ALGEBRA

STRUCTURE AND METHOD

Book 1   new edition

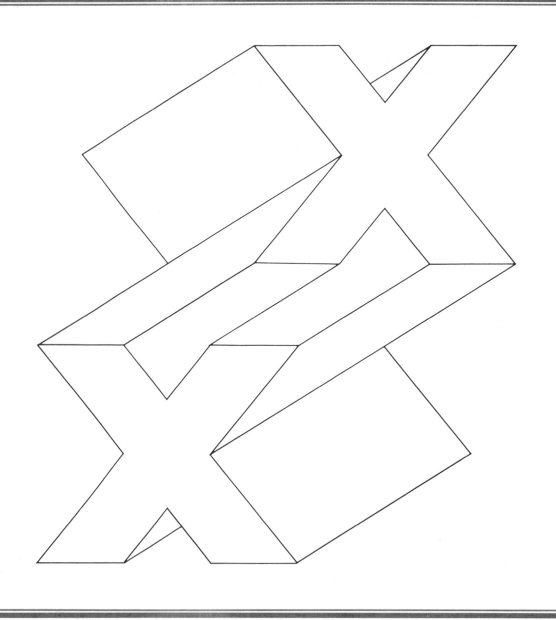

ALGEBRA

STRUCTURE AND METHOD

Book 1   new edition

Mary P. Dolciani

Richard G. Brown

Frank Ebos

William L. Cole

EDITORIAL ADVISERS
Robert H. Sorgenfrey
William Wooton

TEACHER CONSULTANTS
William T. Stanford
Lois B. Whitman

HOUGHTON MIFFLIN COMPANY · BOSTON

Atlanta   Dallas   Geneva, Ill.   Hopewell, N.J.   Palo Alto   Toronto

THE AUTHORS

Mary P. Dolciani, Professor of Mathematical Sciences, Hunter College of the City University of New York.

Richard G. Brown, Mathematics Teacher, The Phillips Exeter Academy, Exeter, New Hampshire.

Frank Ebos, Professor of Mathematics Education, University of Toronto.

William L. Cole, Associate Professor of Mathematics Education, Michigan State University.

EDITORIAL ADVISERS

Robert H. Sorgenfrey, Professor of Mathematics, University of California, Los Angeles.

William Wooton, former Professor of Mathematics, Los Angeles Pierce College.

TEACHER CONSULTANTS

William T. Stanford, Coordinator of Mathematics, Waco Independent School District, Waco, Texas.

Lois B. Whitman, Mathematics Teacher, James Monroe High School, Sepulveda, California.

CONTENTS

3 Solving Equations

4 Polynomials and Problem Solving

5 *Factoring Polynomials*

6 *Fractions*

7 *Applying Fractions*

8 *Linear Equations and Systems*

9 *Introduction to Functions*

10 *Inequalities*

11   *Rational and Irrational Numbers*

12   *Quadratic Functions*

Looking Ahead

SYMBOLS

Metric Units of Measure

Length:
- cm   centimeter
- m   meter
- km   kilometer

Area:
- cm^2 square centimeter
- m^2 square meter
- km^2 square kilometer
- ha   hectare

Time:
- s   second
- min minute
- h   hour

Speed:
- m/s   meters per second
- km/h   kilometers per hour

Mass:
- g   gram
- kg   kilogram

Volume:
- cm^3 cubic centimeter
- mL   milliliter
- L   liter

Temperature: °C   degrees Celsius

WHY STUDY ALGEBRA?

The study of algebra can help you in two ways:
(1) It will help you organize your thoughts to solve mathematical problems that you will meet in your everyday life.
(2) It will prepare you to continue your studies in mathematics and the sciences.

Whatever you choose to do in the future—from teaching children to running a business to doing scientific or social research—you will need to use mathematics.

Information about some possible careers appears throughout the book in the Career Notes: Programmer (page 20); Carpenter (page 35); Nutritionist (page 139); Meteorologist (page 182); Accountant (page 231); Bilingual Math Teacher (page 267); Drafter (page 279); Agricultural Engineer (page 323); Darkroom Technician (page 385); Architect (page 458).

You may think that calculators and computers will do all your problem solving for you, but they can only help. Machines do not think; *you* must do the thinking. If you know what steps to take—what numbers and operations to use—then calculators and computers can be made to do a great deal of the work for you.

The study of physics, biology, astronomy, and social sciences requires mathematics. The caption that accompanies the photograph at the opening of each chapter suggests one of the scientific, natural, or social phenomena that are studied using mathematics. Although an understanding of some applications requires a thorough study of advanced concepts, there are many applications that you can understand. For example, see the Applications about Electrical Energy (page 94), Optics (page 249), Gear Ratios (page 268), Nutrition Labeling (page 397), and Newton's Law of Motion (page 463).

Sky divers must be aware of the distance they can fall before having to open their parachutes in order to land safely. See the chart on the facing page that shows the speed at which a sky diver falls in the first several seconds after jumping.

1

INTRODUCTION TO ALGEBRA

VARIABLES AND EQUATIONS

1-1 *Variables*

OBJECTIVE To simplify numerical expressions and evaluate variable expressions.

A skydiver fell for several seconds before the parachute opened. The table below shows the downward speed one, two, three, and four seconds after the start of the fall.

Number of seconds of fall	Speed in meters per second
1	9.8×1
2	9.8×2
3	9.8×3
4	9.8×4

Each of the expressions for speed fits the pattern

$$9.8 \times n$$

where the letter n stands for 1, 2, 3, or 4. We call n a *variable*.

A **variable** is a symbol used to represent one or more numbers. The numbers are called the **values of the variable.**

An expression, such as $9.8 \times n$, which contains a variable is called a **variable expression.** Expressions, such as 9.8×2, which name a particular number are called **numerical expressions** or **numerals.**

When you write a product that contains a variable, you usually omit the multiplication symbol.

$$9.8 \times n \text{ is usually written } 9.8n.$$

$$y \times z \text{ is usually written } yz.$$

In numerical expressions for products like 9.8×2, you must use a multiplication symbol to avoid confusion. The raised dot $\cdot$ is also used as a multiplication sign.

$$9.8 \times 2 \text{ can be written } 9.8 \cdot 2.$$

The number named by a numerical expression is called the **value of the expression.** Since the expressions $2 + 5$ and 7 name the same number, they have the same value. To show that these expressions have the same value, you use the *equals sign,* $=$. You write

$$2 + 5 = 7$$

and say "two plus five *equals* (or *is equal to*) seven." Of course, 7 is the *simplest,* or most common, name for the number seven.

The symbol $\neq$ means "is *not* equal to." You write $2 + 5 \neq 8$ to show that the expressions $2 + 5$ and 8 do not have the same value.

Replacing a numerical expression by the simplest name of its value is called **simplifying the expression.** In simplifying a numerical expression, you use the following principle.

SUBSTITUTION PRINCIPLE

Changing the numeral by which a number is named in an expression does not change the value of the expression.

EXAMPLE 1 Simplify. **a.** $(48 \div 6) + 2$ **b.** $48 \div (6 + 2)$

SOLUTION The parentheses ( ) show how the numerals in the expression are to be grouped.

a. $(48 \div 6) + 2 = 8 + 2 = 10$ **b.** $48 \div (6 + 2) = 48 \div 8 = 6$

Replacing each variable in a variable expression by a given value and simplifying the result is called **evaluating the expression** or **finding its value.**

EXAMPLE 2 Find the value of $(9x) - (4 + y)$ if $x = 3$ and $y = 5$.

SOLUTION Replace x with 3 and y with 5, and insert the necessary multiplication symbol. Then simplify the result.

$$(9x) - (4 + y) = (9 \times 3) - (4 + 5)$$
$$= 27 - 9$$
$$= 18$$

Oral Exercises

State whether or not each statement is true. Give a reason for your answer.

SAMPLE 1 $3 \times 4 = 6 + 6$ **SOLUTION** True, because 3×4 and $6 + 6$ both name the number 12.

SAMPLE 2 $2 \times 5 = 2 + 5$ **SOLUTION** False, because $2 \times 5 = 10$, whereas $2 + 5 = 7$.

1. $8 \times 6 = 6 \times 8$ **2.** $7 \times 0 = 0 \times 5$

3. $6 \div 1 = 1 \div 6$ **4.** $100 \times \frac{1}{5} = 100 \times 0.2$

5. $3 \times (7 \times 2) = (3 \times 7) \times 2$ **6.** $(9 - 2) - 2 = 9 - (2 - 2)$

7. $0.25 \times 36 = 2.5 \times 3.6$ **8.** $\frac{(6 - 3)}{3} = 6 - 1$

Simplify each expression.

9. $6 + (4 \times 3)$ **10.** $(6 + 4) \times 3$ **11.** $18 - (2 \times 5)$

12. $(18 - 2) \times 5$ **13.** $\frac{(22 - 10)}{4}$ **14.** $\frac{(15 + 3)}{(8 - 2)}$

State the value of each expression if $x = 1$, $y = 2$, and $z = 3$.

15. $6y$ **16.** $8x$ **17.** $z - 3$ **18.** $7 - z$

19. $\frac{4}{y}$ **20.** $(yz) + x$ **21.** $z + (xy)$ **22.** $(4y) - 5$

23. $2 \cdot (y + 1)$ **24.** $3 \cdot (2 - x)$ **25.** $\frac{(x + y)}{z}$ **26.** $\frac{x}{(z - y)}$

Written Exercises

Simplify each expression.

A **1.** $(9 - 4) + 5$ **2.** $7 + (19 - 2)$ **3.** $4 \times (12 + 3)$

4. $(15 - 7) \times 8$ **5.** $(9 + 18) \div 3$ **6.** $9 + (18 \div 3)$

7. $6 - (0 \times 2)$ **8.** $4 - (15 \div 5)$ **9.** $(7 \times 18) + (3 \times 18)$

10. $(14 \times 9) - (4 \times 9)$ **11.** $(22 + 8) \div (60 \div 4)$ **12.** $(70 \div 10) \div (7 \times 1)$

Evaluate each expression if $r = 2$, $s = 5$, $t = 7$, $u = 0$, $v = 1$, and $w = 8$.

13. rs

14. tu

15. $w - (vr)$

16. $v + (ts)$

17. $(3r) + (3s)$

18. $(3s) - (2r)$

19. $(wt) - (5s)$

20. $(sw) + (vr)$

21. $(4v) \cdot (r + t)$

22. $(5t) \cdot (w + u)$

23. $\dfrac{(w + r)}{(t - r)}$

24. $\dfrac{(w + v)}{(s - r)}$

B 25. $s \cdot (w - t) \cdot \dfrac{ur}{v}$

26. $(r + w) - \dfrac{(vt)}{(s + r)}$

27. $\dfrac{(r + s)}{(tv)} + (rwu)$

28. $(rw) + (rs) - (t + u + v)$

Simplify the expression on each side of the __?__. Then make a true statement by replacing the __?__ with the symbol $=$ or $\neq$.

29. $(7 + 5) \times (7 - 5)$ __?__ $(7 \times 7) - (5 \times 5)$

30. $(8 + 4) \times (8 + 4)$ __?__ $(8 \times 8) + (4 \times 4)$

31. $(6 - 1) \times (6 - 1)$ __?__ $(6 \times 6) - (1 \times 1)$

32. $(9 + 2) \times (9 - 2)$ __?__ $(9 \times 9) - (2 \times 2)$

Evaluate each expression shown in color for the given values of the variables.

33. lw (Area of a rectangle)
if $l = 28$ and $w = 12$

34. $(2l) + (2w)$ (Perimeter of a rectangle)
if $l = 40$ and $w = 25$

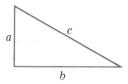

35. $a + b + c$ (Perimeter of a triangle)
if $a = 8$, $b = 15$, and $c = 17$

36. $\dfrac{1}{2}ab$ (Area of a right triangle)
if $a = 12$ and $b = 16$

C 37. Prt (Simple interest on a loan of P dollars)
if $P = 6000$ (dollars), $r = 12\%$ (per year), and $t = 1$ (year)

38. $P + (Prt)$ (Amount of an investment of P dollars at simple interest)
if $P = 2500$ (dollars), $r = 8\%$ (per year), and $t = 6$ (years)

1-2 *Grouping Symbols*

OBJECTIVE   To simplify expressions with and without grouping symbols.

Parentheses have been used to show you how to group the numerals in an expression. Different groupings may produce expressions that name different numbers.

$$(48 \div 6) + 2 \text{ means } 8 + 2, \text{ or } 10.$$
$$48 \div (6 + 2) \text{ means } 48 \div 8, \text{ or } 6.$$

A **grouping symbol** is a device, such as parentheses, used to enclose an expression. Brackets [ ] are also used.

Multiplication symbols are often omitted from expressions with grouping symbols. For example,

$$5 \times (4 - 1) = 5(4 - 1) = 5(3) = 15.$$

Note that 5(3) stands for 5×3. Other ways to write this product using parentheses are (5)3 and (5)(3).

In a fraction such as $\dfrac{12 + 8}{6 - 2}$ the bar is a grouping symbol as well as a division symbol.

$$\frac{12 + 8}{6 - 2} = \frac{20}{4} = 20 \div 4 = 5$$

Throughout your work in algebra you will use these symbols:

GROUPING SYMBOLS		
Parentheses	Brackets	Fraction Bar
5 (4 − 1)	**5 [4 − 1]**	$\dfrac{\mathbf{12 + 8}}{\mathbf{6 - 2}}$

If an expression contains more than one grouping symbol, first simplify the numeral in the innermost grouping symbol. Then work toward the outermost grouping symbol until the simplest expression is found.

EXAMPLE 1   Simplify $9 - [21 \div (3 + 4)]$.

SOLUTION $9 - [21 \div (3 + 4)] = 9 - [21 \div 7] = 9 - 3 = 6$

When there are no grouping symbols, you take the following steps to simplify an expression.

Step 1 Do all multiplications and divisions in order from left to right.

Step 2 Do all additions and subtractions in order from left to right.

$$8 + \underline{5 \times 6}$$
$$\underline{8 + \quad 30}$$
$$38$$

$$9 + 4 - \underline{6 \times 2} \div 4$$
$$9 + 4 - \quad \underline{12 \quad \div 4}$$
$$\underline{9 + 4 -} \qquad 3$$
$$\underline{13 \quad - \qquad 3}$$
$$10$$

EXAMPLE 2 Evaluate $\dfrac{3r + 7s}{5r - s}$ if $r = 2$ and $s = 6$.

SOLUTION Replace r with 2 and s with 6, and insert the necessary multiplication symbols. Then simplify the result.

$$\frac{3r + 7s}{5r - s} = \frac{3(2) + 7(6)}{5(2) - 6}$$

$$= \frac{6 + 42}{10 - 6}$$

$$= \frac{48}{4} = 12$$

Oral Exercises

In Exercises 1–8, the given expression indicates one or more operations to be performed. Describe the operation(s) for each expression.

SAMPLE $4(x + 2)$ *SOLUTION 1* "Multiply 4 by the sum of x and 2."

SOLUTION 2 "Add x and 2, and then multiply the sum by 4."

1. $5x$ **2.** $y - 4$ **3.** $3 + 2x$ **4.** $5z - 8$

5. $7(z + 6)$ **6.** $4(9x - 2)$ **7.** $\dfrac{y - x}{z}$ **8.** $\dfrac{y}{z + x}$

9–16. In Exercises 1–8, evaluate each expression if $x = 3$, $y = 15$, and $z = 2$.

Written Exercises

Evaluate each expression if $a = 1$, $b = 3$, $c = 5$, $x = 0$, $y = 1$, and $z = 6$.

A **1.** $bx + y$ **2.** $cy + a$ **3.** $z - ab$ **4.** $ac - y$
   5. $6z + by$ **6.** $x(a - y) + c$ **7.** $(z - y)c + a$ **8.** $9c - bz$

9. $(2c - 3b)(z + y)$ **10.** $(c - 4a)(4y - b)$ **11.** $\dfrac{ab + c}{y + 3}$

12. $\dfrac{cz - 4y}{15 - 2a}$ **13.** $b(z - c) + \dfrac{yz}{b}$ **14.** $c(b + y) - az$

Simplify each expression.

15. $\dfrac{6 \times 3 + 5 \times 3 \times 3}{10 - 2 - 1}$ **16.** $\dfrac{32 \div 8 + 3}{2 + 5}$

17. $(25 - 4 + 9 \div 3) \div (12 \div 6)$ **18.** $12(11 - 7) - 30 \div (6 - 3)$

Evaluate each expression shown in color for the given values of the variables.

19. $2(a + b)$ (Perimeter of a parallelogram)
if $a = 5.5$ and $b = 25.2$

20. $2a + b + c$ (Perimeter of an isosceles trapezoid)
if $a = 54$, $b = 98$, and $c = 48$

Ex. 19

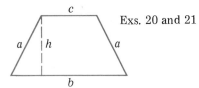
Exs. 20 and 21

21. $\frac{1}{2}h(b + c)$ (Area of a trapezoid)
if $h = 25$, $b = 50$, and $c = 25$

22. $(\pi r)r$ (Area of a circle)
if $r = 14$. Use $\frac{22}{7}$ as an approximate value for π.

Ex. 22

B 23. $2(r + h) + \pi r$ (Perimeter of a Norman window)
if $r = 1.00$ and $h = 3.00$. Use 3.14 as an
approximate value for π.

Ex. 23

Ex. 24

24. $2(lw + wh + lh)$ (Surface area of a rectangular solid)
if $l = 18$, $w = 16$, and $h = 10$

Simplify the expression on each side of the __?__. Then make a true statement by replacing the __?__ with the symbol = or ≠.

25. $\dfrac{12 \times 4}{6 + 2}$ __?__ $\dfrac{6 \times 2}{3 + 1}$

26. $\dfrac{39 + 6}{15 \times 3}$ __?__ $(24 \div 8) - 2$

27. $3[2(2 + 3)]$ __?__ $(6 \times 6) - 6$

28. $4[24 \div (6 + 2)]$ __?__ $4[(24 \div 6) + 2]$

29. $\dfrac{(8 \times 6) \div 12}{4 - (6 \div 2)} + 1$ __?__ $25 - \dfrac{38 + 4}{10 - 8}$

30. $1 + \dfrac{30 - 3}{5 + 4}$ __?__ $\dfrac{(8 \times 6) - 8}{(54 \div 3) + 2} + 2$

C **31.** $([(2 \times 3) + 5]3)3 - 6$ __?__ $2 \times 3 \times 3 \times 3 + 5 \times 3 \times 3 - 6$

32. $([(5 \times 2) - 3]2)2 + 9$ __?__ $5 \times 2 \times 2 - 3 \times 2 \times 2 + 9$

33. $(1 \times 1) + (2 \times 2) + (3 \times 3) + (4 \times 4)$ __?__ $\dfrac{4(4 + 1)[(2 \times 4) + 1]}{6}$

34. $[(3 \times 1) + 1] + [(3 \times 2) + 1] + [(3 \times 3) + 1]$ __?__ $2(3 \times 3) + 3$

35. $\dfrac{[7 - (3 \times 2)] + (4 \times 6)}{[(24 \div 4) + 2] - 3}$ __?__ $[2 + (2 \times 2) - (30 \div 6)] \times \dfrac{12 - 2}{5 - 2}$

36. $\dfrac{78 - [(11 \times 18) \div 3]}{[(8 \times 3) + 8] - (4 \times 5)}$ __?__ $\dfrac{(16 \times 6) \div 3}{(32 \times 2) \div 8} - \dfrac{20 - 4}{2 \times 4}$

Calculator Key-In _____

Does your calculator follow the steps for simplifying an expression stated on page 6? Experiment with your calculator by entering the following example exactly as it appears here:

$$5 + 2 \times 3 =$$

If your calculator displays the answer 11, it followed the order of operations you learned for simplifying expressions: multiplication before addition. Your calculator has an algebraic operating system. The answer 11 is correct.

If your calculator displays the answer 21, it performed the addition and the multiplication in the order in which you pressed the keys. One way to get the correct answer on your calculator is to multiply 2 and 3 first and then add 5, just as you would if you were using pencil and paper.

Use a calculator to simplify each expression.

1. $17 - 2.5 \times 6.8$

2. $1.8 + 0.6 \div 0.3$

3. $0.25 \div 0.5 \times 0.6 - 0.2$

4. $369 \times 0.75 + 369 \times 0.25$

5. $308 \div 11 \times 15873 - 7 \times 5291 \times 3$

1-3 *Equations*

OBJECTIVE To find solution sets of open sentences.

Here are three equations:

$$8 - 2 = 6 \qquad\qquad 3x + 1 = 7 \qquad\qquad y + 2 = 2 + y$$

the two sides $\qquad$ the two sides $\qquad$ the two sides

An **equation** is formed by placing an equals sign between two numerical or variable expressions, called the **sides** of the equation.

Equations containing variables are called **open sentences.** The given set of numbers that a variable may represent is called the **domain** of the variable. When you replace each variable in an open sentence by one of the numbers in its domain, you obtain a true statement or a false statement.

You may use *braces* { } to show a set of numbers. A short way to write "the set whose members are 1, 2, and 3" is $\{1, 2, 3\}$.

EXAMPLE 1 The domain of x is $\{1, 2, 3\}$. Find any values in the domain of x for which $3x + 1 = 7$ becomes a true statement.

SOLUTION Replace x in turn by 1, 2, and 3.

$3x + 1 = 7$
$3(1) + 1 = 7$ False
$3(2) + 1 = 7$ True
$3(3) + 1 = 7$ False

∴ (read "therefore") the required value of x is 2. ***Answer***

Any value of a variable that converts an open sentence into a true statement is called a **solution** or **root** of the sentence, and is said to **satisfy** the sentence.

The set of *all* solutions of an open sentence is called the **solution set** of the sentence. Finding the solution set is called **solving** the sentence.

You may use braces to show a solution set. Thus, for Example 1, you may say either

"The solution is 2" or "The solution set is $\{2\}$."

You can see that the solution set of the equation $x + 2 = 2 + x$ is the set of *all* numbers, because the sentence is true no matter what number is substituted for x. If you are asked to solve this equation *over the domain* $\{0, 1, 2, 3\}$, however, you should state that the solution set is $\{0, 1, 2, 3\}$.

EXAMPLE 2 Solve the equation $y(3 - y) = 2$ if $y \in \{0, 1, 2, 3\}$ (read "y *is a member of* (or *belongs to*) the set whose members are 0, 1, 2, and 3").

SOLUTION Replace y in turn by 0, 1, 2, and 3.

$$y(3 - y) = 2$$
$$0(3 - 0) = 2 \quad \text{False}$$
$$1(3 - 1) = 2 \quad \text{True}$$
$$2(3 - 2) = 2 \quad \text{True}$$
$$3(3 - 3) = 2 \quad \text{False}$$

∴ the solution set is $\{1, 2\}$. *Answer*

Oral Exercises

Solve each equation if $x \in \{0, 1, 2, 3, 4, 5, 6\}$. If there is no solution over the given domain, state "no solution."

1. $x + 1 = 5$ **2.** $x - 1 = 3$ **3.** $3x = 6$ **4.** $x \div 2 = 1$

5. $x - 2 = 4$ **6.** $x + 3 = 6$ **7.** $x + 1 = 1 + x$ **8.** $x + 1 = x$

9. $2x = x + x$ **10.** $3x = x + 2$ **11.** $x + x = 0$ **12.** $(6 - x)x = 0$

Written Exercises

Solve each equation if $x \in \{0, 1, 2, 3, 4, 5, 6\}$.

A   **1.** $x + 4 = 9$ **2.** $7 + x = 9$ **3.** $x - 1 = 4$ **4.** $x - 3 = 1$

    5. $4 - x = 3$ **6.** $5 - x = 2$ **7.** $2x = 10$ **8.** $3x = 12$

    9. $3x = 9$ **10.** $2x = 12$ **11.** $x \div 2 = 1$ **12.** $x \div 2 = 2$

    13. $\frac{1}{2}x = 3$ **14.** $\frac{1}{3}x = 1$ **15.** $x - x = 0$ **16.** $x \cdot x = 1$

Solve each equation over the domain $\{0, 1, 2, 3, 4, 5, 6, 7, 8, 9\}$.

B   **17.** $2a + 7 = 15$ **18.** $3b - 2 = 13$ **19.** $12 = 8c - 4$

    20. $14 = 6d - 4$ **21.** $7 + 7r = 49$ **22.** $4 + 4s = 40$

    23. $2x = x + 4$ **24.** $4t = t(4)$ **25.** $3z = z(z)$

    26. $x(9 - x) = 0$ **27.** $(9 - t)(8 + t)t = 0$ **28.** $8s = (2s)(2s)(2s)$

Write an equation for which the solution set over the domain $\{0, 1, 2, 3, 4\}$ is the given set.

C   **29.** $\{2\}$ **30.** $\{0\}$ **31.** $\{0, 1, 2, 3, 4\}$ **32.** $\{0, 4\}$

Self-Test 1

VOCABULARY

variable (p. 1)
value of a variable (p. 1)
variable expression (p. 2)
value of a numerical
    expression (p. 2)
simplify an expression (p. 2)
substitution principle (p. 2)
evaluate an expression (p. 2)
grouping symbol (p. 5)

equation (p. 9)
open sentence (p. 9)
domain of a variable (p. 9)
solution (p. 9)
root (p. 9)
satisfy an open sentence (p. 9)
solution set (p. 9)
solve an open sentence (p. 9)

Evaluate each expression if $x = 6$, $y = 3$, and $z = 5$.

1. $(2x + 1) + (3y - z)$

2. $\dfrac{x}{y} \cdot z$

Obj. 1-1, p. 1

3. $x - 2(z - y)$

4. $\dfrac{3(x + 4)}{5y - z}$

Obj. 1-2, p. 5

Solve each equation if $x \in \{0, 1, 2, 3, 4\}$.

5. $x + 1 = 3$

6. $12 - 2x = 4$

Obj. 1-3, p. 9

Check your answers with those at the back of the book.

ḟistorical Ոote

Why We Call It "Algebra"

In ninth-century Baghdad, the mathematician and astronomer Muhammed ibn-Musa al-Khwarizmi wrote a mathematical treatise entitled *hisab al-jabr w'al muqabalah,* which means "the science of reduction and comparison" and which probably refers to the solving of equations. For the first time, algebra was systematically discussed as a distinct branch of mathematics. Al-Khwarizmi's book made its way to Europe and in the twelfth century was translated into Latin, the common language of European scholars. As the book was studied throughout Europe, the word "al-jabr" in the title grew into "algebra," which is what this branch of mathematics is called today.

APPLICATIONS

1-4 *Words into Symbols: Numerical Relationships*

OBJECTIVE To represent numerical relationships stated in words by mathematical expressions or equations.

To apply algebra, you must often translate word phrases into numerical or variable expressions, and word sentences into equations.

Suppose you think of two numbers, one five more than the other. If x stands for the smaller number, then the greater number is represented by

$$x + 5.$$

EXAMPLE 1 Represent each word phrase by a variable expression.

      a. Five less than a number x

      b. Five times a number x

SOLUTION **a.** $x - 5$ **b.** $5x$

EXAMPLE 2 Represent each word sentence by an equation.

      a. The sum of the number n and eight is thirty-three.

      b. Three is seven less than twice the number n.

SOLUTION **a.** $n + 8 = 33$ **b.** $3 = 2n - 7$

The numbers

$$0, 1, 2, 3, 4, \ldots$$

are called the **whole numbers.** The three dots are read "and so on" and indicate that the list continues without end. When you count by *ones* from any whole number, you obtain **consecutive numbers.** For example, 7, 8, and 9 are three consecutive numbers.

EXAMPLE 3 A whole number is represented by n.

      a. Write the next three whole numbers after n.

      b. Write an equation which states that the sum of four consecutive numbers is 70, given that the first number is n.

SOLUTION **a.** $n + 1, \quad n + 2, \quad n + 3$

             b. $n + (n + 1) + (n + 2) + (n + 3) = 70$

Six is called an *even* number because $6 = 2 \times 3$. The numbers which are the product of 2 and any whole number are the **even whole numbers:**

$$0, 2, 4, 6, 8, \ldots$$

The **odd whole numbers** are those which are not even:

$$1, 3, 5, 7, 9, \ldots$$

If you count by *twos* from any even number, you obtain **consecutive even numbers.** If you count by *twos* from any odd number, you obtain **consecutive odd numbers.**

Three consecutive even numbers: 10; $10 + 2$, or 12; $12 + 2$, or 14
Three consecutive odd numbers: 11; $11 + 2$, or 13; $13 + 2$, or 15

Thus,

$$n, \quad n + 2, \quad n + 4$$

are consecutive even numbers if n is even, and consecutive odd numbers if n is odd.

Oral Exercises

Represent each word phrase by a variable expression. Use n to represent the number referred to.

SAMPLE Five less than twice the number   *SOLUTION* $2n - 5$

1. Four times the number
2. One third of the number
3. Six greater than the number
4. The product of six and the number
5. The number decreased by three
6. The number increased by nine
7. Five less than half the number
8. Seven more than twice the number

Represent each sentence by an equation. Use n to represent the number.

9. Five more than the number is fifty-four.
10. Eight less than the number is twenty-six.
11. The sum of nine and twice the number is thirty-one.
12. If one is subtracted from five times the number, the difference is fourteen.

Represent the required numbers in terms of the given variables.

13. If w is a whole number, what is the next consecutive whole number? the next consecutive whole number after that one?
14. If v is an even whole number, what is the even whole number just before v? the even whole number just before that one?
15. If n is a whole number, is $2n$ even or odd? Is $2n + 1$ even or odd? Is $2n + 2$ even or odd?

Written Exercises

Match the word sentence in Column I with the corresponding open sentence in Column II. (You will not use all the open sentences.)

Column I

A 1. Ten less than half a number is seven.
2. Three times the sum of a number and two is fifteen.
3. Nine decreased by twice a number is one.
4. The product of six and one less than a number is eighteen.
5. The sum of three times a number and two is fifteen.
6. If twice a number is decreased by five, the difference is three.

Column II

a. $3x + 2 = 15$
b. $2x - 9 = 1$
c. $6(x - 1) = 18$
d. $\frac{1}{2}(x - 10) = 7$
e. $3(x + 2) = 15$
f. $9 - 2x = 1$
g. $\frac{1}{2}x - 10 = 7$
h. $6x - 1 = 18$
i. $2x - 5 = 3$
j. $2(x - 5) = 3$

Represent each word phrase by a variable expression.

7. Eight times the number t
8. Five times the number s
9. Half the number n
10. One third of the number g
11. Seven greater than the number a
12. Five less than the number k
13. Two less than the number b
14. Nine more than the number m

Represent the required numbers in terms of the given variables.

15. What number is one more than twice the number q?
16. What number is two less than half the number w?
17. If t is a whole number, what is the whole number just before t? the whole number just before that one?
18. If s is an odd whole number, what is the next consecutive odd whole number? the next consecutive odd whole number after that one?
19. The sum of two numbers is fifteen. One number is y. What is the other number?
20. The sum of two numbers is eight. One number is n. What is the other number?

B 21. The difference between two numbers is six. The greater number is x. What is the smaller number?
22. The difference between two numbers is ten. The smaller number is s. What is the greater number?
23. Does $2n + 5$ represent an even number or an odd number? What is the next greater even number? the next greater odd number?

24. Does $2k + 4$ represent an even number or an odd number? What is the next greater odd number? the next greater even number?

Represent each sentence by an equation.

25. One half of the number r is thirty-four.

26. One sixth of the number t is forty.

27. Fifteen is three more than twice the number z.

28. Twenty is seven less than one half of the number h.

29. When you increase one third of the number x by five, you obtain nine.

30. When you decrease nine times the number y by six, you obtain four.

31. Three times the sum of four and the number t is forty-two.

32. If five is subtracted from the number y, six times the difference is ninety.

33. Twice the number x is eight more than x itself.

34. Half the number a is ten less than a itself.

35. The first of three consecutive whole numbers is x, and the sum of the three numbers is one hundred fifty-three.

36. The first of three consecutive even numbers is y, and the sum of the three numbers is twenty-four.

C **37.** The first of three consecutive odd numbers is d, and the sum of the first and second exceeds the third by nine.

38. The first of three consecutive even numbers is x, and the sum of the three numbers is three tenths of the product of the first two.

Just for Fun

1, 3, 6, 10, 15, . . . are called triangular numbers because they can be represented by dots arranged to form triangles.

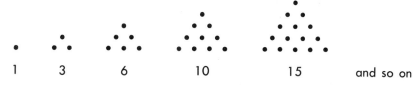

| 1 | 3 | 6 | 10 | 15 | and so on |

1. Draw diagrams for the next five triangular numbers.

2. If *n* represents the number of the triangular number in the list (*n* = 1 for 1, *n* = 2 for 3, and so on), verify for the first ten triangular numbers that the *n*th triangular number $= \dfrac{n(n + 1)}{2}$.

Calculator Key-In

1. Solve each equation if the domain of n is $\{1, 2, 3, 4\}$.

   a. $\dfrac{n(n + 1)}{2} = 1$

   b. $\dfrac{n(n + 1)}{2} = 1 + 2$

   c. $\dfrac{n(n + 1)}{2} = 1 + 2 + 3$

   d. $\dfrac{n(n + 1)}{2} = 1 + 2 + 3 + 4$

2. First guess what value of n in the set of whole numbers satisfies each equation. Then use a calculator to check your guess.

   a. $\dfrac{n(n + 1)}{2} = 1 + 2 + 3 + 4 + \cdots + 10$

   b. $\dfrac{n(n + 1)}{2} = 1 + 2 + 3 + 4 + \cdots + 15$

   (The three dots indicate that all the whole numbers between 4 and 10 are to be included in the sum.)

   c. $\dfrac{n(n + 1)}{2} = 1 + 2 + 3 + 4 + \cdots + 26$

Biography Annie Jump Cannon

Annie Jump Cannon (1863–1941), by examining astronomical plates photographed through a prism, classified almost 400,000 stars according to their stellar spectra or temperatures. She was a graduate of Wellesley College and did graduate work in mathematics, physics, and astronomy there and at Radcliffe College.

In 1896 she began her lifelong career at Harvard classifying stars and developing a new system for this classification. She greatly reduced the number of species to which the vast majority of stars belong and proved that these species, for the most part, form a continuous series. In 1925 she became the first woman to receive an honorary Doctor of Science degree from Oxford University.

1-5 *Words into Symbols: Problem Situations*

OBJECTIVE   **To represent problem situations by mathematical expressions or equations.**

To apply algebra, you often use *formulas*. **Formulas** are equations that state rules about measurements. Here are four formulas:

$A = lw$ Area of rectangle = length of rectangle × width of rectangle

$P = 2l + 2w$ Perimeter of rectangle = (2 × length) + (2 × width)

$D = rt$ Distance traveled = rate × time traveled

$C = np$ Cost = number of items × price per item

EXAMPLE 1

Using the given variable, write an expression for the measure required to complete each statement.

1. A rectangle has length 8 units and width w units.
The area is __?__ square units

2. A rectangle has length 6 cm (centimeters) and width x cm.
The perimeter is __?__ cm.

3. You travel for $(x + 2)$ hours at 70 km/h (kilometers per hour).
The distance you travel is __?__ km.

4. You buy 2 pens at x cents each and 3 notebooks at y cents each.
The total cost is __?__ cents.

SOLUTION

1. Area = length × width = $8w$

2. Perimeter = (2 × length) + (2 × width) = $2(6) + 2x = 12 + 2x$

3. Distance = rate × time = $70(x + 2)$

4. Cost of pens = $2x$; cost of notebooks = $3y$; total cost = $2x + 3y$

The next examples show how you can choose a variable to represent a number and then write an equation to represent the facts in a given situation.

EXAMPLE 2   Jan paid two dollars less than Bob at the pizza parlor. Together, they paid $3.90.

     a. Choose a variable to represent the amount Bob paid and use it to write an expression for the amount Jan paid.

     b. Write an equation that represents the given facts.

SOLUTION   **a.** Let x = amount Bob paid; then $x - 2$ = amount Jan paid.

     b. $x + (x - 2) = 3.90$

EXAMPLE 3

The length of a rectangular rug is 1 m (meter) more than the width. It takes 14 m of fringe to go around the edges of the rug.

a. Choose a variable to represent the width in meters and use it to write an expression for the length.

b. Write an equation that represents the given facts.

SOLUTION

a. Let w = width in meters.
Then $w + 1$ = length in meters.

b. Draw a sketch to help you see the relationships given.

$2(w + 1) + 2w = 14$ *Answer*

Oral Exercises

Give a variable expression for the measure required to complete each statement.

1. A rectangle has width 4 units and length $(x + 5)$ units. Its area is __?__ square units.

2. You travel for $(t - 1)$ hours at 60 km/h. The distance traveled is __?__ km.

3. You buy $(n + 2)$ hamburgers at 85 cents each. The cost is __?__ cents.

4. Lanette earns $(w + 2)$ dollars per hour. In h hours, she earns __?__ dollars.

5. Joe is two years older than Fred. The sum of their ages is 30.
   a. Choose a variable for Fred's age and use it to express Joe's age.
   b. State an equation that represents the given facts.

Written Exercises

Using the given variable, write an expression for the measure required to complete each statement.

A 1. Dick is y years old. Bill is three years older than Dick. Bill is __?__ years old.

2. Mary is t cm tall. Marcia is 5 cm shorter than Mary. Marcia is __?__ cm tall.

3. A book costs x dollars. Six copies of the book cost __?__ dollars.

4. John is m years old. Five years ago he was __?__ years old.

5. In x weeks there are ___?___ days.

6. In y hours there are ___?___ minutes.

7. Kelley bicycles at a rate of 15 km/h. In t hours she bicycles a distance of ___?___ km.

8. Jay walks at a rate of x km/h. In half an hour he walks a distance of ___?___ km.

9. The length of a rectangular lot is 18 m less than twice its width, w m. The length is ___?___ m. The perimeter is ___?___ m.

10. The width of a rectangular field is 2 km more than half the length, l km. The width is ___?___ km. The perimeter is ___?___ km.

In Exercises 11-22:

a. Choose a variable to represent the number indicated by the words in parentheses.

b. Write an equation that represents the given facts.

11. The perimeter of a square is 28 m   (Length of a side)

12. The perimeter of an equilateral triangle (a triangle with three equal sides) is 42 cm.   (Length of a side)

13. Four identical tires cost $120 altogether.   (Cost of one tire)

14. Six bus passengers paid a total fare of $5.40.   (Fare for one passenger)

15. Four years ago Rhoda was 11 years old.   (Rhoda's age now)

16. Max has read all but the last 16 pages of a 250-page book.   (Number of pages Max has read)

B 17. The Science Museum gives students a dollar off the price of admission. Fran, a high school freshman, paid $1.50.   (Admission price)

18. A mail-order firm charges $1.52 for shipping charges on a pair of field glasses. Paulo ordered a pair and sent a check for $34.99.   (Price of the field glasses)

19. A soccer field has a perimeter of 348 m. The length is 37 m more than the width.   (Width)

20. A football team that played 13 games won five times as many games as it lost, and finished one game in a tie.   (Number of games lost)

21. There were five more men than women on a grand jury of 23 people.   (Number of women)

22. There were twice as many dark chocolates as milk chocolates in a box of two dozen.   (Number of milk chocolates)

In Exercises 23–26:

a. Choose a variable to represent the number indicated by the words in parentheses.

b. Write an equation that represents the given facts.

23. On a 1200 km trip, the Watanabe family traveled by car and by plane. They traveled seven times farther by plane than by car. (Distance traveled by car)

24. The coach drove from her home to school and back in 75 minutes. The return trip took three minutes less than the trip to school. (Time to drive to school)

C **25.** On a trip of 600 km, a van traveled at 80 km/h for half of the time and at 100 km/h for the other half of the time. (Time of the trip)

26. The length of one side of a triangular lot is 11 m less than twice the length of the second side. The third side is 7 m longer than the first side. The perimeter of the lot is 235 m. (Length of the second side)

Career Note Programmer

$$x_1 = 1$$
$$x_2 = (x_1 + 2)^2 = (1 + 2)^2 = 9$$
$$x_3 = (x_2 + 3)^2 = (9 + 3)^2 = 144$$
$$x_4 = (x_3 + 4)^2 = (144 + 4)^2 = 21{,}904$$
$$x_5 = (x_4 + 5)^2 = (21{,}904 + 5)^2 = 480{,}004{,}281$$

How long would it take you to find x_{100}? Would you be likely to make a mistake? A computer can find x_{100} and do more complicated calculations accurately in just a fraction of a second. A computer cannot think for itself, however. It must be given detailed, step-by-step instructions in a computer language.

The primary task of the programmer is to write programs or instructions for a computer to follow. Then, after the program has been written, the programmer must check that the desired result will be obtained. A check is made by running the program with a set of typical data for which the results are known. Flowcharts which outline schematically the way in which the program works are sometimes used by programmers to plan their work and explain it to others.

A college degree with either a major or extensive course work in computer science is the usual requirement for a job in this field.

Computer Key-In

How does a computer work? A computer is made up of several connected electronic parts. It works according to the instructions given to it by programs that can be stored in it.

A person called a *programmer* writes programs that tell the computer how to perform various tasks. Such programs are generally written in a programming language, such as BASIC (which is used for the programs shown in this book) or FORTRAN or COBOL. In order for one of these languages to be used, there must be a program stored in the computer that will translate the program instructions into commands that will control the computer circuits.

To get the computer to perform a particular task, the programmer must break the task down into the kinds of steps that the computer can do. These steps must be carefully arranged in the proper order. Sometimes "decision steps" are included to change the order as necessary. The programmer must also consider the numbers and words (*data*) that the computer is to work with (*process*) for them to be *input* as needed. (The work that computers do is sometimes called *data processing*.) The programmer must also arrange for the results to be *output* in a convenient form.

A commonly used business program is one that handles the payroll. Such a program stores payroll records (names of employees, their salaries or wages, and the deductions) and computes and prints the payroll checks.

Other kinds of programs are used to store information in libraries and to retrieve portions of such information on request.

To obtain correct results, a program must be correct in every detail and data must be input correctly. The writing of a successful computer program is a very exciting accomplishment.

1-6 *Solving Problems*

OBJECTIVE   To solve problems using a general method.

A "word problem" describes a situation in which certain numbers are related to each other. If you can state the relationship in an equation, then you can solve the problem by solving the equation.

  Here are two simple examples (which you could solve mentally) to show you a general method for solving word problems.

EXAMPLE 1

Maria bought a hit record album for $10. Her friend bought a cassette of the same music. If the album cost twice as much as the cassette, what was the cost of the cassette?

SOLUTION

Step 1   Read the problem carefully. What numbers are asked for?

> This problem asks for the number of dollars in the cost of the cassette.

Step 2   Choose a variable. Use it with the given facts to represent the number(s) described in the problem.

> Let n = cost of cassette in dollars. Then $2n$ = cost of album in dollars.

Step 3   Write an equation based on the given facts.

> The cost of the album   is $10.
> $$2n \qquad\qquad = \quad 10$$

Step 4   Solve the equation.

> From arithmetic, you know that 5 is the number whose product with 2 is 10.
> $$n = 5$$

Step 5   Check your results with the statement of the problem. Give the answer.

> Is the cost of the album ($10) twice the cost of the cassette?
> $$10 \overset{?}{=} 2 \times 5$$
> $$10 = 10 \ \checkmark$$
> $\therefore$ the cost of the cassette was $5.
>
> ***Answer***

EXAMPLE 2

The approximate height of Yudaki Falls in Japan is 100 m. That is 4 m more than six times the approximate height of Minnehaha Falls in Minnesota. What is the approximate height of Minnehaha Falls?

SOLUTION

Step 1   The problem asks for the number of meters in the approximate height of Minnehaha Falls.

Step 2   Let h = approximate height of Minnehaha Falls in meters. Then $6h + 4$ = approximate height of Yudaki Falls in meters.

Step 3 The approximate height of Yudaki Falls is 100 m.

$$6h + 4 \qquad\qquad = 100$$

Step 4 The sketch shows that $6h = 96$.
From arithmetic, you know that
16 is the number whose product
with 6 is 96.

$$h = 16$$

Step 5 Checking the result of Step 4
is left to you.

∴ the approximate height of
Minnehaha Falls is 16 m.

Answer

The five steps used to solve the problems in Examples 1 and 2 form a
plan that usually helps in solving any word problem.

PLAN FOR SOLVING A WORD PROBLEM

Step 1 Read the problem carefully and decide what numbers are
asked for.

Step 2 Choose a variable and use it with the given facts to represent the number(s) described in the problem. Making a
sketch may be helpful.

Step 3 Write an open sentence based on the given facts.

Step 4 Solve the open sentence and find the required numbers.

Step 5 Check your results with the words of the problem. Give
the answer.

Problems

Solve each problem by writing out the five steps.

A **1.** Last year Hal scored three times as many touchdowns as Bryce. If
Hal scored 15 touchdowns, how many did Bryce score?

2. A truck driver is traveling at a constant rate of 100 km/h. How long
will it take her to reach Oklahoma City, which is 200 km away?

3. Ruby Francis bought a used car for $2400. Her friend Lillian Chen
bought a new moped. The car cost six times as much as the moped.
What was the cost of Lillian's moped?

4. For $8.00 Jim and his friends can get 16 pieces of pizza if they buy whole pizza pies and share them. Find the cost per piece of pizza.

5. Senior citizens pay a dollar less than the general admission price to the Museum of Science. Anna Raciti, a senior citizen, paid $2.50. What is the general admission price?

6. Including the tip, the cost of a meal was $5.00. The tip was $.75. What was the cost of the meal before the tip?

7. The number of students enrolled in Massapoag High School is 150 less today than it was ten years ago when 1800 students were enrolled. How many are enrolled today?

8. In one year 218,899 poodles were registered with the Kennel Club. This was 117,500 more than the number of German shepherds registered in that year. How many German shepherds were registered?

B 9. a. If a number is decreased by 6, the result is 30. Find the number.
      b. If four times another number is decreased by 6, the result is 30. Find the number.

10. a. If a number is increased by 15, the result is 25. Find the number.
    b. If one half of another number is increased by 15, the result is 25. Find the number.

11. Jane dives from a platform that is 10 m high. Joe dives from a springboard. The height of the platform is 1 m more than three times the height of the springboard. What is the height of the springboard?

12. Fourteen-year-old Manuel is two years older than twice the age of his brother Juan. How old is Juan?

13. A ski jacket costing $60 is priced $20 less than twice the cost of a matching pair of ski pants. How much are the ski pants?

14. The total height of the Sutherland Falls in New Zealand is 580 m. That is 20 m less than ten times the approximate height of Niagara Falls (between New York State and Ontario, Canada). What is the approximate height of Niagara Falls?

C 15. Dorothy Lee will authorize her bank to transfer a fixed amount each month from her checking account to a savings account. She has $125 in the savings account now. In six months she wishes to have $1325 in the savings account to pay her real estate tax. What fixed amount should she have transferred each month? (Do not consider the amount of interest her account may draw during this time.)

16. At the beginning of a seven-week speed reading course, Ted read at the rate of 250 words per minute (wpm). At the end of the course, his reading speed was 1020 wpm. What was the average weekly increase in his reading speed over the course?

Self-Test 2

VOCABULARY
whole numbers (p. 12)
consecutive numbers (p. 12)
even number (p. 13)
odd number (p. 13)
consecutive even number (p. 13)
consecutive odd number (p. 13)
formula (p. 17)

Represent each sentence by an equation.

1. The sum of the number n and three is five.

Obj. 1-4, p. 12

2. If one is subtracted from twice the number t, the difference is eleven.

3. Five years ago, Gina was nine years old.

Obj. 1-5, p. 17

   a. Choose a variable to represent Gina's age now and use it to write an expression for Gina's age five years ago.

   b. Write an equation that represents the given facts.

4. Use the five-step method to solve this problem: Noriko sold twice as many tickets to the school play as Lou. If Noriko sold 10 tickets, how many did Lou sell?

Obj. 1-6, p. 22

Check your answers with those at the back of the book.

Chapter Summary

1. A numerical expression represents a particular number. Replacing a numerical expression by the simplest name of the number represented by the expression is called simplifying the expression.

2. A variable expression is evaluated by replacing each variable with its value and simplifying the resulting numerical expression.

3. Grouping symbols are used to show the order in which operations are to be performed to simplify an expression. If no grouping symbols appear, the steps listed on page 6 are followed.

4. Replacing each variable in an open sentence by each of its values, in turn, is a way to find solutions of the open sentence.

5. A problem can often be solved by writing an open sentence based on the given facts and solving the open sentence.

Chapter Review ━━━━━━━━━━

Give the letter of the correct answer.

1. Simplify $(84 \div 7) \div (10 + 2)$. 1-1

    a. 0   **b.** 1   **c.** 24   **d.** 144

2. Evaluate $(3a) - (b - c)$ if $a = 2$, $b = 5$, and $c = 1$.

    a. 0   **b.** 1   **c.** 2   **d.** 3

3. Simplify $\dfrac{19 \times 5 - 7 \times 5}{3 \times 3 + 1}$. 1-2

    a. 5   **b.** 6   **c.** 19   **d.** 44

4. Evaluate $\dfrac{r}{2} + (4s - 1)t$ if $r = 6$, $s = 3$, and $t = 4$.

    a. 11   **b.** 14   **c.** 47   **d.** 56

5. Solve the equation $2x + 9 = 15$ if $x \in \{0, 1, 2, 3, 4, 5, 6\}$. 1-3

    a. 3   **b.** 4   **c.** 5   **d.** 6

6. Which equation represents the word sentence "Five more than twice the number n is nineteen"? 1-4

    a. $2(n + 5) = 19$ **b.** $2(n - 5) = 19$ **c.** $2n - 5 = 19$ **d.** $5 + 2n = 19$

7. A rectangle is 4 cm longer than it is wide. If it is y cm wide, then what is the number of centimeters in its perimeter? 1-5

    a. $4y + 4$ **b.** $y(y + 4)$ **c.** $y + (y + 4)$ **d.** $2y + 2(y + 4)$

8. Alma has four times as much money as Wally. Together they have $40. How much money does Wally have? 1-6

    a. $8   **b.** $10   **c.** $36   **d.** $160

Chapter Test ━━━━━━━━━━

1. Simplify $(18 + 3) \div (56 \div 8)$. 1-1

2. Evaluate $(xy) - (5x)$ if $x = 4$ and $y = 7$.

3. Simplify $9 \times 8 \div 4 \times 2 \div 36 + 1$. 1-2

4. Evaluate $\dfrac{4q - w + 5}{3q - p}$ if $p = 1$, $q = 2$, and $w = 3$.

5. Find the solution set of $4z - 1 = 19$ if $z \in \{1, 2, 3, 4, 5, 6, 7\}$. 1-3

6. Represent this word sentence by an equation: Twelve less than half the number n is twenty. 1-4

7. The sum of two test scores is 178. If x represents one score, represent the other score in terms of x. 1-5

8. The novel has twice as many pages as the poetry book. If the novel has 512 pages, how many pages does the poetry book have? 1-6

Maintaining Skills

Perform the indicated operations.

SAMPLE 1
$$\begin{array}{r} \overset{112}{1025} \\ 37 \\ 429 \\ + 856 \\ \hline 2347 \end{array}$$

SAMPLE 2
$$\begin{array}{r} 398\overset{115}{25} \\ - 7406 \\ \hline 32419 \end{array}$$

SAMPLE 3
$$\begin{array}{r} 5133 \\ \times 407 \\ \hline 35931 \\ 0 \\ 20532 \\ \hline 2089131 \end{array}$$

SAMPLE 4
$$72\overline{)6194} \quad 86 \text{ R}2$$
$$\begin{array}{r} 576 \\ \hline 434 \\ 432 \\ \hline 2 \end{array}$$

1.
$$\begin{array}{r} 7702 \\ 1946 \\ 57 \\ + 813 \end{array}$$

2.
$$\begin{array}{r} 12898 \\ 26065 \\ + 3442 \end{array}$$

3.
$$\begin{array}{r} 4 \\ 521 \\ 98 \\ +6376 \end{array}$$

4.
$$\begin{array}{r} 50483 \\ 39017 \\ + 646 \end{array}$$

5.
$$\begin{array}{r} 9250 \\ 28 \\ 774 \\ +3216 \end{array}$$

6.
$$\begin{array}{r} 4025 \\ -3917 \end{array}$$

7.
$$\begin{array}{r} 8610 \\ - 218 \end{array}$$

8.
$$\begin{array}{r} 5376 \\ -5193 \end{array}$$

9.
$$\begin{array}{r} 19401 \\ - 795 \end{array}$$

10.
$$\begin{array}{r} 68224 \\ -46808 \end{array}$$

11.
$$\begin{array}{r} 1273 \\ \times 56 \end{array}$$

12.
$$\begin{array}{r} 4095 \\ \times 710 \end{array}$$

13.
$$\begin{array}{r} 8162 \\ \times 348 \end{array}$$

14.
$$\begin{array}{r} 30146 \\ \times 98 \end{array}$$

15.
$$\begin{array}{r} 59281 \\ \times 612 \end{array}$$

16. $24\overline{)7260}$ 17. $57\overline{)4854}$ 18. $108\overline{)4428}$ 19. $371\overline{)35616}$

Round each number (a) to the nearest ten; (b) to the nearest thousand.

SAMPLE 5   14,325

SOLUTION   (a) The ones' digit, 5, is greater than or equal to 5; round up to 14,330.   (b) The hundreds' digit, 3, is less than 5; round down to 14,000.

20. 6184   21. 70,569   22. 39,752   23. 87,918   24. 104,055

Estimate each answer to the nearest hundred.

SAMPLE 6
$$\begin{array}{r} 2813 \\ + 952 \end{array}$$
SOLUTION
$$\begin{array}{r} 2800 \\ +1000 \\ \hline 3800 \end{array}$$

25.
$$\begin{array}{r} 837 \\ +651 \end{array}$$

26.
$$\begin{array}{r} 382 \\ -179 \end{array}$$

27.
$$\begin{array}{r} 2091 \\ - 509 \end{array}$$

28.
$$\begin{array}{r} 419 \\ 682 \\ +904 \end{array}$$

29.
$$\begin{array}{r} 2055 \\ 7996 \\ +5247 \end{array}$$

Limpets, crabs, seaworms, an unknown variety of fish, and large tube worms were photographed near an undersea vent at −2800 m. Hot currents rich in dissolved minerals enter the ocean floor at these vents and nourish an abundance of animal life.

2

WORKING WITH
REAL NUMBERS

BASIC PROPERTIES

2-1 *Real Numbers*

OBJECTIVE   To graph real numbers on a number line.

To show how numbers relate to each other, you may represent them as points on a line, called a *number line*. To construct a number line:

1. Choose a starting point on a line and label it "0" (zero). This point is called the **origin.** The origin separates the line into two sides, the **positive side** and the **negative side.** If the line is horizontal, the side to the right of the origin is usually taken to be the positive side.

2. Mark off equal units of distance on both sides of the origin. On the positive side, pair the endpoints of successive units with the **positive integers**

$$1, 2, 3, 4, 5, \ldots .$$

On the negative side, pair the endpoints with the **negative integers**

$$^-1, \ ^-2, \ ^-3, \ ^-4, \ ^-5, \ldots .$$

You read $^-1$ as "negative one." You usually read 1 as "one." You may also read 1 as "positive one," and you may write it as $^+1$.

The positive integers, the negative integers, and zero make up the set of **integers.** The integers which are the product of 2 and any integer are the *even* integers.

$$\{\text{the integers}\} = \{\ldots, {}^-3, {}^-2, {}^-1, 0, 1, 2, 3, \ldots\}$$

$$\{\text{the even integers}\} = \{\ldots, {}^-6, {}^-4, {}^-2, 0, 2, 4, 6, \ldots\}$$

$$\{\text{the odd integers}\} = \{\ldots, {}^-5, {}^-3, {}^-1, 1, 3, 5, \ldots\}$$

In general, a **positive number** is a number paired with a point on the positive side of a number line. A **negative number** is a number paired with a point on the negative side of a number line. For example:

P is $1\frac{1}{3}$ units from 0 on the *positive* side.
The *positive* number $1\frac{1}{3}$ is paired with P.

Q is $1\frac{1}{3}$ units from 0 on the *negative* side.
The *negative* number ${}^-1\frac{1}{3}$ is paired with Q.

On a number line, the point paired with a number is called the **graph** of the number. The number paired with a point is called the **coordinate** of the point. On the number line above, point T is the graph of 2.5, and 2.5 is the coordinate of T.

Any number which is either a positive number, a negative number, or zero is called a **real number.** When you graph real numbers, you take the following facts for granted:

1. Each real number is paired with exactly one point on a number line.
2. Each point on a number line is paired with exactly one real number.

Thus, the graphs of *all* the real numbers make up the entire number line:

The arrowheads indicate that the number line and the graphs go on indefinitely in both directions.

Because positive and negative numbers suggest opposite directions, they are sometimes called *directed numbers.* You use them for measurements that have *direction* as well as *size.* For example:

A *profit* of $75: 75

6 km *north:* 6

A temperature *rise* of
2.5°C (degrees Celsius): 2.5

The charge on a proton: ${}^+1$

A *loss* of $75: ${}^-75$

6 km *south:* ${}^-6$

A temperature *drop* of
2.5°C: ${}^-2.5$

The charge on an electron: ${}^-1$

Oral Exercises

Exercises 1-16 refer to the number line below.

Name the point that is the graph of the given number.

SAMPLE 1 ⁻5   *SOLUTION* Point *D*

1. 3   **2.** 0   **3.** ⁻2   **4.** ⁻1   **5.** 7   **6.** ⁻7

State the coordinate of the given point.

7. *K*   **8.** *F*   **9.** *I*   **10.** *Q*   **11.** *C*   **12.** *R*

SAMPLE 2   The point halfway between *L* and *M*   *SOLUTION* 3.5

13. The point halfway between *J* and *K*
14. The point halfway between *C* and *D*
15. The point one fourth of the way from *P* to *Q*
16. The point one third of the way from *I* to *H*

For each exercise, state the temperature if the mercury in the thermometer shown has reached the level indicated.

17. *A*   **18.** *B*   **19.** *C*   **20.** *D*

Written Exercises

Write a positive number for each measurement. Then write the opposite of that number and describe the measurement indicated by that opposite.

A **1.** Two floors up   **2.** One step to the right
   3. 250 m above sea level   **4.** Five degrees above freezing (0°C)
   5. A gain of 6 points   **6.** Three wins
   7. 8 km east   **8.** Latitude 44° north
   9. One second after liftoff **10.** 2 above par
   11. Receipts of $28.09   **12.** A bank deposit of $5.75

Name the coordinates of the points shown in color.

13.
-3 -2 -1 0 1 2 3

14.
-3 -2 -1 0 1 2 3

15.
-1 0 1 2 3 4 5

16.
-2 -1 0 1 2 3 4

17.
-6 -5 -4 -3 -2 -1 0

18.
0 1 2 3 4 5 6

19.
-3 -2 -1 0 1 2 3

20.
-3 -2 -1 0 1 2 3

List the letters for the points whose coordinates are given.

A   B   C   D   E H F   G   I   J M K   L   N   P   Q

-8 -7 -6 -5 -4 -3 -2 -1 0 1 2 3 4 5 6 7 8

21. -3, 4   **22.** -1, 5   **23.** 0, -7   **24.** 2, -5
25. -6, 6   **26.** -4, 3   **27.** -2, -2.5   **28.** 1, 1.5

Graph the given numbers on a number line. Draw a separate line for each exercise.

29. -3, -1, 1, 3

30. 2, 4, -2, -4

31. 1, $\frac{1}{2}$, 0, -2

32. -3, -2.5, -2, 0

B 33. -2, $-1\frac{2}{3}$, $-1\frac{1}{3}$, 0

34. -1, -0.5, 0, 0.5

35. $-2\frac{1}{4}$, $\frac{-1}{4}$, $\frac{1}{4}$, $\frac{3}{4}$

36. $\frac{-1}{3}$, $\frac{1}{3}$, $\frac{4}{3}$, $\frac{7}{3}$

On a horizontal number line, point P has coordinate -2 and point Q has coordinate 2. Write the coordinate of each point described.

37. 3 units to the right of Q

38. 3 units to the left of P

39. 3 units to the left of Q

40. 3 units to the right of P

41. Halfway between P and Q

42. One fourth of the way from P to Q

C 43. On a number line, point A has coordinate 3, and point D has coordinate 6. What is the coordinate of the point between A and D that is half as far from A as it is from D?

44. On a number line, point X has coordinate -1, and point Y has coordinate 5. What is the coordinate of the point between X and Y that is twice as far from X as it is from Y?

2-2 *Comparing Real Numbers*

OBJECTIVE   To show the order of real numbers.

You know that 2 is less than 6 and that 6 is greater than 2. **Inequality symbols** can be used to show the *order* of pairs of real numbers as follows.

$$< \text{ means "is less than": } \quad 2 < 6$$

$$> \text{ means "is greater than": } \quad 6 > 2$$

To avoid confusing the symbols $>$ and $<$, notice that the name of the greater number is placed at the greater (or open) end of the inequality symbol. The statements $2 < 6$ and $6 > 2$ give the same information.

The graphs of real numbers on a number line show the order of the numbers. Compare the graphs of 2 and 6 below. The graph of the smaller number, 2, lies to the left of the graph of the greater number, 6.

On a horizontal number line, such as the one above, the numbers increase from left to right and decrease from right to left. By studying the number line, you can see that the following statements are true.

$$\begin{array}{ccc} {}^-6 < {}^-4 & {}^-6 < 0 & {}^-6 < 2 \\ {}^-4 > {}^-6 & 0 > {}^-6 & 2 > {}^-6 \end{array}$$

EXAMPLE   Graph the numbers 3, $^-1$, 5.5, 0, $^-2$, $^-4$ on a number line, and then name them in order from least to greatest.

SOLUTION

From least to greatest, the numbers are $^-4$, $^-2$, $^-1$, 0, 3, 5.5.

Oral Exercises

Translate the following statements into words.

1. $2 < 7$ **2.** $0 < 1$ **3.** $0 > {}^-1$ **4.** $^-2 > {}^-6$

5. $^-4 > {}^-10$ **6.** $\dfrac{1}{10} < \dfrac{1}{4}$ **7.** $0.35 < 0.4$ **8.** $^-0.5 > {}^-2.5$

In Exercises 9–16, tell whether or not the given statement is true. Give a reason for your answer.

SAMPLE $8 \times 4 > 8 + 4$ **SOLUTION** True, because $8 \times 4 = 32$, $8 + 4 = 12$, and $32 > 12$.

9. $^-3 < 0 + \dfrac{3}{5}$

10. $\dfrac{3}{4} \times \dfrac{1}{4} < \dfrac{3}{4} + \dfrac{1}{4}$

11. $4 \times 3 < 3 \times 4$

12. $18 + (1 + 19) > (18 + 1) + 19$

13. $\dfrac{7 + 1}{4} > \dfrac{7 - 1}{3}$

14. $\dfrac{10 + 2}{4 + 8} > {}^-1$

15. $4(6 - 3) < 3(6 - 4)$

16. $7(0 + 6) < (7 \times 0) + (7 \times 6)$

Written Exercises

Translate each statement into symbols.

A **1.** Five is greater than negative two.

    2. Negative seven is less than negative one.

    3. Negative ten is greater than negative fifteen.

    4. Nine is greater than six.

    5. Four is less than four and five tenths.

    6. Zero is greater than negative five tenths.

    7. Negative twelve is less than zero.

    8. One fourth is less than seven.

Replace each _?_ with one of the symbols $<$ or $>$ to make a true statement.

9. $^-7 \underline{\ ?\ } 0$ **10.** $0 \underline{\ ?\ } {}^-9$ **11.** $5 \underline{\ ?\ } 4 + 3$ **12.** $2 - 1 \underline{\ ?\ } {}^-6$

13. $7 \times 9 \underline{\ ?\ } 8 \times 6$ **14.** $1 \times 3 \underline{\ ?\ } 2 \times 2$ **15.** $1 \times 1 \underline{\ ?\ } {}^-1$ **16.** $^-1.23 \underline{\ ?\ } {}^-1.24$

17. $49 - 7 \times 7 \underline{\ ?\ } 2(24 \div (5 + 3))$ **18.** $(7 \times 7) - 7 \underline{\ ?\ } (4 + 3)(4 - 3)$

19. $7.2 - 2.2 \underline{\ ?\ } \dfrac{7.2 + 2.2}{2}$ **20.** $\dfrac{4.5 + 3.5}{4} \underline{\ ?\ } (4.5 - 3.5)5$

Write the given numbers in order from least to greatest.

B **21.** $0,\ ^-4,\ 7,\ ^-6$ **22.** $^-5,\ ^-7,\ 0,\ ^-9$ **23.** $^-1,\ 3,\ ^-5,\ 2$

    24. $^-8,\ 9,\ ^-9,\ 1$ **25.** $\dfrac{^-1}{2},\ \dfrac{^-1}{5},\ \dfrac{^-1}{3},\ \dfrac{^-1}{4}$ **26.** $\dfrac{^-2}{3},\ \dfrac{^-3}{4},\ \dfrac{^-1}{6},\ \dfrac{^-1}{9}$

    27. $1.5,\ ^-1.4,\ ^-0.6,\ 0.8$ **28.** $2.6,\ ^-3.4,\ ^-2,\ 3$

    29. $3.142,\ 3.14,\ 3.1416$ **30.** $^-6\dfrac{1}{3},\ ^-6\dfrac{1}{7},\ ^-6\dfrac{1}{2}$

    31. $^-2\dfrac{1}{4},\ ^-2\dfrac{1}{6},\ ^-2\dfrac{1}{2}$ **32.** $1.414,\ 1.4,\ 1.41$

Let x be any positive number and y any negative number. State whether or not the given sentence is true.

C 33. $x < y$　　　　34. $y < 0$　　　　35. $x > y$　　　　36. $0 > x$

37. Some value of x is equal to zero.

38. No value of y is equal to zero.

39. On a number line, the graphs of x and y are on opposite sides of the origin.

40. On a number line, the graph of x is on the same side of the origin as the graph of 1.

Career Note Carpenter

Have you ever used a miter box, a level, a try square, a vise, or a bevel? If you have, then you were probably doing some carpentry work, because these are all hand tools used by carpenters.

Skilled carpenters are involved in almost every aspect of construction. They construct scaffolding, temporary buildings on construction sites, partitions, rafters, sub-floors, and molds for concrete. This work would all be called "rough" carpentry.

Carpenters also do "finish" work. They make cabinets, doors, and stairs. They install floors, paneling, and molding.

To become a skilled carpenter, a student is advised to finish high school or vocational school and then enroll in an apprenticeship program. An apprenticeship program generally includes four years of on-the-job training in carpentry techniques and 144 hours of classroom instruction each year in drafting, blueprint reading, and mathematics.

2-3 *Using Basic Properties*

OBJECTIVE   To use number properties to simplify expressions.

Addition and multiplication of real numbers have several basic properties that you are asked to take for granted. For example, you may accept the following statements as facts.

1. Every pair of real numbers has a unique (one and only one) sum
   which is also a real number.

2. Every pair of real numbers has a unique product which is also a real
   number.

3. When you add two real numbers, you get the same sum no matter
   what order you use in adding them.

$$7 + 5 = 5 + 7 \qquad 1.2 + 0.4 = 0.4 + 1.2$$

4. When you multiply real numbers, you get the same product no matter what order you use in multiplying them.

$$0 \times 13 = 13 \times 0 \qquad \frac{1}{3} \times \frac{2}{5} = \frac{2}{5} \times \frac{1}{3}$$

Statements that are assumed to be true are called **axioms,** or **postu-
lates.** Statements (1) and (2) above may be stated more formally as
follows.

AXIOMS OF CLOSURE

For all real numbers a and b:

$a + b$ is a unique real number.

ab is a unique real number.

Statements (3) and (4) above may be stated as follows.

COMMUTATIVE AXIOMS

For all real numbers a and b:

$$a + b = b + a$$

$$ab = ba$$

In the sum $a + b$, a and b are called **terms.** In the product ab, a and b are called **factors.**

You find a sum or a product by working with two numbers at a time. To find the sum of several numbers, such as

$$87 + 75 + 25,$$

you usually do the additions in order from left to right:

$$(87 + 75) + 25 = 162 + 25 = 187.$$

This example would be easier to compute if the terms were grouped as follows:

$$87 + (75 + 25) = 87 + 100 = 187.$$

Note that the sum is 187 no matter which way the terms of $87 + 75 + 25$ are grouped. When you add three or more real numbers, you get the same sum no matter how you group, or *associate*, the numbers.

Similarly, products of three or more real numbers do not depend on the way you group the factors. For example, you can verify that

$$\left(7 \times \tfrac{1}{2}\right) \times 20 = 7 \times \left(\tfrac{1}{2} \times 20\right).$$

ASSOCIATIVE AXIOMS

For all real numbers a, b, and c:

$$(a + b) + c = a + (b + c)$$

$$(ab)c = a(bc)$$

The commutative and associative axioms permit you to add or multiply numbers *in any order* and *in any groups of two*. Thoughtful use of these axioms can sometimes help you simplify expressions.

EXAMPLE 1 Simplify $3 \times 25 \times 42 \times 4$.

SOLUTION
$$\begin{aligned} 3 \times 25 \times 42 \times 4 &= (3 \times 42)(25 \times 4) \\ &= 126 \times 100 \\ &= 12{,}600 \end{aligned}$$

EXAMPLE 2 Simplify $3 + 7x + 2$.

SOLUTION
$$\begin{aligned} 3 + 7x + 2 &= 7x + 3 + 2 \\ &= 7x + 5 \end{aligned}$$

You use the sign $=$ to show that two expressions name the same number (page 2). In your work, you will usually use the following properties of equality without mention.

For all real numbers a, b, and c:

Reflexive Property $a = a$

Symmetric Property   If $a = b$, then $b = a$.

Transitive Property   If $a = b$ and $b = c$, then $a = c$.

Throughout the rest of this book, the domain of all variables is the set of real numbers unless otherwise specified.

Oral Exercises

Name the axiom or property illustrated.

SAMPLE $6 + 5 = 5 + 6$ *SOLUTION*   Commutative axiom for addition

1. $7 \times 8 = 8 \times 7$

2. $(65 + 99) + 1 = 65 + (99 + 1)$

3. $\frac{1}{2} + 3 = 3 + \frac{1}{2}$

4. $(9)(6 \times 0) = (9 \times 6)(0)$

5. $y + 2.5 = 2.5 + y$

6. If $8y = 56$, then $56 = 8y$.

7. $\frac{1}{2}(4t) = \left(\frac{1}{2} \cdot 4\right)t$

8. If $r + 3 = 7$, then $7 = r + 3$.

9. $(12 + x) + 3 = (x + 12) + 3$

10. There is only one real number that is the sum of 3.9 and 0.7.

11. Every real number is equal to itself.

12. If $x + 4 = 5$ and $5 = 1 + 4$, then $x + 4 = 1 + 4$.

13. $x + 26 + 14 + y = x + (26 + 14) + y$

Name the axiom that justifies each step. A check ($\checkmark$) shows that the step is justified by the substitution principle (page 2).

14. $49 + (28 + 11) = 49 + (11 + 28)$ (1) $\underline{\ \ ?\ \ }$

$= (49 + 11) + 28$ (2) $\underline{\ \ ?\ \ }$

$= 60 + 28$ (3) $\underline{\ \ \checkmark\ \ }$

$= 88$ (4) $\underline{\ \ \checkmark\ \ }$

15. $(25 \times 93) \times 4 = 4 \times (25 \times 93)$ (1) $\underline{\ \ ?\ \ }$

$= (4 \times 25) \times 93$ (2) $\underline{\ \ ?\ \ }$

$= 100 \times 93$ (3) $\underline{\ \ \checkmark\ \ }$

$= 9300$ (4) $\underline{\ \ \checkmark\ \ }$

Written Exercises

In each of Exercises 1-16, simplify the expression.

A   1. $329 + 45 + 71 + 5$
    3. $2 \times 33 \times 5 \times 3$
    5. $25 \times 57 \times 2 \times 2$
    7. $7\frac{1}{2} + 5\frac{1}{3} + 1\frac{1}{2} + \frac{2}{3}$
    9. $0.1 + 1.5 + 7.9 + 0.5$

2. $422 + 36 + 78 + 14$
4. $50 \times 11 \times 11 \times 20$
6. $4 \times 19 \times 7 \times 25$
8. $99\frac{6}{7} + 1\frac{2}{5} + \frac{1}{7} + \frac{3}{5}$
10. $6.75 + 8.95 + 1.05 + 3.25$

SAMPLE $x + 1 + y + 15 = x + y + 1 + 15 = x + y + 16$

B   11. $x + 2 + y + 9 + z + 4$
    13. $(5k)(3p)(2q)$
    15. $(75a)(3b)(10c)(2)$

12. $t + 3 + 8 + s + 16 + r$
14. $(4x)(10y)(7z)$
16. $(25t)(25p)(25q)(4)(8)$

In each of Exercises 17-19, an operation * is defined over the set of positive integers.

a. Find $2 * 3$.
b. State whether or not * has a commutative property.
c. State whether or not * has an associative property.

C   17. $a * b = a + (b + 1)$ 18. $a * b = a + 2b$ 19. $a * b = 2(a + b)$

Self-Test 1

VOCABULARY   origin (p. 29)
                 positive side (p. 29)
                 negative side (p. 29)
                 integers (p. 30)
                 positive number (p. 30)
                 negative number (p. 30)
                 graph (p. 30)
                 coordinate (p. 30)

real number (p. 30)
inequality symbols (p. 33)
axiom (p. 36)
axioms of closure (p. 36)
commutative axioms (p. 36)
terms (p. 37)
factors (p. 37)
associative axioms (p. 37)

1. Graph the given numbers on the same number line: Obj. 2-1, p. 29
   $^-4, ^-1, 0, 2$

2. Translate the given statement into words: $^-3 < 2$.   Obj. 2-2, p. 33

3. Write the given numbers in order from least to greatest:
   $5, 0, ^-6, ^-1$

Simplify.

4. $25 \times 89 \times 4$ 5. $5 + 2x + 6$ Obj. 2-3, p. 36

Check your answers with those at the back of the book.

ADDING REAL NUMBERS

2-4 *Addition on a Number Line*

OBJECTIVE To use a number line to add real numbers.

You can use a horizontal number line to help you find the sum of two real numbers. To find the sum of ⁻3 and ⁻5, draw a number line and follow these directions. Starting at the origin, move your pencil along your number line 3 units to the left. Then, from that position, move your pencil 5 units to the left. Moves to the *left* represent *negative* numbers. Together, the two moves amount to a move of 8 units to the left from the origin. The arrows in the diagram below show the moves.

Thus, ⁻3 + ⁻5 = ⁻8.

To find the sum ⁻3 + 5, first move 3 units to the left from the origin. Then, from that position, move 5 units to the right. Moves to the *right* represent *positive* numbers. The two moves amount to a move of 2 units to the right, as shown below.

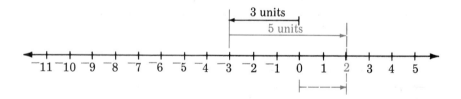

Thus, ⁻3 + 5 = 2

The next diagram shows how to find the sum 3 + ⁻5.

Thus, 3 + ⁻5 = ⁻2.

You can use a number line to help you find the sum of any two real numbers. Can you visualize $^-3 + 0$ on a number line? Interpret "add 0" to mean "move no units." Then you can see that

$$^-3 + 0 = ^-3 \quad \text{and} \quad 0 + ^-3 = ^-3.$$

These equations illustrate the special property of zero for addition of real numbers: When 0 is added to any given number, the sum is *identical* to the given number. We call 0 the **identity element for addition.**

IDENTITY AXIOM FOR ADDITION

There is a unique real number 0 such that for every real number a,

$$a + 0 = a \quad \text{and} \quad 0 + a = a.$$

Oral Exercises

Give an addition statement illustrated by each diagram.

1.

2.

3.

4.

Simplify each expression. If necessary, think of moves along a number line.

5. $^-7 + 0$	**6.** $0 + ^-4$	**7.** $^-6 + 6$	**8.** $5 + ^-5$
9. $^-4 + ^-5$	**10.** $^-9 + ^-1$	**11.** $3 + ^-1$	**12.** $^-4 + 7$
13. $^-8 + 6$	**14.** $5 + ^-3$	**15.** $17 + ^-20$	**16.** $^-1 + ^-99$
17. $101 + ^-1$	**18.** $^-100 + 1$	**19.** $^-10 + 0$	**20.** $^-59 + 59$

Written Exercises

Simplify each expression. If necessary, draw a number line such as the one below to help you.

A   **1.** $(^-2 + 5) + ^-3$ **2.** $(7 + ^-4) + ^-11$

    3. $(15 + ^-21) + 5$ **4.** $(^-10 + ^-17) + 10$

    5. $^-71 + (^-14 + 21)$ **6.** $(48 + ^-8) + (1 + ^-1)$

    7. $(^-45 + ^-25) + (0 + 2)$ **8.** $43 + (6 + ^-12)$

    9. $^-3 + ^-2 + ^-6 + ^-7$ **10.** $^-12 + ^-8 + ^-22 + ^-2$

   11. $^-3.2 + 1.6 + 1.2$ **12.** $4.8 + ^-1.5 + ^-2.3$

   13. $\frac{^-2}{3} + 4\frac{1}{3} + (^-6) + \left(^-1\frac{1}{3}\right)$ **14.** $^-6\frac{1}{2} + \left(^-1\frac{1}{2}\right) + 5 + 2\frac{1}{2}$

   15. $5.50 + (^-2.25) + (^-1)$ **16.** $3.1 + (^-2.8) + (^-8)$

In Exercises 17–34, solve each equation. Use a number line as needed.

SAMPLE $^-3 + y = 4$

SOLUTION

The equation states that $^-3$ plus a certain number is 4. To arrive at 4 from $^-3$ on a number line, you move 7 units to the right.

∴ the solution is 7.   *Answer*

B **17.** $^-4 + y = ^-5$ **18.** $^-2 + x = 17$ **19.** $0 = 12 + z$

   20. $v + 0 = ^-8$ **21.** $^-13 + k = ^-9$ **22.** $^-1 + r = ^-6$

   23. $^-20 = 4 + d$ **24.** $11 = ^-3 + m$ **25.** $^-3.5 + n = ^-4$

   26. $^-1.25 + t = ^-2$ **27.** $^-4 + q = ^-4$ **28.** $0 = ^-50 + w$

C **29.** $r + ^-2 = ^-3 + 5$ **30.** $^-8 + a = ^-3 + ^-10$ **31.** $a + a = 0$

   32. $b + b = ^-12$ **33.** $9 = 2y + ^-1$ **34.** $6x + ^-3 = 0$

2-5 Opposites and Absolute Values

OBJECTIVE To use opposites and absolute values.

The diagram below shows pairings of points on a number line. The paired points are at the same distance from the origin but on opposite sides of the origin. The origin is paired with itself.

The coordinates of the paired points can also be paired:

0 with 0 ⁻1 with 1 ⁻4 with 4 ⁻6.5 with 6.5

The sum of the numbers in such a pair is 0. You can think of adding ⁻4 and 4 on a number line to check that

$$^-4 + 4 = 0.$$

Each number in a pair such as 4 and ⁻4 is called the **opposite,** or **additive inverse,** of the other number. The symbol for the opposite, or additive inverse, of a number a is

$-a$ (note the lowered position of the minus sign).

For example:

$-4 = {}^-4$, read "The opposite of four equals negative four."

$-({}^-1) = 1$, read "The opposite of negative one equals one."

$-0 = 0$. read "The opposite of zero equals zero."

The following axiom is a formal way of saying that every real number has one and only one opposite and that the sum of a number and its opposite is always zero.

AXIOM OF OPPOSITES

For every real number a, there is a unique real number $-a$ such that

$$a + (-a) = 0 \quad \text{and} \quad -a + a = 0.$$

Note that the numerals -4 (lowered minus sign) and ⁻4 (raised minus sign) name the same number. Thus -4 can mean "negative 4" as well as "the opposite of 4."

To simplify notation, lowered minus signs will be used in the numerals for negative numbers throughout the rest of this book.

Be sure you understand the meaning of a variable expression like $-a$. If a represents -7, then $-a$ is the positive number 7. In general:

1. If a is a positive number, then $-a$ is a negative number;
   if a is a negative number, then $-a$ is a positive number;
   if a is 0, then $-a$ is 0.

2. The opposite of $-a$ is a; that is, $-(-a) = a$.

EXAMPLE 1 Simplify.

          a. $-(7 + 5)$ **b.** $-(-2.5)$ **c.** -0 **d.** $-(-n)$

SOLUTION   **a.** -12 **b.** 2.5 **c.** 0 **d.** n

EXAMPLE 2 $-(-10) + (-14) = 10 + (-14) = -4$

In any pair of nonzero opposites, such as -4 and 4, one number is negative and the other is positive. The positive number of any pair of opposite nonzero real numbers is called the **absolute value** of each number in the pair.

The absolute value of a number a is denoted by $|a|$. For example,

$$|-4| = 4 \quad \text{and} \quad |4| = 4.$$

The absolute value of a number may be thought of as the distance of the graph of the number from the origin on a number line. The graphs of both -4 and 4 are 4 units from the origin.

The absolute value of 0 is defined to be 0 itself: $|0| = 0$.

EXAMPLE 3 $8|-2| + |-5| = (8 \times 2) + 5 = 16 + 5 = 21$

Oral Exercises

Name the opposite of each number.

   1. 8   **2.** 5   **3.** -1 **4.** -3 **5.** 1000

   6. -101 **7.** 0   **8.** 0.5   **9.** 2.4   **10.** $-1\frac{1}{2}$

Simplify.

  11. $-(-6)$ **12.** $-(-14)$ **13.** $-\left[-\left(-\frac{1}{2}\right)\right]$

  14. $-[-(-0)]$ **15.** $(-3 + 6) + (-6)$ **16.** $(8 + 2) + (-8)$

  17. $5 + [-(-1)]$ **18.** $-(-4) + 4$ **19.** $|2.1|$

20. $|-32|$ **21.** $6 + |6|$ **22.** $6 + |-6|$
23. $-8 + |-8|$ **24.** $-|9| + |-9|$ **25.** $-(-|2| + |1|)$

Complete.

26. If r is a negative number, then $-r$ is a __?__ number.

27. If r is a positive number, then $-r$ is a __?__ number.

28. The absolute value of every real number is __?__ than zero or equal to zero.

Written Exercises

Simplify.

A **1.** $-(-6) + 12$ **2.** $-(-8) + 2$ **3.** $-7 + [-(-3)]$
   4. $5 + [-(-1)]$ **5.** $-(8 + 9)$ **6.** $-(-5 + 6)$
   7. $-(-10) + 10$ **8.** $-(31 + 49)$ **9.** $-20 + [-(-15)]$
   10. $-[8 + (-3)]$ **11.** $-[-3 + (-3)]$ **12.** $-[11 + (-9)]$
   13. $7 + |-8|$ **14.** $|-6| + |0|$ **15.** $|-7| + |10|$
   16. $|1.2| + |-1.2|$ **17.** $|3 + (-2)| + 6$ **18.** $|9 + (-3)| + (-6)$
   19. $-|-13 + 5|$ **20.** $-|8 + (-10)|$ **21.** $3|-1| + |-4|$
   22. $5\left|-\dfrac{1}{5}\right| + |-2|$ **23.** $-(2|6|) + (-|6|)$ **24.** $-[5|-2| + (-8)]$

In Exercises 25–36, let the domain of the variable be $\{-2, -1, 0, 1, 2\}$. For each number in the given domain, tell whether the open sentence is true or false. Then solve the open sentence.

SAMPLE $-x < 1$ *SOLUTION* $-(-2) < 1$;   that is, $2 < 1$;   false
                        $-(-1) < 1$;   that is, $1 < 1$;   false
                        $-(0) < 1$;   that is, $0 < 1$;   true
                        $-(1) < 1$;   that is, $-1 < 1$;   true
                        $-(2) < 1$;   that is, $-2 < 1$;   true

The solution set is $\{0, 1, 2\}$.

B **25.** $-y = 2$ **26.** $-1 = -a$ **27.** $-2 + b = 0$
   28. $x + (-1) = 1$ **29.** $1 - [-(-z)] = -1$ **30.** $-(-s) + 2 = 0$
   31. $|x| = 1$ **32.** $|-x| = 2$ **33.** $|y| + 1 = 3$
   34. $-6 + |n| = -4$ **35.** $-z > 1$ **36.** $-t < 0$

In Exercises 37–40, suppose that a can be any nonzero real number. State whether the given sentence is always true, only sometimes true, or never true.

C **37.** $|-a| > 0$ **38.** $|-a| < 0$ **39.** $|a| > -a$ **40.** $|a| < -a$

41. Explain why the following statement is true.

If a is a real number, then
$$|a| = a \quad \text{if } a > 0;$$
$$|a| = a \quad \text{if } a = 0;$$
$$|a| = -a \text{ if } a < 0.$$

Computer Key-In _____

If you type the following program into a computer that accepts the language BASIC, the computer will then be ready to add any two numbers that you give it.

```
10  PRINT "TYPE IN TWO NUMBERS TO BE ADDED."
20  INPUT A
30  INPUT B
40  PRINT "SUM =";A+B
50  END
```

Now type RUN. When the computer prints a question mark, type in any positive or negative integer or decimal and then press the RETURN key.

To add more than two numbers (except zero), try the following program. This program uses zero to indicate the end of your list of numbers to be added.

```
10  PRINT "TYPE IN A NUMBER AFTER EACH QUESTION MARK."
20  PRINT "TO END INPUT AND PRINT SUM, TYPE ZERO."
30  LET S=0
40  INPUT N
50  IF N=0 THEN 80
60  LET S=S+N
70  GOTO 40
80  PRINT "SUM=";S
90  END
```

Just for Fun _____

Find the sum of each row, column, and diagonal in the table at the right.

For example, in the first row:
$[3 + (-4)] + 1 = \underline{\quad?\quad}$

			?
3	−4	1	?
−2	0	2	?
−1	4	−3	?
?	?	?	?

2-6 Rules for Addition

OBJECTIVE   To add real numbers.

The expression $-(4 + 3)$ represents the opposite of the sum of 4 and 3. Since $4 + 3 = 7$,

$$-(4 + 3) = -7.$$

The expression $-4 + (-3)$ represents the sum of the opposite of 4 and the opposite of 3. As you saw earlier, you can use a number line to find $-4 + (-3)$ as shown below.

$$\text{Thus, } -4 + (-3) = -7.$$

Since $-(4 + 3) = -7$ and $-4 + (-3) = -7$, the following equation is true.

$$-(4 + 3) = -4 + (-3)$$

Using a number line, you can show that the following equations are also true.

$$-[-5 + (-2)] = 5 + 2 \qquad -[9 + (-4)] = -9 + 4 \qquad -(-7 + 6) = 7 + (-6)$$

These equations suggest the following property.

PROPERTY OF THE OPPOSITE OF A SUM

The opposite of a sum of real numbers is equal to the sum of the opposites of the numbers. That is, for all real numbers a and b,

$$-(a + b) = -a + (-b).$$

Using the property of the opposite of a sum along with axioms you have learned and the familiar addition facts for positive numbers, you can compute sums of any real numbers without thinking of a number line.

EXAMPLE 1   Simplify $-9 + (-5)$. 　　SOLUTION 　　$\begin{aligned} -9 + (-5) &= -(9 + 5) \\ &= -14 \end{aligned}$

EXAMPLE 2   Simplify $12 + (-7)$.

SOLUTION $\begin{aligned}
12 + (-7) &= (5 + 7) + (-7) \\
&= 5 + [7 + (-7)] \\
&= 5 + 0 \\
&= 5
\end{aligned}$

After computing many sums by using either a number line or the methods of Examples 1 and 2, you would probably discover the short-cut methods permitted by the following rules.

RULES FOR ADDITION OF POSITIVE AND NEGATIVE NUMBERS

1. If a and b are both positive, then $a + b = |a| + |b|$.
   Example. $2 + 6 = 8$

2. If a and b are both negative, then $a + b = -(|a| + |b|)$.
   Example. $-4 + (-5) = -(4 + 5) = -9$

3. If a is positive and b is negative and a has the greater absolute value, then $a + b = |a| - |b|$.
   Example. $7 + (-3) = 7 - 3 = 4$

4. If a is positive and b is negative and b has the greater absolute value, then $a + b = -(|b| - |a|)$.
   Example. $6 + (-9) = -(9 - 6) = -3$

5. If a and b are opposites, then $a + b = 0$.
   Example. $4 + (-4) = 0$

The following examples show how to add more than two real numbers.

EXAMPLE 3   Simplify $6 + (-10) + 12 + (-5)$.

SOLUTION 1   Add the numbers in order from left to right.

$$6 + (-10) = -4; \quad -4 + 12 = 8; \quad 8 + (-5) = 3 \quad \textbf{\textit{Answer}}$$

SOLUTION 2
Add positive numbers.	Add negative numbers.	Add the sums.
6	-10	18
$\underline{12}$	$\underline{-\ 5}$	$\underline{-15}$
18	-15	**3** *Answer*

EXAMPLE 4 Add. $\begin{array}{r} -142 \\ 263 \\ 184 \\ -357 \\ \hline \end{array}$ **SOLUTION**

Step 1	*Step 2*	*Step 3*
$\begin{array}{r} -142 \\ -357 \\ \hline -499 \end{array}$	$\begin{array}{r} 263 \\ 184 \\ \hline 447 \end{array}$	$\begin{array}{r} -499 \\ 447 \\ \hline \mathbf{-52} \end{array}$
		Answer

Oral Exercises

Add.

1. $\begin{array}{r} 7 \\ 7 \\ \hline \end{array}$ **2.** $\begin{array}{r} -3 \\ -2 \\ \hline \end{array}$ **3.** $\begin{array}{r} -9 \\ 5 \\ \hline \end{array}$ **4.** $\begin{array}{r} 7 \\ -11 \\ \hline \end{array}$ **5.** $\begin{array}{r} -13 \\ -27 \\ \hline \end{array}$ **6.** $\begin{array}{r} -1 \\ 9 \\ \hline \end{array}$

7. $\begin{array}{r} -15 \\ 6 \\ \hline \end{array}$ **8.** $\begin{array}{r} -12 \\ -5 \\ \hline \end{array}$ **9.** $\begin{array}{r} -14 \\ 34 \\ \hline \end{array}$ **10.** $\begin{array}{r} 55 \\ -75 \\ \hline \end{array}$ **11.** $\begin{array}{r} -89 \\ 24 \\ \hline \end{array}$ **12.** $\begin{array}{r} 55 \\ -39 \\ \hline \end{array}$

Simplify.

13. $-8 + (-2)$ **14.** $-17 + 9$ **15.** $12 + (-12)$

16. $13 + (-4)$ **17.** $2 + (-11)$ **18.** $-7 + 15$

19. $7 + (-1) + (-6)$ **20.** $-1 + (-3) + 3$ **21.** $-5 + (-6) + 11$

Written Exercises

Add.

A **1.** $\begin{array}{r} 7 \\ 6 \\ -1 \\ 3 \\ \hline \end{array}$ **2.** $\begin{array}{r} -4 \\ -7 \\ 5 \\ 2 \\ \hline \end{array}$ **3.** $\begin{array}{r} 43 \\ -23 \\ 52 \\ -10 \\ \hline \end{array}$ **4.** $\begin{array}{r} -35 \\ 31 \\ 48 \\ -70 \\ \hline \end{array}$ **5.** $\begin{array}{r} 148 \\ -72 \\ -26 \\ -9 \\ \hline \end{array}$ **6.** $\begin{array}{r} -137 \\ 241 \\ -85 \\ -66 \\ \hline \end{array}$

Simplify.

7. $-19 + 6 + (-10) + 41$ **8.** $-14 + (-7) + 12 + 24$

9. $111 + (-58) + (-93) + 28$ **10.** $-310 + (-90) + 275 + 65$

11. $-[35 + (-7)] + [-(-3 + 8)]$ **12.** $[-5 + (-3)] + [-(3 + 5)]$

13. $33 + (-44) + (-23) + 0 + 64 + 128$ **14.** $-70 + 114 + (-81) + (-92) + 4$

15. $29 + 41 + (-15) + 13 + (-57) + 5 + (-38) + (-18)$

16. $48 + (-31) + 16 + 0 + (-95) + (-4) + (-36)$

Replace each __?__ with a numeral to make a true statement.

B **17.** $\underline{\ ?\ } + (-8) = 2$ **18.** $-11 + \underline{\ ?\ } = 4$ **19.** $6 + \underline{\ ?\ } = -5$

20. $\underline{\ ?\ } + (-7) = 2$ **21.** $0.4 + \underline{\ ?\ } = -1$ **22.** $\underline{\ ?\ } + 0.75 = -0.25$

In Exercises 23–26, write equations leading to the given equation. Justify each step.

SAMPLE $(a + b) + [-a + (-b)] = 0$

SOLUTION

$(a + b) + [-a + (-b)] = [a + (-a)] + [b + (-b)]$ Commutative and associative axioms

$\qquad\qquad\qquad\qquad\quad = 0 + 0$ Axiom of opposites

$\qquad\qquad\qquad\qquad\quad = 0$ Identity axiom for addition

C **23.** $-8 + (-x + x + 8) = 0$ **24.** $-(-a + b) + b = a$

     25. $a + b + [-(a + b + c)] = -c$ **26.** $m + [-(m + p)] = -p$

Problems

a. Name a positive or a negative number to represent each measurement given in the problem.

b. Compute the sum of the numbers.

c. Answer the question.

SAMPLE

During a period of unsettled weather, the temperature fell 9°C, rose 3°C, fell 4°C, and then rose 6°C. How did the temperature at the end of the period compare with the temperature at the beginning?

SOLUTION

a. $-9, 3, -4, 6$

b. $-9 + 3 + (-4) + 6 = -4$

c. At the end, the temperature was 4°C lower than at the beginning.

A **1.** On one play a football team gained 5 yards. On the next play it lost 7 yards but then gained 9 yards on the third play. What was the team's net gain on the three plays?

     2. An elevator starts at the 16th floor. It then goes down nine floors and up five floors. At what floor is the elevator then located?

     3. Henry LeBlanc has $237 in his checking account. He deposits $63 and then writes a check for $28. How much is then in the checking account?

     4. The stock of Acme Rotors opened in the morning at $38 per share. By noon it had lost $5, but during the afternoon it gained $3. What was its closing value?

     5. A jet plane flying at an altitude of 7800 m dropped 900 m and then rose 750 m. What was its new altitude?

6. A submarine dove to a level 240 m below the surface of the ocean. Later it climbed 80 m and then dove 45 m. What was the new depth of the submarine?

7. A helicopter was flying in Death Valley at an altitude of 13 m below sea level. If it climbed 37 m and then dropped 29 m, at what altitude was it then flying?

8. A submarine 38 m below the ocean surface descended 15 m and then fired a rocket which rose 265 m. How far above the ocean surface did the rocket rise?

9. During their first year after opening a restaurant, the Taylors had a loss of $12,760. During their second and third years of operation, they had gains of $19,350 and $25,180. What was the restaurant's net gain or loss over the three-year period?

10. During a four-day period, Milville Hospital received 24 new patients and discharged 6, received 8 and discharged 11, received 12 and discharged 21, and received 9 and discharged 13. How did the number of patients in the hospital at the end of the fourth day compare with the number at the start of the four-day period?

B 11. A passenger on a train traveling at 133 km/h walks toward the back of the train at the rate of 7 km/h. What is the passenger's rate of travel with respect to the ground?

12. Departing from Center City at noon, Sandra flew to Westville. The flight took 3.5 hours, but the time in Westville is 2 hours earlier than it is in Center City. What time was it in Westville when Sandra landed?

13. A golfer played six rounds of golf with the following scores: 2 under par, 4 over par, par, 3 over par, 1 under par, 5 over par. How did she finish with respect to par?

14. On opening a revolving charge account, Jim Halloran bought $168.40 worth of clothing, and $88.20 worth of garden equipment. He then made two monthly payments of $35.00 each. If the interest charges for the two-month period totaled $6.50, what did Jim then owe on the account?

C 15. During a training exercise, an astronaut's heart rate rose 33 beats per minute, then fell 18 beats per minute, then rose 21 beats per minute, and after the exercise was completed, fell 30 beats per minute. If the rate was 74 beats per minute after the exercise was completed, what was it at the beginning?

16. During a ten-year period, the population of Windham increased by 2500. Over the next three ten-year periods, the population grew by 1500, decreased by 3000, and then decreased again by 2000. What was the population at the beginning of the forty-year period if the population was 15,000 at the end of the period?

Self-Test 2

VOCABULARY   identity element for addition (p. 41)
opposite (p. 43)

absolute value (p. 44)
opposite of a sum (p. 47)

Simplify.

1. $^-3 + {}^-2$
2. $^-5 + 17 + {}^-6$
3. $-(-8) + 5$
4. $-|-7 + 3|$
5. $-11 + (-1)$
6. $-16 + 0 + (-12) + 8$

Obj. 2-4, p. 40

Obj. 2-5, p. 43

Obj. 2-6, p. 47

Check your answers with those at the back of the book.

Calculator Key-In

Use a calculator to add.

1.
```
  $50.00
-  19.99
-   6.59
    3.25
```

2.
```
- 3679
  5153
- 2768
  4627
```

3.
```
  0.1000
- 0.0100
  0.0010
- 0.0001
```

Historical Note Plus and Minus

In one Egyptian papyrus dated around 1550 B.C., a pair of legs drawn walking in one direction was used to indicate addition and a pair of legs drawn walking in the opposite direction was used to indicate subtraction.

The symbols + and − that are used today for addition and subtraction were not used universally until the eighteenth century, although variations of these two symbols were in common use in Europe at about the time Columbus explored the Americas.

During the nineteenth century, as mathematicians turned to the foundations of algebra, they tried various ways of differentiating between "plus and minus" and "positive and negative." At about the beginning of the twentieth century, the small raised symbols, $^+$ for positive and $^-$ for negative, that are used in the early work with integers in this book came into general use in the United States.

2-7 *The Distributive Axiom*

OBJECTIVE: To use the distributive axiom to simplify expressions.

The fare on the ferry from Port Alice to Seagate was $5 for each motorbike and $4 for the rider. Therefore, the total fare in dollars for three friends and their bikes was

$$3(5 + 4) = 3 \times 9 = 27.$$

The total fare was also the sum of the fares for the bikes and the fares for the riders:

$$(3 \times 5) + (3 \times 4) = 15 + 12 = 27.$$

Either way you compute it, the total fare is the same. That is,

$$3(5 + 4) = (3 \times 5) + (3 \times 4).$$

Note that 3 is *distributed* as a multiplier of each term of 5 + 4. This example illustrates another axiom that we use in working with real numbers: multiplication is *distributive with respect to addition.*

DISTRIBUTIVE AXIOM OF MULTIPLICATION WITH
RESPECT TO ADDITION

For all real numbers a, b, and c,

$$a(b + c) = ab + ac \quad \text{and} \quad (b + c)a = ba + ca.$$

By applying the symmetric property of equality, you can also state the distributive axiom in the following form.

For all real numbers a, b, and c,

$$ab + ac = a(b + c) \quad \text{and} \quad ba + ca = (b + c)a.$$

For example, the diagram below illustrates that

$$(4 \times 3) + (4 \times 2) = 4(3 + 2).$$

Area:
4×3

Area:
4×2

Area:
$4 \times (3 + 2)$

The following examples show some uses of the distributive axiom.

EXAMPLE 1 **a.** $45\left(\frac{1}{3} + \frac{1}{5}\right) = \left(45 \times \frac{1}{3}\right) + \left(45 \times \frac{1}{5}\right) = 15 + 9 = 24$

b. $8(7.5) = 8(7 + 0.5) = (8 \times 7) + (8 \times 0.5) = 56 + 4 = 60$

c. $28 \times 7 = (20 + 8) \times 7 = (20 \times 7) + (8 \times 7) = 140 + 56 = 196$

d. $(25 \times 9) + (75 \times 9) = (25 + 75)9 = (100)9 = 900$

EXAMPLE 2 Show that $5x + 8x = 13x$ for every real number x.

SOLUTION $5x + 8x = (5 + 8)x$ Distributive axiom
$\qquad\qquad = 13x$ Substitution principle

Because properties of real numbers and equality guarantee that for all values of the variable

$$5x + 8x \quad \text{and} \quad 13x$$

represent the same number, the two expressions are said to be **equivalent.** The expression $5x + 8x$ has two terms. The expression $13x$ has one term. Replacing an expression containing a variable by an equivalent expression with as few terms as possible is called **simplifying the expression.**

EXAMPLE 3 Simplify $5y + 1 + (-3)y + 19$.

SOLUTION $5y + 1 + (-3)y + 19 = [5y + (-3)y] + (1 + 19)$
$\qquad\qquad\qquad\qquad\qquad = [5 + (-3)]y + 20$
$\qquad\qquad\qquad\qquad\qquad = 2y + 20$

Oral Exercises

Use the distributive axiom to simplify each expression.

1. $2(50 + 1)$

2. $3(40 + 2)$

3. $5(20 + 7)$

4. $4(30 + 5)$

5. 4×2.5

6. $6 \times 1\frac{1}{3}$

7. $10\left(3\frac{1}{2}\right)$

8. $12(2.25)$

9. $(25 + 75)\left(\frac{1}{5}\right)$

10. $(49 + 77)\left(\frac{1}{7}\right)$

11. $\left(\frac{1}{3} \times 16\right) + \left(\frac{1}{3} \times 2\right)$

12. $\left(17 \times \frac{1}{4}\right) + \left(3 \times \frac{1}{4}\right)$

Simplify.

13. $3x + 11x$

14. $10y + 18y$

15. $x + 7x$

16. $4r + r$

17. $(-2)t + (-4)t$

18. $(-3)s + (-7)s$

19. $5b + (-2)b$

20. $7a + (-3)a$

21. $3(2 + x) + 5$

Written Exercises

Simplify.

A **1.** $80\left(\frac{1}{4} + \frac{1}{5}\right)$

2. $3\left(1\frac{1}{3}\right)$

3. $\frac{1}{6}(13) + \frac{1}{6}(11)$

4. $(0.25)(9) + (0.75)(9)$

5. $(4 \times 37) + (6 \times 37)$

6. $(33 \times 89) + (67 \times 89)$

7. $2x + 13x$

8. $20y + 14y$

9. $z + 29z$

10. $99w + w$

11. $45t + (-30)t$

12. $-16s + 36s$

13. $3x + 2x + 8$

14. $5 + 7y + 4y$

15. $2(a + 1) + 5$

16. $9(b + 7) + 7$

17. $8c + (-5)c + 16$

18. $21 + (-4)d + 12d$

19. $6a + 1 + 7a + 3$

20. $4 + 11c + 4c + 11$

21. $10x + (-3) + (-3)x + 5$

22. $-9y + 7 + 18y + (-6)$

23. $-12 + 12x + 12 + (-1)x$

24. $16y + 8 + (-8)y + (-8)$

25. $8b + (-2)b + (-4)b$

26. $(-9)c + (-2)c + 22c$

B **27.** $3m + 5k + (-1)m + 12k$

28. $5h + (-2)g + 4h + 7g$

29. $7x + 9y + 3 + x + y$

30. $8r + s + (-6)r + 2 + 4s$

SAMPLE $2(x + y + z) + 3(2x + 3y)$

SOLUTION $2(x + y + z) + 3(2x + 3y) = (2x + 2y + 2z) + (6x + 9y)$
$$= (2x + 6x) + (2y + 9y) + 2z$$
$$= 8x + 11y + 2z$$

31. $7(n + r) + 13(n + r)$

32. $3(u + v) + 17(u + v)$

33. $8(x + 3) + 9(4 + x) + x$

34. $6(y + 2) + 9(4 + y) + y$

35. $5(z + 2x + 4) + 3(2z + 8)$

36. $16(k + 2) + 4(3p + 5k + 4)$

Represent each word expression by a variable expression. Then simplify it.

37. Six times the sum of x and y, increased by twice the sum of $3x$ and $2y$.

38. Twice the sum of seven and m, increased by three times the sum of eleven and m.

39. Ten more than the sum of negative seven and x, increased by one half the sum of $10x$ and $12y$.

40. Three more than twice the sum of p and q, increased by the product of negative five and q.

Simplify.

C **41.** $9[7x + 5(4 + 3x)] + (-16)x + (-8)$

42. $-21 + (-1)y + 2[6y + 3(5y + 12)]$

43. $10(2q + p) + 17[2q + 4(3q + 9p + 5)]$

44. $8[9(3v + 4w + 1) + 14(v + 7)] + 5(8v + 3w)$

Biography John Cunningham McLennan

Sir John Cunningham McLennan (1867–1935) was born in Ingersoll, Ontario. He graduated from the University of Toronto in 1892 and was professor of physics there from 1907 to 1931. His major contributions in physics were made in the study of the flow of electricity in metals at very low temperatures.

McLennan's research in other areas included work in radioactivity and the use of radium in treating cancer. During World War I, he aided in the development of magnetic detection devices for submarines. He and another physicist were able to obtain a spectrum similar to that of the aurora by passing electrons through thin oxygen. Another achievement was his success in liquefying helium in 1932.

2-8 Rules for Multiplication

OBJECTIVE To multiply real numbers.

When you multiply any given real number by 1, the product is identical to the given number. For example,

$$3 \times 1 = 3 \quad \text{and} \quad 1 \times 3 = 3.$$

The **identity element for multiplication** is 1.

IDENTITY AXIOM FOR MULTIPLICATION

There is a unique real number 1 such that for every real number a,

$$a \cdot 1 = a \quad \text{and} \quad 1 \cdot a = a.$$

The equations

$$3 \times 0 = 0 \quad \text{and} \quad 0 \times 3 = 0$$

illustrate the *multiplicative property of zero:* When one of the factors of a product is zero, the product itself is zero.

MULTIPLICATIVE PROPERTY OF ZERO

For every real number a,

$$a \cdot 0 = 0 \quad \text{and} \quad 0 \cdot a = 0.$$

Would you guess that $3 \times (-1) = -3$? You can verify this product by noticing that

$$3 \times (-1) = (-1) + (-1) + (-1) = -3.$$

Multiplying *any* real number by -1 produces the opposite of the number.

MULTIPLICATIVE PROPERTY OF -1

For every real number a,

$$a(-1) = -a \quad \text{and} \quad (-1)a = -a.$$

A special case of the multiplicative property of -1 occurs when the value of a is -1:

$$(-1)(-1) = 1.$$

Using the multiplicative property of -1 with the familiar multiplication facts for positive numbers and axioms that you have learned, you can compute the product of *any* two real numbers. Here are some examples:

1. $3(4) = 12$
2. $(-3)(4) = (-1)(3)(4) = (-1)(12) = -12$
3. $3(-4) = 3(-1)(4) = (-1)(12) = -12$
4. $(-3)(-4) = (-1)(3)(-1)(4) = (-1)(-1)(12) = (1)(12) = 12$

Similarly, the following property can be shown.

PROPERTY OF OPPOSITES IN PRODUCTS

For all real numbers a and b:

$$-a(b) = -ab \qquad a(-b) = -ab \qquad -a(-b) = ab$$

Practice in computing products will lead you to discover the following rules.

RULES FOR MULTIPLICATION OF POSITIVE AND NEGATIVE NUMBERS

1. The product of a positive number and a negative number is a negative number.
2. The product of two positive numbers or of two negative numbers is a positive number.
3. The absolute value of the product of two real numbers is the product of the absolute values of the numbers:

$$|ab| = |a| \times |b|.$$

By pairing the negative numbers in a product of more than two factors, you will find that

the product of an *even* number of negative numbers is *positive;*

the product of an *odd* number of negative numbers is *negative.*

EXAMPLE 1 State whether the expression names a positive number, a negative number, or zero. Then simplify the expression.

        a. $-8(-4)(-3)$ **b.** $15(-73)(0)$ **c.** $4(-3)(-2)$

SOLUTION   **a.** Negative; -96 **b.** 0   **c.** Positive; 24

EXAMPLE 2 Simplify.   **a.** $(-3x)(-12y)$ **b.** $7t + (-8t)$

SOLUTION   **a.** $(-3x)(-12y) = (-3)(-12)(x)(y) = 36xy$

              b. $7t + (-8t) = 7t + (-8)t = [7 + (-8)]t = (-1)t = -t$

Oral Exercises

Simplify.

1. $(-8)(-1)$	**2.** $10(-9)$	**3.** $(-3)(-7)$
4. $(-9)(-5)$	**5.** $(-1)(3)(-3)$	**6.** $2(-5)(-1)$
7. $(-1)(-3)(-5)$	**8.** $(-2)(-4)(-6)$	**9.** $15(0)(-21)$
10. $-8(-12)(0)$	**11.** $(-7)(-10x)$	**12.** $(-6)(11y)$
13. $(-2a)(-3b)$	**14.** $(4x)(-6y)$	**15.** $(-7w)(11z)$
16. $5t + (-4t)$	**17.** $8u + (-8u)$	**18.** $-9xy + 8xy$
19. $-4mn + (-6mn)$	**20.** $-a + 12a$	**21.** $(-39k) + (-k)$

Written Exercises

Simplify.

A

1. $(-30)(-4)$	**2.** $21(-4)$	**3.** $(-4)(12)(-10)$
4. $(-6)(-11)(20)$	**5.** $(-7)(-3)(-5)$	**6.** $(-8)(-4)(-2)$
7. $(-18)(-19)(0)$	**8.** $(-45)(55)(0)$	**9.** $4(-2)(-10)(-5)$
10. $(-6)(15)(-2)(-10)$	**11.** $(-4)(-1)(-6)(-10)$	**12.** $(-8)(-5)(-1)(-3)$
13. $-2[-1 + (-8)]$	**14.** $(-6 + 15)(-1)$	**15.** $(9 \times 1) + 9(-11)$
16. $(-3 \times 8) + (-3 \times 2)$	**17.** $(-6 \times 8) + (-6 \times 2)$	**18.** $21(-1) + 21(11)$

19. $6(-r + 7t)$	**20.** $-7[2x + (-y)]$
21. $-3[-a + (-5)b]$	**22.** $-2(3m + 4k)$
23. $-m + 3 + 3m + (-4)$	**24.** $3 + (-b) + (-7) + (-2b)$
25. $15q + (-4p) + (-7q) + (-8p)$	**26.** $n + (-5k) + 3n + (-4n) + k$

B

27. $2.3a + 0.5b + (-1.7a) + (-2.5b)$	**28.** $-0.1m + 3.1n + (-3.9m) + (-2.3n)$
29. $-x + \frac{3}{4}x + \frac{1}{2}y + \frac{5}{2}y$	**30.** $-3v + (-\frac{1}{2}t) + 2\frac{1}{2}v + (-\frac{1}{2}t)$
31. $2(a + 3b) + (-3)(3a + b)$	**32.** $6[x + (-y)] + 5(3y + x)$

Simplify.

33. $-2(3t + s) + 7[t + (-s)]$

34. $-3(6a + c) + (-2)(a + 10c)$

35. $-4(-d + 2e) + (-3)[d + (-5e)]$

36. $-6[q + (-3t)] + (-5)(3q + t)$

37. $2[-3(m + 4n) + (-n)] + (-m)$

38. $3[2(-3k + g) + (-k)] + (-6g)$

39. $-10 + (-3)[2(-1 + w) + (-2w)]$

40. $3r + (-2)[3(-r + 1) + r]$

C 41. To show that $a(-1)$ is the opposite of a for every real number a, you can show that the sum of $a(-1)$ and a is zero as follows. Name the axiom or property that justifies each step.

$$\begin{aligned} a(-1) + a &= a(-1) + a(1) & (1) \ \underline{\ ?\ } \\ &= a[(-1) + 1] & (2) \ \underline{\ ?\ } \\ &= a(0) & (3) \ \underline{\ ?\ } \\ &= 0 & (4) \ \underline{\ ?\ } \end{aligned}$$

Calculator Key-In _____

Use a calculator to simplify each expression.

1. $34(-34)$

2. $(-334)334$

3. $(-3334)(-3334)$

4. $3(-5)(-37)$

5. $2(-3)(-4)(-37)$

6. $-3(-3)(-3)(-37)$

7. $(1234)(8) + 4$

8. $(-12345)(8) - 5$

9. $(-123456)(-8) + 6$

Just for Fun _____

Copy the diagram and write the products in the boxes. (Use a calculator if you like.) Do you see a pattern in the results?

$142857 \times 1 = \underline{\ ?\ }$
$142857 \times 2 = \underline{\ ?\ }$
$142857 \times 3 = \underline{\ ?\ }$
$142857 \times 4 = \underline{\ ?\ }$
$142857 \times 5 = \underline{\ ?\ }$
$142857 \times 6 = \underline{\ ?\ }$

2-9 *The Reciprocal of a Real Number*

OBJECTIVE To use reciprocals.

Two numbers whose product is 1 are called **reciprocals,** or **multiplicative inverses,** of each other. For example:

1. 3 and $\frac{1}{3}$ are reciprocals because $3 \times \frac{1}{3} = 1$.

2. -1.25 and -0.8 are reciprocals because $(-1.25)(-0.8) = 1$.

3. $\frac{2}{3}$ and $\frac{3}{2}$ are reciprocals because $\frac{2}{3} \cdot \frac{3}{2} = 1$.

4. 1 is its own reciprocal because $1 \times 1 = 1$.
5. -1 is its own reciprocal because $(-1)(-1) = 1$.
6. 0 has no reciprocal because the product of 0 and *any* real number is 0, *not* 1.

The symbol for the reciprocal, or multiplicative inverse, of a nonzero real number a is $\frac{1}{a}$.

Every real number except 0 has a reciprocal. This fact is stated as an axiom.

AXIOM OF RECIPROCALS

For every nonzero real number a, there is a unique real number $\frac{1}{a}$ such that

$$a \cdot \frac{1}{a} = 1 \quad \text{and} \quad \frac{1}{a} \cdot a = 1.$$

You know that -3 and $-\frac{1}{3}$ are reciprocals because $(-3)\left(-\frac{1}{3}\right) = 1$.

You can show in general that $(-a)\left(-\frac{1}{a}\right) = 1$ for $a \neq 0$ as follows:

$$(-a)\left(-\frac{1}{a}\right) = (-1 \cdot a)\left(-1 \cdot \frac{1}{a}\right) = [(-1)(-1)]\left(a \cdot \frac{1}{a}\right) = 1 \times 1 = 1.$$

Therefore, for every nonzero real number a,

$$\frac{1}{-a} = -\frac{1}{a}, \text{ read "The reciprocal of } -a \text{ is } -\frac{1}{a}."$$

EXAMPLE 1 Simplify each expression.

a. $(8 \times 9)\left(\frac{1}{8} \times \frac{1}{9}\right)$

b. $(ab)\left(\frac{1}{a} \cdot \frac{1}{b}\right)$, $a \neq 0$, $b \neq 0$

SOLUTION **a.** $(8 \times 9)\left(\frac{1}{8} \times \frac{1}{9}\right) = \left(8 \times \frac{1}{8}\right)\left(9 \times \frac{1}{9}\right) = 1 \times 1 = 1$

b. $(ab)\left(\frac{1}{a} \cdot \frac{1}{b}\right) = \left(a \cdot \frac{1}{a}\right)\left(b \cdot \frac{1}{b}\right) = 1 \times 1 = 1$

Example 1(b) shows that the product of ab and $\frac{1}{a} \cdot \frac{1}{b}$ is 1. Therefore, $\frac{1}{a} \cdot \frac{1}{b}$ is the reciprocal of ab. This fact can be stated as follows.

PROPERTY OF THE RECIPROCAL OF A PRODUCT

The reciprocal of a product of nonzero real numbers is the product of the reciprocals of the numbers. That is, for all nonzero real numbers a and b,

$$\frac{1}{ab} = \frac{1}{a} \cdot \frac{1}{b}.$$

EXAMPLE 2 Simplify the product $\frac{1}{3} \cdot \frac{1}{-5}$.

SOLUTION $\frac{1}{3} \cdot \frac{1}{-5} = \frac{1}{3(-5)} = \frac{1}{-15} = -\frac{1}{15}$

Oral Exercises

State the reciprocal of each number.

1. 7   **2.** 1   **3.** -1 **4.** $\frac{1}{6}$

5. -2 **6.** $\frac{3}{4}$ **7.** 0.25   **8.** $-\frac{1}{8}$

9. $-\frac{5}{6}$ **10.** d, $d \neq 0$ **11.** $\frac{a}{5}$, $a \neq 0$ **12.** $-\frac{1}{t}$, $t \neq 0$

Simplify.

13. $\frac{1}{6} \cdot \frac{1}{7}$ **14.** $\frac{1}{-3} \cdot \frac{1}{-2}$ **15.** $\frac{1}{4} \cdot \frac{1}{-5}$ **16.** $\frac{1}{-x} \cdot \frac{1}{y}$

Written Exercises

Simplify each expression.

SAMPLE 1
$$-63xy\left(-\frac{1}{7}\right) = (-1 \cdot 63)xy\left(-1 \cdot \frac{1}{7}\right)$$
$$= [(-1)(-1)]\left(63 \cdot \frac{1}{7}\right)xy$$
$$= 1 \cdot \left(9 \cdot 7 \cdot \frac{1}{7}\right)xy$$
$$= 1 \cdot (9 \cdot 1)xy = 9xy$$

A

1. $\frac{1}{5}(-20)$

2. $-\frac{1}{12}(36)$

3. $-100\left(\frac{1}{10}\right)$

4. $-60\left(-\frac{1}{6}\right)$

5. $96\left(-\frac{1}{8}\right)\left(-\frac{1}{12}\right)$

6. $-51\left(-\frac{1}{3}\right)\left(-\frac{1}{17}\right)$

7. $\frac{1}{-4}(48)\left(\frac{1}{3}\right)$

8. $-90\left(\frac{1}{2}\right)\left(\frac{1}{-3}\right)$

9. $6xy\left(-\frac{1}{6}\right)$

10. $22kt\left(-\frac{1}{11}\right)$

11. $\frac{1}{x}(7xy)$, $x \neq 0$

12. $(3mn)\frac{1}{n}$, $n \neq 0$

SAMPLE 2
$$\frac{1}{4}[28t + (-4s)] = \frac{1}{4}(28t) + \frac{1}{4}(-4s)$$
$$= \left(\frac{1}{4} \times 28\right)t + \left[\frac{1}{4}(-4)\right]s$$
$$= 7t + (-1)s$$
$$= 7t + (-s)$$

13. $\frac{1}{2}(-10x + 6)$

14. $\frac{1}{3}[12y + (-27)]$

15. $-\frac{1}{7}(-21c + 14d)$

16. $-\frac{1}{9}(45u + 81v)$

17. $[16a + (-24b)]\left(-\frac{1}{8}\right)$

18. $[-26p + (-39)q]\left(-\frac{1}{13}\right)$

B

19. $\frac{1}{2}(6x + 4y) + \frac{1}{3}(-3x + 15y)$

20. $\frac{1}{5}(-5z + 10w) + \frac{1}{2}(-8w + 2z)$

21. $12\left[\frac{1}{3}a + \left(-\frac{1}{2}b\right)\right] + 21\left[\frac{1}{7}b + \frac{1}{3}a\right]$

22. $-8\left[\frac{1}{8}d + \left(-\frac{1}{8}e\right)\right] + \frac{1}{3}[6d + (-9e)]$

23. $-\frac{1}{6}[48r + (-6)] + \left(-\frac{1}{4}\right)(64r + 4)$

24. $-4\left(\frac{1}{2}p + 4\right) + \frac{1}{5}(-30p + 5)$

25. $-3\left[\frac{1}{4}(8w + 1) + \left(-\frac{1}{4}\right)\right] + 7w$

26. $5h + \left(-\frac{1}{2}\right)\left[8 + 40\left(-\frac{1}{5} + \frac{1}{4}h\right)\right]$

Use the definition of reciprocals to find the value of x.

C

27. $-\frac{1}{3}x = 1$

28. $-0.5x = 1$

29. $x \cdot \frac{1}{\pi} = 1$

30. $\frac{1}{x} = 3$

31. $\frac{1}{\frac{1}{x}} = 3$

32. $\frac{1}{\frac{1}{x}} = -2$

Calculator Key-In _____

Use the reciprocal key on a calculator to find the reciprocal of each number.

1. 0.125   **2.** −8   **3.** −0.0625   **4.** 15625

5. For each number in Exercises 1–4, press the reciprocal key twice. Your results illustrate the property: The reciprocal of the reciprocal of a number is __?__ .

6. a. Copy and complete the table.

a	b	$\dfrac{1}{ab}$	$\dfrac{1}{a} \cdot \dfrac{1}{b}$
4	8	?	?
0.678	0.789	?	?
−64	−0.5	?	?
999	888	?	?

b. What property does your completed table illustrate?

7. If you have not done Exercises 27–32 on page 63, you may wish to try them now and to check your answers using the reciprocal key on a calculator. To check Exercise 29, you will also need to use the key labeled "π."

Self-Test 3 _____

VOCABULARY   distributive axiom (p. 53)
equivalent expressions (p. 54)
simplify a variable expression (p. 54)
identity element for multiplication (p. 57)
reciprocals (p. 61)
reciprocal of a product (p. 62)

Simplify.

1. $-7x + 12x + 5$ **2.** $3(y - 2) + 1$ Obj. 2-7, p. 53

3. $6(-7)$ **4.** $a(-1) + (-2)(-3)$ Obj. 2-8, p. 57

5. $\dfrac{1}{8} \cdot 8x$ **6.** $-\dfrac{1}{2}[12a + (-2)b]$ Obj. 2-9, p. 61

Check your answers with those at the back of the book.

Application Balancing a Checkbook

The amount of a check or a deposit and the date written are recorded in a checkbook register or on a check stub. To calculate the new balance, subtract the amount of a check from the previous balance or add the amount of a deposit to the previous balance.

CHECK NO.	DATE	CHECK ISSUED TO	AMOUNT OF CHECK		√	DATE OF DEP.	AMOUNT OF DEPOSIT		BALANCE	
		BALANCE BROUGHT FORWARD →							904	21
319	3/15	Zelkova Stationery	12	43					891	78
320	3/21	Phoenix Realty	205	00					691	78
321	4/11	Shorts Sports, Inc.	21	50					670	28
						4/12	793	81	1464	09

Banks send each customer a monthly statement, which is accompanied by the canceled checks. The customer then balances the checkbook by comparing his or her records with the bank statement.

As a preliminary step in balancing your checking account, you indicate in your records all checks that have been canceled and all deposits that have been recorded. On a separate sheet of paper, you do the following:

1. Write down the current balance according to your records.
2. Add the amount of any check not yet canceled.
3. Subtract any deposits not yet credited to your account.
4. Subtract any service charges.
5. Compare the last amount with the closing balance on the bank statement. They should agree.

If the balances do not agree, search for the error. First, go over the arithmetic so far. If the error is not discovered, add the sum of the deposits to the previous correct balance and subtract the total of the amounts of the checks written. If this result agrees with the corrected bank balance, then there is simply an error in computing the running balances. If this result does not agree, then find the difference between the balances. Does it suggest a check or a deposit that was not recorded?

Balance the checkbook register shown above with the bank statement at the right. Be sure to check for arithmetic errors.

OPENING DATE THRU CLOSING DATE		
3/13/8X	4/12/8X	
PREVIOUS BALANCE	NEW BALANCE	
904.21	1480.59	
DATE	CHECKS PAID	DEPOSITS
3/16	12.43	
4/3	205.00	
4/12		793.81

Chapter Summary

1. The positive numbers, the negative numbers, and zero make up the real numbers and can be paired with the points on a number line, thereby showing their order.

2. A number line can be used to find the sum of two real numbers.

3. Opposites and absolute values are used in the rules for adding real numbers (page 48) and multiplying real numbers (page 58).

4. Real number axioms are statements about numbers that are accepted as true and are the basis for computation in arithmetic and in algebra. The following statements are true for all real values of each variable except as noted.

Equality:	Reflexive property	$a = a$
	Symmetric property	If $a = b$, then $b = a$.
	Transitive property	If $a = b$ and $b = c$, then $a = c$.

	Addition	Multiplication
Axioms of closure	$a + b$ is a unique real number.	ab is a unique real number.
Commutative axioms	$a + b = b + a$	$ab = ba$
Associative axioms	$(a + b) + c = a + (b + c)$	$(ab)c = a(bc)$
Identity axioms	$a + 0 = 0 + a = a$	$a \cdot 1 = 1 \cdot a = a$
Axiom of opposites	$a + (-a) = (-a) + a = 0$	
Axiom of reciprocals		$a \cdot \dfrac{1}{a} = \dfrac{1}{a} \cdot a = 1;\ a \neq 0$
Distributive axiom	$a(b + c) = ab + ac$ and $(b + c)a = ba + ca$	

5. Other useful properties about addition or multiplication:

Property of the opposite of a sum: $-(a + b) = -a + (-b)$

Multiplicative property of zero: $a \cdot 0 = 0 \cdot a = 0$

Multiplicative property of -1: $a(-1) = (-1)a = -a$

Property of opposites in products: $-a(b) = -ab;\quad a(-b) = -ab;\quad -a(-b) = ab$

Property of the reciprocal of a product. $\dfrac{1}{ab} = \dfrac{1}{a} \cdot \dfrac{1}{b};\ a \neq 0,\ b \neq 0$

Chapter Review

Give the letter of the correct answer.

1. Refer to the number line above. Give the coordinate of the point halfway between the origin and $^-1$.

    a. 1   **b.** $^-2$ **c.** $\dfrac{^-1}{2}$ **d.** $\dfrac{1}{2}$

2-1

2. Refer to the number line above. Name the point that is the graph of $\dfrac{7}{2}$.

    a. A **b.** B **c.** C **d.** D

3. Which of the following statements is true?

2-2

    a. $^-5 > 0$ **b.** $^-5 > 5$ **c.** $^-5 < 2$ **d.** $2 < 0$

4. Name the axiom illustrated: $4n + 5 = 5 + 4n$.

2-3

    a. axiom of closure for addition

    b. commutative axiom for addition

    c. associative axiom for multiplication

    d. commutative axiom for multiplication

5. Simplify $7 + 5m + 2$.

    a. $12m + 2$ **b.** $7 + 7m$ **c.** $14m$ **d.** $5m + 9$

6. Simplify $^-2 + 0$.

2-4

    a. $^-2$ **b.** 0 **c.** 2 **d.** $^-1$

7.

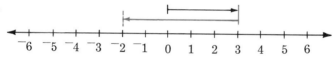

The diagram above suggests that $3 + \underline{\quad?\quad} = {^-2}$.

    a. 5   **b.** $^-5$ **c.** $^-2$ **d.** $^-1$

8. Simplify $-(-7) + 3$.

2-5

    a. -4 **b.** 4 **c.** -10 **d.** 10

9. Simplify $-(-6 + |-3|)$.

    a. 3 **b.** -3 **c.** 9 **d.** -9

10. Simplify $-12 + (-10) + 14 + (-3)$.

2-6

    a. 11 **b.** -5 **c.** -39 **d.** -11

11. Simplify $4(a + 2) + 6$.

2-7

    a. $4a + 14$ **b.** $4a + 32$ **c.** $4a + 8$ **d.** $8a + 6$

12. Simplify $7x + 1 + 9x + 5$.

   a. $8x + 14$ **b.** $79x + 6$ **c.** $63x + 6$ **d.** $16x + 6$

13. Simplify $(-3)(-1)(-2)(-6)$.   2-8

   a. -36 **b.** 36 **c.** -12 **d.** 12

14. Simplify $-6x + 2y + 5x + (-2y)$.

   a. $-xy$ **b.** $-4x + 3y$ **c.** $-x$ **d.** $-11x - 4y$

15. Simplify $8rs\left(-\dfrac{1}{8}\right)$.   2-9

   a. $-rs$ **b.** rs **c.** $-64rs$ **d.** $7\dfrac{7}{8}rs$

16. Simplify $\dfrac{1}{-p} \cdot \dfrac{1}{q}$.

   a. $-\dfrac{q}{p}$ **b.** $\dfrac{1}{-p + q}$ **c.** $-pq$ **d.** $-\dfrac{1}{pq}$

Chapter Test

1. Graph the numbers $^-4$, 0, 1.5, and 2 on a number line.   2-1

2. Name the greater of the two numbers 7 and $^-10$.   2-2

3. Replace the $\underline{\ \ ?\ \ }$ with one of the symbols $<$ or $>$ to make a true statement: $(6 \times 6) + 6 \underline{\ \ ?\ \ } (6 + 6)(6 + 6)$.

4. Simplify $54 + 27 + 6 + 73$.   2-3

5. Name the two axioms that guarantee that for all real numbers h, j, and k,
$$h + (j + k) = (h + k) + j.$$

6. The diagram below suggests that $\underline{\ \ ?\ \ } + \underline{\ \ ?\ \ } = \underline{\ \ ?\ \ }$.   2-4

7. Simplify $-(-5) + 7$.   **8.** Simplify $|2| + |0| + |-3|$.   2-5

9. Simplify $8 + (-2) + 9 + (-7)$.   2-6

10. Simplify $(64 \times 271) + (36 \times 271)$.   2-7

11. Simplify $35 + (-8)x + 15x + (-10)$.

12. Simplify $(-6)(-9) + (7)(-5)(0)$.   **13.** Simplify $-4[7v + (-w)]$.   2-8

14. Simplify $-\dfrac{1}{2}[14q + (-2q)]$.   **15.** Simplify $\dfrac{1}{w} \cdot \dfrac{1}{-x}$.   2-9

Maintaining Skills

Perform the indicated operations.

SAMPLE 1 $1.9 + 5.62 + 1.493$

SOLUTION
```
  1.900
  5.620
+ 1.493
  9.013
```

SAMPLE 2 $35.6 - 1.872$

SOLUTION
```
  35.600
-  1.872
  33.728
```

SAMPLE 3 1.87×0.043

SOLUTION
```
    1.87
  ×0.043
     561
     748
 0.08041
```

SAMPLE 4 $12.04 \div 2.8$

SOLUTION
```
         4.3
  2.8)12.0.4
       112
        84
        84
         0
```

1.
```
   37.5
   8.616
+  0.99
```

2.
```
  0.0192
  1.7
  5.16
+ 3.057
```

3.
```
   57.12
  193.4
+   4.581
```

4.
```
   47.03
    6.8
    0.46
+ 52.511
```

5. $5.4 + 7.86 + 9.3$

6. $12.2 + 6.051 + 4$

7. $29.41 + 0.058 + 103.6$

8.
```
   204.91
 - 153.64
```

9.
```
   70.038
 -  7.129
```

10.
```
   4.615
 - 0.28
```

11.
```
   36.71
 -  1.648
```

12. $6.8 - 0.591$

13. $34.227 - 12.4$

14. $871.2 - 0.0391$

15.
```
    50.8
  × 1.26
```

16.
```
   1.954
 ×  0.31
```

17.
```
   62.15
 ×  0.07
```

18.
```
    0.724
  × 0.015
```

19. $0.2107 \div 0.86$

20. $3657.7 \div 0.79$

21. $327.68 \div 0.032$

Estimate each answer by using rounded numbers. Then find the exact product or quotient.

SAMPLE 5 0.39×7.12 **SOLUTION** $0.4 \times 7 = 2.8;\ 0.39 \times 7.12 = 2.7768$

SAMPLE 6 $0.039 \div 0.15$ **SOLUTION** $0.04 \div 0.2 = 0.2;\ 0.039 \div 0.15 = 0.26$

22. 0.29×0.73

23. 1.4×0.077

24. 3.85×1.68

25. 49.2×0.93

26. $0.031)\overline{0.868}$

27. $0.48)\overline{17.16}$

28. $6.2)\overline{0.589}$

29. $7.5)\overline{50.91}$

A gymnasium must provide adequate room overhead for people to jump and for balls to be thrown. To design a large roof that can be supported with a minimum number of beams and posts requires a knowledge of the mathematics of architecture and engineering.

3

SOLVING EQUATIONS

USING ADDITION AND SUBTRACTION

3-1 *Transforming Equations: Addition*

OBJECTIVE To solve equations using addition.

Two competing gymnasts are tied: 48.3 to 48.3. If each gymnast scores 12 points in the next event, then the score is still tied:

$$48.3 + 12 = 48.3 + 12$$

This example illustrates the **addition property of equality:** *If the same number is added to equal numbers, the sums are equal.*

ADDITION PROPERTY OF EQUALITY

If a, b, and c are any real numbers and $a = b$, then

$$a + c = b + c \quad \text{and} \quad c + a = c + b.$$

Another property of real numbers is suggested by the following calculation.

$$(8 + 9) + (-9) = 8 + [9 + (-9)]$$
$$= 8 + 0$$
$$= 8$$
$$\therefore (8 + 9) + (-9) = 8$$

The calculation suggests a useful idea: *To "undo" the addition of a number, add the opposite of that number to the sum.* This idea can be stated more formally as follows.

For all real numbers a and b,

$$(a + b) + (-b) = a.$$

You can use the idea of "undoing" an addition along with the addition property of equality to solve equations. Study the following equations.

$$
\begin{array}{ll}
(1) & x + 7 = 4 \\
(2) & x + 7 + (-7) = 4 + (-7) \\
(3) & x = -3
\end{array}
$$

When you add -7 to each side of equation (1) and simplify the result, you obtain equation (3).

On the other hand, when you add 7 to each side of equation (3), you obtain equation (1), as shown below.

$$
\begin{array}{ll}
(3) & x = -3 \\
(2') & x + 7 = -3 + 7 \\
(1) & x + 7 = 4
\end{array}
$$

The addition property of equality guarantees that any root, or solution, of equation (1) is also a root of equation (3), and any root of (3) is also a root of (1). Therefore the two equations have the same solution, namely -3.

Equations having the same solution set over a given domain are called **equivalent equations** over that domain. To solve an equation, you usually try to change, or *transform*, it into a simple equivalent equation whose solution or solutions can be seen at a glance.

WAYS TO TRANSFORM AN EQUATION INTO AN EQUIVALENT EQUATION

Transformation by Substitution: Substitute for any expression in a given equation an equivalent expression.

Transformation by Addition: Add the same real number to each side of a given equation.

EXAMPLE 1 Solve $t + (-5) = 8$.

SOLUTION
$$
\begin{array}{l}
t + (-5) = 8 \\
t + (-5) + 5 = 8 + 5 \\
t = 13
\end{array}
$$
$\left\{ \begin{array}{l} \text{To obtain } t \text{ alone as the left side, add the} \\ \text{opposite of } -5, \text{ namely } 5, \text{ to each side.} \end{array} \right.$

Because errors may occur in transforming equations, always check your work by showing that each root of the transformed equation satisfies the original equation.

$$\textit{Check: } t + (-5) = 8 \quad \leftarrow \text{original equation}$$
$$13 + (-5) \overset{?}{=} 8$$
$$8 = 8 \quad \checkmark$$

$\therefore$ the solution is 13. **Answer**

EXAMPLE 2 Solve $-12 = 20 + z$.

SOLUTION

$$-12 = 20 + z$$
$$-20 + (-12) = -20 + 20 + z$$
$$-32 = z$$

To obtain z alone as the right side, add the opposite of 20, namely -20, to each side.

$$\textit{Check: } -12 = 20 + z$$
$$-12 \overset{?}{=} 20 + (-32)$$
$$-12 = -12 \quad \checkmark$$

$\therefore$ the solution is -32. **Answer**

Oral Exercises

State the number that must be added to each side of the given equation to produce an equivalent equation with the variable alone as one side. Then state this equivalent equation.

SAMPLE $u + 8 = 12$ **SOLUTION** Add -8; $u = 4$

1. $x + 5 = 6$
2. $y + 4 = 13$
3. $v + (-1) = 6$
4. $w + (-11) = 3$
5. $z + 10 = 1$
6. $s + 8 = 6$
7. $5 + h = -5$
8. $-1 + q = 1$
9. $-1 + p = -1$
10. $16 + m = 16$
11. $4 = u + (-6)$
12. $-7 = y + (-10)$
13. $-8 = -2 + a$
14. $9 = -1 + t$
15. $0 = 0.6 + b$
16. $\frac{3}{5} = \frac{1}{5} + c$
17. $\frac{9}{7} + y = \frac{5}{7}$
18. $-1.7 + d = -2.3$

Written Exercises

Use transformation by addition to solve each equation.

A
1. $t + (-11) = 14$
2. $v + (-8) = 14$
3. $x + 5 = 24$
4. $m + 15 = 23$
5. $-17 + a = 13$
6. $-59 + m = 41$
7. $z + (-3) = -19$
8. $n + (-23) = -17$
9. $k + 14 = -22$
10. $a + 80 = -25$
11. $28 + b = 0$
12. $0 = x + (-13)$
13. $x + (-27) = -54$
14. $y + (-84) = -100$
15. $9 + c = -18$

Use transformation by addition to solve each equation.

16. $16 + m = -36$ **17.** $55 = t + 7$ **18.** $46 = s + 5$

19. $-17 + z = -21$ **20.** $-30 + j = -80$ **21.** $t + 6 = |-14|$

22. $u + (-4) = |20|$ **23.** $v + 5 = |2 - 7|$ **24.** $q + (-6) = |8 - 14|$

SAMPLE
$$-a + 12 = 3$$
$$-a + 12 + (-12) = 3 + (-12)$$
$$-a = -9$$
$$\therefore a = 9 \quad \text{(By definition of the opposite of a number)}$$

B **25.** $-a + 7 = 5$ **26.** $-x + 1 = 19$ **27.** $20 + (-z) = 26$

 28. $-5 + (-b) = 11$ **29.** $7 = 10 + (-s)$ **30.** $10 = -s + 7$

 31. $(y + 2) + 5 = 3$ **32.** $(r + 3) + 8 = 1$ **33.** $1 = 11 + (-1 + x)$

 34. $7 = 19 + (m + 1)$ **35.** $-2 + (1 + x) = 8$ **36.** $-3 + (1 + q) = 5$

SAMPLE
$$|z| + 3 = 7$$
$$|z| + 3 + (-3) = 7 + (-3)$$
$$|z| = 4$$
$$\therefore z = 4 \text{ or } z = -4 \quad \text{(By definition of absolute value)}$$

C **37.** $|x| + (-2) = 4$ **38.** $|y| + (-1) = 1$ **39.** $-5 + |r| = 0$ **40.** $6 + |w| = 2$

Problems

Solve each problem by using an equation. (Though you may be able to solve some by mental arithmetic, using equations provides practice for more difficult problems later.)

SAMPLE

Sam has a temperature of $39°$C. This is two degrees above normal body temperature. What is normal temperature?

SOLUTION

Step 1   The problem asks for the number of degrees in normal body temperature.

Step 2   Let n = normal temperature in degrees.
         Then $n + 2$ = Sam's temperature in degrees.

Step 3 $n + 2 = 39$

Step 4 $n + 2 + (-2) = 39 + (-2)$
             $n = 37$

Step 5   The check is left to you.
       $\therefore$ normal temperature is $37°$C.   *Answer*

A 1. Seven more than a number is 36. Find the number.

   2. Nine more than a number is 67. Find the number.

   3. A number increased by 5 is -2. Find the number.

   4. A number increased by 3 is -11. Find the number.

   5. In his final game of the season Tom scored two touchdowns, making his touchdown record for the season 11. How many touchdowns had he scored in that season before the final game?

   6. The monthly rent for an apartment was increased by $16. If the new monthly rent is $279, what was the previous rent?

   7. If the temperature of the water in the beaker rises three degrees Celsius above what it is now, the water will be at the boiling point ($100°C$). What is the temperature of the water now?

   8. The temperature this morning is $-4°C$. How many degrees will the temperature have to rise to reach $4°C$ today?

B 9. The school principal arrived at school at 7:55 A.M. This is 25 minutes later than her usual time of arrival. At what time does she usually arrive?

   10. Fred sold a dozen magazine subscriptions during the last six days in January. During the whole month of January he sold 44 subscriptions. How many subscriptions had he sold during the first 25 days in January?

   11. A factory hired 125 new employees during a year in which 17 employees retired. If there were 526 employees in the factory at the end of that year, how many were there at the beginning?

   12. After cashing a check for $75 and then spending $28.75, Jeanne LePage had $134 in her purse. How much did she have in her purse before she cashed the check?

ჩistorical ΠΟte The Equals Sign

The symbols shown were all used in the sixteenth and seventeenth centuries to denote equality. It was not until the eighteenth century that the current equals sign $=$ was universally adopted.

The Englishman Robert Recorde is credited with the invention of the symbol $=$. He published a mathematics book in 1557 in which he used ═══ "to avoid the tedious repetition of the words 'is equal to.'" He said that he chose a pair of line segments of the same length because "no two things could be more equal." With the passage of time, the segments were shortened until the symbol became $=$.

3-2 Subtracting Real Numbers

OBJECTIVE   To subtract real numbers and to simplify expressions involving differences.

If you pay for a 45-cent soda with a half dollar, the cashier may hand you a nickel and say,

"45 and 5 is 50."

The cashier is using addition,

$45 + 5 = 50,$

to do subtraction,

$50 - 45 = 5.$

   In general, the **difference** $a - b$ is the number whose sum with b is a. Thus, the equations

$$a - b = x \quad \text{and} \quad b + x = a$$

have the same solution and are equivalent.

   Using this definition, you can compute a difference such as $6 - 2$ by asking yourself, "What number *added* to 2 gives me 6?" The answer is 4.

EXAMPLE 1   Simplify $4 - (-3)$.

SOLUTION   Ask, "What number added to -3 gives 4?"
On the number line below, think of moving from the graph of -3 to the graph of 4.

From -3 you move 7 units to the right to reach 4.
Thus, $4 - (-3) = 7.$ ***Answer***

   It would be helpful to find a way to simplify a difference such as $4 - (-3)$ without using a number line. In general, to compute $a - b$, you can ask, "What number added to b gives a?" and solve $b + x = a$ for x to find the answer. You can use transformation by addition and transformation by substitution as follows:

$$b + x = a$$
$$x + b = a$$
$$x + b + (-b) = a + (-b)$$
$$x + 0 = a + (-b)$$
$$x = a + (-b)$$

Since $a + (-b)$ is the value of x that satisfies the last equation, it also satisfies the equations $b + x = a$ and $a - b = x$. The following rule can be stated.

RULE FOR SUBTRACTION

For all real numbers a and b,

$$a - b = a + (-b).$$

To subtract b, add the opposite of b.

EXAMPLE 2 Simplify.

   a. $4 - (-3)$ **b.** $-8 - 2$ **c.** $-5 - (-6)$ **d.** $x - (x + 7)$

SOLUTION   **a.** $4 - (-3) = 4 + 3 = 7$

   b. $-8 - 2 = -8 + (-2) = -10$

   c. $-5 - (-6) = -5 + 6 = 1$

   d. $x - (x + 7) = x + [-(x + 7)] = x + (-x) + (-7) = -7$
   Note that the property of the opposite of a sum is used. The opposite of $(x + 7)$ is $-x + (-7)$.

Using the rule for subtraction, you may replace any difference with a sum. For example,

$$10 - 7 - 5 + 6 \text{ means } 10 + (-7) + (-5) + 6.$$

You may evaluate this expression by grouping from left to right:

$$\underbrace{\underbrace{\underbrace{10 - 7}_{3} - 5}_{-2} + 6}_{4}$$

This method is convenient if you are doing the work mentally or with a hand calculator. For written work, you may want to group positive terms and negative terms:

$$10 - 7 - 5 + 6 = (10 + 6) - (7 + 5) = 16 - 12 = 4$$

Certain sums are usually replaced by differences. For example,

$$8 + (-3x) \text{ is usually written as } 8 - 3x.$$

Here are some important questions and answers about subtraction of real numbers:

1. Is subtraction commutative? No, for example,

$$9 - 3 = 6 \quad \text{but} \quad 3 - 9 = -6.$$

2. Is subtraction associative? No, for example,

$$(5 - 4) - 8 = -7 \quad \text{but} \quad 5 - (4 - 8) = 9.$$

3. Is multiplication distributive with respect to subtraction? Yes. (See Exercise 43.) For all real numbers a, b, and c,

$$a(b - c) = ab - ac \quad \text{and} \quad (b - c)a = ba - ca.$$

Oral Exercises

Simplify.

1. $36 - 4$

2. $18 - 11$

3. $7 - 12$

4. $9 - 29$

5. $0 - 6$

6. $0 - (-4)$

7. $-15 - 0$

8. $-8 - 2$

9. $3 - (-1)$

10. $8 - (-2)$

11. $-9 - (-14)$

12. $-7 - (-3)$

13. $x - (x + 1)$

14. $v - (v + 3)$

15. $a - (a - 2)$

16. $b - (b - 5)$

Written Exercises

Simplify.

A

1. $42 - 212$

2. $134 - 241$

3. $29 - (-22)$

4. $27 - (-29)$

5. $-17 - (-3)$

6. $-23 - (-9)$

7. $-26 - 42$

8. $-41 - 57$

9. $153 - (-23)$

10. $-201 - (-58)$

11. $182 - (-103)$

12. $195 - (-155)$

13. $123 - (65 - 59)$

14. $265 - (90 - 75)$

15. $342 - (72 - 85)$

16. $193 - (35 - 60)$

17. $(33 - 44) - (66 - 77)$

18. $(53 - 60) - (82 - 90)$

19. $(2 - 7) - (-14 + 17)$

20. $(32 - 23) - (-7 + 9)$

21. $1066 - 1492 - 1776$

22. $1914 - 1939 + 2001$

23. $13 - (-7) - [6 - (-5)]$

24. $-10 - 8 - [-5 - (-7)]$

25. $3 - 4 + 7 - 16 + 32$

26. $19 - 15 + 13 + 6 - 23$

27. $38x - 18x - 43x + 17x - 27x$

28. $43y - 18y + 11y - 23y - 35y$

29. $2x - (-3 + x)$

30. $y - (-y + 5)$

B 31. $x + y - (x - y) - y$

32. $u - v - (u + v) + v$

33. $2h + 9 - (-7 + h)$

34. $-(10 - 3k) - (12 + k)$

Write each phrase using symbols of algebra. Then simplify.

35. -11 decreased by 7

36. -8 decreased by -3

37. $(a - 4)$ less than a

38. $(7 + z)$ less than z

39. $(\pi + 1)$ subtracted from $(\pi - 6)$

40. $(8 - 2\pi)$ subtracted from $(5 - 2\pi)$

41. The sum of -8 and -9, decreased by -5

42. -32 decreased by the sum of -27 and 14

C **43.** Name the axiom, property, or rule that justifies each step.

$$
\begin{aligned}
a(b - c) &= a[b + (-c)] &\quad (1) &\ \underline{\ ?\ } \\
&= a(b) + a(-c) &\quad (2) &\ \underline{\ ?\ } \\
&= ab + (-ac) &\quad (3) &\ \underline{\ ?\ } \\
&= ab - ac &\quad (4) &\ \underline{\ ?\ }
\end{aligned}
$$

Problems

Express the answer to each question as the difference between two real numbers. Compute the difference. Answer the question.

SAMPLE

The Qattara Depression in Egypt is about 133 m below sea level. The Dead Sea is about 396 m below sea level. How much higher is the Qattara Depression than the Dead Sea?

SOLUTION $-133 - (-396) = -133 + 396 = 263$

The Qattara Depression is about 263 m higher.

A **1.** One winter evening the temperature dropped from $-3°$C to $-8°$C. How many degrees did the temperature drop?

2. The temperature was $19°$C in the classroom and $-2°$C outdoors. How much warmer was it in the classroom than outdoors?

3. In one round of a game, Mike's score dropped from 50 points to -25 points. How many points did he lose in that round?

4. Jan's team's score is 125 points. The other team's score is -175 points. How many points higher is Jan's team's score than the other team's score?

B **5.** Winnipeg's latitude is about $50°$N. Rio de Janeiro's latitude is about $23°$S. What is the approximate difference in latitude between the two cities?

6. The North Pole is located at latitude $90°$N. The South Pole is located at latitude $90°$S. What is the difference in latitude between the two poles?

7. The town of Aucanquilcha, Chile, is about 5334 m above sea level. Several villages on the shores of the Dead Sea are about 396 m below sea level. About how many meters higher is Aucanquilcha than the Dead Sea villages?

8. New Orleans, the lowest point in Louisiana, is 1.524 m below sea level. Driskill Mountain, the highest point in the state, is 163.068 m above sea level. What is the difference in elevation between the highest and lowest points in Louisiana?

9. The highest recorded weather temperature on earth is 58.0°C. The lowest is −88.3°C. What is the difference between these two extremes?

10. Mercury is a metallic element that melts at −38.87°C and boils at 356.9°C. How many degrees are there in the range between the melting and boiling points of mercury?

Calculator Key-In

Use a calculator to simplify each expression.

1. $1332 - 369$ 2. $1332 + (-396)$ 3. $-1332 - (-639)$
4. $9265 - 12221$ 5. $9526 + (-12221)$ 6. $-9625 - (-12221)$
7. $5296 - 5692 + (-5962) - (-5629) + 6925 + (-6529) - 6259 + 6592$

Biography Andres Manuel del Río

Andres Manuel del Río (1764–1849) introduced modern mining techniques in Mexico. Born in Madrid, Spain, del Río studied the classics at the Colegio de San Isidro in Madrid. After winning a public competition in physics, he was subsidized first by King Charles III and later by the state to study mineralogy at the Mining Academy of Almadén and at mining centers in France, England, and Germany.

In 1794 he sailed to Mexico to become professor of mineralogy at Colegio de Minería, which had just been founded in Mexico City. He discovered the new chemical element vanadium in 1801, but it was not until some thirty years later that this discovery was verified.

3-3 *Transforming Equations: Subtraction*

OBJECTIVE To solve equations using addition or subtraction.

EXAMPLE 1 Solve $z - 4 = 13$.

SOLUTION

$$z - 4 = 13$$
$$z + (-4) = 13$$
$$z + (-4) + 4 = 13 + 4$$
$$z = 17$$

CONDENSED SOLUTION

$$z - 4 = 13$$
$$z - 4 + 4 = 13 + 4$$
$$z = 17$$

Check: $z - 4 = 13$
$$17 - 4 \overset{?}{=} 13$$
$$13 = 13 \;\surd$$

$\therefore$ the solution is 17. ***Answer***

EXAMPLE 2 Solve $a + 8 = 1$.

SOLUTION

$$a + 8 = 1$$
$$a + 8 - 8 = 1 - 8$$
$$a = -7$$

Check: $a + 8 = 1$
$$-7 + 8 \overset{?}{=} 1$$
$$1 = 1 \;\surd$$

$\therefore$ the solution is -7. ***Answer***

The method used in Example 2 is called **transformation by subtraction,** because 8 is *subtracted* from each side of the equation. Of course, transformation by subtraction is just a special case of transformation by addition, since you can just as well add -8 to solve the equation in Example 2.

Oral Exercises

State the number that must be added to or subtracted from each side of the given equation to produce an equivalent equation with the variable alone as one side. Then state this equivalent equation.

SAMPLE 1 $x + 6 = -1$ *SOLUTION* Subtract 6; $x = -7$

SAMPLE 2 $x - 10 = -4$ *SOLUTION* Add 10; $x = 6$

1. $x + 3 = 11$
2. $y + 5 = -1$
3. $z - 2 = 8$
4. $t - 8 = 3$
5. $s + 6 = 21$
6. $r + 7 = 1$
7. $x - 9 = -4$
8. $y - 3 = -6$
9. $q - 14 = -18$
10. $z - \dfrac{1}{2} = \dfrac{1}{2}$
11. $w + 0.25 = -0.50$
12. $p - 1.5 = -3$

Written Exercises

Solve.

A 1. $x + 16 = 42$ 2. $y + 31 = 79$ 3. $-1 = a + 51$

    4. $-22 = b + 7$ 5. $1.5 + c = 1.5$ 6. $0.4 + d = 0.4$

    7. $p - 4 = 13$ 8. $q - 6 = 8$ 9. $s - 2 = 19$

   10. $t - 6 = 23$ 11. $18 = x - 1$ 12. $14 = y - 10$

B 13. $34 - x = 10$ 14. $17 - y = -6$ 15. $(z + 8) - 3 = -2$

   16. $(w - 5) + 19 = 144$ 17. $(v - 4) + 6 = 11$ 18. $(h + 1) + 9 = 10$

   19. $y - 8 = |21 - 29|$ 20. $x - 9 = |7 - 16|$ 21. $b + |7 - 12| = -8$

   22. $a + |3 - 5| = -1$ 23. $d - 4 = ||-3| - |6||$ 24. $c - 7 = ||-1| - |-7||$

C 25. $2|a| - (|a| - 3) = 9$ 26. $4(|b| - 1) - 2|b| - 19 = 1$

Problems

Solve each problem by using an equation. (Though you may be able to solve some by mental arithmetic, using equations provides practice for more difficult problems later.)

SAMPLE

Using a coupon that read "35¢ off," Jimmy paid $1.94 for a bag of dry dog food. What was the price of the dog food without the coupon?

SOLUTION

Step 1 The problem asks for the price of the dog food without the coupon.

Step 2 Let p = price of the dog food without the coupon in dollars. Then $p - 0.35$ = price of the dog food with the coupon.

Step 3 $p - 0.35 = 1.94$

Step 4 $p - 0.35 + 0.35 = 1.94 + 0.35$
                $p = 2.29$

Step 5 The check is left to you.
       ∴ the price is $2.29. *Answer*

A 1. Fifteen less than a number is 19. Find the number.

    2. A number decreased by 9 is -10. Find the number.

    3. A number decreased by 22 is 22. Find the number.

    4. Eight less than a number is -7. Find the number.

    5. Three students are absent from Homeroom 101 today. If 26 of the students assigned to the homeroom are present, how many are assigned to Homeroom 101?

6. Five of the chorus members missed the last rehearsal. Twenty-eight of the members did attend the rehearsal. How many members does the chorus have in all?

7. Miguel's grade on today's biology test was 89. This grade was five points lower than his grade on last week's test. What was Miguel's grade on last week's test?

8. Mimi swam the length of the pool in 21 seconds. This was two seconds less than her previous time. What was her previous time?

B 9. A newspaper ad offers a dollar off the price of any album in the record store if a customer brings in the ad. Alicia brought in the ad and paid $9.99 for an album. What would the album have cost Alicia without the ad?

10. The last check Henri wrote was for $18.95. His next bank statement showed an overdraft of $7.64 on his account. How much did he have in his account before he wrote that last check?

11. A rocket landed 17 km from its launching pad. If it fell 1.5 km short of its target, how far was the target from the launching pad?

12. An astronaut spent 32.6 days in space. This was 2.4 days shorter than her previous record. What was her previous record?

Self-Test 1

VOCABULARY equivalent equations (p. 72)
transformation by substitution (p. 72)
transformation by addition (p. 72)

difference (p. 76)
transformation by subtraction (p. 81)

Solve.

1. $x + 12 = 20$

2. $-15 + y = 7$

Obj. 3-1, p. 71

Simplify.

3. $26 - 37$

4. $-9 - 12$

Obj. 3-2, p. 76

5. $15 - (-5)$

6. $x - (x + 6)$

Solve.

7. $18 + w = 59$

8. $16 = z - 10$

Obj. 3-3, p. 81

9. This year the cross-country team has four more runners than last year. This year's team has 11 runners. Find out how many runners were on last year's team by writing an equation and solving it.

Check your answers with those at the back of the book.

3-4 *Transforming Equations: Multiplication*

OBJECTIVE To solve equations using multiplication.

Jim earned the same amount as Millie working at the supermarket on Friday. Each of them earned twice as much working on Saturday. From this information you can conclude that Jim earned the same amount as Millie on Saturday also.

This example illustrates the **multiplication property of equality:** *If equal numbers are multiplied by the same number, the products are equal.*

MULTIPLICATION PROPERTY OF EQUALITY

If a, b, and c are any real numbers and $a = b$, then

$$ca = cb \quad \text{and} \quad ac = bc.$$

This property guarantees another way to transform an equation into an equivalent equation:

Transformation by Multiplication: Multiply each side of a given equation by the same *nonzero* real number.

EXAMPLE 1 Solve $4x = 52$.

SOLUTION

$$4x = 52$$
$$\frac{1}{4}(4x) = \frac{1}{4}(52)$$
$$x = 13$$

To obtain x alone as the left side, multiply each side by the reciprocal of 4, namely $\frac{1}{4}$.

Check: $4x = 52$
$$4(13) \stackrel{?}{=} 52$$
$$52 = 52 \ \surd$$

$\therefore$ the solution is 13. ***Answer***

EXAMPLE 2   Solve $-\frac{1}{5}v = 2$.

SOLUTION $-5\left(-\frac{1}{5}v\right) = -5(2)$ | To obtain v alone as the left side, multiply each side by the reciprocal of $-\frac{1}{5}$, namely -5.

$$v = -10$$

Check: $-\frac{1}{5}v = 2$

$$-\frac{1}{5}(-10) \overset{?}{=} 2$$

$$2 = 2 \quad \checkmark$$

$\therefore$ the solution is -10.   ***Answer***

Examples 1 and 2 suggest a useful idea: To "undo" multiplication by a number, multiply the product by the reciprocal of that number. This idea can be stated more formally as follows.

> For every real number a and every *nonzero* real number b,
>
> $$\frac{1}{b}(ba) = a.$$

EXAMPLE 3   Solve $\frac{2}{3}r = 18$.

SOLUTION $\frac{3}{2} \cdot \frac{2}{3}r = \frac{3}{2} \cdot 18$ | To obtain r alone as the left side, multiply each side by the reciprocal of $\frac{2}{3}$, namely $\frac{3}{2}$.

$$r = 27$$

Check: The check is left to you.

$\therefore$ the solution is 27.   ***Answer***

Do you know why zero is not allowed as a multiplier in transforming an equation? Look at the following equations.

$$(1) \qquad 3y = 18$$
$$(2) \qquad 0 \cdot 3y = 0 \cdot 18$$
$$(3) \quad (0 \cdot 3)y = 0 \cdot 18$$
$$(4) \qquad 0 \cdot y = 0$$

Equation (1) has just one root, namely 6. Equation (4) is satisfied by *any* real number. Equations (1) and (4) are not equivalent (see page 72). *In transforming an equation, never multiply by zero.*

Oral Exercises

State the number by which each side of the given equation must be multiplied to produce an equivalent equation with the variable alone as one side. Then state the equivalent equation.

1. $\frac{1}{2}x = 5$ 2. $\frac{1}{3}z = 8$ 3. $\frac{1}{10}y = 7$ 4. $\frac{1}{9}m = \frac{2}{9}$

5. $5v = 30$ 6. $4w = 24$ 7. $-3n = 12$ 8. $-6p = -54$

9. $-\frac{1}{5}q = -3$ 10. $\frac{1}{13}t = -1$ 11. $\frac{3}{4}c = -\frac{1}{4}$ 12. $-\frac{2}{7}z = \frac{1}{7}$

Written Exercises

Solve each equation.

A 1. $\frac{1}{8}x = 21$ 2. $\frac{1}{9}y = 14$ 3. $\frac{1}{12}r = -12$ 4. $\frac{1}{17}s = -101$

5. $13m = 91$ 6. $8v = -136$ 7. $-5t = 850$ 8. $-11a = 165$

9. $-64 = -\frac{1}{8}x$ 10. $-\frac{1}{6}z = -36$ 11. $12p = -84$ 12. $-25q = 300$

B 13. $\frac{1}{2}y = \frac{5}{2}$ 14. $\frac{1}{3}x = \frac{4}{3}$ 15. $-\frac{3}{5} = \frac{1}{5}b$ 16. $-\frac{5}{7} = -\frac{1}{7}a$

17. $-\frac{3}{8} = -\frac{1}{16}d$ 18. $\frac{5}{6} = -\frac{1}{12}c$ 19. $-3y = \frac{6}{5}$ 20. $-2x = -\frac{8}{9}$

21. $9n = \frac{36}{11}$ 22. $4x = -\frac{48}{23}$ 23. $-17m = \frac{1}{2}$ 24. $10r = -\frac{1}{5}$

C 25. $0.5x = 1$ 26. $1.5t = -3$ 27. $-0.2y = 10$ 28. $-0.25z = -4$

Problems

Solve using an equation.

A 1. A dozen eggs cost $1.08. How much is one egg worth?

2. Six tacos cost $5.70. How much does each taco cost?

3. One eighth of a pizza pie is sold for 65¢. How much will be received when all the pieces of a pie have been sold at this price?

4. Nine-year-old Chico is one fifth as old as his aunt Sofia. How old is Sofia?

5. The perimeter of a square garden plot is 140 m. How long is each side of the plot?

6. The perimeter of an equilateral triangle (a triangle with all sides equal) is 7.5 cm. How long is each side of the triangle?

B   **7.** A rectangular quilt is made up of 195 small squares. The quilt is 15 squares long. How many squares wide is it?

8. A train traveled 448 km at the rate of 128 km/h. How long did it travel?

9. The Ecology Club has $18.25 in its treasury. This is one third the amount in the Computer Club treasury. How much is in the Computer Club treasury?

10. In a scale drawing of a kitchen, dimensions are shown $\frac{1}{100}$ of actual size. The width of the kitchen in the drawing is 3.5 cm. What is the actual width of the kitchen in centimeters? in meters?

Computer Key-In

The following computer program in BASIC will solve simple equations for you.

```
10   PRINT "TO SOLVE AN EQUATION OF THE FORM"
20   PRINT "     X  (SIGN)   A = B"
30   PRINT "INPUT SIGN,A,B";
40   INPUT S$,A,B
50   IF S$="+" THEN 110
60   IF S$="-" THEN 130
70   IF S$="*" THEN 150
80   IF S$="/" THEN 170
90   PRINT "WHAT DID YOU INTEND?"
100  GOTO 30
110  PRINT "X =";B-A
120  STOP
130  PRINT "X =";B+A
140  STOP
150  PRINT "X =";B/A
160  STOP
170  PRINT "X =";B*A
180  END
```

Here is an example of a RUN of this program which solves the equation $x + 4 = 10$.

```
RUN

TO SOLVE AN EQUATION OF THE FORM
     X  (SIGN)   A = B
INPUT SIGN,A,B?"+",4,10
X = 6

END
```

Notice that the operational sign must be typed in quotation marks, and that it and the two numerical values are typed on one line, separated by commas.

3-5 Dividing Real Numbers

OBJECTIVE To divide real numbers and to simplify expressions involving quotients.

In arithmetic when you learned the multiplication fact $8 \times 6 = 48$, you found that you also knew the related division fact $48 \div 8 = 6$.

In general, if b is *not* zero, the **quotient** $a \div b$ is the number whose product with b is a. Thus, the equations

$$a \div b = x \quad \text{and} \quad bx = a$$

are equivalent equations.

A quotient is often represented by a fraction:

$$a \div b = \frac{a}{b}$$

When you studied fractions, you learned facts like these:

$$\frac{4}{9} = 4 \times \frac{1}{9} \qquad \frac{5}{3} = 5 \times \frac{1}{3} \qquad \frac{24}{8} = 24 \times \frac{1}{8}$$

These equations suggest the following rule.

RULE FOR DIVISION

For every real number a and every *nonzero* real number b,

$$a \div b = a \cdot \frac{1}{b}, \quad \text{or} \quad \frac{a}{b} = a \cdot \frac{1}{b}.$$

To divide by b, multiply by the reciprocal of b.

You can use the rule for division to replace any quotient by a product.

$$\frac{15}{3} = 15 \times \frac{1}{3} = 5 \qquad\qquad \frac{-15}{-3} = -15 \times \left(-\frac{1}{3}\right) = 5$$

$$\frac{-15}{3} = -15 \times \frac{1}{3} = -5 \qquad\qquad \frac{15}{-3} = 15 \times \left(-\frac{1}{3}\right) = -5$$

The quotient of two positive or two negative numbers is positive.

The quotient of a positive number and a negative number is negative.

The quotient when zero is divided by any nonzero number is zero.

Here are some important questions and answers about division of real numbers:

1. Why can you never divide by zero? Suppose you allowed division by zero in the definition of $a \div b$. Then $a \div 0 = x$ would mean that $0 \cdot x = a$. If $a \neq 0$, no value of x can satisfy this equation, because $0 \cdot x = 0$ for each value of x. But if $a = 0$, then every value of x would satisfy $0 \cdot x = a$. A "quotient" $a \div 0$ would have either *no* value or *many* values! Therefore, *division by zero has no meaning in the set of real numbers.*

2. You cannot divide zero by zero, but can you divide zero by any other number? Look at these examples:

$$\frac{0}{5} = 0 \times \frac{1}{5} = 0 \qquad 0 \div (-2) = 0 \times \left(-\frac{1}{2}\right) = 0$$

When zero is divided by any nonzero number, the quotient is zero.

3. Is division commutative? *No,* for example,

$$8 \div 2 = 4 \quad \text{but} \quad 2 \div 8 = 0.25.$$

4. Is division associative? *No,* for example,

$$(12 \div 3) \div 2 = 4 \div 2 = 2 \quad \text{but} \quad 12 \div (3 \div 2) = 12 \div 1.5 = 8.$$

5. Is division distributive with respect to addition and with respect to subtraction? Yes. In Exercises 31 and 32 it will be shown that for all real numbers a, b, and c such that $c \neq 0$,

$$\frac{a + b}{c} = \frac{a}{c} + \frac{b}{c} \quad \text{and} \quad \frac{a - b}{c} = \frac{a}{c} - \frac{b}{c}.$$

Oral Exercises

Read each quotient as a product. Then simplify.

SAMPLE 1 $\quad 12 \div \left(-\frac{1}{4}\right) \qquad$ **SOLUTION** $\quad 12 \times (-4); \ -48$

SAMPLE 2 $\quad \dfrac{16x}{-8} \qquad$ **SOLUTION** $\quad 16x \times \left(-\frac{1}{8}\right); \ -2x$

1. $0 \div 8$

2. $-3 \div (-3)$

3. $-1 \div (-1)$

4. $1 \div (-1)$

5. $50 \div (-10)$

6. $40 \div (-5)$

7. $-10 \div \frac{1}{2}$

8. $-1 \div \left(-\frac{1}{5}\right)$

9. $\dfrac{35}{-7}$

10. $\dfrac{-14}{14}$

11. $\dfrac{18}{-1}$

12. $\dfrac{-81}{-9}$

13. $y \div (-1)$

14. $\dfrac{-x}{-1}$

15. $\dfrac{-27r}{3}$

16. $\dfrac{-12a}{-4}$

17. $-3 \div \frac{1}{m}, \ m \neq 0$

18. $-1 \div \left(-\frac{1}{z}\right), \ z \neq 0$

19. $\dfrac{-a}{-a}, \ a \neq 0$

20. $\dfrac{b}{-b}, \ b \neq 0$

Simplify.

SAMPLE 3 $\frac{z}{4} \cdot 4$ **SOLUTION** $\frac{z}{4} \cdot 4 = z \cdot \frac{1}{4} \cdot 4 = z \cdot 1 = z$

21. $5 \cdot \frac{x}{5}$ **22.** $\left(-\frac{t}{8}\right)(-8)$ **23.** $2\left(\frac{a}{-2}\right)$ **24.** $-7 \cdot \frac{b}{7}$

Written Exercises

Simplify.

A 1. $-256 \div 32$ **2.** $204 \div (-17)$ **3.** $36 \div \left(-\frac{1}{3}\right)$ **4.** $0 \div (-23)$

5. $\dfrac{-25}{-\frac{1}{5}}$ **6.** $\dfrac{7}{-\frac{1}{2}}$ **7.** $\dfrac{-10}{\frac{1}{6}}$ **8.** $\dfrac{0}{-\frac{1}{7}}$

9. $\dfrac{165x}{-15}$ **10.** $\dfrac{192y}{-8}$ **11.** $\dfrac{-426a}{3a}, \ a \neq 0$ **12.** $\dfrac{-108c}{-12c}, \ c \neq 0$

13. $-\frac{z}{12}(-12)$ **14.** $-9 \cdot \frac{t}{9}$ **15.** $\frac{3x}{2} \cdot 2$ **16.** $-\frac{5r}{3}(-3)$

Find the average of the numbers given in Exercises 17-20. (The average is the sum of the numbers divided by the number of numbers.)

SAMPLE 1 $15, -7, -14, 2$

SOLUTION $\dfrac{15 + (-7) + (-14) + 2}{4} = \dfrac{17 - 21}{4} = \dfrac{-4}{4} = -1$

17. $-18, 5, -10, 3$ **18.** $9, -20, -6, 13$

19. $21, -2, -17, 3, -15$ **20.** $23, -19, 0, -20, 11$

Evaluate each expression if $x = -2$, $y = -1$, $z = 3$, and $w = 6$.

SAMPLE 2 $\dfrac{xzw}{x - y} = \dfrac{(-2)(3)(6)}{-2 - (-1)} = \dfrac{-6(6)}{-2 + 1} = \dfrac{-36}{-1} = 36$

B 21. $\dfrac{4x + y}{z}$ **22.** $\dfrac{5z + y}{w + 1}$

23. $\dfrac{zw}{xy}$ **24.** $\dfrac{z - w}{x + y}$

25. $\dfrac{w - 7z}{y}$ **26.** $\dfrac{z - 2w}{y - x}$

27. $\dfrac{2z - w}{xyz}$ **28.** $\dfrac{x - 2y}{yzw}$

29. $\dfrac{(x + z)(x - z)}{w - y}$ **30.** $\dfrac{(5x + w)(5x - w)}{y - z}$

In Exercises 31 and 32 assume that a, b, and c are any real numbers and $c \neq 0$.

C **31.** Name the axiom, property, or rule that justifies each numbered step.

$$\frac{a + b}{c} = (a + b) \cdot \frac{1}{c} \qquad (1) \ \underline{\ ? \ }$$

$$= \left(a \cdot \frac{1}{c}\right) + \left(b \cdot \frac{1}{c}\right) \qquad (2) \ \underline{\ ? \ }$$

$$= \frac{a}{c} + \frac{b}{c} \qquad (3) \ \underline{\ ? \ }$$

32. Using the fact that multiplication is distributive with respect to subtraction, show that $\frac{a - b}{c} = \frac{a}{c} - \frac{b}{c}$. (Hint: See Exercise 31.)

Calculator Key-In _____

Use the division key on a calculator to find a decimal equal to each expression.

SAMPLE $\frac{-3}{2}$ *SOLUTION* $\frac{-3}{2} = -3 \div 2 = -1.5$

1. $\frac{1}{4}$ **2.** $\frac{-1}{8}$ **3.** $\frac{1}{-16}$ **4.** $\frac{-1}{-25}$ **5.** $\frac{1}{40}$

6. $\frac{-7}{4}$ **7.** $\frac{6}{-50}$ **8.** $\frac{-5}{-8}$ **9.** $\frac{31}{32}$ **10.** $\frac{37}{-64}$

11–20. Use the reciprocal key on a calculator to find a decimal equal to each expression in Exercises 1–10. Are your answers the same as before?

SAMPLE $\frac{-3}{2}$ *SOLUTION* $\frac{-3}{2} = -3 \times \frac{1}{2} = -1.5$

Just for Fun _____

Find at least three numbers that satisfy all three conditions:

there is a remainder of 1 when the number is divided by 2;
there is a remainder of 2 when the number is divided by 3;
there is a remainder of 3 when the number is divided by 4.

3-6 *Transforming Equations: Division*

OBJECTIVE   To solve equations using multiplication or division.

EXAMPLE 1   Solve $-\frac{z}{4} = -13$.

SOLUTION
$$-\frac{z}{4} = -13$$
$$(-4)\left(-\frac{z}{4}\right) = (-4)(-13)$$
$$z = 52$$

$$Check: \quad -\frac{z}{4} = -13$$
$$-\frac{52}{4} \overset{?}{=} -13$$
$$-13 = -13 \quad \checkmark$$

$\therefore$ the solution is 52.   *Answer*

EXAMPLE 2   Solve $-8a = 72$.

SOLUTION
$$-8a = 72$$
$$\frac{-8a}{-8} = \frac{72}{-8}$$
$$a = -9$$

$Check:$ $-8a = 72$
$$-8(-9) \overset{?}{=} 72$$
$$72 = 72 \quad \checkmark$$

$\therefore$ the solution is -9.   *Answer*

The method used in Example 2 is called **transformation by division,** because each side of the equation is *divided* by -8. Of course, transformation by division is just a special case of transformation by multiplication, since you can just as well multiply by $-\frac{1}{8}$ to solve the equation in Example 2.

Oral Exercises

State the number by which each side of the given equation must be divided to produce an equivalent equation with the variable alone as one side. Then state this equivalent equation.

1. $12a = 72$
2. $8b = -8$
3. $7c = -21$
4. $-4x = 32$
5. $-6y = -6$
6. $-35z = -105$

State the root of each equation.

7. $8t = 48$ **8.** $2m = -22$ **9.** $-5n = 60$ **10.** $-6 = 6x$

11. $0 = -3k$ **12.** $-9r = -27$ **13.** $y \div 3 = 9$ **14.** $\dfrac{y}{2} = -4$

15. $10 = x \div 5$ **16.** $8 = -\dfrac{u}{3}$ **17.** $-7v = -7$ **18.** $11f = 99$

Written Exercises

Solve.

A

1. $17s = 510$ **2.** $30r = 450$ **3.** $-1024 = 64t$ **4.** $-351 = 27g$

5. $-7f = 133$ **6.** $15h = -255$ **7.** $-14x = -364$ **8.** $-5y = 435$

9. $-9a = -216$ **10.** $12b = -576$ **11.** $8y = -344$ **12.** $-11x = 154$

13. $6d = 210$ **14.** $2680 = 40z$ **15.** $-374 = 34m$ **16.** $-18k = 198$

17. $5 = \dfrac{1}{74}p$ **18.** $0 = -\dfrac{1}{89}t$ **19.** $-\dfrac{q}{10} = -68$ **20.** $-77 = -\dfrac{v}{7}$

21. $27c = -675$ **22.** $736 = -32d$ **23.** $-37x = -962$ **24.** $-26f = -858$

Problems

Solve using an equation.

A

1. Twelve times a number is -348. Find the number.

2. Negative seven times a number is 259. Find the number.

3. Eric Danielle paid $86 for a series of four operas. How much is that for each opera?

4. Maria Brilla paid $418 for a season ticket to the 38 home basketball games. How much is that for each game?

5. A package of two AA batteries costs $1.18. How much is that for each battery?

6. A half-dozen blueberry muffins cost $1.80. How much does one muffin cost?

B

7. This week you can get 12 color prints developed for $2.88. How much is that for each print?

8. A monthly commuter ticket costs $39. If it is used for 50 rides, how much does each ride cost?

9. Four diesel-powered sedans cost a company $31,361.60. How much did each sedan cost?

10. A corporation gained $820,000 from the sale of some property. This was a gain of $.25 for each share of stock in the corporation. How many shares of stock are there in the corporation?

Self-Test 2

VOCABULARY   transformation by multiplication (p. 84)
quotient (p. 88)
transformation by division (p. 92)

Solve.

1. $\frac{1}{4}y = 16$ **2.** $-\frac{1}{2}x = 10$ *Obj. 3-4, p. 84*

Simplify.

3. $\dfrac{36}{-6}$ **4.** $-42 \div 7$ *Obj. 3-5, p. 88*

5. $-18 \div (-9)$ **6.** $-2x \div \dfrac{1}{2}$

Solve.

7. $8x = -72$ **8.** $-5z = -35$ *Obj. 3-6, p. 92*

9. Half of the oranges that the coach brought were eaten on the way home from the game. Twelve of the coach's oranges were eaten. By writing an equation and solving it, find out how many oranges the coach brought.

Check your answers with those at the back of the book.

Application

Electrical Power and Energy

Power is associated with the flow of an electric current in a circuit. Electrical power is measured in watts (W). The amount of power that is used depends on the number of volts (V) of the source of electricity and on the current. Current is the rate of flow of electrical charge, measured in amperes (A). Most household appliances (with the exception of large ones, such as stoves or clothes dryers) operate at voltages between 115 V and 125 V. Look at some electrical appliances in your home. The voltage and power are usually labeled.

The watt, ampere, and volt are units in the metric system. Using these units of measurement, power (P) is related to voltage (V) and current (I) by the formula

$$P = VI.$$

EXAMPLE 1   If current from a 120 V source flows through a 100 W light bulb, find the amount of current flowing in the circuit.

SOLUTION   You are given $V = 120$ and $P = 100$. Use the formula:

$$P = VI$$
$$100 = 120 \cdot I$$
$$I = \frac{100}{120} = \frac{5}{6}$$
$$I = \frac{5}{6}$$

∴ the amount of current is about 0.83 A.

When P watts of power are used for t hours, the energy (e) consumed, measured in watt-hours (W · h), is

$$e = Pt.$$

Electric companies base their charge to their customers on a larger unit, the kilowatt-hour (kW · h), which is equal to one thousand watt-hours.

EXAMPLE 2   A room air conditioner uses about 860 W. If the average cost of electricity is 8.4¢ per kW · h, how much does it cost to operate the air conditioner for six hours?

SOLUTION   Using the formula for energy, find the amount of energy consumed.

$$e = Pt$$
$$e = 860 \cdot 6$$
$$e = 5160$$

∴ the amount of energy consumed is 5160 W · h or 5.160 kW · h.

To compute the cost:

$$\text{cost} = 8.4 \times 5.160$$
$$= 43.344$$

∴ the cost of energy is about 43¢.

1. A desk calculator operates at 115 V with a current of 0.14 A. How much power is used by the calculator?

2. A toaster uses about 1150 W. If it operates at 120 V, how much current flows through the wiring?

3. A 1000 W hair dryer operates on a current of 8.33 A. What is the voltage in the circuit?

4. A solid-state color television uses 200 W. Assuming the cost of electricity is 8.4¢ per kW · h, how much does it cost to watch a three hour movie?

5. The oven in an electric range uses 12,200 W. At 8.4¢ per kW · h, how much does it cost to roast a turkey for five hours?

3-7 *Using Several Transformations*

OBJECTIVE To use several transformations to solve an equation.

To solve the equation $3x + 8 = 20$, you transform it into an equivalent equation which has x alone as one side. Look at the side with x in it: $3x + 8$. To get x alone, first subtract 8 and then divide by 3, as follows.

$$3x + 8 = 20$$
$$3x + 8 - 8 = 20 - 8 \quad \leftarrow \text{Subtract 8.}$$
$$3x = 12$$
$$\frac{3x}{3} = \frac{12}{3} \quad \leftarrow \text{Divide by 3.}$$
$$x = 4$$

To "undo" the *addition* of a number, you use the *subtraction* of that number. Addition and subtraction are called **inverse operations.** Multiplication and division are also inverse operations.

The following steps are usually helpful when you solve an equation in which all the variables are on the same side.

---

1. Simplify each side of the equation.

2. If there are still indicated additions or subtractions, use the inverse operations to undo them.

3. If there are indicated multiplications or divisions involving the variable, use the inverse operations to undo them.

EXAMPLE 1 Solve $8x + 5x - 3 = 23$.

SOLUTION

$$8x + 5x - 3 = 23$$
$$(8 + 5)x - 3 = 23 \qquad \left\{ \begin{array}{l} \text{Use the distributive axiom} \\ \text{to simplify the left side.} \end{array} \right.$$
$$13x - 3 = 23$$
$$13x - 3 + 3 = 23 + 3 \quad \leftarrow \text{Add 3 to each side.}$$
$$13x = 26$$
$$\frac{13x}{13} = \frac{26}{13} \quad \leftarrow \text{Divide each side by 13.}$$
$$x = 2$$

CONDENSED SOLUTION

$$8x + 5x - 3 = 23$$
$$13x - 3 = 23$$
$$13x = 26$$
$$x = 2$$

Check: $8x + 5x - 3 = 23$
$$8(2) + 5(2) - 3 \overset{?}{=} 23$$
$$16 + 10 - 3 \overset{?}{=} 23$$
$$23 = 23 \quad \sqrt{}$$

$\therefore$ the solution is 2. *Answer*

Oral Exercises

Describe how you would solve each equation.

SAMPLE $\frac{1}{3}x + 1 = -2$ **SOLUTION** First subtract 1 from each side; then multiply each side by 3.

1. $4x + 1 = 5$ **2.** $3x - 2 = 8$ **3.** $\frac{1}{2}x - 3 = -1$

4. $-\frac{1}{5}x + 8 = 4$ **5.** $6 + \frac{x}{2} = 7$ **6.** $-2 + \frac{x}{-3} = 4$

7. $5x + x = 18$ **8.** $4y - y = 12$ **9.** $z - 4z = 6$

10. $-5t + 7t = -20$ **11.** $6s + s - 2 = 5$ **12.** $3m - m + 1 = -7$

Written Exercises

Solve.

A **1.** $3x + 5 = 14$ **2.** $2y - 5 = 17$ **3.** $-13 + 4t = -37$

4. $12 + 5s = -78$ **5.** $\frac{a}{2} - 4 = 8$ **6.** $\frac{b}{3} + 6 = 9$

7. $\frac{c}{5} + 20 = -15$ **8.** $\frac{-d}{4} - 2 = -1$ **9.** $9 = 5 - 2m$

10. $12 = -3 - 5n$ **11.** $-6w + 3w = 21$ **12.** $3k - k = -8$

13. $5t + 3t = -32$ **14.** $2p - 5p = -15$ **15.** $3q + 4q = 0$

16. $7s - 11s = 0$ **17.** $2k + 42 = 0$ **18.** $4w + 80 = 0$

19. $5q - 3q + 10 = 0$ **20.** $3w - w - 2 = 0$ **21.** $x - 4x + 2 = 5$

22. $r - 7 - 4r = -4$ **23.** $0 = m - 14 - 3m$ **24.** $0 = u + 15 + 4u$

25. $x + 2x + 3x = 24$ **26.** $3y - 2y + y = 36$ **27.** $5(a - 2) = -35$

28. $6(b + 9) = -30$ **29.** $-3(r - 3) = 12$ **30.** $-8(s + 5) = 56$

B **31.** $3(x + 1) + 2 = -7$ **32.** $2(y - 1) - 7 = 5$

33. $4(w + 8) - 13 = -1$ **34.** $5(z - 2) + 8 = 3$

35. $8 + 3(x + 1) = -4$ **36.** $13 + 4(y + 5) = -3$

37. $4 - 3(a - 1) = -2$ **38.** $7 - 4(b + 1) = -1$

39. $-4 - 3(2y + 1) = -13$ **40.** $-5 + 4(3d - 6) = 7$

41. $(a - 10) + (a - 2) + a = 0$ **42.** $(3 - b) + (4 - b) + (5 - b) = 0$

43. $3(r + 4) - 2r = -5$ **44.** $2(s - 3) - s = -2$

C **45.** $x - 2[6 - (1 - 2x)] = 0$ **46.** $\frac{1}{2}[3(m + 2) - (2 - m)] = 6$

47. $-2[y + 3(5 - y)] - 5(y - 7) = 0$ **48.** $5z + 2[3(1 - z) - 2(1 + z)] = 22$

49. $2|x| - (|x| - 1) = 7$ **50.** $7(|y| - 2) - 3|y| - 16 = 2$

Problems

In the class elections Maria received 53 more votes than Annie. In all, 221 votes were cast for the two girls. How many votes were for Annie?

SOLUTION

Step 1   The problem asks for the number of votes for Annie.

Step 2   Let n = number of votes for Annie.
Then $n + 53$ = number of votes for Maria.

Step 3 $n + (n + 53) = 221$

Step 4 $2n + 53 = 221$

Complete the solution.

A 1. The sum of twice a number and 63 is 191. Find the number.

2. The sum of 17 and three times a number is 80. Find the number.

3. Four times a number, decreased by 43, is -11. Find the number.

4. Six times a number, increased by 9, is 123. Find the number.

5. Seventy, decreased by five times a number, is -100. Find the number.

6. Twice a number, decreased by 37, is -3. Find the number.

7. If you add to 8 the product of 3 and a number, you get 41. Find the number.

8. If you subtract 57 from the product of 4 and a number, you get -1. Find the number.

9. The perimeter of a rectangle is 32 and the length is 10. Find the width.

10. The perimeter of a rectangle is 44 and the width is 8. Find the length.

11. Together, a soft drink and a sandwich cost $2.20. What was the price of each if the sandwich cost three times as much as the drink?

12. Casey's Car Care Center sold 1864 L (liters) of gasoline today. Seven times as much gasoline was bought with credit cards as with cash. How much gasoline was bought on credit?

13. Sally Chin has practiced law three years longer than her younger brother. Together, they have a total of 21 years of practice. How long has her brother practiced law?

14. The home team's score of 102 points was 60 points less than twice the visiting team's score. What was the visiting team's score?

B 15. One number is 17 greater than a second number. When the lesser number is subtracted from twice the greater number, the difference is 157. Find each number.

16. Two numbers differ by 3. Four times the lesser diminished by three times the greater is 7. Find the numbers.

17. The side of a square is twice as long as the side of an equilateral triangle (a triangle with all sides equal). The perimeter of the square is 60 cm more than the perimeter of the triangle. What are the lengths of the sides of the square and the triangle?

18. In woodshop, Lisa cut a board 2 m long into two pieces. One piece is 10 cm shorter than the other. How long is each piece?

19. Juan and Ingrid went selling magazine subscriptions. Ingrid sold four fewer subscriptions than twice as many as Juan sold. Together, they sold 23 subscriptions. How many subscriptions did each sell?

20. With optional equipment, an automobile cost $7840. If the cost of the basic car was $165 more than four times the price of the optional equipment, what was the cost of the basic car?

C 21. The record low temperature at one station in Antarctica is 3.1°C warmer than the record low at a second station. The average of the two record low temperatures is −86.75°C. What is the record low at the first station?

22. The total length of three wilderness trails is 20 km. The first trail is 1 km shorter than twice the length of the second trail. The third trail is 2 km longer than the first. Find the length of each trail.

23. There is a three-year age difference between each child in the Miller family and the next older child. If there are four children in the family and the sum of their ages is 34, how old is the oldest?

24. The perimeter of a rectangular lot is 260 m. The length exceeds the width by 20 m. Find the dimensions of the lot.

25. Mac paid $8.55 for a table tennis set at a 10%-off sale. What was the price of the set before the sale?

Just for Fun

Philanthropic Philomena was trying to get people to contribute $10 to the scholarship fund. She knocked on the door of the first house and said, "Give me as much money as I have of my own in my pocket and I'll put $10 into the fund box in your name." It was done, and Philomena repeated the procedure at a second and a third house, after which she had no money of her own left in her pocket and $30 in the fund box. How much money of her own did Philomena start out with in her pocket?

3-8 *Equations Having the Variable in Both Sides*

OBJECTIVE To solve equations having the variable in both sides.

The variable appears in both sides of the equation

$$4y = y + 12.$$

Are you allowed to transform the equation by subtracting y from both sides? The answer is Yes. Because variables represent numbers, you may transform an equation by adding a variable expression to each side or by subtracting a variable expression from each side.

EXAMPLE 1 Solve $4y = y + 12$.

SOLUTION
$$4y = y + 12$$
$$4y - y = y + 12 - y$$
$$3y = 12$$
$$\frac{3y}{3} = \frac{12}{3}$$
$$y = 4$$

CONDENSED $4y = y + 12$ *Check:* $4y = y + 12$
SOLUTION $3y = 12$ $4(4) \overset{?}{=} 4 + 12$
           $y = 4$ $16 = 16$ $\checkmark$

$\therefore$ the solution is 4.   ***Answer***

It is possible that an equation may have *no* roots, or that it may be satisfied by *every* real number. Study the next two examples.

EXAMPLE 2 Solve $5(1 - x) + 8x = 3(x + 2)$.

SOLUTION
$$5(1 - x) + 8x = 3(x + 2)$$
$$5 - 5x + 8x = 3x + 6$$
$$5 + 3x = 3x + 6$$
$$3x - 3x = 6 - 5$$
$$0 = 1$$

Since the given equation is equivalent to the false statement $0 = 1$, it has no root. ***Answer***

It is convenient to call the set with no members the **empty set,** or the **null set.** It is denoted by the symbol $\emptyset$. Thus, you may say that the solution set of the equation in Example 2 is $\emptyset$.

EXAMPLE 3 Solve $\frac{1}{2}(8t - 18) + 16 = -5 + 4(t + 3)$.

SOLUTION
$$\frac{1}{2}(8t - 18) + 16 = -5 + 4(t + 3)$$
$$4t - 9 + 16 = -5 + 4t + 12$$
$$4t + 7 = 7 + 4t$$

The given equation is equivalent to $4t + 7 = 7 + 4t$, which is satisfied by every real number.

∴ the solution set is the set of real numbers. ***Answer***

An equation which is true for every value of the variable(s) is called an **identity.** Thus, the equation in Example 2,

$$\frac{1}{2}(8t - 18) + 16 = -5 + 4(t + 3),$$

is an identity.

Oral Exercises

Solve.

1. $3x = 2x + 5$
2. $y + 8 = 2y$
3. $4t + 1 = 5t$
4. $2u - 7 = 3u$
5. $x + 5 = 1 + x$
6. $2a = 4 + 2a$
7. $3x = x + 2x$
8. $2m = m$
9. $3x = x + 2$
10. $3b + 1 = 3b + 2$
11. $2(x - 1) = 2x - 2$
12. $3(z + 1) = 3z$

Written Exercises

Solve each equation. If the equation is an identity or if it has no root, state that fact.

A
1. $8u = 6u + 14$
2. $13t = 40 + 8t$
3. $x = 51 - 2x$
4. $z = 84 - 6z$
5. $11h - 91 = 4h$
6. $4i + 49 = 1$
7. $29j + 54 = 23j$
8. $41k - 63 = 34k$
9. $98 - 5x = 2x$
10. $42 + 10s = 4s$
11. $2p = 11p + 45$
12. $11e = 15e + 96$
13. $17x + 66 = 14x$
14. $-6q = q - 35$
15. $-3a = -8a - 30$
16. $-4k - 18 = -13k$
17. $5y = -2 + 5y$
18. $7t = 126 - 7t$
19. $7u + 5 = 5u - 7$
20. $4r - 3 = r + 6$
21. $6x - 2 = x + 13$
22. $6c + 8 = -8 + 6c$
23. $53 - 2d = 2 + d$
24. $3 - f = 6f + 24$

B
25. $3(x + 4) = 2x$
26. $2(y - 5) = y - 1$
27. $5(1 + n) = 2(7 + n)$
28. $3(2 + m) = 2(3 - m)$
29. $4b + 4(1 - b) = b - 9$
30. $2(2 + a) - 3a = a + 10$

Solve each equation. If the equation is an identity or if it has no root, state that fact.

31. $4(2y - 1) + 5 = 3y + 1$

32. $3(x - 4) - x = 2(x - 6)$

33. $4s - 2(1 - s) = 2(3s - 1)$

34. $3z + 2(1 - z) = z - 2$

35. $4(g + 1) = 10 - 2(3 - 2g)$

36. $1 + 3(d + 2) = d + 2(d + 4)$

C **37.** $4[1 - 3(r + 2)] + 2r = 0$

38. $2[3(c + 2) - (c + 1)] = 3(1 + c)$

39. $2[3(2 + v) - (-v)] = 5(v + 3) - 2(1 - v)$

40. $y - 1 - [2(3 - 2y) - 3(3 - y)] = 2(y + 1)$

Problems

Solve.

A **1.** Find a number which is 24 greater than its opposite.

2. Find a number which is 14 less than its opposite.

3. Find a number which is 15 greater than twice its opposite.

4. Find a number whose product with 6 is the same as its sum with 60.

5. The sum of two numbers is 76. One of the numbers is three times the other. Find the numbers.

6. Twice a number, increased by 11, is the same as three times the number, decreased by 12. Find the number.

7. The difference of two numbers is 16. Four times the smaller number is 13 less than three times the larger. What are the numbers?

8. The sum of two numbers is 64. Twice the lesser number is five more than the greater number. Find the numbers.

9. Karla has five steel balls of equal mass. If she puts four of them in one pan of a beam balance and one ball along with a mass of 30 g (grams) in the other pan, the pans balance each other. What is the mass of each steel ball?

10. Sandy has six coins of the same kind. Two fifteen-cent stamps and three of the coins have the same total value as all six coins put together. What kind of coin does she have?

11. Cycles, Inc., manufactures ten-speed and three-speed bicycles. The profit on a ten-speed is three times the profit on a three-speed. If the profit on each kind of bicycle is increased by $15, then the profit on the ten-speed will be twice the profit on the three-speed. What is the current profit on each?

12. During the passage of a cold front, the temperature dropped at the steady rate of 1°C per hour. The temperature at 6:00 P.M. was 3°C more than twice the temperature at midnight. What was the temperature at 6:00 P.M.?

B 13. On Friday, Mike and Steve shot baskets, and Mike made three times as many as Steve. On Saturday, Mike made seven fewer baskets than he did on Friday, while Steve made nine more than he did on Friday. If they tied on Saturday, how many baskets did each make on Friday?

14. The combined length of the Panama and Suez Canals is 250 km. If the Suez Canal were 4 km shorter, it would be twice as long as the Panama Canal. How long is each canal?

15. Angel Falls, the highest waterfall on earth, is 750 m higher than Niagara Falls. If each of the falls were 7 m lower, Angel Falls would be sixteen times as high as Niagara Falls. How high is Angel Falls? Niagara Falls?

16. A cup of coffee contains 20 more mg (milligrams) of caffeine than a cup of tea and 85 more mg of caffeine than the average cola drink. If one cup of tea and four cola drinks contain the same amount of caffeine as one cup of coffee, how many milligrams of caffeine are there in one cup of coffee?

17. "Tom is two times as old as I am," said Dick. "On the other hand, I am four years younger than Harry while Tom is eight years older than Harry. How old are Harry, Tom, and I?"

18. Suppose that five plain hamburgers cost the same as three superburgers. Also, suppose that one superburger costs 30 cents more than one cheeseburger, while one plain hamburger costs 20 cents less than one cheeseburger. What would be the cost of one of each kind of burger?

C 19. Television ratings showed that at nine o'clock on Monday night, 37% more of the city's TV audience watched a new situation comedy than watched an old hit movie. The percent watching the movie was 5% more than twice the percent watching a college football game. The percent watching the comedy was 2% more than six times the percent watching the game. What percent of the TV audience watched the game? the movie? the comedy?

20. The three countries of greatest area in the world are the Soviet Union, Canada, and China, with a combined area of 41,939,000 km² (square kilometers). The area of Canada is 415,000 km² greater than that of China, while the combined area of Canada and China is 2,865,000 km² less than that of the Soviet Union. What is the area of each country?

3-9 *Proving Statements*

OBJECTIVE To prove statements in algebra.

Many rules or number properties have been stated earlier in this book. Some of these are axioms, statements *assumed* to be true. Others are theorems. A **theorem** is a statement that is *shown* to be true by using axioms, definitions, and other theorems in a logical development.

Logical reasoning from known facts and axioms to a theorem is called a **proof.** The following example shows how a theorem is proved in algebra.

EXAMPLE Prove: For all real numbers a and b, $(a + b) + (-b) = a$.

PROOF

STATEMENTS	REASONS
1. $(a + b) + (-b) = a + [b + (-b)]$	1. Associative axiom for addition
2. $\quad b + (-b) = 0$	2. Axiom of opposites
3. $a + [b + (-b)] = a + 0$	3. Substitution principle
4. $\quad a + 0 = a$	4. Identity axiom for addition
5. $(a + b) + (-b) = a$	5. Transitive property of equality

Generally, a shortened form of proof is given, in which only the *key reasons* are stated. (The substitution principle and axioms of equality are usually not stated.)

The proof shown in the example above may be shortened to the three steps shown below.

STATEMENTS	REASONS
1. $(a + b) + (-b) = a + [b + (-b)]$	1. Associative axiom for addition
2. $\qquad\qquad = a + 0$	2. Axiom of opposites
3. $\qquad\qquad = a$	3. Identity axiom for addition

Once a theorem has been proved, it can be used as a reason in other proofs.

You may refer to the Chapter Summaries on pages 66 and 107 for listings of axioms and theorems that you can use as reasons in your proofs.

Oral Exercises

State the missing reasons.

1. Prove the *property of the opposite of a sum:* $-(a + b) = (-a) + (-b)$.

   Proof: Since $-(a + b)$ is the opposite of $a + b$, you can prove that
$$-(a + b) = (-a) + (-b)$$
   by showing that $a + b + [(-a) + (-b)] = 0$.

   1. $a + b + [(-a) + (-b)] = [a + (-a)] + [b + (-b)]$ 1. _?_ and _?_
   2. $\qquad\qquad\qquad\qquad = 0 + 0$ 2. _?_
   3. $\qquad\qquad\qquad\qquad = 0$ 3. _?_

2. Prove the *addition property of equality:*

$$\text{If } a = b, \text{ then } a + c = b + c \text{ and } c + a = c + b.$$

   Proof: 1. $a + c = a + c$ 1. _?_
           2. $a = b$ 2. Given
           3. $a + c = b + c$ 3. _?_
           4. $a + c = c + a;$ 4. _?_
              $b + c = c + b$
           5. $c + a = c + b$ 5. _?_

Written Exercises

Write the missing reasons in Exercises 1-6.

A 1. **a.** Prove: If $b \neq 0$, then $\frac{1}{b}(ba) = a$.

   Proof:

   1. $\frac{1}{b}(ba) = \left(\frac{1}{b} \cdot b\right)a$ 1. _?_
   2. $\qquad = 1 \cdot a$ 2. _?_
   3. $\qquad = a$ 3. _?_

   b. From step 3 prove that $(ab)\frac{1}{b} = a$.

   3. $\frac{1}{b}(ba) = a$ (above)

   4. $(ba)\frac{1}{b} = a$ 4. _?_

   5. $(ab)\frac{1}{b} = a$ 5. _?_

   $\therefore$ if $b \neq 0$, $\frac{1}{b}(ba) = a$ and $(ab)\frac{1}{b} = a$.

2. Prove the *multiplication property of equality:*

$$\text{If } a = b, \text{ then } ca = cb \text{ and } ac = bc.$$

Proof:

1. $ca = ca$ 1. _?_
2. $a = b$ 2. Given
3. $ca = cb$ 3. _?_
4. $ca = ac;$ 4. _?_
   $cb = bc$
5. $ac = bc$ 5. _?_

3. Prove: If $a + c = b + c$, then $a = b$.

Proof:

1. $a + c = b + c$ 1. Given
2. $(a + c) + (-c) = (b + c) + (-c)$ 2. _?_
3. $a = b$ 3. _?_

4. Prove: If $ac = bc$ and $c \neq 0$, then $a = b$.

Proof:

1. $ac = bc$ 1. Given
2. $(ac) \cdot \dfrac{1}{c} = (bc) \cdot \dfrac{1}{c}$ 2. _?_
3. $a = b$ 3. _?_

B 5. Prove: $-(a - b) = b - a$.

Proof:

1. $-(a - b) = -[a + (-b)]$ 1. _?_
2. $\qquad\quad = -a + [-(-b)]$ 2. _?_
3. $\qquad\quad = -a + b$ 3. _?_
4. $\qquad\quad = b + (-a)$ 4. _?_
5. $\qquad\quad = b - a$ 5. _?_

6. Prove: $-(-a - b) = a + b$

Proof:

1. $-(-a - b) = -[-a + (-b)]$ 1. _?_
2. $\qquad\qquad = -(-a) + [-(-b)]$ 2. _?_
3. $\qquad\qquad = a + b$ 3. _?_

Write proofs, including statements and reasons, for Exercises 7–11.

7. Prove: If $a \neq 0$, then $\dfrac{a}{a} = 1$.

8. Prove: If $a \neq 0$ and $b \neq 0$, then $\dfrac{1}{\frac{a}{b}} = \dfrac{b}{a}$.   (Hint: Show that $\dfrac{a}{b} \cdot \dfrac{b}{a} = 1$.)

C   **9.** Prove: If $a = b$ and $c \neq 0$, then $\dfrac{a}{c} = \dfrac{b}{c}$.

10. Prove: If $c \neq 0$ and $\dfrac{a}{c} = \dfrac{b}{c}$, then $a = b$.

11. Prove: If $a \neq 0$ and $b \neq 0$, then $\dfrac{a+b}{ab} = \dfrac{1}{a} + \dfrac{1}{b}$.

Self-Test 3

VOCABULARY   inverse operations (p. 96)   theorem (p. 104)
empty set (p. 100)   proof (p. 104)
identity (p. 101)

Solve.

1. $4x - 3 = 21$ **2.** $y - 3y + 9 = 5$ Obj. 3-7, p. 96

3. $2z - 4 = z + 2$ **4.** $3(1 - t) + 2 = 2(t - 10)$ Obj. 3-8, p. 100

5. Fred is 6 years older than Liz.
This year he is twice as old as Liz.
How old is Liz this year?

6. Write the missing reasons.   Obj. 3-9, p. 104

1. $-a + (a + b) = (-a + a) + b$ 1. _?_
2. $ = 0 + b$ 2. _?_
3. $ = b$ 3. _?_

Check your answers with those at the back of the book.

Chapter Summary

1. Transforming an equation by substitution, or by addition or subtraction, or by multiplication or division (not by zero) produces an equivalent equation. These transformations are used in solving equations.

2. Inverse operations are used in solving equations.

3. The structure of algebra is built up of axioms and definitions and of theorems proved by using the axioms and definitions in a logical development.

Chapter Review

Give the letter of the correct answer.

1. Find the solution of $x + (-6) = -1$. 3-1
   - **a.** -7
   - **b.** -5
   - **c.** 5
   - **d.** 6

2. Find the solution of $9 + y = 7$.
   - **a.** 2
   - **b.** 16
   - **c.** -16
   - **d.** -2

3. Simplify $12 - (-6)$. 3-2
   - **a.** -18
   - **b.** 18
   - **c.** -6
   - **d.** 6

4. Simplify $185 - (75 - 90)$.
   - **a.** -200
   - **b.** 20
   - **c.** 170
   - **d.** 200

5. Find the solution of $w - 6 = 9$. 3-3
   - **a.** -15
   - **b.** 15
   - **c.** -3
   - **d.** 3

6. Find the solution of $15 = 7 + z$.
   - **a.** -22
   - **b.** -8
   - **c.** 8
   - **d.** 22

7. Find the solution of $\frac{1}{3}x = -12$. 3-4
   - **a.** -36
   - **b.** -4
   - **c.** 36
   - **d.** 4

8. Find the solution of $-\frac{1}{2}t = -34$.
   - **a.** -17
   - **b.** -68
   - **c.** 17
   - **d.** 68

9. Simplify $-100 \div (-50)$ 3-5
   - **a.** $\frac{1}{2}$
   - **b.** 2
   - **c.** -5000
   - **d.** -2

10. Simplify $\frac{-96x}{8x}$, $x \neq 0$.
    - **a.** -12
    - **b.** $-12x$
    - **c.** 12
    - **d.** $12x$

11. Find the solution of $27y = -81$. 3-6
    - **a.** -54
    - **b.** -108
    - **c.** -3
    - **d.** $-\frac{1}{3}$

12. Find the solution of $-220 = -5t$.
    - **a.** -1100
    - **b.** -44
    - **c.** 1100
    - **d.** 44

13. Find the solution of $4s - 2s - 2 = -42$. 3-7
    - **a.** -42
    - **b.** -20
    - **c.** -22
    - **d.** 20

14. Find the solution of $29 - 3k = 1 + k$. 3-8
    - **a.** -7
    - **b.** -4
    - **c.** 4
    - **d.** 7

15. A statement assumed to be true is called:

   a. a theorem   **b.** an axiom   **c.** a definition   **d.** a proof

3-9

16. Which axiom guarantees that for every real number n, $(n + 3) + 7 = n + (3 + 7)$?

   a. commutative axiom for multiplication

   b. axiom of closure for addition

   c. transitive property of equality

   d. associative axiom for addition

Chapter Test

Solve.

1. $y + (-4) = -15$

2. $w + 12 = 33$

3-1

Simplify.

3. $9 - (-1)$

4. $218 - (14 - 59)$

3-2

Solve.

5. $t - 15 = 2$

6. $-7 = v + 8$

3-3

7. $\frac{1}{3}u = -18$

8. $-8 = -\frac{1}{8}a$

3-4

Simplify.

9. $24 \div (-12)$

10. $\frac{-56t}{-7t}$, $t \neq 0$

3-5

Solve.

11. $4b = -32$

12. $-9t = -108$

3-6

13. $3q + 1 = -17$

14. $p - 6 - 6p = 14$

3-7

15. $3c + 2 = 4c - 9$

3-8

16. Paula had four times as much money as her brother Larry, but after their aunt gave each of them four dollars, Paula had three times as much as Larry. How much did each have originally?

Write the missing reasons.

17. $10x - 12 = 78$

      $10x - 12 + 12 = 78 + 12$ <u> ? </u>

3-9

18. $(\frac{1}{x} \cdot x)y = 1 \cdot y$ <u> ? </u>

Cumulative Review (Chapters 1-3)

Simplify.

1. $7(18 \div 2) - 6$

2. $\dfrac{72 \div 4}{5 + 2 \cdot 2}$

3. $-15 + 22 + (-30)$

4. $|0| + 2|-5|$

5. $-[-10 - (-2)]$

6. $-29 + [-(-5 + 8)]$

7. $5(-r + 2) + 6r$

8. $\dfrac{1}{10}(210xy)\left(-\dfrac{1}{7}\right)$

9. $\dfrac{1}{3}[-27 + (-3t)]$

10. $(18 - 20) - (-2 + 5)$

11. $(-4)(-2)(-1)$

12. $(5a + 2) - (4 - 3a)$

13. $120z \div \left(-\dfrac{1}{5}\right)$

14. $-174 \div (-29)$

15. $\dfrac{1}{4}(8m - 4n) + (-7m)$

Evaluate each expression if $a = 3$, $b = 7$, $c = \dfrac{1}{3}$, $d = -1$, and $e = -4$.

16. $3b - 4a$

17. $\dfrac{2ac + b}{a}$

18. $c(d - e)$

19. $\dfrac{a - b}{de}$

20. Graph the given numbers on one number line: $-1, 4, 0, -3$.

21. Write the numbers in order from least to greatest: $-2, 1, -3.5, 0$.

Solve each equation if $x \in \{-6, -3, 0, 3, 6\}$.

22. $5x - 7 = 8$

23. $x(x - 3) = 0$

24. $-(-x) = -3$

25. $|x| + 1 = 7$

Solve. If the equation is an identity or has no root, state that fact.

26. $-1 = a + 5$

27. $b - 7 = |-2|$

28. $3 = -10 - c$

29. $d - 11 = -4$

30. $2.8 + e = 2.8$

31. $f + 9 = 1$

32. $-5 = -\dfrac{1}{3}g$

33. $9h = 126$

34. $\dfrac{1}{2}j = -\dfrac{7}{4}$

35. $-15k = 795$

36. $8 - 3m = -1$

37. $9 = n + 3 - 2n$

38. $q - 3 = -(3 - q)$

39. $4(2 - r) = 2 + r$

40. $6(s + 5) = 4 + 6s$

Solve.

41. Nine less than a number is 2. Find the number.

42. The Farrens were driving to Palo Alto. They had driven 243.8 km when they had a flat tire 12.4 km from the city. How far do the Farrens live from Palo Alto?

43. Five pads of paper cost $4.15. What is the cost of three pads?

44. Half a number, increased by 2, is -5. Find the number.

Maintaining Skills ━━━━━━━━━━

Express each fraction as a decimal to the nearest hundredth.

SAMPLE 1 $\frac{26}{25}$ **SOLUTION** $\frac{26}{25} = \frac{26}{25} \cdot \frac{4}{4} = \frac{104}{100} = 1.04$

SAMPLE 2 $\frac{3}{7}$ **SOLUTION** $\frac{3}{7} = 3 \div 7;$ 0.428; 0.43 **Answer**

$$7\overline{)3.000}$$

1. $\frac{37}{50}$ **2.** $\frac{13}{20}$ **3.** $\frac{7}{4}$ $\frac{28}{}$

                                          20

4. $\frac{5}{8}$ **5.** $\frac{5}{6}$ **6.** $\frac{25}{23}$ $\frac{14}{}$

                                          60

Express each percent as a fraction in simplest form.

                                          $\frac{56}{}$

                                          4

SAMPLE 3 3.2%   **SOLUTION** $3.2\% = \frac{3.2}{100} = \frac{3.2}{100} \cdot \frac{10}{10} = \frac{32}{1000} = \frac{4}{125}$

7. 28%   **8.** 5%   **9.** 93%   **10.** 108%   **11.** 1.6%   **12.** 0.02%

Express each decimal as a percent.

SAMPLE 4 0.32   **SOLUTION 1** $0.32 = \frac{32}{100} = 32\%$

                                 SOLUTION 2 $0.32 = 32\%$

SAMPLE 5 0.192   **SOLUTION** $0.192 = 19.2\%$

13. 0.37   **14.** 0.04   **15.** 0.3   **16.** 2.56   **17.** 0.075   **18.** 0.003

Find each number.

SAMPLE 6 15% of 18   **SOLUTION** $0.15 \times 18 = 2.7$

19. 4% of 135   **20.** 29% of 82   **21.** 0.5% of 450

22. 75.4% of 200   **23.** 120% of 40.8   **24.** 256% of 30

Find the value of x or of n to the nearest tenth.

SAMPLE 7 12% of $x = 3$ **SOLUTION** $0.12x = 3;$ $x = \frac{3}{0.12} = \frac{300}{12} = 25$

25. 15% of $x = 9$ **26.** 10% of $x = 3.2$ **27.** 4% of $x = 18$

28. 0.8% of $x = 0.5$ **29.** 120% of $x = 7$ **30.** 45% of $x = 8$

SAMPLE 8 $n\%$ of $6 = 3$ **SOLUTION** $\frac{n}{100} \times 6 = 3;$ $\frac{n}{100} = \frac{3}{6};$ $n = \frac{300}{6} = 50$

31. $n\%$ of $4 = 1$ **32.** $n\%$ of $3 = 1$ **33.** $n\%$ of $25 = 16$

34. $5 = n\%$ of 18   **35.** $15 = n\%$ of 16   **36.** $48 = n\%$ of 40

Archaeologists excavate an American Indian settlement in Wyoming. Carbon dating can be used to determine the ages of artifacts less than 4000 years old that are made of wood, leather, or other organic material. The formulas used in carbon dating involve expressions such as $A_0 e^{-kt}$.

4

POLYNOMIALS AND
PROBLEM SOLVING

ADDITION AND SUBTRACTION

4-1 *Exponents*

OBJECTIVE To write and simplify exponential expressions.

The number 32 can be written as $2 \times 2 \times 2 \times 2 \times 2$ and is called a *power* of 2. Here is how other powers of 2 are defined and written:

First power of 2: $2^1 = 2$ (read "two to the first power")

Second power of 2: $2^2 = 2 \times 2$ (read "two to the second power," or "two squared," or "the square of two")

Third power of 2: $2^3 = 2 \times 2 \times 2$ (read "two to the third power," or "two cubed," or "the cube of two")

Fourth power of 2: $2^4 = 2 \times 2 \times 2 \times 2$ (read "two to the fourth power")

In general, if b is any real number and n is any positive integer, the **nth power of b** is written b^n and is defined as follows:

$$b^n = \underbrace{b \cdot b \cdot b \cdot \ \ldots \ \cdot b}_{n \text{ factors}}$$

In b^n, the value of b is called the **base** and the value of the small raised symbol ^{n} is called the **exponent**.

$$\text{Exponent} \longrightarrow b^n = \text{the } n\text{th power of } b \longleftarrow \text{Base}$$

The exponent indicates the number of times the base occurs as a factor.

113

The third power of b can be written in the **exponential form** b^3 or in the **factored form** $b \cdot b \cdot b$.

EXAMPLE 1   Evaluate y^4 if $y = -7$.

SOLUTION   Replace y with -7, and simplify the result.
$$y^4 = (-7)^4 = (-7)(-7)(-7)(-7) = 2401$$

The expression $-2t^3$ represents $-2(t \cdot t \cdot t)$; that is, 3 is the exponent of the base t. On the other hand, $(-2t)^3$ stands for $(-2t)(-2t)(-2t)$. In this case, the parentheses show that the base is $-2t$. Study the following examples.

$5 \times 4^2 = 5(4 \times 4) = 80$ but $(5 \times 4)^2 = (5 \times 4)(5 \times 4) = 400$.

$-3^4 = -(3 \cdot 3 \cdot 3 \cdot 3) = -81$ but $(-3)^4 = (-3)(-3)(-3)(-3) = 81$.

$xz^3 = x(z \cdot z \cdot z)$ but $(xz)^3 = (xz)(xz)(xz)$.

$9 + a^2 = 9 + (a \cdot a)$ but $(9 + a)^2 = (9 + a)(9 + a)$.

The following steps are used to simplify numerical expressions which contain powers.

SUMMARY OF ORDER OF OPERATIONS

1. First simplify expressions within grouping symbols.
2. Then simplify powers.
3. Then simplify products and quotients in order from left to right.
4. Then simplify sums and differences in order from left to right.

EXAMPLE 2   Evaluate $\dfrac{(x + 1)^3}{9} + 5(x - 8)^2 - 1$ if $x = 2$.

SOLUTION   Replace x with 2 and simplify the result.
$$\frac{(x + 1)^3}{9} + 5(x - 8)^2 - 1 = \frac{(2 + 1)^3}{9} + 5(2 - 8)^2 - 1$$
$$= \frac{3^3}{9} + 5(-6)^2 - 1$$
$$= \frac{27}{9} + 5(36) - 1$$
$$= 3 + 180 - 1$$
$$= 182$$

Oral Exercises

For each exercise state the power, the base of that power, and the exponent. Then state the expression with the power in factored form.

SAMPLE $7r^5$ **SOLUTION**   Power r^5; base r; exponent 5; factored form $7 \cdot r \cdot r \cdot r \cdot r \cdot r$

1. 12^2

2. c^5

3. $4a^3$

4. $-6b^4$

5. $2(xy)^2$

6. $(u + v)^3$

Simplify.

7. $(4 \times 5)^2$

8. 2×3^2

9. $2 \times \left(\dfrac{1}{3}\right)^2$

10. $(12 - 2)^3$

11. $(2 \times 3)^2 - 4 + 1$

12. $10 \times 2^2 \div 5$

13. $2 \times 3^2 - 1 \times 3 + 7$

14. $5(-2)^2 - 3(-2) - 10$

15. $\left(\dfrac{6}{2} - 1\right)(2 + 3)^2$

16. $(-1)^2$

17. $(-1)^3$

18. $(-1)^4$

Complete each statement with the word *positive* or *negative*.

19. An even power of a negative number is a __?__ number.

20. An odd power of a negative number is a __?__ number.

Written Exercises

Write each expression in exponential form.

A   **1.** $x \cdot x \cdot x$

2. $m \cdot m \cdot m \cdot m$

3. z cubed

4. y squared

5. $7 \cdot b \cdot b$

6. $-11 \cdot n \cdot n \cdot n$

7. $-5 \cdot r \cdot r \cdot s$

8. $2 \cdot a \cdot b \cdot b \cdot b$

9. $6 \cdot y \cdot y \cdot y \cdot t \cdot t$

10. $\dfrac{1}{3} \cdot s \cdot s \cdot t \cdot t \cdot t$

11. $(a + b)(a + b)(a + b)$

12. $(x + y)(x - y)(x - y)$

13. $(c - 2)$ squared

14. the fourth power of $5d$

15. The product of 17 and the cube of $(m + p)$

16. -47 divided by the square of $(c - d)$

17. The sixth power of the sum of d and e

18. The fifth power of the product of a and b

Simplify.

19. $2 + 2^2 + 6 \div 2 - 1$

20. $2 + (2^2 + 6) \div 2 - 1$

21. $(2 + 2^2 + 6) \div 2 - 1$

22. $(2 + 2^2 + 6) \div (2 - 1)$

23. $3 \times 4^2 - 5 \times 1 - 4$

24. $3 \times 4^2 - (5 \times 1 - 4)$

Simplify.

B 25. $6^3 \div [5^2 - 3^2 - (-2)^2]$

26. $(6^2 - 3 \times 2^2 + 1) \div [0 + (-5)^2]$

27. $6(3^2 - 2^2) \div 3 + 4 \div (-4)$

28. $7(3^2 - 1) + 2^4 \times 3 \div (-3)2^2$

29. $8 \times (-1)^3 - 7(-1)^2 + 2(-1) + 4$

30. $15(-2)^4 - 6(-2)^3 + 5(-2)^2 + 1$

Evaluate each expression if $x = 4$ and $y = -3$.

31. $x^2 - 2xy + y^2$

32. $(x - y)^3$

33. $\dfrac{(x^2 + y^2)}{5^2}$

34. $\dfrac{(x - 2y)^3}{x^3 + (2y)^2}$

35. $\dfrac{3x + 2y}{3 - y^2}$

36. $3x \div 6 + 2y^3 \div 18$

Evaluate each expression for the given value of x.

C 37. $(x^2 + 4x - 5)(2x^2 - 7x + 1)$, $x = -5$

38. $(3x^2 + 8x - 1)(x^2 + x - 6)$, $x = -2$

39. $2(x - 1)^3 - 11(x - 1)^2 + 12(x - 1) + 9$, $x = 3$

40. $4(x + 1)^3 - 2(x + 1)^2 - 8(x + 1) + 6$, $x = \dfrac{1}{2}$

Calculator Key-In _____

Simplify each of the following mentally. Then use a calculator to check your answers.

1. $(0.1)^2$

2. $(0.3)^2$

3. $(0.4)^2$

4. $(1.2)^2$

5. $(0.12)^2$

6. $(0.05)^2$

7. $(0.03)^2$

8. $(0.011)^2$

9. $(0.2)^3$

10. $(0.3)^3$

11. $(0.5)^3$

12. $(0.09)^3$

Just for Fun _____

Recall (page 15) that the triangular numbers are

$$1, 3, 6, 10, 15, \text{ and so on.}$$

The square numbers are

$$1, 4, 9, 16, 25, \text{ and so on.}$$

1. Verify that each square number from 4 to 100 is the sum of two consecutive triangular numbers.

2. Illustrate Exercise 1 by dividing the square array of dots shown at the right into two triangular arrays.

4-2 Adding and Subtracting Polynomials

OBJECTIVE To add and subtract polynomials.

Each of the expressions below is a *monomial*.

$$5 \quad z \quad \tfrac{1}{3}b \quad -2xy^2$$

A **monomial** is an expression that is either a numeral, a variable, or a product of a numeral and one or more variables. A numeral, such as 5, is also called a **constant monomial,** or a **constant.**

A sum of monomials is called a **polynomial.** A polynomial such as $x^2 + (-5x) + (-6)$ is usually written as $x^2 - 5x - 6$. Some polynomials have special names:

Binomials (two terms): $\quad 3x + 7 \qquad 4a^2 - 8b$
Trinomials (three terms): $\quad x^2 - 5x - 6 \qquad 3a^2 + 2ab - b^2$

A monomial may be thought of as a polynomial of one term.

In the monomial $-2xy^2$, the number -2 is called the **coefficient,** or **numerical coefficient.** Two monomials which are exactly alike or which differ only in their numerical coefficients are called **similar,** or **like.** The following monomials are all similar:

$$-2xy^2, \quad 5y^2x, \quad xy^2, \quad \text{and} \quad \tfrac{1}{2}xy^2.$$

The following monomials are *not* similar: $-2xy^2$ and $-2x^2y$.

A polynomial is **simplified,** or **in simplest form,** when no two of its terms are similar. You may use the distributive property to add similar terms.

EXAMPLE 1   Simplify $-2x^3 + 3x^2 + 5x^2 + 2x^3 - 6$.

SOLUTION
$$\begin{aligned}
-2x^3 + 3x^2 + 5x^2 + 2x^3 - 6 &= (-2 + 2)x^3 + (3 + 5)x^2 - 6 \\
&= 0x^3 + 8x^2 - 6 \\
&= 8x^2 - 6
\end{aligned}$$

The **degree of a monomial in a variable** is the number of times that variable occurs as a factor in the monomial. For example,

$$-4x^2yz^3 \text{ is of degree} \begin{cases} 2 \text{ in } x; \\ 1 \text{ in } y; \\ 3 \text{ in } z. \end{cases}$$

The **degree of a monomial** is the total number of times its variables occur as factors. Thus, the degree of $-4x^2yz^3$ is $2 + 1 + 3$, or 6. The degree of any nonzero constant monomial is 0.

The **degree of a polynomial** is the greatest of the degrees of its terms *after it has been simplified*. Since the polynomial $-2x^3 + 3x^2 + 5x^2 + 2x^3 - 6$, in Example 1, can be simplified to $8x^2 - 6$, the degree of the polynomial is 2, *not* 3.

To add two polynomials, you write the sum and simplify by adding similar terms.

EXAMPLE 2 Add $3x^2y - 7x^2 + y^2 + 2$ and $x^2y + 5x^2 - 9$.

SOLUTION 1 $(3x^2y - 7x^2 + y^2 + 2) + (x^2y + 5x^2 - 9) =$
$(3 + 1)x^2y + (-7 + 5)x^2 + y^2 + (2 - 9) = 4x^2y - 2x^2 + y^2 - 7$

SOLUTION 2 You may also add vertically:

$$3x^2y - 7x^2 + y^2 + 2$$
$$\underline{x^2y + 5x^2 - 9}$$
$$4x^2y - 2x^2 + y^2 - 7$$

Subtracting polynomials is very much like subtracting real numbers. To subtract a number, you add the opposite of that number. To subtract a polynomial, you add the opposite of that polynomial and simplify.

EXAMPLE 3 Subtract $-3a^2 - 2ab + b^2 - 3$ from $5a^2 - 3ab - 7b^2 + 4$.

SOLUTION 1 $(5a^2 - 3ab - 7b^2 + 4) - (-3a^2 - 2ab + b^2 - 3) =$
$5a^2 - 3ab - 7b^2 + 4 + 3a^2 + 2ab - b^2 + 3 =$
$(5 + 3)a^2 + (-3 + 2)ab + (-7 - 1)b^2 + (4 + 3) =$
$8a^2 - ab - 8b^2 + 7$

SOLUTION 2 Subtract the lower polynomial from the one above it.

$$5a^2 - 3ab - 7b^2 + 4$$
$$\underline{-3a^2 - 2ab + b^2 - 3}$$
$$8a^2 - ab - 8b^2 + 7$$

To subtract one polynomial from another, add the opposite of each term you are subtracting.

Oral Exercises

1. State the degree of the monomial $3xy^3z^2$ in each variable.

State the degree of each polynomial. If the polynomial is a binomial or a trinomial, state this fact.

2. $3 + 2x - x^2$ **3.** $x^2 + y^2$ **4.** $x^2y^2 - z^3$

5. $t^3 - 3t^2 + 4t$ **6.** $uv^3 + u^3v + u^2v + uv^2$ **7.** $r^4 + 3s^4 + 2rs + r^3s^3$

Name the similar monomials.

8. $5a, 7ab, -2a, -4b, 8b, -9ab$ **9.** $9xy, -2x, 3y, -xy, 5yx, 11y$

10. $4x^2$, $-8x^2y$, $-3x$, $-9x^2$, $-2xy^2$, $3x^2y$, x, $-y$

11. $13m^2n^2$, $-6m^2$, $4n^2$, $7m^2n$, $-4n^2m^2$, $-3n^2$, $8m^2n$, $9mn^2$

Add the polynomials.

12. $5x - 5$
$\underline{2x + 7}$

13. $7a + 5b$
$\underline{5a - b}$

14. $7n - 4k$
$\underline{5n + 2k}$

15. $3a - 2b + 1$
$\underline{4a + 9b - 7}$

16. $4x^2 - 3x + 2$
$\underline{x^2 + 1}$

17. $9y^2 - 3y + 2$
$\underline{y^2 - 4y}$

18. $a^2 + 3ab + b^2$
$\underline{2a^2 + 5ab - b^2}$

19. $2x - 3y + 4z$
$\underline{-4x - 4z}$

20. $1 - 6x$
$\underline{5 - 4x + 3x^2}$

21–29. In Exercises 12–20, state the opposite of the lower polynomial. Then subtract by adding that opposite to the upper polynomial.

Simplify.

30. $(2x + 5) + (3x - 1)$

31. $(4y + 7) - (y - 1)$

Written Exercises

Copy each polynomial and underline similar terms in the same way. Then simplify the polynomial.

SAMPLE $\underline{4n^2t} - \underline{3nt^2} + \underline{n^2t} - \underline{nt^2}$; $5n^2t - 4nt^2$

A
1. $2rt - 6 + rt$
2. $-4a + 3b - b$
3. $2x^2 - 4x + 5x - 3x^2$
4. $4y^3 - 3y^2 + 2y^3 - 5y$
5. $-5abc + 2bc - 3ac + abc$
6. $-6r^2t - 6r^2 + rt^2 - r^2t$
7. $-3m^2n - 2mn^2 + 5m^2n - 2mn$
8. $3xy^2z - 2xyz^2 + 7xyz^2 - 3x^2yz$

Add.

9. $4x - 3$
$\underline{2x + 4}$

10. $9a + 2b$
$\underline{4a - 3b}$

11. $3r - 2s$
$\underline{-5r + 7s}$

12. $5a - 2b$
$\underline{2a + 6b}$

13. $3s + 7t - 1$
$\underline{5s + t - 2}$

14. $4x - 2xy + y$
$\underline{3x - xy - y}$

15. $3x^2 + 5x + 2$
$\underline{x^2 - 2x - 1}$

16. $y^2 - y - 7$
$\underline{3y^2 + y - 8}$

17. $2n^2 - 5$
$\underline{-n^2 + 4n - 2}$

18. $3a - 2b + c$
$\underline{-a + 4b}$

19. $5x^2 - 3x - 4$
$2x^2 - 5$
$\underline{x^2 + 5x + 7}$

20. $6r^2 - s^2$
$s^2 - 8$
$\underline{-2r^2 + 3s^2 - 2}$

21–30. In Exercises 9–18, subtract the lower polynomial from the one above it.

Simplify.

31. $(2a + 3b - 4) + (5a - b + 7)$

32. $(2x^2 - 3x + 5) + (x^2 - 7x - 9)$

33. $(7a^2 - 2ab + b^2) + (-a^2 - b^2)$

34. $(1 - c - c^2) + (2c - 3c^2)$

35. $(x^3 - x - 7) + (2x^2 + 4x - 9)$

36. $(5n^4 - 2n^3 - 1) + (2 + n^2 - n^4)$

37. $(9b - 3) - (4b + 6)$

38. $(4a - 7) - (5a - 9)$

39. $(2a - 3b - 5) - (6a - 7b - 2)$

40. $(7c - 8d - 11) - (-c + 5d + 2)$

41. $(x^2 - 5x + 9) - (2x^2 + 3x + 1)$

42. $(-3a^2 + 5a - 2) - (3a^2 - a + 1)$

43. $(2a^2 - b^2) - (a^2 - ab + b^2)$

44. $(c^2 + cd) - (-c^2 + cd + d^2)$

Solve.

B 45. $5x - (x + 3) = 5$

46. $(12n - 3) - (3n - 1) = 34$

47. $(2a - 5) - (3a + 2) = 5 - 3a$

48. $(5p - 3) - (p - 8) = 2p - 7$

49. $(4 - 2t) - (t - 5) = 2t - 1$

50. $(4s - 7) - (2 - 3s) = -23$

51. $2x^2 - 5x = (3x^2 - 7x) - (x^2 - 4)$

52. $(x^2 + 2x + 1) - (x^2 + 4x + 3) = 4$

53. $2x^2 = (3x^2 - 5x - 7) - (x^2 - x + 1)$

54. $4 - (a^2 - 2a - 9) = 9 - (2a + a^2)$

55. The sum of $a^4 - 3a^2 + 2a - 1$ and $2a^4 - a^3 + a^2 - 2a - 2$ is subtracted from the sum of $6 + 3a^3 - a^4$ and $-6 - 2a^2 - 2a^4$. What is the difference?

56. By what does the sum of $3x^3 - 2x^2 + 5x$ and $x^3 + 7x^2 - 3x$ exceed the sum of $2x^3 + x^2 - 5x$ and $2x^3 - 6x + 7$?

Integer Problems

Solve.

A 1. Find two consecutive integers whose sum is 33.

2. Find three consecutive integers whose sum is -147.

3. Find four consecutive even integers whose sum is 116.

4. Find four consecutive odd integers whose sum is 0.

5. The sum of the least and greatest of three consecutive integers is 50. What is the middle integer?

6. The sum of the least and greatest of three consecutive odd integers is 110. What are the integers?

7. The greater of two consecutive integers is 10 greater than twice the lesser. Find the integers.

8. The greater of two consecutive odd integers is 7 greater than twice the lesser. Find the integers.

B 9. Find three consecutive odd integers such that the sum of the greatest and twice the least is 25.

10. Find four consecutive integers such that the sum of the two greatest subtracted from twice the sum of the two least is 15.

11. Find four consecutive integers such that five times the third decreased by twice the fourth is 55.

12. Find four consecutive odd integers such that the third is the sum of the fourth and twice the second.

13. The measures in meters of two adjacent sides of a rectangle are consecutive odd integers. The perimeter is 96 m. What are the dimensions of the rectangle?

14. The atomic numbers of radium, thorium, and uranium are consecutive even integers in increasing order. If three times the atomic number of radium is 82 more than the sum of the atomic numbers of thorium and uranium, what are the atomic numbers of these three elements?

For Exercises 15–16 use this definition: The product of any real number and an integer is called a *multiple* of the real number.

C 15. The ages of three sisters are consecutive multiples of 4. Three years ago the sum of their ages was 39. Find their present ages.

16. Find four consecutive multiples of 3 such that twice the sum of the two greatest integers exceeds three times the least by 21.

Self-Test 1

VOCABULARY
power (p. 113)
base (p. 113)
exponent (p. 113)
exponential form (p. 114)
factored form (p. 114)
monomial (p. 117)
constant (p. 117)
polynomial (p. 117)

binomial (p. 117)
trinomial (p. 117)
coefficient (p. 117)
similar terms (p. 117)
simplify a polynomial (p. 117)
degree of a monomial (p. 117)
degree of a polynomial
   (p. 118)

1. Write in exponential form: $2 \cdot a \cdot a \cdot a \cdot b \cdot c \cdot c$ Obj. 4-1, p. 113

2. Simplify $3 + (-3)^2 \times (-1)^3$.

3. Evaluate $\dfrac{(2x - y)^3}{12x^2 - (2y)^2}$ if $x = -1$ and $y = 2$.

4. Add.   5. Subtract the lower polynomial. Obj. 4-2, p. 117

$$\begin{array}{l} x^2 - 3x - 5 \\ \underline{5x^2 + 3x + 1} \end{array} \qquad \begin{array}{l} 4a^2 + 2ab - b^2 \\ \underline{2a^2 - 2ab - 7b^2} \end{array}$$

Check your answers with those at the back of the book.

MULTIPLICATION

4-3 *Multiplying Monomials*

OBJECTIVE   To multiply monomials.

When you multiply two powers having the same base, you add the exponents as shown below.

$$x^3 \cdot x^4 = x^{3+4} = x^7$$
$$y^6 \cdot y^2 = y^{6+2} = y^8$$

You can understand why you add exponents if you remember that an exponent indicates the number of times the base is used as a factor.

$$x^3 \cdot x^4 = \overbrace{(x \cdot x \cdot x)}^{3 \text{ factors}} \cdot \overbrace{(x \cdot x \cdot x \cdot x)}^{4 \text{ factors}} = x^7$$
$$\underbrace{\qquad\qquad\qquad\qquad\qquad}_{7 \text{ factors}}$$

$$a^m \cdot a^n = \overbrace{(a \cdot a \cdot \ldots \cdot a)}^{m \text{ factors}} \cdot \overbrace{(a \cdot a \cdot \ldots \cdot a)}^{n \text{ factors}} = a^{m+n}$$
$$\underbrace{\qquad\qquad\qquad\qquad\qquad}_{m + n \text{ factors}}$$

The following general rule applies when two powers to be multiplied have the same base.

RULE OF EXPONENTS FOR MULTIPLICATION

For all positive integers m and n,

$$a^m \cdot a^n = a^{m+n}$$

When you multiply two monomials, you use the rule of exponents along with the commutative and associative axioms for multiplication.

EXAMPLE 1

$(2x^3y^4)(-3xy^5) = [2 \cdot (-3)](x^3 \cdot x)(y^4 \cdot y^5)$ Commutative and associative axioms for multiplication

$\qquad\qquad\quad = -6x^4y^9$ Rule of exponents for multiplication

EXAMPLE 2

$(3a^5b)(-2ab^3) + (4a^3b^2)(a^3b^2) = -6a^6b^4 + 4a^6b^4$
$$= -2a^6b^4$$

Oral Exercises

Simplify each expression.

1. $a^4 \cdot a^6$ **2.** $a^{12} \cdot a^3$ **3.** $b^3 \cdot b^3$ **4.** $a^n \cdot a^n$

5. $a^n \cdot a$ **6.** $b^{2n} \cdot b^{3n}$ **7.** $(2x)(3x)$ **8.** $(2x)(3x)(4x)$

9. $2p \cdot p^2$ **10.** $\left(-\frac{1}{2}x\right)(4x^2)$ **11.** $(-c^4d^2)(-c^3d^3)$ **12.** $(9x^9)(2x^2)$

13. $(2x^3y^2)(1.2xy^4)$ **14.** $(3rs)(-2r^4s^3)$ **15.** $(-x)^2(-x)^3$ **16.** $(-x)^2 \cdot x^3$

Written Exercises

Simplify each expression.

A **1.** $a^3 \cdot a^5 \cdot a^2$ **2.** $2 \cdot b^3 \cdot b^2 \cdot b$ **3.** $(3c^4)(5c^2)$

   4. $(4x^3)(2x^5)(3x)$ **5.** $(2c^5)(3c^4)(5c)$ **6.** $(-4a^3)(-3a)$

   7. $(xy^2)(x^3y)$ **8.** $(ab^3)(a^2b)(b^2)$ **9.** $(5n^2m)(6nm^2)(3m^4)$

   10. $(-ab)(-ac)(-bc)$ **11.** $(-x^2y^5)(-3x^4y^7)$ **12.** $(4c^2bd^4)(3c^5b^2)(2d^5)$

   13. $\left(\frac{1}{2}n^2p\right)(2np^2)(np)$ **14.** $\left(\frac{1}{7}a^3b\right)(7ab^4)(a^5)$ **15.** $(-3n^2m)(-2nm^4)(n^2)$

   16. $a^n \cdot a^3$ **17.** $b^{3n} \cdot b^{2n} \cdot b^n$ **18.** $c^{1+n} \cdot c^n$

   19. $2^k \cdot 2^{k+1} \cdot 2^2$ **20.** $3^r \cdot 3^{r+1} \cdot 3$ **21.** $x^n \cdot x^{2n+3} \cdot x^4$

   22. $(-2)^m(-2)^{2m}(-2)^{3m}$ **23.** $(-x)^2(-x)^3(-x)^5$ **24.** $(-x^2)(-x^3)(-x^5)$

B **25.** $(2a^3)(4a^2) + (3a^4)(a)$ **26.** $(4n^3)(5n^7) - (2n^6)(4n^4)$

   27. $(3x^3)(2x^2)(5x) + (7x)(2x^5)$ **28.** $(4r^5)(3r)\left(\frac{1}{2}r^6\right) - (3r^4)(2r^6)(-r^2)$

   29. $(8a^2b)\left(\frac{1}{4}a^4b^4\right) + (5ab^3)(2a^5b^2)$ **30.** $(7n^2)(3m^4) - (2n)(3m^4n)$

   31. $(4a^3b^2)(2b^3) - (-3ab)(a^2b^4)$ **32.** $(4r^4s^2)(s^5) + (2s^3r^2)(s^4r^2)$

   33. $(5ab^2c^3)(3abc) + (2ab^2c)(abc^3)$ **34.** $(xy^2z^3)(3x^3yz^4) - (4xyz)(x^3y^2z^6)$

Find in simplest form the area of each shaded region.
(Area of a rectangle = length × width)

35.

36.

37.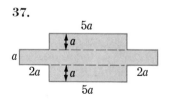

Find the total surface area of each solid. (The total surface area of a solid is the sum of the areas of all its faces.)

C 38.

39.

40.

41–43. Find the volume of each solid above. (The volume can be found by multiplying the area of the bottom or top of the solid by the height of the solid.)

EXTRA

Scientific Notation

Some numbers are so large or so small that they are difficult to read and write. For example, consider the numbers

$$1,370,000,000,000,000 \quad \text{and} \quad 0.0000000165.$$

Scientific notation makes it easier to read such numbers and to calculate with them. Scientific notation is based on positive and negative powers of 10 as defined below.

Positive Powers of 10

$10^1 = 10$
$10^2 = 100$
$10^3 = 1000$
$10^4 = 10,000$
and so on

Negative Powers of 10

$10^{-1} = 0.1$
$10^{-2} = 0.01$
$10^{-3} = 0.001$
$10^{-4} = 0.0001$
and so on

To express a number in **scientific notation**, write it as the product of a number between 1 and 10 and an integral power of 10.

$51,400 = 5.14 \times 10^4$	Decimal point moved 4 places left
$7,080,000,000 = 7.08 \times 10^9$	Decimal point moved 9 places left
$0.009 = 9 \times 10^{-3}$	Decimal point moved 3 places right
$0.0000325 = 3.25 \times 10^{-5}$	Decimal point moved 5 places right

Numbers written in scientific notation can be multiplied easily, using the rule of exponents for multiplication.

$$(4.1 \times 10^4)(2 \times 10^5) = (4.1 \times 2) \times (10^4 \times 10^5) = 8.2 \times 10^9$$
$$(7 \times 10^{-4})(3.1 \times 10^6) = (7 \times 3.1) \times (10^{-4} \times 10^6) = 21.7 \times 10^2 = 2.17 \times 10^3$$

Exercises

Express each of the following numbers in scientific notation.

1. 200,000
2. 159,000,000
3. 40,800,000,000
4. 0.0007
5. 0.00000019
6. 0.0000000000325

Express each product in scientific notation.

7. $(3 \times 10^5)(2 \times 10^9)$
8. $(4.1 \times 10^7)(2 \times 10^{-3})$
9. $(3 \times 10^{-4})(1.2 \times 10^{-5})$
10. $(8 \times 10^7)(6 \times 10^4)$
11. $(3.1 \times 10^4)(4 \times 10^{-3})$
12. $(8 \times 10^{-5})(3 \times 10^{-2})$

13. If you have a calculator with directions for entering numbers in scientific notation, calculate $(5.2 \times 10^{13})(4.73 \times 10^{-5})$.

14. Study the positive and negative powers of 10 defined in this section. Then guess how 10^0 is defined.

15. The metric system is based on powers of 10. Complete each statement by writing a power of 10.

   a. 1 m = _?_ cm
   b. 1 km = _?_ m
   c. 1 km = _?_ cm
   d. 1 g = _?_ mg
   e. 1 kg = _?_ g
   f. 1 mg = _?_ kg

Calculator Key-In

To display very large numbers, most calculators use a form of exponential notation similar to that described in the Extra on the opposite page. Try this on a calculator:

Press the 9 key until the display is filled with 9's. Next, estimate what the answer would be if you were to multiply this large number by 2. Write your estimate on paper. Now go ahead and multiply by 2 on the calculator. Compare the displayed answer with your estimate. They should be two different forms of the same number.

Enter 9's again. Predict what the calculator will display when you multiply by 20. Try it. Were you right? What will be displayed if you multiply by 400 instead of 20?

4-4 *Powers of Monomials*

OBJECTIVE   To find powers of a monomial.

To find a power of a monomial that is itself a power, you can apply the definition of a power and the rule of exponents for multiplication.

EXAMPLE 1 $(x^2)^3 = x^2 \cdot x^2 \cdot x^2 = x^{2+2+2} = x^6$

Note that $(x^2)^3 = x^6$, or $x^{2 \times 3}$. In general:

$$\overset{a^m \text{ is a factor } n \text{ times}}{\qquad} \qquad \overset{n \text{ terms}}{\qquad}$$
$$(a^m)^n = \overbrace{(a^m)(a^m) \cdots (a^m)} = \overbrace{a^{m+m+\cdots+m}} = a^{mn}$$

Thus, *to find a power of a power, you multiply the exponents.*

> ### RULE OF EXPONENTS FOR A POWER OF A POWER
>
> For all positive integers m and n,
>
> $$(a^m)^n = a^{mn}.$$

EXAMPLE 2 $(y^8)^7 = y^{56}$ *EXAMPLE 3* $[(-a)^5]^4 = (-a)^{20} = a^{20}$

To find a power of a product, you can apply the definition of a power and the commutative and associative axioms for multiplication.

EXAMPLE 4 $(3x)^2 = 3x \cdot 3x = 3 \cdot 3 \cdot x \cdot x = 3^2 \cdot x^2 = 9x^2$

Note that *both* the 3 and the x are squared when the product $3x$ is squared. In general:

$$\overset{ab \text{ is a factor}}{\underset{m \text{ times}}{\qquad}} \qquad \overset{m \text{ factors}}{\qquad} \quad \overset{m \text{ factors}}{\qquad}$$
$$(ab)^m = \overbrace{(ab)(ab) \cdots (ab)} = \overbrace{(a \cdot a \cdot \ldots \cdot a)}\overbrace{(b \cdot b \cdot \ldots \cdot b)} = a^m b^m$$

Thus, *to find a power of a product, you find the power of each factor and then multiply.*

> ### RULE OF EXPONENTS FOR A POWER OF A PRODUCT
>
> For every positive integer m,
>
> $$(ab)^m = a^m b^m.$$

EXAMPLE 5 $(3a)^4 = 3^4 \cdot a^4 = 81a^4$

EXAMPLE 6 $(-4y)^3 = (-4)^3 \cdot y^3 = -64y^3$

The rules of exponents for powers are applied in the following example.

EXAMPLE 7 $(-2x^6y^4)^3 = (-2)^3 \cdot (x^6)^3 \cdot (y^4)^3 = -8x^{18}y^{12}$

Oral Exercises

Simplify.

1. $(x^3)^2$ **2.** $(y^5)^3$ **3.** $(a^7)^4$ **4.** $(3^7)^2$

5. $(5a)^2$ **6.** $\left(\frac{1}{2}b\right)^2$ **7.** $\left(\frac{1}{3}ab\right)^2$ **8.** $\left(\frac{2}{3}x\right)^3$

9. $(3a^2)^2$ **10.** $(5n^3)^3$ **11.** $(-4x^5)^2$ **12.** $(-x^2)^4$

13. $(2y^3)^4$ **14.** $2(y^3)^4$ **15.** $(-4a^4)^2$ **16.** $-(4a^4)^2$

17. $(a^n)^2$ **18.** $(a^2)^n$ **19.** $[(-a)^n]^2$ **20.** $(x^ny^m)^3$

21. Find the values of $3a^2$ and $(3a)^2$ if $a = 4$.

22. Find the values of $-b^4$ and $(-b)^4$ if $b = 2$.

Written Exercises

Simplify.

A   **1.** $(x^4)^2$ **2.** $(a^8)^3$ **3.** $(2b)^3$ **4.** $(5nm)^3$

   5. $(2a^3)^4$ **6.** $\left(\frac{1}{3}n^4\right)^2$ **7.** $\left(\frac{1}{2}x^2\right)^5$ **8.** $(6x^3y^2)^2$

   9. $(-2b^2y^5)^3$ **10.** $(-4n^2y^6)^3$ **11.** $(-3t^2s^4)^4$ **12.** $(-x^3y)^5$

   13. $(4a)(3a)^2$ **14.** $(3n^2)(2n)^3$ **15.** $(-5a)^2(5a^2)$ **16.** $(-x^2y)^3(3x^4y)$

   17. $(4n)^3(3n)^2$ **18.** $(2a^2b)^3(a^2b^3)^4$ **19.** $(-3r^4s)^4\left(\frac{1}{9}rs^2\right)^2$ **20.** $\left(\frac{1}{2}a^3\right)^4(4a^7)^3$

Evaluate each expression if $a = 2$, $b = 3$, and $c = -4$.

21. $5b^2$ **22.** $(5b)^2$ **23.** $-7a^2$ **24.** $(-7a)^2$

25. $(3a + 2c)^3$ **26.** $3a^3 + 2c^3$ **27.** $(b + c)^2$ **28.** $b^2 + c^2$

Simplify.

B   **29.** $(2c)^3(3c)^2(-c)^4$ **30.** $(5n)^3(2n^2)^2\left(\frac{1}{10}n\right)^3$ **31.** $(u^2v^4)^3(4u^2v)^2$

   32. $(2a^4b^7)^3\left(\frac{1}{2}ab^4\right)^5$ **33.** $(a^n)^3(2a^n)^4$ **34.** $(c^2)^n(c^3)^{2n}$

   35. $(x^2y)^n(x^2y^3)^n$ **36.** $(a^{n+1})^3(a^n)^3$ **37.** $(2a^2b^3)^4 - (3a^4b^6)^2$

   38. $(5p^2q^4)^3 + (-pq^2)^6$ **39.** $x^3(xy^2)^2 + x(-xy)^4$ **40.** $s^2(r^2s^2)^2 + r^2(rs^3)^2$

C **41. a.** Find the volumes of the two cubes shown.

b. How many times larger is the volume of the bigger cube than that of the smaller cube?

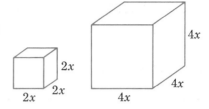

Computer Key-In _____

If you type the following program into a computer that accepts the language BASIC, the computer will then be ready to multiply any two numbers that you give it.

```
10   PRINT "TYPE IN TWO NUMBERS TO BE MULTIPLIED."
20   INPUT A
30   INPUT B
40   PRINT "PRODUCT =";A*B
50   END
```

If the absolute value of the product is greater than 999999, it will be printed in an exponential notation. For example, if you multiply 3452 by 675, the answer will be printed in this form:

$$2.33010E+06$$

The "E+06" means "times 10^6," and so

   $2.33010E+06$ means 2.33010×10^6,   or   2,330,100.

This happens to be the exact answer. However, if you multiply 67892 by 543, the answer may be printed as:

$$3.68654E+07$$

This is not an exact answer. It gives *six significant digits* of the answer 36,865,400, although the exact answer would be 36,865,356. Computers using BASIC commonly give such answers rounded to six significant digits.

   Verify that 999×999 is less than 999999. Then add 1 successively to one factor until the product is greater than 999999.

   Verify that 9999×99 is less than 999999. Then keep one factor fixed and add 1 successively to the other factor until the product is greater than 999999. Do this with each factor.

   To find the product of several numbers, you can use the second program on page 46 if you change the words in lines 20 and 80 and change lines 30 and 60 as follows:

$$30 \quad LET \ P=1$$
$$60 \quad LET \ P=P*N$$

4-5 Multiplying a Polynomial by a Monomial

OBJECTIVE To multiply a polynomial by a monomial.

The distributive axiom and the rules of exponents enable you to multiply any polynomial by a monomial. For example:

$$3a(5a^2 - 2a + 4) = 3a(5a^2) + 3a(-2a) + 3a(4) = 15a^3 - 6a^2 + 12a$$

You may multiply either horizontally or vertically:

$$-2xy(5xy + 3x - y) = -10x^2y^2 - 6x^2y + 2xy^2$$

or

$$5xy + 3x - y$$
$$-2xy$$
$$\overline{-10x^2y^2 - 6x^2y + 2xy^2}$$

Recall that to simplify an expression containing more than one grouping symbol, you work with the expression within the innermost grouping symbol first.

EXAMPLE Solve $20x^2 - 2[4x - 2x(1 - 5x)] = 8$

SOLUTION
$$20x^2 - 2[4x - 2x(1 - 5x)] = 8$$
$$20x^2 - 2[4x - 2x + 10x^2] = 8$$
$$20x^2 - 8x + 4x - 20x^2 = 8$$
$$-4x = 8$$
$$x = -2$$

The check is left for you.

$\therefore$ The solution is -2. *Answer*

Oral Exercises

Multiply.

1. $2(a + 5)$ **2.** $3(x - 8)$ **3.** $-7(2x + 5)$ **4.** $-\frac{1}{2}(2x - 2)$

5. $x(x - 6)$ **6.** $3a(2a + b)$ **7.** $5x(x + y)$ **8.** $-a(a - b)$

9. $x(x^3 + 3x^2 + 2x)$ **10.** $2c^2(3c - cd)$ **11.** $x^2y^3(x^2y + 2xy^2)$

Written Exercises

Multiply.

A   **1.** $3(2x^2 + 5y + 4)$ **2.** $4(3y^2 - 2y + 7)$
     3. $-7(2x^3 - x^2 + 5x)$ **4.** $-(2a - 3a^2 - a^3)$
     5. $3x^2(x^2 - 2xy + y^2)$ **6.** $5n^3(3n^2 + 7n - 2)$

Multiply.

7. $\frac{1}{3}a(3a^2 + 6ab - 12b^2)$

8. $\frac{1}{2}y(4x^2 - 8xy - 2y^2)$

9. $(8n^3 - 3n^2m + m^2)(2m)$

10. $(5x^2y - 2xy^2 + 4y^3)(3xy)$

11. $-2ab(3a^2b^2 - 7ab^3)$

12. $(p^3 - 4p^2q + 6q^2)(-3pq)$

13. $4n^2 + 3n + 7$
$\underline{2n}$

14. $5a^3 - 3a^2 - 2$
$\underline{3a}$

15. $\quad 4a^2b - 3ab^2 + b^3$
$\underline{-2a}$

16. $\quad y^2z - 3yz^2 + z^3$
$\underline{-3yz}$

Simplify.

17. $2x(3x - 5) + 4x(x + 2)$

18. $5n(2n + 4) - 3n(n - 2)$

19. $-2a(a^2 - 5) + 3a(a^2 - 6)$

20. $7x(3x - 2y) - 4(5x^2 - y)$

21. $\frac{2}{3}(6x - 9) - \frac{1}{2}(8x + 6)$

22. $\frac{1}{10}c(10 - 30c) - 2c(4 - c)$

23. $2a(a^2 - a + 2) - (a^3 + 5a^2 - 7a)a$

24. $2x^2(x + 3) - 5(x^2 - x)x$

Solve.

25. $5(x - 2) - 3x = 10$

26. $4(y - 3) - 12 = 8$

27. $\frac{1}{3}(6 - 3n) = -12$

28. $2y = -\frac{1}{2}(4y - 8)$

29. $5x(x - 2) = 5x^2 + 40$

30. $6a(a - 3) = 3a(2a + 12)$

31. $3a\left(5 - \frac{1}{3}a\right) - (15 - a^2) = 0$

32. $4(n - 7) - 2(1 - 3n)n = 6n^2$

Simplify.

B 33. $\frac{3}{5}(5a - 10b - 1) - 2\left(a - 3b + \frac{1}{5}\right)$

34. $\frac{1}{2}(4x + 3y - 1) + \frac{1}{4}(6y - 8x - 2)$

35. $2pq(1 - 4r - 3p) - 3p(2q - qr)$

36. $(4k^2 + 3kn + 2n^2)(-5k) + n(7k^2 - kn)$

37. $4a^3 - a[3 - 2a(a - 5)]$

38. $7n^2 - n[4n - 3n(2n - 1)]$

Solve.

39. $3(2y + 5) - 4(1 - 5y) = 9(3 + 2y)$

40. $x - 5(x + 2) = x + 3(3 - 2x)$

41. $2(5n - 4) - 3(n - 5) = 8(2n - 7)$

42. $2\left(a + \frac{3}{2}\right) - 3(a - 2) = 2(a - 3)$

43. $18a^2 - 2a[6a - 3(1 - a)] = -6$

44. $5n - \frac{2}{3}\left[2n^2 - \frac{1}{2}n(3 + 4n)\right] = -24$

Simplify. Each variable in an exponent represents a positive integer.

C 45. $x^n(2x^n - 3x + 4)$

46. $a^{n+1}(a^n + a)$

47. $(2b^{n+1} + 3b^2)b^{n+1}$

48. $(-s)^{2n}(s^{2n} - 1)$

4-6 *Multiplying Two Polynomials*

OBJECTIVE To multiply polynomials.

You have learned to use the distributive axiom to multiply a polynomial by a monomial:

$$(3x + 4)(2x) = 3x(2x) + 4(2x)$$

If you replace $2x$ in the example above by the polynomial $2x + 5$, the distributive axiom can still be applied:

$$
\begin{aligned}
(3x + 4)(2x + 5) &= 3x(2x + 5) + 4(2x + 5) \\
&= 6x^2 + 15x + 8x + 20 \\
&= 6x^2 + 23x + 20
\end{aligned}
$$

Here is another example in which a polynomial is multiplied by a polynomial, but the work is done in vertical form.

STEP 1 Multiply by $3a$.

$$
\begin{array}{r}
5a^2 - 3a - 7 \\
3a + 2 \\
\hline
15a^3 - 9a^2 - 21a
\end{array}
$$

STEP 2 Multiply by 2.

$$
\begin{array}{r}
5a^2 - 3a - 7 \\
3a + 2 \\
\hline
15a^3 - 9a^2 - 21a \\
10a^2 - 6a - 14
\end{array}
$$

STEP 3 Add.

$$
\begin{array}{r}
5a^2 - 3a - 7 \\
3a + 2 \\
\hline
15a^3 - 9a^2 - 21a \\
10a^2 - 6a - 14 \\
\hline
15a^3 + a^2 - 27a - 14
\end{array}
$$

It is often helpful to rearrange the terms of a polynomial so that their degrees in a particular variable are in either decreasing or increasing order.

In order of decreasing degree in x: $3x^4 + 5x^3 - 6x + 4$

In order of increasing degree in x: $4 - 6x + 5x^3 + 3x^4$

In order of decreasing degree in a
and increasing degree in b: $-4a^3 + a^2b + 5ab^2 + 3b^3$

To see the advantage of rearranging terms, first multiply the polynomials at the left below. Then compare your work with that shown at the right, where the terms of both polynomials have been rearranged.

$$
\begin{array}{l}
a^3 - ab^2 + 3b^3 + 2a^2b \\
b + a \\
\hline
\end{array}
$$

Rearrange in order of decreasing degree in a.

$$
\begin{array}{r}
a^3 + 2a^2b - ab^2 + 3b^3 \\
a + b \\
\hline
a^4 + 2a^3b - a^2b^2 + 3ab^3 \\
a^3b + 2a^2b^2 - ab^3 + 3b^4 \\
\hline
a^4 + 3a^3b + a^2b^2 + 2ab^3 + 3b^4
\end{array}
$$

Oral Exercises

Arrange in order of decreasing degree in the variable indicated in color.

1. $x - 3 + x^2$; x

2. $3x^2 + x^3 - 5$; x

3. $4a^2b + 3b^2a - a^3$; a

4. $2r^4 - 3s^2r + 4sr^2 + s^3$; r

Arrange in order of increasing degree in the variable indicated in color.

5. $x^2 + 2 - 3x$; x

6. $5y + 3y^3 - 7y^2$; y

7. $c^2d^2 + cd + c^4$; c

8. $c^2d^2 + c^3d + c^4$; d

Complete.

9. $(2x + 5)(x + 3) = 2x(x + 3) + (?)(x + 3)$

10. $(3a - 4)(a - 1) = 3a(a - 1) - (?)(a - 1)$

11. $(a + 1)(a + 2) = a(a + 2) + 1(?) = a^2 + 2a + (?) + 2$

12. $(r + 2)(r + 3) = r(?) + 2(?) = r^2 + (?)r + 2r + 6$

13. $(t + 2)(t + 4) = t^2 + 4t + 2t + (?)$

14. $(x + 2)(x - 3) = x^2 - 3x + 2x + (?)$

15. $(v - 2)(v - 5) = v^2 - 5v - 2v + (?)$

Written Exercises

Multiply. Use the horizontal form.

A
1. $(n + 3)(n + 4)$

2. $(x + 2)(x + 5)$

3. $(y + 3)(y - 7)$

4. $(z + 5)(z - 5)$

5. $(2a + 4)(a + 7)$

6. $(2b - 3)(b + 5)$

7. $(c - 4)(2c + 1)$

8. $(5x + 7)(2x - 3)$

9. $(3p - 4)(p - 5)$

10. $(a + 1)(a^2 + 2a + 3)$

11. $(x + 2)(x^2 - 3x + 1)$

12. $(y - 1)(3y^2 + y + 5)$

13. $(2b + 1)(3b^2 + 4b + 2)$

14. $(c - 7)(5c^2 - c - 2)$

15. $(3n - 8)(n^3 - 3n^2 + n)$

Multiply. Use the vertical form.

16. $4n + 1$
$\underline{ n + 2}$

17. $3a - 2$
$\underline{ 2a - 1}$

18. $2n^2 + 5n + 1$
$\underline{ n + 7}$

19. $3x^2 + x - 2$
$\underline{ 2x + 5}$

20. $2a + b$
$\underline{ a + b}$

21. $3r - s$
$\underline{2r + 3s}$

22. $a^2 + ab + b^2$
$\underline{ a + b}$

23. $2c^2 - cd + d^2$
$\underline{ c - d}$

Multiply using whichever form you prefer. Arrange the terms in each factor in order of decreasing or increasing degree in some variable.

B 24. $(3r + 2s)(5r^2 - 2rs + s^2)$

25. $(2n - 5)(n^2 - 3n - 7)$

26. $(a - 2)(3a^2 - 5a - 4)$

27. $(x - 1)(x^2 + x + 1)$

28. $(a^2 - 5)(a^2 + 5)$

29. $(2p - 5q)(p^3 - 3p^2q - 7pq^2)$

30. $(4c - 9)(c + c^2 - 7)$ **31.** $(5x - y)(x^2 - xy - y^2)$

32. $(3n - 7)(2 - n^2 - 4n)$ **33.** $(4a - b)(ab - b^2 + 3a^2)$

34. $(x + 3)(x + 3)(x + 3)$ **35.** $x(2x + 5)(4x + 1)$

36. $(x^2 - 2x + 3)(x^2 + 2x + 1)$ **37.** $(3a^2 + 2ab + b^2)(a^2 - ab - b^2)$

Solve.

38. $(x + 2)(x + 3) - x(x + 4) = 7$

39. $(a + 7)(a + 3) - a(a + 1) = 21$

40. $(3n + 1)(4n + 5) - (2n + 3)(6n + 1) = 15$

41. $(8n + 5)(n - 1) + 12 = (4n + 3)(2n - 1)$

42. $(6x - 5)(x + 3) - (2x - 4)(3x - 1) = 35$

43. $(3y + 2)(4y - 1) - (-2y - 1)(-6y - 2) = -24$

C **44.** When a certain polynomial is divided by $x - 3$, the quotient is $x^2 + x + 2$. Find the polynomial.

45. When a certain polynomial is divided by $2x + 5$, the quotient is $2x^2 - 3x + 1$. Find the polynomial.

Multiply.

46. $(2b^n + 1)(b^n - 2)$ **47.** $(a^n + 1)(a^n - 1)$

48. $(s^{2n} + 3)(s^{2n} - 3)$ **49.** $(b^m + a^n)(b^m - a^n)$

Self-Test 2

Simplify.

1. $x^2 \cdot x^5 \cdot x$ **2.** $(-3y^4)(-2y^3)$ Obj. 4-3, p. 122

3. $(a^3)^5$ **4.** $(-3x^2y^3)^2$ Obj. 4-4, p. 126

5. $5x(x + 4)$ **6.** $2a^2(a^2 - ab + b^2)$ Obj. 4-5, p. 129

7. $(n + 3)(n - 3)$ **8.** $(x - 2)(x^2 + 3x - 6)$ Obj. 4-6, p. 131

Check your answers with those at the back of the book.

Just for Fun

Write the number 260 using only three 4's and one other mathematical symbol.

Write the number 24 using a digit other than 8 three times and using one other mathematical symbol.

4-7 *Organizing Information*

OBJECTIVE   To organize facts given in a problem and write formulas in convenient form in order to solve problems.

In Chapter 1 you learned a five-step problem-solving method which included the following step:

Step 2   Choose a variable and use it with the given facts to represent the number(s) described in the problem.

Making a chart is a helpful way to carry out this step in solving certain kinds of problems. Before you can solve puzzles involving ages of people, you must learn how to use variables to represent their present ages as well as their ages in the past and in the future. For example, if you are told that Dan is two years older than Valerie, you can let x represent Valerie's age now and make the following chart.

	Age now
Valerie	x
Dan	$x + 2$

If you are then given some more information about their ages five years ago, you can enlarge the chart this way:

	Age now	Age 5 years ago
Valerie	x	$x - 5$
Dan	$x + 2$	$(x + 2) - 5$, or $x - 3$

The following example shows the solution of a word problem using this technique of organizing given facts.

EXAMPLE 1

Uncle Louis is three times as old as Michelle. In eight years their ages will total 100. How old are they now?

SOLUTION

Step 1   The problem asks for the ages of Michelle and Uncle Louis.

Step 2   Let x = Michelle's age now. Make a chart of the given facts.

	Age now	Age in 8 years
Michelle	x	$x + 8$
Louis	$3x$	$3x + 8$

Step 3 The only fact not recorded in the chart is that in 8 years their ages will total 100. Use this fact to write an equation.

$$(x + 8) + (3x + 8) = 100$$

Step 4
$$4x + 16 = 100$$
$$4x = 84$$
$$x = 21$$

Step 5 The check is left to you.

$\therefore$ Michelle is now 21 and Uncle Louis is 63. ***Answer***

Many problems, such as those involving area, distance, and interest, require the application of a known formula. In applying a formula, it is often useful to find an equivalent but different form in which a particular variable is expressed in terms of the other variables. For example, if you know the perimeter and the width of a rectangle, you can find a formula for the length as follows.

EXAMPLE 2 Solve $P = 2l + 2w$ for l.

SOLUTION
$$P = 2l + 2w$$
$$P - 2w = 2l$$
$$\frac{P - 2w}{2} = l \quad \textbf{\textit{Answer}}$$

Oral Exercises

Use the given information to complete each chart.

1. Karl is 4 years younger than Tom.

	Age now	Age last year
Tom	x	?
Karl	?	?

2. Tony is half as old as Lynn.

	Age now	Age 3 years ago
Lynn	x	?
Tony	?	?

3. Kim was twice as old as Kit last year.

	Age last year	Age now
Kit	x	?
Kim	?	?

4. A mat is 4 cm longer than it is wide. A second mat is 1 cm wider and 2 cm longer than the first.

	length	width
First mat	?	x
Second mat	?	?

Solve each equation for x.

5. $x - a = b$ **6.** $-x = d - 2x$ **7.** $y = kx$ **8.** $ax + b = c$

Solve each formula for the variable shown in color.

9. $P = a + b + c$; a **10.** $V = Bh$; h **11.** $A = \frac{1}{2}bh$; h **12.** $I = Prt$; r

Written Exercises

A   **1. a.** Solve $lw = A$ for w.
     b. Copy and complete the chart.

length	width	Area
$2x + 5$	x	?
$x + 4$	$x - 3$	?
$a + 1$	?	24
$3n + 2$	?	15

2. a. Solve $rt = D$ for r.
     b. Copy and complete the chart.

rate	time	Distance
x	2	?
30	$n + 2$	?
?	x	20
?	$5 - t$	12

Use the given information to complete each chart.

3. Sylvia has a collection of coins. She has three more quarters than dimes and five more dimes than nickels.

	number $\times$ value per coin = Total value		
nickels	x	?	?
dimes	?	?	?
quarters	?	?	?

4. Frank bought several boxes of strawberries costing $1 a box. He also bought three fewer boxes of cherries costing 75 cents a box.

	number of boxes $\times$ price per box (in cents) = Cost		
strawberries	x	?	?
cherries	?	?	?

5. The length of a rectangle is 12 cm more than the width. A second rectangle is 5 cm wider but 2 cm shorter than the first rectangle.

	length $\times$ width = Area		
first rectangle	?	x	?
second rectangle	?	?	?

6. Jo has 20 coins. She has twice as many dimes as nickels and the rest are quarters.

	number × value per coin = Total value		
nickels	x	?	?
dimes	?	?	?
quarters	?	?	?

Use the given information to complete each chart and each equation.

7. Janet is seven times as old as her dog Woofie. In two years Janet will be four times as old as Woofie.

a.

	Age now	Age in 2 years
Woofie	x	?
Janet	?	?

b. $7x + 2 = 4(?)$

8. Jean has three times as much money as her brother Jim, but when each of them earns three dollars, Jean will have twice as much as Jim.

a.

	Money now	Money after earnings
Jim	x	?
Jean	?	?

b. $\underline{\ ?\ } = 2(x + 3)$

9. Sam bought several apples at 10 cents each. He ate two and sold the rest at 15 cents each. He made a profit of 20 cents.

a.

	number × price = Cost		
Apples bought	n	?	?
Apples sold	?	?	?

b. $(n - 2)15 - \underline{\ ?\ } = 20$

10. Pete jogs to the gym at a rate of 15 km/h and walks back at a rate of 5 km/h. His total travel time is one hour. Pete traveled along the same route both ways.

a.

	rate × time = Distance		
Jogging	?	t	?
Walking	?	?	?

b. $15t = \underline{\ ?\ }$

Solve for the variable shown in color.

11. $x + c = a$; x 12. $y + 2b = b$; y 13. $2a - z = a$; z

14. $\dfrac{x + d}{3} = c$; x 15. $a - y = 3y$; y 16. $\dfrac{a + z - b}{2} = c$; z

17. $I = Prt$; t 18. $V = \dfrac{1}{3}Bh$; h 19. $s = \dfrac{1}{2}at^2$; a

B 20. $v^2 = u^2 + 2as$; s 21. $A = P + Prt$; t 22. $S = (n - 2)180$; n

23. $C = 2\pi r$; r 24. $V = \dfrac{1}{3}\pi r^2 h$; h 25. $T = 2\pi r^2 + 2\pi rh$; h

26. The formula

$$s = c + o + p$$

relates the selling price s of an item to the wholesale cost c, overhead expenses o, and profit p for the item.

   a. Solve the formula for o.

   b. What is the overhead on a television set selling at $349 if it cost the dealer $260 and she makes a $70 profit on the sale?

27. The formula

$$P = \dfrac{3}{4}R + 25$$

is used to convert a raw score R on a certain test to a percentage score P.

   a. Convert the raw score 60 to a percentage score.

   b. Solve the formula for R.

   c. What raw score corresponds to a percentage score of 82?

Age Problems

Solve.

A 1. Ben is four years older than Juan. In two years, their ages will total 50. How old is each now?

2. Pearl is seven years younger than Dot. Five years ago their ages totaled 25. How old is each now?

3. Bill is half as old as his father. Next year, their ages will total 62. How old is each now?

4. Len is ten years older than Marie. In six years, Len will be twice as old as Marie. How old is each now?

5. Lou is 8 and his mother is 31. How long will it be before his mother is twice as old as he is?

6. Bonita is 12, exactly one third as old as her father. In how many years will she be half as old as he is?

B 7. Jill's age next year will be twice Ann's age last year. Their present ages total 54. How old is each now?

8. Matt is five years older than Noriko and three years younger than Cindy. Seven years ago, Cindy's age totaled the ages of Noriko and Matt. How old is each now?

9. George Washington was born eleven years before Thomas Jefferson. In 1770 Washington's age was three years more than seven times the age of Jefferson in 1748. How old was each man in 1750?

C 10. Susan is six years older than Mary. She is also twice as old as Mary was when Susan was as old as Mary is now. How old is each now?

11. In 1901 Northwestern University had been in existence five times as long as Stanford University. By 1931 Northwestern was only twice as old as Stanford. In what year was Northwestern University founded?

12. For six consecutive years, a man's age was a multiple of his granddaughter's age. How old was each during the sixth year?

Career Note Nutritionist

Who plans your school menus and what factors contribute to the choice of foods? Nutritionists plan menus for individuals and for groups. To maintain health, the human body requires certain amounts of food energy, protein, vitamins, and minerals each day. These nutrients can be supplied by the food we eat.

It is the job of the nutritionist to plan menus which are appealing and which satisfy a significant portion of these nutritional requirements. Nutritionists also plan special menus which are salt free, low in cholesterol, high in protein, or sugar free for individuals with certain health problems. Once a menu has been planned, a nutritionist may supervise the purchasing, preparation, and serving of the food.

The minimum requirement for a career as a nutritionist is a bachelor's degree with a major in foods and nutrition. Courses should be taken in physiology, bacteriology, chemistry, food selection, meal preparation, and nutrition. Nutritionists may continue their training after graduation with an internship in a hospital.

4-8 Cost, Wage, and Money Problems

OBJECTIVE To solve some problems involving money.

The problems in this section all involve money. Organizing the given facts in a chart will help you solve such problems.

EXAMPLE

Les spent $4.40 for several pencils costing 10 cents each and some notebooks costing 80 cents each. He bought 8 more pencils than notebooks. How many notebooks did he buy?

SOLUTION

Step 1 The problem asks for the number of notebooks Les bought.

Step 2 Let x = number of notebooks Les bought. Make a chart.

	number $\times$	price $=$	Cost
notebooks	x	80	$80x$
pencils	$x + 8$	10	$10(x + 8)$

Step 3 The only fact not recorded in the chart is that the total cost is $4.40. Use this fact to write an equation. (Since the prices are given in terms of cents, write the total cost as 440 cents.)

$$10(x + 8) + 80x = 440$$

Step 4
$$10x + 80 + 80x = 440$$
$$90x = 360$$
$$x = 4$$

Step 5 *Check:* If the number of notebooks is 4, then the number of pencils is $4 + 8$, or 12.
12 pencils at 10¢ each cost 12×10, or 120¢.
4 notebooks at 80¢ each cost 4×80, or 320¢.
$120 + 320 = 440$, or 440¢; that is, $4.40. $\checkmark$

$\therefore$ Les bought 4 notebooks. *Answer*

Problems

Copy and complete each chart and solve each problem.

A **1.** At the beach refreshment stand, hot dogs cost 80 cents each and lemonade costs 50 cents. A group of students ordered twice as many hot dogs as lemonades. If their bill was $16.80, how many hot dogs were ordered?

	number $\times$	price $=$	Cost
hot dogs	x	?	?
lemonade	?	?	?

2. Susan makes $3 an hour working after school and $4 an hour working on Saturdays. Last week she worked a total of 12 hours and made $42.50. How many hours did she work on Saturday?

	hours worked $\times$	wage per hour $=$	Income
Saturday	x	?	?
Weekdays	?	?	?

Solve.

B **3.** A student company made some school book covers at a cost of 10 cents each. They sold all but three of them at 15 cents each. Their profit was 90 cents. How many covers did they make?

4. Some Booster Club members made cupcakes at a cost of 20 cents each. They sold all but two at 30 cents each. If the club's profit was $3.00, how many cupcakes did they make?

5. Acme Appliance Company bought several Model H television sets costing $325 each. They gave away one set as a door prize and sold the rest for $399 each. If their profit was $1821, find how many sets they bought.

6. Joyce has a collection of dimes and quarters worth $13.60. She has four more quarters than dimes. How many dimes does she have?

7. Hank has a pocketful of nickels, dimes, and quarters. He has 18 coins in all worth $2.00. Find how many of each coin he has, if he has twice as many dimes as nickels.

8. In a collection of coins worth $9.13, there are twice as many dimes as quarters, four more nickels than dimes, and twice as many pennies as nickels. How many of each kind of coin are in the collection?

C **9.** Nadia has seven more nickels than Dora has dimes. If Dora gives Nadia four of her dimes, then Dora will have the same value of money as Nadia. How much money do they have together?

10. Ned has some nickels, Dick has some dimes, and Quincy has some quarters. Dick has five more dimes than Quincy has quarters. If Ned gives Dick a nickel, Dick gives Quincy a dime, and Quincy gives Ned a quarter, they will all have the same value of money. How many coins did each have originally?

4-9 Distance-Rate-Time Problems

OBJECTIVE   To solve some problems involving uniform motion.

An object is said to be in **uniform motion** when it moves without changing its speed, or rate. The three examples which follow illustrate three types of problems involving uniform motion. Each is solved using a chart, a sketch, and the formula:

$$\text{Distance} = \text{rate} \times \text{time}$$
$$D = rt$$

   In your work you will use the symbols s for seconds, min for minutes, and h for hours.

EXAMPLE 1   (Motion in opposite directions)

Bud and Ruth leave the same point driving in opposite directions. Traffic conditions enable Bud to average 10 km/h more than Ruth. After two hours they are 308 km apart. Find the rate of each.

SOLUTION

Step 1   The problem asks for Ruth's rate and Bud's rate.

Step 2   Let x = Ruth's rate. Make a chart and a sketch of the given facts.

	rate	$\times$ time	= Distance
Ruth	x	2	$2x$
Bud	$x + 10$	2	$2(x + 10)$

Step 3   The sketch will help you write this equation:
$$2x + 2(x + 10) = 308$$

Step 4
$$2x + 2x + 20 = 308$$
$$4x = 288$$
$$x = 72$$
$$x + 10 = 82$$

Step 5   *Check:* In two hours, Ruth traveled 2(72), or 144 km. In two hours, Bud traveled 2(72 + 10), or 164 km. 144 + 164 = 308   √

   ∴ Ruth's rate is 72 km/h and Bud's rate is 82 km/h.   *Answer*

EXAMPLE 2   (Motion in the same direction)

Jay begins bicycling north at 20 km/h at noon. Alex leaves from the same place fifteen minutes later to catch him. If Alex bicycles north at 24 km/h, when will he catch Jay?

SOLUTION

Step 1 The problem asks for the time at which Alex will catch Jay.

Step 2 Let x = Jay's time. Make a chart and a sketch of the given facts. Since the rates are given in terms of kilometers per hour, time must be expressed in hours. Fifteen minutes is a quarter of an hour.

	rate $\times$	time	= Distance
Jay	20	x	$20x$
Alex	24	$x - \frac{1}{4}$	$24\left(x - \frac{1}{4}\right)$

Step 3 When Alex catches Jay, the distances both have traveled will be equal. Thus, you have this equation to solve:

$$20x = 24\left(x - \frac{1}{4}\right)$$

Step 4
$$20x = 24x - 6$$
$$-4x = -6$$
$$x = 1\frac{1}{2}$$

Step 5 The check is left to you.

∴ Alex will catch Jay $1\frac{1}{2}$ hours after noon, or at 1:30 P.M. *Answer*

EXAMPLE 3 (Round trip)

Jill walks from her home to the movies at 8 km/h and gets a ride back home at 40 km/h. If her total traveling time is half an hour, how long did it take Jill to walk to the movies and how far was it?

SOLUTION

Step 1 The problem asks for the time and the distance of Jill's walk.

Step 2 Let x = time of Jill's walk in hours. Make a chart and a sketch of the given facts.

	rate $\times$	time	= Distance
To movies	8	x	$8x$
Return home	40	$0.5 - x$	$40(0.5 - x)$

Step 3 In all round-trip problems, the distance going equals the distance returning. Thus, you have this equation to solve:

$$8x = 40(0.5 - x)$$

Steps 4 and 5 are left to you. You should find that it took Jill 25 min to walk about 3.3 km to the movies. *Answer*

Problems

Solve.

A
1. Two jets leave Washington, D.C., at the same time, one traveling north at 850 km/h and the other traveling south at 750 km/h. In how many hours will they be 4800 km apart?

2. Barry and Juan live 36 km apart. At noon each leaves his house and bicycles toward the other. Barry bicycles at 11 km/h and Juan at 13 km/h. At what time will they meet?

3. At 7:00 A.M. a train which averages 100 km/h leaves Charleville headed for Mirabeau. At 8:00 A.M. a train which also averages 100 km/h leaves Mirabeau headed for Charleville. The distance between the two cities is 900 km. At what time will the trains pass each other?

4. A car and a bike set out at 1:00 P.M. from the same point headed in the same direction. After 1 hour the car is 60 km ahead of the bike. Find how fast each travels, given that the car travels four times as fast as the bike.

5. Jeanne and Teresa leave their campsite and paddle their canoe down a river at a constant rate of 6 km/h. Four hours later, Mei Ling leaves the campsite in a motorboat and travels down the river with the camping supplies. If the motorboat travels at 18 km/h, how long does it take to overtake the canoe?

6. A mover's van left Middleton at 8:00 A.M. and drove to Bayside at an average speed of 70 km/h. At 9:00 A.M. the same day, the Rileys left Middleton following the same route as the van. If both arrived in Bayside at 4:00 P.M. what was the Rileys' average speed?

7. Walt rode his bike from home to the bicycle repair shop and then walked home. He averaged 18 km/h riding and 6 km/h walking. If his total travel time was one hour, how far is it to the shop from Walt's home?

8. Running at the average rate of 400 m/min, Pam dashed to the end of the course. She then walked back to her starting position at an average rate of 80 m/min. How long was the course if it took her 6 min to make the dash and walk back?

B
9. Using the butterfly stroke to swim the length of the pool, Rita averaged 1.5 m/s. Swimming back, she used the breast stroke and averaged 1.2 m/s. The entire swim took 1 min 15 s. How long was the pool?

10. Helaine Fabre left on a business trip at 9:00 A.M. traveling at 30 km/h through the downtown traffic. After she left, her secretary discovered that some important papers had been left behind. The secretary set out at 9:10 A.M. to catch her. If the secretary traveled at 50 km/h, at what time did she catch up with Helaine?

11. A ski lift carries Claude up a slope at the rate of 4 km/h, and he returns from the top to the bottom on a path parallel to the lift at 36 km/h. How long is the lift if the round trip traveling time is 20 min?

12. If I leave now and drive at 60 km/h, I can be in Ashton in time for my appointment. On the other hand, if I eat first and leave in half an hour, I will have to drive at 80 km/h to make my appointment. How far is it to Ashton?

13. The Walkers averaged 60 km/h driving from their house to the airport but they arrived 15 min late. If they had averaged 90 km/h they would have been on time. How far is it from their house to the airport?

14. Two cars heading for Montreal on the same route left a service area at the same time. Their average speeds differed by 16 km/h. Four hours later, the faster car reached Montreal, and the other car reached Montreal an hour after that. Find the average speed of each car.

Biography Elijah McCoy

Elijah McCoy (1844–1929) was an American engineer and inventor. Born in Ontario, Canada, he went to Edinburgh, Scotland, in 1858 to serve as an apprentice to a mechanical engineer. Upon returning to the United States, he took a job on the Michigan Central Railroad. There he received the inspiration for his life's work—the invention and improvement of an automatic lubricator. He took out the first of over fifty patents in 1872 for a "lubricator cup," which allowed oil to drip continuously onto the moving parts of a machine while it was operating. Elijah McCoy's invention saved a great deal of time and work, because previously, machines had to be stopped regularly so that their parts could be lubricated.

The expression "the real McCoy" which is used to indicate that a thing is genuine probably came from buyers who wanted only the quality McCoy lubricator for their machines.

4-10 *Area Problems*

OBJECTIVE To solve some problems involving area.

To solve some problems involving area, you will need to multiply and add or subtract polynomials. Sketches are especially helpful in solving such problems.

The units of square measure that you will use most often are square centimeters (cm²) and square meters (m²).

A photograph 10 cm wide and 16 cm long is surrounded by a border 2 cm wide. To find the area of the border, you subtract the areas of the two rectangles.

Area of Border = Area of outer rectangle − Area of inner rectangle
$$= (16 + 4)(10 + 4) - 16 \cdot 10$$
$$= (20)(14) - 160 = 280 - 160 = 120$$

Thus, the area of the border is 120 cm².

EXAMPLE

A photograph is twice as long as it is wide. It is mounted so that a border 2 cm wide completely surrounds the photograph. Find the dimensions of the photograph if the area of the border is 136 cm².

SOLUTION

Step 1 The problem asks for the dimensions of the photograph.

Step 2 Let x = width of the photograph. Show the other dimensions in a sketch.

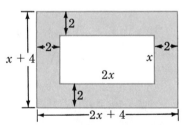

Step 3 Area of border = Area of photograph and border − Area of photograph
$$136 = (2x + 4)(x + 4) - (2x)(x)$$

Step 4
$$136 = 2x^2 + 12x + 16 - 2x^2$$
$$136 = 12x + 16$$
$$120 = 12x$$
$$10 = x$$

Step 5 *Check:* Area of photograph and border = $(2x + 4)(x + 4) = (24)(14) = 336$
Area of photograph = $(2x)(x) = (20)(10) = 200$
Area of Border = $336 - 200 = 136$ √

∴ The dimensions of the photograph are 20 cm and 10 cm. ***Answer***

Problems

Solve.

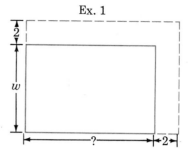

A 1. A rectangle is twice as long as it is wide. If its length and width are both increased by 2 cm, the area of the rectangle is increased by 40 cm². Find the dimensions of the original rectangle.

2. A photo is 10 cm longer than it is wide. It is mounted in a frame 3 cm wide. The area of the frame is 156 cm². Find the dimensions of the picture.

Ex. 2

3. A rectangular pool is 8 m longer than it is wide. A walkway 1 m wide surrounds the pool. Find the dimensions of the pool if the area of the walkway is 100 m².

4. A poster is three times as long as it is wide. It is mounted on a piece of cardboard so that there is a strip 10 cm wide all around the poster. If the area of this bordering strip is 2800 cm², find the dimensions of the poster.

B 5. A page of a book is 6 cm longer than it is wide. By increasing the length by 3 cm and the width by 2 cm, the book designer can increase the area of the page by 68 cm². Find the dimensions of the page.

6. An instrument is mounted on a rectangular base twice as long as it is wide. A design engineer must reduce the length of the base by 3 cm and the width by 1 cm to fit the instrument into the space available on a space vehicle. This change will reduce the area of the base by 27 cm². Find the original dimensions of the base.

7. A circular pool is surrounded by a walkway 2 m wide. Find the radius of the pool if the area of the walkway is 176 m². (*Hint:* The formula for the area of a circle with radius r is $A = \pi r^2$. Use $\frac{22}{7}$ as an approximation for π.)

8. When the radius of a circular ripple in a pond increases by 4 cm, the area it encloses increases by 352 cm². Find the radius of the ripple after the increase. (See the hint for Exercise 7.)

Ex. 7

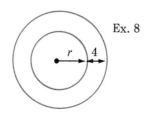

Ex. 8

C 9. Two plastic containers have square bases, but the base of one container is 10 cm longer and wider than that of the other. Both containers are filled with water to a depth of 30 cm. Find the dimensions of the base of each container if the volume of water in the larger container exceeds that in the smaller container by 15,000 cm³ (cubic centimeters). (*Hint:* Use the formula: Volume of a box = length × width × height.)

10. One planting box has a rectangular base that is 8 cm longer than it is wide. A larger planter is 2 cm wider and 4 cm longer than the first one. If each is filled to a depth of 10 cm, the larger planter has 840 cm³ more soil than the smaller. What are the dimensions of the base of the smaller planter? (See the hint for Exercise 9.)

Self-Test 3

VOCABULARY   uniform motion (p. 142)

1. Copy and complete the chart. Use the fact that Ruth is three years younger than Dan.

Obj. 4-7, p. 134

	Age now	Age in 5 years
Dan	x	?
Ruth	?	?

2. Solve the formula $V = lwh$ for w.

Solve.

Obj. 4-8, p. 140

3. At a lunch stand, a hamburger costs 85 cents and a slice of pizza costs 65 cents. A family bought twice as many hamburgers as slices of pizza for a total cost of $4.70. How many slices of pizza did the family buy?

Obj. 4-9, p. 142

4. Two planes leave an airport at the same time, one traveling east at 750 km/h and the other traveling west at 850 km/h. In how many hours will they be 3200 km apart?

Obj. 4-10, p. 146

5. The screen of a Model A television set is a rectangle that is 10 cm wider than it is high. Model B has a screen 2 cm wider and 3 cm higher and has 241 cm² more area than the Model A screen. Find the dimensions of the Model A screen.

Check your answers with those at the back of the book.

Chapter Summary

1. The expression b^n is an abbreviation for $\underbrace{b \cdot b \cdot b \cdot \ldots \cdot b}_{n \text{ factors}}$.

   The base is b and the exponent is n.

2. To simplify expressions that contain powers, the steps listed on page 114 are followed.

3. To add (or subtract) polynomials, you add (or subtract) their similar terms. Similar terms have the same variables to the same powers.

4. Rules of Exponents

   $$a^m \cdot a^n = a^{m+n} \qquad (a^m)^n = a^{mn} \qquad (ab)^m = a^m b^m$$

5. Polynomials can be multiplied in a vertical or horizontal form by applying the distributive property (p. 131). Before multiplying, it is wise to rearrange the terms of each polynomial in order of increasing or decreasing degree in one variable.

6. Organizing the facts of a word problem in a chart is often helpful. A three-column chart can be used to solve problems about costs, coins, distances, and areas. The formulas which head these columns are all similar:

   $$\text{number} \times \text{price} = \text{Cost}$$
   $$\text{number} \times \text{value per coin} = \text{Total value}$$
   $$\text{rate} \times \text{time} = \text{Distance}$$
   $$\text{length} \times \text{width} = \text{Area}$$

Chapter Review

Give the letter of the correct answer.

1. Express the square of $(a + b)$ in exponential form.   4-1

   a. $a + b^2$ **b.** $a^2 + b$ **c.** $a^2 + b^2$ **d.** $(a + b)^2$

2. Find the value of $4xy^2 - 2y^3$ if $x = 3$ and $y = -2$.

   a. 32   **b.** 64   **c.** 112   **d.** -16

3. Simplify $(4x^2 - 2x + 5) + (2x^2 - 2x - 8)$.   4-2

   a. $2x^2 + 13$ **b.** $6x^2 - 3$

   c. $6x^2 - 4x - 3$ **d.** $6x^2 - 4x + 13$

4. Subtract $4a^2 + 7a - 5$ from $3a^2 - 2a - 4$.

   a. $-a^2 - 9a + 1$ **b.** $-a^2 - 9a - 9$

   c. $-a^2 + 5a + 1$ **d.** $7a^2 + 5a - 9$

5. Solve $5x^2 - 3x = (3x^2 - 7x) + (8x - 2 + 2x^2)$.

   a. $x = -2$ **b.** $x = 2$ **c.** $x = -\dfrac{1}{2}$ **d.** $x = \dfrac{1}{2}$

6. Simplify $\left(-\frac{1}{2}a^3b^2\right)(4ab^4)(-ab^2)$. 4-3

    a. $2a^4b^8$ **b.** $-2a^5b^8$ **c.** $2a^5b^8$ **d.** $2a^3b^{16}$

7. Simplify $(4x^3y^2)(2y^3) - (-3xy)(x^2y^4)$.

    a. $11x^3y^5$ **b.** $5x^3y^5$ **c.** $11x^3y^6$ **d.** $5x^3y^6$

8. Simplify $(-2a^2b^3)^3$. 4-4

    a. $-6a^6b^9$ **b.** $-6a^5b^6$ **c.** $-8a^5b^6$ **d.** $-8a^6b^9$

9. Simplify $(2n)^3(3n^4)^2$.

    a. $72n^{11}$ **b.** $36n^{11}$ **c.** $36n^9$ **d.** $6n^{11}$

10. Find the solution of $21x - 6x(4x - 1) = 9 - (4x)(6x)$. 4-5

    a. $\frac{1}{2}$ **b.** $\frac{1}{3}$ **c.** $\frac{3}{5}$ **d.** $\frac{2}{3}$

11. Multiply: $(x - 2)(x + 1)$. 4-6

    a. $x^2 - 2$ **b.** $x^2 - 2x - 2$ **c.** $x^2 - x - 2$ **d.** $2x - 1$

12. Multiply: $(2x - 3y)(x^3 - 4x^2y - 6xy^2)$.

    a. $2x^4 - 11x^3y - 18xy^3$ **b.** $2x^4 - 11x^3y - 24x^2y - 18xy^3$

    c. $2x^4 - 11x^3y + 18xy^3$ **d.** $2x^4 - 11x^3y - 24x^2y + 18xy^3$

13. Kit is x years old and Judy is seven years younger. How old will Judy be in five years? 4-7

    a. $x + 12$ **b.** 2 **c.** $2x - 2$ **d.** $x - 2$

14. Solve the formula $F = 1.8C + 32$ for C.

    a. $C = \frac{F}{1.8} - 32$ **b.** $C = \frac{F + 32}{1.8}$ **c.** $C = \frac{F - 32}{1.8}$ **d.** $C = 1.8(F - 32)$

15. What is the value in cents of q quarters and twice as many dimes? 4-8

    a. $25q + 20$ **b.** $27q$ **c.** $35q$ **d.** $45q$

16. The Varsity Club bought several oranges at ten cents each. They sold all but two for fifteen cents each at the track meet and made a profit of $1.10. How many oranges did the club buy?

    a. 26 **b.** 28 **c.** 24 **d.** 20

17. Cindy bicycles to the beach at 20 km/h and returns by car at 60 km/h. If the car trip is two hours shorter than the bicycle trip, how far did she bicycle? 4-9

    a. $20\,\text{km}$ **b.** $40\,\text{km}$ **c.** $60\,\text{km}$ **d.** $80\,\text{km}$

18. A photo is twice as long as it is wide. It is mounted in a frame 2 cm wide. If the area of the frame is $112\,\text{cm}^2$, find the area of the photo. 4-10

    a. $8\,\text{cm}^2$ **b.** $16\,\text{cm}^2$ **c.** $128\,\text{cm}^2$ **d.** $240\,\text{cm}^2$

Chapter Test

1. Write $11 \cdot a \cdot a \cdot b \cdot c \cdot c \cdot c$ in exponential form.

4-1

2. Evaluate $2x^3 + y^2$ if $x = -3$ and $y = 4$.

Simplify.

3. $(x^3 - 2x^2 + 7) + (4 + 2x - 4x^3)$

4-2

4. $(2a^2 - 3a - 4) - (7a^2 - 5a - 9)$

Simplify.

5. $(2x^3y)(-3x^2y^3)$

6. $(4n^4)(5n^5)(6n^6)$

4-3

7. $(-2k^2)^3$

8. $(-xy^3)(3x)^2 - (xy)^3$

4-4

9. $(p^3 - 3p^2q - 2q^2)(-4pq)$

10. $\frac{2}{5}(5a - 10) - 3(4a - b + 1)$

4-5

Multiply.

11. $2c^3 - c^2d + 3cd^2$
$\underline{ c - 2d}$

12. $(4a - 5)(7a + a^2 - 2)$

4-6

13. Copy and complete the chart.
Use the fact that Peg is twice as old as Jon.

4-7

	Age now	Age 2 years ago
Jon	x	?
Peg	?	?

14. Solve the formula $A = P + Prt$ for r.

Solve.

15. The cashier's drawer has four more nickels than dimes in it. The value of the nickels and dimes together is $2.45. How many dimes are there?

4-8

16. Some campers leave a campsite and paddle a canoe down a river at a steady rate of 8 km/h. Three hours later, a motorboat leaves the campsite and travels down the river at 20 km/h. How long does it take the motorboat to overtake the canoe?

4-9

17. A pool in the city plaza is 7 m longer than it is wide. A border of plants around the pool is 1 m wide. Find the dimensions of the pool if the area of the border is 58 m².

4-10

Cumulative Review (Chapters 1-4)

Simplify each expression.

1. $-\frac{1}{3}(56 - 83)$

2. $10t \div \left(-\frac{1}{2}\right)$

3. $[-6 - (-8)] \div 4$

4. $8(3 + z) + (-5z)$

5. $-5|-6| + 7$

6. $-4(2x - y + 3z)$

7. $2^3 + 9 \div 3$

8. $(-2j^2k^3)(-3jk^5)$

9. $(m + 3n) - (5m - 3n)$

10. $(-r^2s)^3(4rs^4)^2$

11. $(8 - 3b)(-1 + 2b)$

12. $-5x(x^2 + 7xy - 3y^2)$

Evaluate if $q = 5$, $r = -2$, $s = 1$, $t = -3$, and $u = -0.5$.

13. $u(2q + 3t)$

14. $\dfrac{2t - 9s}{q + r}$

15. $(r - s)^3$

16. $2r^2u$

Solve each equation if $x \in \{-2, -1, 0, 1, 2\}$.

17. $-8 = x - 7$

18. $2(x - 1) = x$

19. $x(3x - 5) = 10 + 3x^2$

Solve. (The equation may be an identity or have no root.)

20. $-9 + z = -2$

21. $y - 3 = |0|$

22. $3 = x + 12$

23. $-80w = 16$

24. $-2 = 0.2v$

25. $-52u = 0$

26. $-6t + 4 = t - 3$

27. $4(s + 1) = 2 + 4s$

28. $3(-1 - r) = 9$

29. $2q - 5 = -(5 - 2q)$

30. $-\frac{1}{4}(4p + 8) = p + 2$

31. $n(7 + n) = n^2 + 7n$

32. $5(2 - 3m) = -4(4m + 9)$

33. $(2k + 1)(2k - 3) = (4k - 3)(k - 1)$

34. Solve for y: $ax + by = c$.

Solve.

35. Find three consecutive even integers such that the sum of the least and the greatest is -20.

36. Clyde is one fourth as old as his grandfather. Ten years ago, their ages totaled 60. How old is each now?

37. Florence and Trudy started hiking toward each other from opposite ends of a trail 13.5 km long. Florence's average rate was 4 km/h and Trudy's was 5 km/h. How far had each hiked when they met?

38. One side of a square is increased by 1 cm, and an adjacent side is decreased by 3 cm. The area of the resulting rectangle is 21 cm² less than that of the square. Find the dimensions of the square.

Maintaining Skills

Express each fraction in simplest form.

SAMPLE 1 $\dfrac{24}{60}$ **SOLUTION** $\dfrac{24}{60} = \dfrac{2 \times 12}{5 \times 12} = \dfrac{2}{5}$

1. $\dfrac{10}{15}$ **2.** $\dfrac{7}{56}$ **3.** $\dfrac{18}{49}$ **4.** $\dfrac{42}{90}$ **5.** $\dfrac{57}{76}$ **6.** $\dfrac{24}{54}$

Express each answer in simplest form.

SAMPLE 2 $\dfrac{7}{16} - \dfrac{3}{16}$ **SOLUTION** $\dfrac{7}{16} - \dfrac{3}{16} = \dfrac{7-3}{16} = \dfrac{4}{16} = \dfrac{1}{4}$

7. $\dfrac{1}{9} + \dfrac{2}{9}$ **8.** $\dfrac{5}{18} + \dfrac{11}{18}$ **9.** $\dfrac{11}{15} + \dfrac{2}{15}$ **10.** $\dfrac{17}{22} + \dfrac{5}{22}$

11. $\dfrac{7}{8} - \dfrac{3}{8}$ **12.** $\dfrac{17}{20} - \dfrac{9}{20}$ **13.** $\dfrac{22}{27} - \dfrac{7}{27}$ **14.** $\dfrac{27}{28} - \dfrac{3}{28}$

SAMPLE 3 $\dfrac{7}{12} + \dfrac{9}{10}$ **SOLUTION** The least common denominator is 60.

$$\dfrac{7}{12} \times \dfrac{5}{5} + \dfrac{9}{10} \times \dfrac{6}{6} = \dfrac{35}{60} + \dfrac{54}{60} = \dfrac{89}{60}$$

15. $\dfrac{1}{4} + \dfrac{7}{12}$ **16.** $\dfrac{3}{5} + \dfrac{2}{9}$ **17.** $\dfrac{3}{10} + \dfrac{7}{8}$ **18.** $\dfrac{11}{16} + \dfrac{5}{12}$

19. $\dfrac{20}{27} - \dfrac{3}{7}$ **20.** $\dfrac{13}{14} - \dfrac{8}{21}$ **21.** $\dfrac{19}{24} - \dfrac{1}{6}$ **22.** $\dfrac{2}{3} - \dfrac{7}{15}$

SAMPLE 4 $\dfrac{8}{9} \times \dfrac{5}{12}$ **SOLUTION** $\dfrac{8}{9} \times \dfrac{5}{12} = \dfrac{\overset{2}{\cancel{8}} \times 5}{9 \times \underset{3}{\cancel{12}}} = \dfrac{10}{27}$

23. $\dfrac{6}{11} \times \dfrac{1}{2}$ **24.** $\dfrac{5}{28} \times \dfrac{24}{25}$ **25.** $\dfrac{3}{17} \times \dfrac{7}{10}$ **26.** $9 \times \dfrac{2}{3}$

27. $\dfrac{7}{12} \times \dfrac{27}{35}$ **28.** $\dfrac{3}{26} \times \dfrac{12}{13}$ **29.** $\dfrac{5}{21} \times 3$ **30.** $\dfrac{2}{15} \times \dfrac{5}{18}$

SAMPLE 5 $\dfrac{2}{3} \div \dfrac{8}{15}$ **SOLUTION** $\dfrac{2}{3} \div \dfrac{8}{15} = \dfrac{2}{3} \times \dfrac{15}{8} = \dfrac{2 \times \overset{5}{\cancel{15}}}{\underset{1}{\cancel{3}} \times \underset{4}{\cancel{8}}} = \dfrac{5}{4}$

31. $\dfrac{13}{16} \div \dfrac{11}{12}$ **32.** $\dfrac{7}{8} \div \dfrac{5}{2}$ **33.** $15 \div \dfrac{5}{21}$ **34.** $\dfrac{5}{9} \div \dfrac{10}{3}$

35. $\dfrac{9}{20} \div \dfrac{3}{4}$ **36.** $\dfrac{8}{15} \div 4$ **37.** $\dfrac{10}{21} \div \dfrac{24}{35}$ **38.** $\dfrac{18}{25} \div \dfrac{16}{45}$

*The height above water of each dolphin at a given time (t) is given by
an expression in the form $at^2 + bt + c$.*

5

FACTORING POLYNOMIALS

QUOTIENTS AND FACTORING

5-1 *Factoring Integers*

OBJECTIVE   To factor integers.

When you write

$$48 = 6 \cdot 8 \quad \text{or} \quad 48 = (2)(24),$$

you have *factored* 48. In the first case the factors are 6 and 8; in the second case they are 2 and 24. You could also write $48 = \left(\frac{1}{2}\right)(96)$ and call $\frac{1}{2}$ and 96 factors of 48. Usually, however, you are interested only in factors drawn from a specified set. The given number is then said to be **factored** over the given set, called the **factor set.** In this text *integers will be factored over the set of integers* unless some other set is specified. Such factors are called *integral* factors.

You can find factors by dividing. If the remainder is zero, the divisor is a factor. For example, -4 is a factor of 108 because $108 \div (-4) = -27$, but 8 is not a factor of 108 because $108 \div 8 = 13$ R4.

You can find the *positive factors* of a positive integer by dividing it by the positive integers in succession until a previous factor is repeated. Thus:

$$48 = (1)(48) = (2)(24) = (3)(16) = (4)(12) = (6)(8)$$

A set of numbers useful in factoring is the set of *prime numbers* or *primes.* A **prime number,** or **prime,** is an integer greater than 1 that has no positive integral factor other than itself and 1. The first prime numbers are

$$2, 3, 5, 7, 11, 13, 17, 19, 23, 29, \ldots.$$

A systematic way to find the prime factors of positive integers is to try the primes, in order, as divisors. You divide by each prime as many times as possible before going on to the next. This technique is illustrated at the right. The final result is

$$588 = 2 \cdot 294$$
$$= 2 \cdot 2 \cdot 147$$
$$= 2 \cdot 2 \cdot 3 \cdot 49$$
$$= 2 \cdot 2 \cdot 3 \cdot 7 \cdot 7$$
$$= 2^2 \cdot 3 \cdot 7^2$$

$$588 = 2^2 \cdot 3 \cdot 7^2.$$

The expression of a positive integer as a product of prime factors is called the **prime factorization** of the integer.

It can be proved by advanced methods that the prime factorization of an integer is *unique* (one and only one) except for the order in which the factors may be written. (If 1 were to be considered a prime factor, the factorization would not be unique because 1 could be considered to be a factor any number of times.)

A factor of two or more integers is called a *common factor* of the integers. The greatest integer which is a factor of two or more integers is called the **greatest common factor** (GCF) of the integers.

The following example shows how you can use prime factorization to find the greatest common factor of two integers.

EXAMPLE   Find the GCF of 504 and 945.

SOLUTION   First find the prime factorizations of each integer. Then form the product of the smaller powers of each common prime factor.

$$504 = 2^3 \cdot 3^2 \cdot 7 \qquad 945 = 3^3 \cdot 5 \cdot 7$$

smaller power: 3^2 smaller power: 7

The greatest common factor of 504 and 945 is $3^2 \cdot 7$, or 63.   *Answer*

Oral Exercises

Give all the positive factors of each number.

1. 12   2. 40   3. 75   4. 83   5. 51

State whether or not each number is a prime.

6. 7   7. 15   8. 31   9. 81   10. 91

Give the prime factorization of each number.

11. 12   12. 40   13. 1000   14. 68   15. 300

Find the GCF of each pair of numbers.

16. 12 and 18   17. 30 and 55   18. 27 and 45   19. 3 and 13

Written Exercises

List all of the positive factors of each number.

A **1.** 18 **2.** 30 **3.** 37 **4.** 63 **5.** 64
  6. 49 **7.** 101 **8.** 15 **9.** 23 **10.** 65

11–20. Write all the pairs of positive and negative factors of the integers in Exercises 1-10.

SAMPLE 20

SOLUTION $(1)(20)$, $(2)(10)$, $(4)(5)$, $(-1)(-20)$, $(-2)(-10)$, $(-4)(-5)$

21–30. Write all the pairs of positive and negative factors of the opposites of the integers in Exercises 1-10.

Give the prime factorization of each number.

B **31.** 34 **32.** 45 **33.** 63 **34.** 104 **35.** 128
  36. 250 **37.** 476 **38.** 539 **39.** 408 **40.** 576

Give the GCF of each group of numbers.

41. 18, 24 **42.** 15, 21 **43.** 12, 24, 30
44. 36, 54, 81 **45.** 21, 35, 48 **46.** 144, 180

Calculator Key-In _____

You can use the calculator to evaluate a polynomial for a given value of the variable. One way is to evaluate the polynomial term by term using the calculator's memory to store the partial sums.

Another way is to express the polynomial in a form that suggests a sequence of steps on the calculator. For example, to evaluate $3x^2 - 4x + 5$, you could first rewrite it as follows:

$$3x^2 - 4x + 5 = (3x - 4)x + 5$$

To evaluate the polynomial for a particular value, you can just work through the rewritten expression from left to right substituting the appropriate value for x.

Evaluate the polynomial for the given value of the variable.

1. $4x^2 + 3x - 8$; 2   **2.** $6z^2 - 3z - 5$; 4   **3.** $2x^2 + 5x + 9$; -3
4. $y^2 - 2y - 3$; 1.5   **5.** $15k^2 - 35k + 90$; 10   **6.** $40v^2 - 20v + 80$; 17
7. $14x^2 - 15x - 5$; -8 **8.** $4y^2 + 4y - 5$; 0.4   **9.** $10z^2 - 5z + 5$; -0.5

5-2 Dividing Monomials

OBJECTIVE To divide and factor monomials.

There are three basic rules that are used to simplify fractions and quotients of monomials. The property of quotients (see Exercise 45 on page 161) enables you to express a fraction as a product.

PROPERTY OF QUOTIENTS

If c, d, x, and y are any real numbers, $d \neq 0$, and $y \neq 0$, then

$$\frac{cx}{dy} = \frac{c}{d} \cdot \frac{x}{y}.$$

EXAMPLE 1 $\dfrac{35}{48} = \dfrac{5 \cdot 7}{6 \cdot 8} = \dfrac{5}{6} \cdot \dfrac{7}{8}$

If you let $d = c$ in the quotient rule, you derive the cancellation rule stated below (see Exercise 46 on page 161).

CANCELLATION RULE FOR FRACTIONS

If c, x, and y are any real numbers, $c \neq 0$, and $y \neq 0$, then

$$\frac{cx}{cy} = \frac{x}{y}.$$

The cancellation rule enables you to divide the numerator and denominator of a fraction by the same nonzero number. In the following examples, assume that no denominator equals 0.

EXAMPLE 2 $\dfrac{4ab}{12a} = \dfrac{4a \cdot b}{4a \cdot 3} = \dfrac{b}{3}$ $\left\{ \begin{array}{l} \text{The red marks indicate that both the numerator} \\ \text{and denominator are divided by } 4a. \end{array} \right.$

    The cancellation rule can be used to simplify a quotient of two powers of the same number.

EXAMPLE 3 $\dfrac{x^7}{x^3} = \dfrac{x^3 \cdot x^4}{x^3} = x^4$ *EXAMPLE 4* $\dfrac{y^2}{y^8} = \dfrac{y^2}{y^2 \cdot y^6} = \dfrac{1}{y^6}$

The previous examples illustrate the rule of exponents for division shown at the top of the next page.

> ## RULE OF EXPONENTS FOR DIVISION
>
> When m and n are positive integers and a is a real number not equal to 0:
>
> If $m > n$:
>
> $$\frac{a^m}{a^n} = a^{m-n}$$
>
> If $n > m$:
>
> $$\frac{a^m}{a^n} = \frac{1}{a^{n-m}}$$
>
> If $n = m$:
>
> $$\frac{a^m}{a^n} = 1$$

In short, the rule above says that when you divide powers you subtract exponents. You have already seen that when you multiply powers you add exponents.

A quotient of monomials is said to be *simplified* when each base appears only once, when there are no powers of powers, and when all fractions have been expressed in simplest form. Examples 5 and 6 show that all three rules presented in this section may be needed to simplify quotients of monomials. In them assume that no variable equals 0. Notice how each rule is used in the examples.

EXAMPLE 5 $\dfrac{8a^3}{-2a^4} = \dfrac{8}{-2} \cdot \dfrac{a^3}{a^4} = -4 \cdot \dfrac{1}{a} = -\dfrac{4}{a}$

EXAMPLE 6 $\dfrac{24x^9y}{16x^3y^8} = \dfrac{24}{16} \cdot \dfrac{x^9}{x^3} \cdot \dfrac{y}{y^8} = \dfrac{3}{2} \cdot x^6 \cdot \dfrac{1}{y^7} = \dfrac{3x^6}{2y^7}$

The **greatest monomial factor** of two monomials is defined to be the common factor which has the greatest coefficient and the greatest degree in each variable. Example 7 shows how to find the greatest monomial factor of two monomials.

EXAMPLE 7 Find the greatest monomial factor of $24x^5yz$ and $32x^3y^8$.

SOLUTION Form the product of the GCF of the numerical coefficients and the smaller power of each variable that appears in both monomials.

GCF of 24 and 32: 8 Smaller power of x: x^3 Smaller power of y: y

The greatest monomial factor of $24x^5yz$ and $32x^3y^8$ is $8x^3y$. *Answer*

Oral Exercises

Simplify each expression, assuming that no denominator equals 0.

1. $\dfrac{3x}{x}$

2. $\dfrac{8a^2}{2a}$

3. $\dfrac{5b}{10}$

4. $\dfrac{3c^2}{c}$

5. $\dfrac{-8x^3}{2x}$

6. $\dfrac{3^{10}}{3^8}$

7. $\dfrac{a^8}{a^3}$

8. $\dfrac{-b^7}{b^9}$

9. $\dfrac{(st)^7}{(st)^5}$

10. $\dfrac{a^{12}b^{15}}{a^{10}b^{20}}$

Simplify each expression, assuming that no denominator equals 0.

11. $(3xy^2)^2$ **12.** $(a^2b)^4$ **13.** $(-2a^2)^3$ **14.** $(-a^2x)^4$ **15.** $(3x^2k^4)^3$

16. $\dfrac{4.8 \times 10^5}{2.4 \times 10^2}$ **17.** $\dfrac{6x^{12}y^2}{2x^8y}$ **18.** $\dfrac{9r^3s}{3rs^3}$ **19.** $\dfrac{-3uv^2}{6uv}$ **20.** $\dfrac{-12c^{12}}{-4c^4}$

Find the greatest monomial factor of the given monomials.

21. $8x$; $2xy$ **22.** $3a^2$; $6a$ **23.** $5x^2y$; $10xy^2$

24. $12u^3v^2$; $5uv^3$ **25.** $14s^5t^2$; $21s^3t^3$ **26.** $35x^2y^4$; $15x^3y^5$

Written Exercises

Simplify each expression, assuming that no variable equals 0.

A

1. $\dfrac{a^7}{a^2}$ **2.** $\dfrac{b^{12}}{b^5}$ **3.** $\dfrac{-c^{14}}{c^{10}}$ **4.** $\dfrac{d^3}{d^9}$

5. $\dfrac{9a^4}{3a}$ **6.** $\dfrac{-18r^3t}{12rt^5}$ **7.** $\dfrac{-8xy}{-24xy^3}$ **8.** $\dfrac{13a^4b^9}{26a^2b^2}$

9. $\dfrac{6(xy)^5}{8(xy)^3}$ **10.** $\dfrac{-36u^5v^4}{27uv^6}$ **11.** $\dfrac{-16a^5b^3}{-24a^5b^7}$ **12.** $\dfrac{14x^2yz^3}{35xy^3z}$

13. $\dfrac{(x^2)^4}{(x^3)^3}$ **14.** $\dfrac{(3a)^3}{3a^3}$ **15.** $\dfrac{(3y)^2}{(3y)^3}$ **16.** $\dfrac{5k^3}{(5k)^3}$

17. $\dfrac{(2x)^4}{2x^4}$ **18.** $\dfrac{(-x)^8}{-x^6}$ **19.** $\dfrac{(-2y)^3}{(y^2)^3}$ **20.** $\dfrac{(a^5)^3}{(a^4)^4}$

21. $\dfrac{(4ab^2)^3}{(2a^2b)^4}$ **22.** $\dfrac{(3a^5)(2a^4)}{(6a^3)^2}$ **23.** $\dfrac{(13c^4d)^2}{(13cd^2)^3}$ **24.** $\dfrac{-(8x^2y)^4}{(8x^2y)^5}$

Find the missing factor.

SAMPLE $36a^5b^8 = (12a^3b^2)(\underline{\ ?\ })$ *SOLUTION* $\dfrac{36a^5b^8}{12a^3b^2} = 3a^2b^6$ *Answer*

25. $9a^5 = (3a)(\underline{\ ?\ })$ **26.** $12a^2b = (3a)(\underline{\ ?\ })$

27. $-4c^3d^3 = (2cd^2)(\underline{\ ?\ })$ **28.** $35u^5v^6 = (7uv)(\underline{\ ?\ })$

29. $24x^6y^4 = (-3x^2y^2)(\underline{\ ?\ })$ **30.** $-18x^3y^5 = (-9x^2y)(\underline{\ ?\ })$

31. $98a^7b^4 = (\underline{\ ?\ })(14a^7b)$ **32.** $156k^3z^5n = (-13k^2z)(\underline{\ ?\ })$

B **33.** $(a^2b)^6 = (a^2b)^4(\underline{\ ?\ })$ **34.** $(3xy)^5 = (3xy)^4(\underline{\ ?\ })$

35. $144x^6y^3 = (-12xy)^2(\underline{\ ?\ })$ **36.** $42x^4y^5 = (3x^2y)(2xy)(\underline{\ ?\ })$

37. $36a^8b^5 = (6ab^2)(3a^4b)(\underline{\ ?\ })$ **38.** $72x^5y^8 = (3xy^2)^2(2y^3)(\underline{\ ?\ })$

Find the greatest monomial factor of the given monomials.

39. $5x^3$; $15x$ **40.** $18k^2n$; $27kn$ **41.** $2rs^2t^3$; $5r^3s^3t^2$

42. $24x^2y$; $36xz^3$ **43.** $25ab^2$; $15ab^2$; $36a^2b^2$ **44.** $21m^3n^2$; $14m^2n^3$; $35m^4n$

Give a reason for each step in the proofs of the property of quotients and the cancellation rule for fractions. Assume that c, d, x, and y are real numbers, $c \neq 0$, $d \neq 0$, and $y \neq 0$. Once you prove the property of quotients, you may use it in the proof of the cancellation rule.

C **45.** Property of Quotients: $\dfrac{cx}{dy} = \dfrac{c}{d} \cdot \dfrac{x}{y}$

$$\dfrac{cx}{dy} = cx\left(\dfrac{1}{dy}\right) \qquad (1) \underline{\;?\;}$$

$$= cx\left(\dfrac{1}{d} \cdot \dfrac{1}{y}\right) \qquad (2) \underline{\;?\;}$$

$$= \left(c \cdot \dfrac{1}{d}\right)\left(x \cdot \dfrac{1}{y}\right) \qquad (3) \underline{\;?\;} ;$$
$$\underline{\;?\;}$$

$$= \dfrac{c}{d} \cdot \dfrac{x}{y} \qquad (4) \underline{\;?\;}$$

46. Cancellation Rule for Fractions: $\dfrac{cx}{cy} = \dfrac{x}{y}$

$$\dfrac{cx}{cy} = \dfrac{c}{c} \cdot \dfrac{x}{y} \qquad (1) \underline{\;?\;}$$

$$= 1 \cdot \dfrac{x}{y} \qquad (2) \underline{\;?\;}$$

$$= \dfrac{x}{y} \qquad (3) \underline{\;?\;}$$

Computer Key-In

If you have access to a computer that will accept BASIC, you can use it to test or to find factors of integers.

You need to know that INT(N) will give the greatest integer less than or equal to N. Thus:

$$\text{INT}(4) = 4, \qquad \text{INT}(4.9) = 4, \qquad \text{INT}(-6.3) = -7$$

This function may then be used to find factors as follows:

(a) To test whether 5 is a factor of 12, you divide:

$$12/5 = 2.4$$

Let Q = 2.4. Then INT(2.4) = 2, and so Q $\neq$ INT(Q).

(b) To test whether 6 is a factor of 12, you divide:

$$12/6 = 2$$

Here Q = 2; INT(2) = 2, and so Q is equal to INT(Q).

To print whole-number factors of a whole number, use this program:

```
10  PRINT "WHAT IS YOUR WHOLE NUMBER";
20  INPUT W
30  FOR F=1 TO W/2
40  LET Q=W/F
50  IF Q <> INT(Q) THEN 70
60  PRINT F;" AND";Q;" ARE FACTORS OF";W;"."
70  NEXT F
80  END
```

5-3 *Monomial Factors of Polynomials*

OBJECTIVE   To divide a polynomial by a monomial and to find a monomial factor of a polynomial.

The following result was proved earlier (see page 91) when a, b, and c are real numbers and $c \neq 0$:

$$\frac{a + b}{c} = \frac{a}{c} + \frac{b}{c}$$

This result is also true when a, b, and c are monomials and $c \neq 0$. It suggests a technique for dividing a polynomial by a monomial. To divide a polynomial by a monomial, divide each term of the polynomial by the monomial, and then add the quotients.

The examples below illustrate this technique. In them assume that no variable equals 0.

EXAMPLE 1 $\dfrac{3x^4 + 6x^3y - 9x^2y^2}{3x^2}$

SOLUTION $\dfrac{3x^4 + 6x^3y - 9x^2y^2}{3x^2} = \dfrac{3x^4}{3x^2} + \dfrac{6x^3y}{3x^2} - \dfrac{9x^2y^2}{3x^2} = x^2 + 2xy - 3y^2$

EXAMPLE 2 $\dfrac{x^2y^2 + x - y}{xy}$

SOLUTION $\dfrac{x^2y^2 + x - y}{xy} = \dfrac{x^2y^2}{xy} + \dfrac{x}{xy} - \dfrac{y}{xy} = xy + \dfrac{1}{y} - \dfrac{1}{x}$

One polynomial is said to be **evenly divisible,** or simply **divisible,** by another polynomial if the quotient is also a polynomial. Example 1 shows that $3x^4 + 6x^3y - 9x^2y^2$ is evenly divisible by $3x^2$; Example 2 shows that $x^2y^2 + x - y$ is not evenly divisible by xy.

You factor a polynomial by expressing it as a product of other polynomials. Unless otherwise stated, the *factor set for a polynomial having integral coefficients is the set of all polynomials having integral coefficients.*

You can use division to test for factors of a polynomial. Example 1 shows that you can factor $3x^4 + 6x^3y - 9x^2y^2$ as $3x^2(x^2 + 2xy - 3y^2)$. Notice that 3 and x^2 are also factors of $3x^4 + 6x^3y - 9x^2y^2$. In general, you factor the greatest monomial factor from a polynomial. The **greatest monomial factor of a polynomial** is the greatest monomial factor of its terms. Notice the factoring in Examples 3 and 4.

EXAMPLE 3   Factor $4a^2b - 6ab^2$.

SOLUTION   1. The greatest monomial factor of $4a^2b - 6ab^2$ is $2ab$.
2. Divide $4a^2b - 6ab^2$ by $2ab$ to get $2a - 3b$.
3. $4a^2b - 6ab^2 = 2ab(2a - 3b)$ *Answer*

EXAMPLE 4 Factor $12x^3 - 18x^2 + 6x$.

SOLUTION
1. The greatest monomial factor of $12x^3 - 18x^2 + 6x$ is $6x$.
2. Divide $12x^3 - 18x^2 + 6x$ by $6x$ to get $2x^2 - 3x + 1$.
3. $12x^3 - 18x^2 + 6x = 6x(2x^2 - 3x + 1)$ ***Answer***

Oral Exercises

Divide. Assume that no denominator is zero.

1. $\dfrac{6a + 12}{6}$
2. $\dfrac{9x - 6y}{3}$
3. $\dfrac{6c - 18}{6}$
4. $\dfrac{33ab - 22b}{11b}$

5. $\dfrac{27a - 18b + 9c}{9}$
6. $\dfrac{4a^3 - 10a^2 + 6a}{2a}$
7. $\dfrac{6x^2y - 4xy^2}{2xy}$
8. $\dfrac{9a^3b - 12ab^4}{3ab}$

Factor each polynomial as a product of its greatest monomial factor and another polynomial.

9. $9ab - 6$
10. $8a^2 - 4a$
11. $16xy - 12yz$
12. $14ab - 21bc$

Written Exercises

Divide. Assume that no denominator is zero.

A
1. $\dfrac{3a + 6}{3}$
2. $\dfrac{18a - 12}{6}$
3. $\dfrac{30x - 15}{5}$

4. $\dfrac{9a + 6b + 3}{3}$
5. $\dfrac{4x - 8y + 12}{4}$
6. $\dfrac{x^3 + 4x^2 + x}{x}$

7. $\dfrac{10xy - 15x^2}{5x}$
8. $\dfrac{6a - 12a^2 - 18a^3}{6a}$
9. $\dfrac{14y - 21y^2 - 7y^3}{7y}$

10. $\dfrac{9a^2b - 6ab^2}{3ab}$
11. $\dfrac{24cd^3 - 18c^2d - 12c}{-6c}$
12. $\dfrac{25x^4y^3 - 15x^2y^5}{5xy}$

13. $\dfrac{42s^4t^4 - 35st^2}{7st^2}$
14. $\dfrac{8yz^2 - 24y^3z - 32yz}{-8yz}$

15. $\dfrac{45d^4k^2 - 75d^3k + 30d^4}{15d^2}$
16. $\dfrac{32k^4z^2 - 96k^2z^4 - 48k^6z^2}{16k^2z^2}$

Evaluate by factoring.

SAMPLE $4 \times 21 + 4 \times 79 = 4(21 + 79) = 4(100) = 400$

17. $3 \times 78 + 7 \times 78$
18. $28 \times 43 - 18 \times 43$
19. $13 \times 19 + 4 \times 19 + 3 \times 19$

20. $9 \times 11^2 - 9 \times 11$
21. $81^2 + 81 \times 19$

22. $(18)^2 - 4 \times 9$
23. $32 \times 17 + 17^2 + 17$

24. $216 + 2 \times 36 + 5 \times 6$
25. $22 \times 14 \times 25 - 11 \times 21 \times 30$

Factor each polynomial as the product of its greatest monomial factor and another polynomial.

26. $6x + 12y$

27. $14a - 12b$

28. $9p - 6q + 3$

29. $4x - 8y + 16$

30. $15a^2 - 9a$

31. $6x^2 + 12x$

32. $4a^3 + 8a^2$

33. $12x^3 - 6x^2 + 24x$

34. $10y^3 - 5y^2 + 15y$

B 35. $24a^4x - 18a^3x + 12a^2x^2$

36. $14s^2 + 7st$

37. $7s^2y - 21xy^2$

38. $8a^2b - 16ab - 24a$

39. $25c^3d - 15c^2d^2 + 5cd^3$

40. $-40r^8s^6 - 16r^9s^5$

41. $21e^3k - 49e^2k^2 + 84k^3$

42. $\pi r^2 h + 2\pi r^2$

43. $\frac{1}{2}bh - \frac{1}{2}ah$

Simplify.

SAMPLE $\quad \dfrac{5x - 10}{5} - \dfrac{12x - 9}{3} = (x - 2) - (4x - 3)$

$$= x - 2 - 4x + 3 = -3x + 1$$

C 44. $\dfrac{3x - 6}{3} - \dfrac{4 - 8x}{2}$

45. $\dfrac{15a - 5}{5} - \dfrac{9a - 12}{3}$

46. $\dfrac{24x - 18}{6} + \dfrac{14x + 7}{7}$

47. $\dfrac{12a^2b - 6ab^2}{3ab} + \dfrac{4a^2 + 10ab}{2a}$

48. $\dfrac{a^2b + 2a^2b^2}{ab} - \dfrac{2a^3 - 6a^2b}{2a}$

49. $\dfrac{a^4b^3 - b^2a^3}{a^3b} + \dfrac{b^3c - ab^3c}{bc}$

Problems

Write an expression in factored form for the area A of each shaded region.

SAMPLE

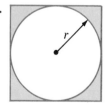

SOLUTION

A = Area of rectangle $- 2 \cdot$ area of circle
$= (4r \cdot 2r) - 2\pi r^2$
$= 2r^2(4 - \pi)$ *Answer*

A 1.

2.

3.

4.

B 5.

6.

7.

8.

Self-Test 1

VOCABULARY factor (p. 155)
factor set (p. 155)
prime number (p. 155)
prime factorization (p. 156)
common factor (p. 156)
greatest common factor
(p. 156)

simplify (p. 159)
greatest monomial factor
(p. 159)
divisible (p. 162)
greatest monomial factor of
a polynomial (p. 162)

1. Find the prime factorization of 75.

2. Find all pairs of integral factors of 45.

3. Find the greatest common factor of 45 and 75.

Obj. 5-1, p. 155

Simplify, assuming no variable equals 0.

4. $-\dfrac{21x^2y^5}{7xy^6}$

5. $\dfrac{8k^2m^7}{32k^3m^3}$

Obj. 5-2, p. 158

Find the missing factor.

6. $-84 = -7(\underline{\ ?\ })$

7. $-35a^2b^5 = (7ab)(\underline{\ ?\ })$

8. Simplify $\dfrac{21t^4 + 15t^3 - 9t^2}{3t^2}$. $(t \neq 0)$

Obj. 5-3, p. 162

9. Factor $4x^4y^3 - 8x^2y^2 + 6xy^2$.

Check your answers with those at the back of the book.

PRODUCTS AND FACTORING

5-4 *Multiplying Binomials Mentally*

OBJECTIVE   To find the product of two binomials.

Study the multiplication below and notice how the three terms of the product are formed. Do you see where the distributive axiom is used?

$$
\begin{array}{r}
3x \;+\; 4 \\
5x \;-\; 2 \\
\hline
15x^2 + 20x \\
-\; 6x - 8 \\
\hline
15x^2 + 14x - 8
\end{array}
$$

You can use the following short method to multiply binomials.

Think:

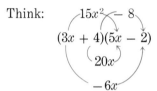

Write: $15x^2 + 14x - 8$

To find the terms in the trinomial product of two binomials $(ax + b)(cx + d)$:

1. Multiply the first terms of the binomials.
2. Multiply the first term of each polynomial by the last term of the other and add these products.
3. Multiply the last terms of the binomials.

Each term of a trinomial like $15x^2 + 14x - 8$ has a standard name. A **quadratic term** is a term of degree two. A **linear term** is a term of degree one. As defined earlier, a *constant term* is a numerical term with no variable factor. The trinomial itself is called a quadratic polynomial.

$$15x^2 - 14x - 8$$

quadratic term ⌐
linear term ⌐
constant term ⌐

Oral Exercises

State the quadratic, linear, and constant term of each product, and read the product as a polynomial.

SAMPLE $(z - 4)(z + 3)$

SOLUTION   Quadratic term, z^2; linear term, $-z$; constant term, -12; polynomial, $z^2 - z - 12$.

1. $(x + 2)(x + 1)$ **2.** $(a + 3)(a + 4)$ **3.** $(b + 4)(b + 1)$ **4.** $(y + 5)(y + 6)$

5. $(x - 3)(x - 4)$ **6.** $(a - 2)(a - 4)$ **7.** $(b - 5)(b - 1)$ **8.** $(y - 9)(y - 2)$

9. $(c - 3)(c + 4)$ **10.** $(d - 2)(d + 5)$ **11.** $(x - 5)(x + 3)$ **12.** $(z - 1)(z + 7)$

13. $(a + 5)(2a + 1)$ **14.** $(3a + 1)(a + 2)$ **15.** $(y - 1)(2y - 1)$ **16.** $(x - 3)(2x - 5)$

Written Exercises

Write each product as a trinomial.

A **1.** $(x + 7)(x + 2)$ **2.** $(y + 3)(y + 2)$ **3.** $(a - 4)(a - 5)$

   4. $(b - 7)(b - 6)$ **5.** $(c + 3)(c + 7)$ **6.** $(k - 3)(k - 11)$

   7. $(a - 5)(a - 9)$ **8.** $(1 + x)(2 + x)$ **9.** $(2a + 1)(a + 5)$

   10. $(4x + 3)(x + 5)$ **11.** $(2a + 9)(a - 3)$ **12.** $(3a - 1)(2a - 1)$

   13. $(x - 9)(x + 7)$ **14.** $(a - 5)(a + 7)$ **15.** $(b - 3)(b + 8)$

   16. $(c - 7)(c + 8)$ **17.** $(3k + 1)(2k + 5)$ **18.** $(4a - 5)(2a - 3)$

   19. $a(7a - 5)(5a - 7)$ **20.** $b(3b + 2)(7b + 8)$ **21.** $2x(2x - 5)(3x + 1)$

   22. $n(4n - 7)(3n + 6)$ **23.** $k(2k - 5)(7k + 4)$ **24.** $3n(n - 3)(2n + 7)$

Express each product as a trinomial.

SAMPLE $(4x - 3y)(2x - 4y)$

SOLUTION $8x^2 - 22xy + 12y^2$

B **25.** $(2x + 4y)(3x + 2y)$ **26.** $(3x - 2y)(4x + y)$ **27.** $(9a - 2b)(3a - 5b)$

   28. $(x^2 + y^2)(x^2 + 3y^2)$ **29.** $(a^2 - 3)(2a^2 + 7)$ **30.** $(r^2 - 2s)(3r^2 + s)$

   31. $(x^4 + 7x^2)(x^2 - 3)$ **32.** $(x^3 - 2y)(3x^3 + 4y)$ **33.** $(3a^4 - 5b^2)(a^4 - 2b^2)$

Solve and check:

34. $(x + 5)(x - 3) = (x - 4)(x + 9)$ **35.** $(a - 4)(a + 4) = (a + 7)(a - 6)$

36. $(6y - 5)(6y + 5) = (4y + 3)(9y - 7)$ **37.** $(y + 1)(2y - 1) = (y - 1)^2 + (y + 1)^2$

38. $(3a - 4)(4a + 5) = (6a - 2)(2a + 10)$ **39.** $2(x + 1)(2x + 5) = (x + 3)(4x + 3)$

40. Show that $(ax + by)(cx + dy) = acx^2 + (ad + bc)xy + bdy^2$.

5-5 *Differences of Squares*

OBJECTIVE   To simplify products of the form $(a + b)(a - b)$ and to factor differences of squares.

Observe what happens when you simplify the product $(a + b)(a - b)$.

$$\begin{array}{r} a\ +\ b \\ a\ -\ b \\ \hline a^2 + ab \\ -\ ab - b^2 \\ \hline a^2 -\qquad b^2 \end{array}$$

Two of the terms are opposites so the product is just a difference of two squares. This result is so useful that you should remember it in either of the following forms:

$$(a + b)(a - b) = a^2 - b^2$$

$$\begin{bmatrix}\text{Sum of two} \\ \text{numbers}\end{bmatrix} \cdot \begin{bmatrix}\text{Difference of} \\ \text{the numbers}\end{bmatrix} = [\text{First number}]^2 - [\text{Second number}]^2$$

EXAMPLE 1   Express each product as a binomial.

   a. $(x + 3)(x - 3)$ **b.** $(4y + 5)(4y - 5)$ **c.** $(6b^2 + 7c)(6b^2 - 7c)$

SOLUTION   **a.** $(x + 3)(x - 3) = x^2 - 9$
b. $(4y + 5)(4y - 5) = 16y^2 - 25$
c. $(6b^2 + 7c)(6b^2 - 7c) = 36b^4 - 49c^2$

You can use the symmetric property of equality to write the statement $(a + b)(a - b) = a^2 - b^2$ in a form useful for factoring the difference of two squares.

$$a^2 - b^2 = (a + b)(a - b)$$

EXAMPLE 2   Factor.   **a.** $n^2 - 16$ **b.** $4a^2 - 9b^2$

SOLUTION   **a.** $n^2 - 16 = (n + 4)(n - 4)$
b. $4a^2 - 9b^2 = (2a)^2 - (3b)^2 = (2a + 3b)(2a - 3b)$

In Example 2b it was important to recognize that both terms were *squares*. A monomial is a square if all powers in it are even and the numerical coefficient is the square of an integer. You can use the table at the back of the book or a calculator to determine whether or not an integer is a square. For example, the table shows that 2916 is the square of 54.

EXAMPLE 3   Factor $16x^4 - 1$.

SOLUTION $16x^4 - 1 = (4x^2 + 1)(4x^2 - 1)$ $\Big\{$ Continue factoring because
$\qquad\qquad = (4x^2 + 1)(2x + 1)(2x - 1)$ $\ 4x^2 - 1$ can be factored.

Oral Exercises

Square each monomial.

SAMPLE $-3k^2$ *SOLUTION* $(-3k^2)^2 = 9k^4$

1. $3x$ **2.** $-4z$ **3.** $3y^4$ **4.** $-2r^2$ **5.** $7x^2y$ **6.** $-5xy^3$

Express each product as a binomial.

7. $(x + 2)(x - 2)$ **8.** $(a + 5)(a - 5)$ **9.** $(s - t)(s + t)$

10. $(4b + 3)(4b - 3)$ **11.** $(2n - 3)(2n + 3)$ **12.** $(5x - 7)(5x + 7)$

Tell whether or not each binomial is the difference of two squares. If it is, factor it.

13. $x^2 - 16$ **14.** $a^2 - 10$ **15.** $k^3 - 4$

16. $4y^2 - 81$ **17.** $a^4 - 1$ **18.** $b^2 + 9$

Written Exercises

Express each product as a binomial.

A   **1.** $(a - 3)(a + 3)$ **2.** $(2 - x)(2 + x)$ **3.** $(3b - 5)(3b + 5)$
    4. $(7x - y)(7x + y)$ **5.** $(9a - 7)(9a + 7)$ **6.** $(8 + 3x)(8 - 3x)$
    7. $(8a - 5b)(8a + 5b)$ **8.** $(x^2 - 5)(x^2 + 5)$ **9.** $(3u^2 + v)(3u^2 - v)$
    10. $(2a^2 - 5b^2)(2a^2 + 5b^2)$ **11.** $(rs + t^2)(rs - t^2)$ **12.** $(a^7 - b^4)(a^7 + b^4)$

Multiply using the form $(a + b)(a - b)$.

SAMPLE 1 $77 \times 83 = (80 - 3)(80 + 3) = 6400 - 9 = 6391$

13. 17×23 **14.** 28×32 **15.** 62×58 **16.** 45×55

17. 51×49 **18.** 102×98 **19.** 204×196 **20.** 70×130

Factor. Use the table of squares.

21. $25y^2 - 9$ **22.** $49a^2 - 16$ **23.** $144 - x^2$ **24.** $169b^2 - 49c^2$

25. $9a^2 - b^2c^2$ **26.** $121 - 400r^2$ **27.** $x^6 - y^6$ **28.** $a^4 - 100$

29. $-9 + 16x^4$ **30.** $-1 + 81x^4$ **31.** $225 - a^2b^4$ **32.** $16x^4 - y^4$

B **33.** $a^4b^4 - c^8$ **34.** $x^8 - 256$ **35.** $a^{16} - 1$ **36.** $81k^8 - n^8$

Factor.

SAMPLE 2 $(y + 3)^2 - y^2 = [(y + 3) - y][(y + 3) + y] = 3(2y + 3)$

37. $(x + 3)^2 - x^2$ **38.** $y^2 - (y - 1)^2$

39. $(a + 1)^2 - (a - 1)^2$ **40.** $9(x + 1)^2 - 4(x - 1)^2$

First factor out the greatest monomial factor. Then complete the factoring.

SAMPLE 3 $3x^3 - 75x = 3x(x^2 - 25) = 3x(x - 5)(x + 5)$

41. $2x^2 - 50$ **42.** $3y^2 - 48$ **43.** $45 - 5a^2$ **44.** $36x^2 - 81y^2$

45. $x^3 - 9x$ **46.** $2xy - 72x^3y$ **47.** $324 - 4k^4$ **48.** $\pi R^2 - \pi r^2$

Factor, assuming that n is a positive integer.

SAMPLE 4 $x^{2n} - y^2 = (x^n)^2 - y^2 = (x^n - y)(x^n + y)$

49. $x^{2n} - y^{2n}$ **50.** $a^{2n} - 9$ **51.** $b^{2n} - c^{4n}$ **52.** $2x^{2n} - 98$

C **53.** $a^{4n} - b^{6n}$ **54.** $x^{2n+1} - x$ **55.** $y^{2n+3} - y^3$ **56.** $ab^{4n} - a$

EXTRA
Sums and Differences of Cubes

The following factoring patterns indicate that both sums and differences of cubes can be factored.

$$x^3 + y^3 = (x + y)(x^2 - xy + y^2)$$

$$x^3 - y^3 = (x - y)(x^2 + xy + y^2)$$

EXAMPLE   Factor $a^3 + 8$.

SOLUTION $a^3 + 8 = (a + 2)(a^2 - 2a + 4)$

1. Verify the factoring pattern for the sum of two cubes by multiplying $(x + y)(x^2 - xy + y^2)$.

2. Verify the factoring pattern for the difference of two cubes by multiplying $(x - y)(x^2 + xy + y^2)$.

Factor.

3. $n^3 + 27$ **4.** $a^3 - 8$ **5.** $x^3 + 64$ **6.** $125 - 27b^3$

7. a. Factor $z^6 - 1$ as a difference of cubes to show that
$$z^6 - 1 = (z - 1)(z + 1)(z^4 + z^2 + 1).$$

b. Factor $z^6 - 1$ as a difference of squares to show that
$$z^6 - 1 = (z - 1)(z + 1)(z^2 + z + 1)(z^2 - z + 1).$$

c. Show that the factorizations given in parts (a) and (b) are equivalent by writing
$$z^4 + z^2 + 1 = (z^4 + 2z^2 + 1) - z^2$$
and then factoring the difference of squares on the right.

5-6 *Squares of Binomials*

OBJECTIVE   To find squares of binomials and to factor trinomial squares.

Note what happens when you square
the binomial $a + b$.

$$
\begin{array}{r}
a + b \\
a + b \\
\hline
a^2 + ab \\
ab + b^2 \\
\hline
a^2 + 2ab + b^2
\end{array}
$$

1. Square of the first term._____

2. Twice the product of the two terms._____

3. Square of the last term._____

When you square the binomial
difference $a - b$, the middle term
in the product will be preceded by
a minus sign.

$$
\begin{array}{r}
a - b \\
a - b \\
\hline
a^2 - ab \\
- ab + b^2 \\
\hline
a^2 - 2ab + b^2
\end{array}
$$

1. Square of the first term._____

2. Twice the product of the two terms._____

3. Square of the last term._____

These results may be expressed as these two useful formulas.

$$(a + b)^2 = a^2 + 2ab + b^2$$
$$(a - b)^2 = a^2 - 2ab + b^2$$

These formulas can be used to write squares of binomials as trinomials.

EXAMPLE 1 $(x + 4)^2 = x^2 + 8x + 16$

EXAMPLE 2 $(3c + 5)^2 = 9c^2 + 30c + 25$

EXAMPLE 3 $(2s - 7t)^2 = 4s^2 - 28st + 49t^2$

EXAMPLE 4 $(6x^2 - y^3)^2 = 36x^4 - 12x^2y^3 + y^6$

The symmetric property of equality enables you to rewrite the formulas for squaring a binomial in a form useful for factoring.

$$a^2 + 2ab + b^2 = (a + b)^2$$
$$a^2 - 2ab + b^2 = (a - b)^2$$

The expressions on the left sides of the two equations above are called **trinomial squares**.

To determine whether or not a trinomial is a trinomial square, ask the three questions illustrated in the next examples.

EXAMPLE 5   Is $25x^2 - 30x + 9$ a trinomial square?

SOLUTION
1. Is the first term a square?   Yes, $25x^2 = (5x)^2$
2. Is the last term a square?   Yes, $9 = 3^2$
3. Is the middle term, neglecting the   Yes, $30x = 2(5x \cdot 3)$
    sign, twice the product of $5x$ and 3?

Thus, $25x^2 - 30x + 9$ is a trinomial square, and
$25x^2 - 30x + 9 = (5x - 3)^2$.   ***Answer***

EXAMPLE 6   Is $16x^2 + 28xy + 49y^2$ a trinomial square?

SOLUTION
1. Is the first term a square?   Yes, $16x^2 = (4x)^2$
2. Is the last term a square?   Yes, $49y^2 = (7y)^2$
3. Is the middle term twice the product   No, $28xy \neq 2(4x \cdot 7y)$
    of $4x$ and $7y$?

Thus, $16x^2 + 28xy + 49y^2$ is not a trinomial square.   ***Answer***
(It would be a trinomial square if the middle term were $56xy$.)

Oral Exercises

Express each square as a trinomial.

1. $(x + 1)^2$ **2.** $(y + 3)^2$ **3.** $(a - 5)^2$ **4.** $(x - y)^2$
5. $(a + 6)^2$ **6.** $(b - 8)^2$ **7.** $(3x + 1)^2$ **8.** $(2k + 1)^2$
9. $(y^2 - 1)^2$ **10.** $(a^2 + 3)^2$ **11.** $(5x - 2)^2$ **12.** $(2 - 5x)^2$

Decide whether or not each polynomial is a trinomial square. If so, factor it.

13. $x^2 + 14x + 49$ **14.** $a^2 - 6a + 9$ **15.** $b^2 - 8b + 16$
16. $y^2 + 2y + 4$ **17.** $9n^2 - 12n + 4$ **18.** $25x^2 - 10xy + 4y^2$

19. Find the square of 31 by thinking of it as $(30 + 1)^2$.

Written Exercises

Express each square as a trinomial.

A **1.** $(x + 2)^2$ **2.** $(y - 3)^2$ **3.** $(a - 4)^2$ **4.** $(b + 9)^2$
   5. $(2x + 3)^2$ **6.** $(3y + 8)^2$ **7.** $(4k - 5)^2$ **8.** $(7k - 2)^2$
   9. $(4p + 3q)^2$ **10.** $(8x - 5y)^2$ **11.** $(3x + 7y)^2$ **12.** $(2a - 9b)^2$
   13. $(ab - 5)^2$ **14.** $(x^2 + 3)^2$ **15.** $(y^2 - 7)^2$ **16.** $(2x^2 - y^2)^2$
   17. $(-3 + 5a)^2$ **18.** $(-7 - 6b)^2$ **19.** $(-8x^2 + 1)^2$ **20.** $(-11a^2 - b^2)^2$

Factor each trinomial as the square of a binomial if possible. If it is not possible, so state.

21. $n^2 - 2n + 1$ **22.** $k^2 + 6k + 9$ **23.** $r^2 - 4r + 4$

24. $a^2 + 12a + 24$ **25.** $b^2 - 18b + 81$ **26.** $49 - 7k + k^2$

27. $4x^2 + 4x + 1$ **28.** $9 + 12y + 4y^2$ **29.** $36 - 60a + 25a^2$

30. $25d^2 - 50d + 100$ **31.** $64x^2 - 16xy + y^2$ **32.** $81n^2 + nt + 9t^2$

B   **33.** $x^4 + 2x^2 + 1$ **34.** $y^4 + 10y^2 + 25$ **35.** $a^2b^2 - 12ab + 36$

    36. $25a^2 + 55a + 121$ **37.** $a^4 - 24a^2 + 144$ **38.** $(x + 1)^2 + 2(x + 1) + 1$

39. Express each square as a trinomial
    a. $(5x - 2)^2$ **b.** $(2 - 5x)^2$
    c. Notice that the answers to parts (a) and (b) are equal even though $(5x - 2)$ is not equal to $(2 - 5x)$. Explain why the squares of these binomials are equal.

40. Show that $a^4 - 8a^2 + 16$ can be factored as $(a - 2)^2(a + 2)^2$.

41. Show that $x^4 - 18x^2 + 81$ can be factored as $(x - 3)^2(x + 3)^2$.

Solve and check.

42. $x(x + 5) = (x + 2)^2$ **43.** $(x - 4)^2 = (x - 6)(x - 1)$

44. $(x - 1)(x + 1) = (x + 5)(x - 2)$ **45.** $(x + 4)^2 = x^2 + 16$

First factor out a common monomial factor. Then complete the factoring.

SAMPLE $12x^3 + 36x^2 + 27x = 3x(4x^2 + 12x + 9) = 3x(2x + 3)^2$

46. $6x^2 + 12x + 6$ **47.** $3a^2 + 18a + 27$ **48.** $a^3 - 10a^2 + 25a$

49. $18x^2 - 12x + 2$ **50.** $24b - 24b^2 + 6b^3$ **51.** $20x^4 + 60x^2 + 45$

52. $2a^6 - 24a^4 + 72a^2$ **53.** $16k^5 - 48k^3 + 36k$ **54.** $3v^8 - 48v^5 + 192v^2$

Solve and check.

55. $(x + 3)(x + 5) = (x + 1)^2 + 13x$

56. $(2x + 1)^2 - (2x - 1)^2 = (x + 6)^2 - x^2$

57. $(2x - 1)^2 - (4x - 3)(x + 2) = 1 - 7x$

58. $(5x + 4)^2 - (3x + 2)^2 = (4x + 4)(4x - 4)$

59. The length of a rectangle is equal to four times its width. If the width of the rectangle is increased by 4 cm and its length is decreased by 4 cm, its area will be increased by 32 cm². Find the dimensions of the original rectangle.

60. The sum of the squares of three consecutive integers is 22 less than three times the product of the two greater integers. Find the integers.

C **61.** The square of a two-digit number ending in 5 always ends in 25. The digits before the 25 are found by multiplying the ten's digit by one more than the ten's digit. Thus,

$$25^2 = 625 \qquad \text{and} \qquad 45^2 = 2025$$
$$(2 \times 3) \qquad\qquad (4 \times 5)$$

a. Use this rule to find the squares of 35, 55, and 85.

b. Prove the rule works by letting $10t + 5$ represent a two-digit number ending in 5. Square this number and show that the result equals $t(t + 1) \times 100 + 25$.

Self-Test 2

VOCABULARY   linear term (p. 166)   trinomial square (p. 171)
                  quadratic term (p. 166)

Express each product as a polynomial.

1. $(3y + 5)(2y - 6)$ **2.** $2x(x - 4)(3x - 2)$ Obj. 5-4, p. 166

3. $(x - 7)(x + 7)$ **4.** $(2a + 7b)(2a - 7b)$ Obj. 5-5, p. 168

Factor.

5. $4x^2 - 49$ **6.** $36x^4 - 81$

Express each square as a trinomial.

7. $(2y + 5)^2$ **8.** $(3z - 5k)^2$ Obj. 5-6, p. 171

Factor.

9. $9a^2 + 12a + 4$ **10.** $16m^2 - 24mn + 9n^2$

Check your answers with those at the back of the book.

Biography Rosalind Franklin

Rosalind Elsie Franklin (1920–1958), a British chemist and molecular biologist, contributed significantly to the determination of the structure of deoxyribonucleic acid, or DNA. DNA appears in all cells of all living things and is responsible for determining the form and function of these cells. It is the means by which hereditary characteristics are passed on. Rosalind Franklin's X-ray studies of DNA were instrumental in the construction and verification of the DNA model.

5-7 Factoring Pattern for $x^2 + bx + c$, c positive

OBJECTIVE To factor quadratic trinomials whose quadratic coefficient is 1 and whose constant term is positive.

In this section you will study trinomials that can be factored as a product of the form $(x + r)(x + s)$ where r and s are both positive or both negative. First look at some products of this form to see what clues they give you for factoring the trinomial.

EXAMPLE 1 $(x + 2)(x + 3) = x^2 + 5x + 6$

sum of
2 and 3

product of
2 and 3

EXAMPLE 2 $(x - 5)(x - 7) = x^2 - 12x + 35$

sum of
-5 and -7

product of
-5 and -7

EXAMPLE 3 $(x + r)(x + s) = x^2 + (r + s)x + rs$

Example 3 suggests the following technique for factoring polynomials with quadratic term x^2 and a positive constant term:

1. List the pairs of factors that have a product equal to the constant term.
2. Find the pair of factors in the list that have a sum equal to the coefficient of the linear term.

Examples 1 and 2 suggest that in Step 1 you can just look at the factors with the same sign as the linear term.

EXAMPLE 4 Factor $x^2 + 7x + 12$.

SOLUTION
1. List the pairs of positive factors of 12.
2. Find the factors that have a sum of 7: 3, 4.
3. $x^2 + 7x + 12 = (x + 3)(x + 4)$ *Answer*

	12
1	12
2	6
3	4 √

Instead of writing down the factors of the constant term, it is often faster to review them mentally.

EXAMPLE 5 Factor $y^2 - 14y + 24$.

SOLUTION
1. The factoring pattern is $(y - \;\;)(y - \;\;)$.
2. Select the factors of 24 with sum -14: $-2, -12$.
3. $y^2 - 14y + 24 = (y - 2)(y - 12)$ *Answer*

A polynomial that cannot be rewritten as a product of polynomials of lower degree is called **irreducible.** An irreducible polynomial whose greatest monomial factor is 1 is a **prime polynomial.**

EXAMPLE 6   Factor $x^2 - x + 8$.

SOLUTION   1. List the pairs of negative factors of -8: $-1, -8; -2, -4$.
  2. Neither of these pairs of factors has a sum of -1.
  3. Thus, $x^2 - x + 8$ cannot be factored. It is irreducible and prime. ***Answer***

Oral Exercises

For each trinomial, state the factors of the constant term whose sum is equal to the coefficient of the linear term.

SAMPLE $x^2 - 10x + 21$ *SOLUTION* $-3, -7$

1. $x^2 + 3x + 2$	**2.** $x^2 + 5x + 4$	**3.** $y^2 + 6y + 8$
4. $y^2 + 7y + 10$	**5.** $a^2 + 11a + 10$	**6.** $b^2 + 9b + 20$
7. $x^2 - 4x + 3$	**8.** $x^2 - 8x + 7$	**9.** $r^2 - 7r + 12$
10. $s^2 - 8s + 15$	**11.** $a^2 - 10a + 24$	**12.** $z^2 + 10z + 21$

Written Exercises

Factor. Check by multiplying the factors. If the polynomial is not factorable, write "prime."

A
1. $x^2 + 6x + 5$	**2.** $y^2 + 7y + 6$	**3.** $a^2 - 4a + 3$
4. $b^2 - 10b + 16$	**5.** $r^2 + 9r + 18$	**6.** $v^2 - 20v + 51$
7. $k^2 - 11k + 28$	**8.** $x^2 - 13x + 22$	**9.** $z^2 - 13z + 42$
10. $y^2 + 15y + 44$	**11.** $a^2 - 17a + 50$	**12.** $b^2 - 14b + 45$
13. $y^2 + 16y + 55$	**14.** $d^2 - 14d + 32$	**15.** $p^2 - 17p + 72$
16. $72 - 38z + z^2$	**17.** $20 - 12c + c^2$	**18.** $40 - 15a + a^2$

SAMPLE 1 $a^2 - 8ab + 12b^2$

SOLUTION $a^2 - 8ab + 12b^2 = (a - \quad)(a - \quad)$
$\qquad\qquad\qquad\quad = (a - 2b)(a - 6b)$ ***Answer***

19. $x^2 - 12xy + 35y^2$	**20.** $a^2 - 11ab + 24b^2$	**21.** $s^2 - 11st + 30t^2$
22. $c^2 - 19cd + 48d^2$	**23.** $b^2 + 13bc + 40c^2$	**24.** $x^2 + 15xy + 50y^2$
25. $s^2 - 13st + 42t^2$	**26.** $a^2 + 10ab + 25b^2$	**27.** $k^2 - 18ka + 36a^2$
28. $y^2 - 14yz + 49z^2$	**29.** $d^2 + 12de + 27e^2$	**30.** $y^2 - 28yz + 75z^2$

B
31. $a^2 - 23a + 120$	**32.** $y^2 + 22y + 96$	**33.** $108 - 21a + a^2$
34. $180 - 41b + b^2$	**35.** $98n^2 - 21nx + x^2$	**36.** $112y^2 - 22yz + z^2$

Determine all integral values for k for which the trinomial can be factored.

SAMPLE 2 $x^2 + kx + 35$

SOLUTION   35 can be factored as a product of two integers in these ways:
$$1 \cdot 35 \quad 5 \cdot 7 \quad (-1)(-35) \quad (-5)(-7)$$
The corresponding values of k are 36, 12, -36, -12. ***Answer***

37. $x^2 + kx + 10$ **38.** $y^2 + ky + 4$ **39.** $z^2 + kz + 15$
40. $u^2 + ku + 21$ **41.** $r^2 + kr + 12$ **42.** $n^2 + kn + 18$

Factor. Check by multiplying the factors.

C **43.** $(x + 2)^2 + 5(x + 2) + 4$ **44.** $(y - 2)^2 + 7(y - 2) + 10$
45. $(a + b)^2 - 6(a + b) + 8$ **46.** $(a + 4)^2 - 8(a + 4) + 16$
47. $a^4 - 10a^2 + 9$ **48.** $b^4 - 26b^2 + 25$
49. $x^4 - 6x^2 - 27$ **50.** $x^5 - 13x^3 + 36x$

ꜰistorical ꞥote Exponents

Down through the centuries, many forms of notation were used to represent powers of a variable before the current notation became standard. As early as 1485, Nicolas Chuquet in France used a form of exponent to describe powers, but his notation omitted the variable. He wrote

$.2.^0, .2.^1, .2.^2, \ldots$ for 2, 2x, 2x^2, ...

To represent what you would write as

$$x^4 + 3x^2 - 7x,$$

Jobst Burgi (1552–1632), a Swiss clockmaker, used

$$\overset{\text{iv}}{1} + \overset{\text{ii}}{3} - \overset{\text{i}}{7}$$

and Simon Stevin (1548–1620), a Flemish engineer, wrote

$$\overset{4}{1} + \overset{2}{3} - \overset{1}{7}.$$

In 1637 it was René Descartes, a French mathematician, who introduced the use of small numerals with variables, and expressed powers as x, xx, x^3, x^4, ... Eventually, mathematicians used x^2 for xx.

As you can see from the dates, all this was going on while other Europeans were exploring and settling North America.

5-8 *Factoring Pattern for* $x^2 + bx + c$, *c negative*

OBJECTIVE To factor a quadratic polynomial whose quadratic coefficient is 1 and whose constant term is negative.

The factoring which you did in the last section had this form:

$$x^2 + bx + c = (x + r)(x + s)$$

positive r and s both positive
or both negative

By contrast, the factoring which you will do in this section has the following form:

$$x^2 + bx + c = (x + r)(x + s)$$

negative r and s have
opposite signs

The procedure that you will use in this section is the same as before. You find two numbers r and s whose product is c and whose sum is b.

If a quadratic polynomial of the form $x^2 + bx + c$ (c negative) can be factored, its factors will be of the form

$$(x + r)(x + s)$$

where one of r and s, say r, is negative and s is positive.

EXAMPLE 1 Factor $a^2 + 2a - 8$.

SOLUTION
1. List the pairs of factors of -8.
2. Find the pair of factors with a sum of 2: $-2, 4$
3. $a^2 + 2a - 8 = (a + 4)(a - 2)$. **Answer**

-8	
-1	8
1	-8
-2	4 √
2	-4

It is often faster to review the factors of the constant term mentally.

EXAMPLE 2 Factor $n^2 - 6n - 27$.

SOLUTION
1. The factoring pattern is
$$(n - \ )(n + \ ).$$
2. Find the pair of factors of -27 with a sum of -6:
$-9, 3$.
3. $n^2 - 6n - 27 = (n - 9)(n + 3)$ **Answer**

Oral Exercises

For each trinomial, state the factors of the constant term whose sum is equal to the coefficient of the linear term.

SAMPLE $x^2 - 7x - 8$ **SOLUTION** $1, -8$

1. $a^2 + 3a - 4$ **2.** $x^2 + 2x - 3$ **3.** $t^2 + 5t - 6$

4. $y^2 + y - 6$ **5.** $y^2 - y - 6$ **6.** $b^2 - 8b - 9$

7. $b^2 + 8b - 9$ **8.** $u^2 - 3u - 10$ **9.** $r^2 + 5r - 14$

Written Exercises

Factor each expression. Check by multiplying the factors. If the expression is not factorable, write "prime."

A **1.** $a^2 + 4a - 5$ **2.** $x^2 - 2x - 3$ **3.** $y^2 - 5y - 6$

4. $b^2 + 2b - 15$ **5.** $c^2 - 11c - 10$ **6.** $r^2 + 6r - 16$

7. $x^2 - 6x - 18$ **8.** $y^2 - 10y - 24$ **9.** $a^2 + 2a - 35$

10. $k^2 - 2k - 20$ **11.** $z^2 + 5z - 36$ **12.** $r^2 - 3r - 40$

13. $p^2 - 4p - 21$ **14.** $a^2 + 3a - 54$ **15.** $y^2 - 5y - 30$

16. $z^2 - z - 72$ **17.** $a^2 - ab - 20b^2$ **18.** $y^2 - 2yz - 3z^2$

19. $p^2 - 5pq - 50q^2$ **20.** $a^2 - 4ab - 77b^2$ **21.** $k^2 - 11kd - 60d^2$

22. $s^2 + 14st - 72t^2$ **23.** $x^2 - 9xy - 22y^2$ **24.** $p^2 - pq - 72q^2$

B **25.** $1 - 8ab - 20a^2b^2$ **26.** $1 - 7pq - 60p^2q^2$ **27.** $1 - ab - 56a^2b^2$

28. $n^2 - 13nm + 48m^2$ **29.** $r^2 - 18r - 144$ **30.** $a^2 + 19a - 150$

31. $800 - 20b - b^2$ **32.** $a^2 + 3a - 270$ **33.** $320 - 32x - x^2$

Find all the integral values of k for which the given polynomial can be factored.

34. $x^2 + kx - 12$ **35.** $y^2 + ky - 20$ **36.** $15 - kz - z^2$

Find two negative values for k for which the given trinomial can be factored.

C **37.** $x^2 - 3x + k$ **38.** $y^2 + 2y + k$ **39.** $z^2 + 4z + k$

40. $k - 6x - x^2$ **41.** $n^2 + 11n + k$ **42.** $k + 4m - m^2$

Factor.

43. $(x + 1)^2 - 2(x + 1) - 15$ **44.** $(a + b)^2 - 3(a + b) - 70$

45. $(2x - y)^2 + 16(2x - y) + 60$ **46.** $4(a^2 - 1) - x^2(a^2 - 1)$

47. $x^4 - 8x^2 - 9$ **48.** $2x^4 - 34x^2 + 32$

49. $3a^4 - 63a^2 - 300$ **50.** $(3a + b)^4 - (a + b)^4$

5-9 *Factoring Pattern for* $ax^2 + bx + c$

OBJECTIVE   To factor quadratic trinomials when the coefficient of the quadratic term is a positive integer greater than 1.

If $ax^2 + bx + c$ $(a > 1)$ can be factored, the factors will have the pattern

$$(px + r)(qx + s).$$

EXAMPLE 1   Factor $5x^2 - 13x + 6$.

SOLUTION

First clue: Because the trinomial has a positive constant term and a negative linear term, both r and s will be negative.

Second clue: The product of the linear terms of the binomial factors is $5x^2$, and the product of their constant terms is 6. Thus, you can determine the possible factors as follows:

Factors of $5x^2$	Factors of 6
x and $5x$	-1 and -6
	-2 and -3

Test the possibilities to see which produces the correct linear term.

Possible Factors	Linear Term
$(x - 1)(5x - 6)$	$-6x - 5x = -11x$
$(x - 6)(5x - 1)$	$-x - 30x = -31x$
$(x - 2)(5x - 3)$	$-3x - 10x = -13x$ √
$(x - 3)(5x - 2)$	$-2x - 15x = -17x$

The third possibility produces the correct linear term.

$$5x^2 - 13x + 6 = (x - 2)(5x - 3)   \textit{Answer}$$

EXAMPLE 2   Factor $8x^2 + 26x - 7$.

SOLUTION

First clue: Because the trinomial has a negative constant term, one of r and s will be negative and the other will be positive.

Second clue: You can determine the possible factors of the quadratic and constant terms as follows:

Factors of $8x^2$	Factors of -7
x and $8x$	-1 and 7
$2x$ and $4x$	1 and -7

Test the possibilities to see which produces the correct linear term.

Possible Factors	Linear Term
$(x + 1)(8x - 7)$	x
$(x - 7)(8x + 1)$	$-55x$
$(x - 1)(8x + 7)$	$-x$
$(x + 7)(8x - 1)$	$55x$
$(2x + 1)(4x - 7)$	$-10x$
$(2x - 7)(4x + 1)$	$-26x$
$(2x - 1)(4x + 7)$	$10x$
$(2x + 7)(4x - 1)$	$26x$ $\sqrt{}$

The last possibility gives the correct linear term.

$$8x^2 + 26x - 7 = (2x + 7)(4x - 1) \quad \textbf{\textit{Answer}}$$

As you practice factoring, you will become able to select the correct factors without writing all the possibilities.

EXAMPLE 3   Factor $7x^2 - 16x - 15$.

SOLUTION
$$
\begin{aligned}
7x^2 - 16x - 15 &= (7x \quad)(x \quad) \\
&= (7x + \ )(x - \ ) \\
&= (7x + 5)(x - 3) \quad \textbf{\textit{Answer}}
\end{aligned}
$$

Note: If you had written $(7x - \ )(x + \ )$ as the second step, you would have found that no such combination of factors would produce the desired linear term $-16x$.

Written Exercises

Factor. Check by multiplying the factors. If the expression is not factorable, write "prime."

A 1. $2x^2 + 5x + 3$
   2. $2n^2 + 7n + 3$
   3. $5a^2 + 6a + 1$

   4. $8n^2 + 6n + 1$
   5. $7n^2 - 8n + 1$
   6. $14k^2 - 9k + 1$

   7. $5y^2 - 16y + 3$
   8. $7y^2 - 18y + 8$
   9. $3k^2 - 5k + 1$

   10. $3z^2 + z - 2$
   11. $2t^2 - t - 6$
   12. $3a^2 + 2a - 5$

   13. $4y^2 - y - 3$
   14. $9a^2 + 3a - 2$
   15. $7k^2 + 19k - 6$

   16. $3x^2 - 7x + 6$
   17. $1 + b - 6b^2$
   18. $10 + 3y - y^2$

   19. $10 + y - 2y^2$
   20. $6 - 23a - 4a^2$
   21. $a^2 + ab - 2b^2$

   22. $x^2 - xy - 56y^2$
   23. $9r^2 - 25rs - 6s^2$
   24. $3a^2 - 5ab - 12b^2$

B 25. $25a^2 + 10ab - 3b^2$
   26. $36d^2 - 5d - 24$
   27. $12x^2 + 19xy - 18y^2$

   28. $20k^2 + 27k - 8$
   29. $12x^2 - 4x - 21$
   30. $24a^2 - 31a - 15$

Factor. Check by multiplying the factors. If the expression is not factorable, write "prime."

31. $-48c^2 + 29c + 15$ **32.** $-21b^2 + 4b + 12$ **33.** $108x^2 + 15x - 7$

34. $6x^2 - 17x - 45$ **35.** $42y^2 + 41y + 9$ **36.** $40a^2 - 7a - 21$

C **37.** $2(y + 4)^2 - (y + 4) - 3$ **38.** $3(a + b)^2 - 17(a + b) - 6$

    39. $(x^2 - 1)^2 - 14(x^2 - 1) - 15$ **40.** $(x^2 - 5x - 1)^2 - 25$

41. Show that the product of $6x^2 - 13x - 5$, $15x^2 - 16x - 7$, and $10x^2 - 39x + 35$ is a *perfect square* by showing that it is the square of another polynomial.

Self-Test 3

VOCABULARY   irreducible (p. 176)
                   prime polynomial (p. 176)

Factor.

1. $y^2 + 8y + 15$ **2.** $x^2 - 10x + 16$ Obj. 5-7, p. 175

3. $n^2 - 3n - 28$ **4.** $v^2 + 9v - 36$ Obj. 5-8, p. 178

5. $6x^2 - 19x + 15$ **6.** $3x^2 + 10x - 8$ Obj. 5-9, p. 180

Check your answers with those at the back of the book.

Career Note Meteorologist

Meteorologists study the atmosphere and atmospheric phenomena. The majority of meteorologists specialize in the study of the weather. They make predictions about the weather by examining data on air pressure, temperature, humidity, wind velocity, cloud formations, air masses, and fronts. Most of this data is now collected by weather satellites and processed by computers.

Other meteorologists specialize in atmospheric pollution, weather map analysis, or meteorological instrumentation. Hydrometeorologists study the water cycle. Climatologists specialize in the study of average weather patterns.

The minimum educational requirement for a career in this field is a bachelor's degree with a major in meteorology. General background work includes courses in physics, mathematics, and chemistry.

5-10 *Factoring by Grouping*

OBJECTIVE   To factor polynomials using the distributive axiom.

One of the key tools in factoring is the distributive axiom:

$$ab + ac = a(b + c).$$

This axiom holds not only when a represents a monomial, but also when a represents any polynomial. If $a = 3 + x$,

$$(3 + x)b + (3 + x)c = (3 + x)(b + c).$$

If $a = p - 2q + r$,

$$(p - 2q + r)b + (p - 2q + r)c = (p - 2q + r)(b + c).$$

It will help you in factoring if you learn to recognize factors which are opposites of each other.

Factor	Its Opposite
$a - b$	$-(a - b)$, or $-a + b$, or $b - a$
$4z - y$	$-(4z - y)$, or $-4z + y$, or $y - 4z$
$5 - p - 2q$	$-(5 - p - 2q)$, or $-5 + p + 2q$, or $p + 2q - 5$

EXAMPLE 1   Factor $5(a - b) + 3(b - a)$.

SOLUTION   Notice that $(a - b)$ and $(b - a)$ are opposites. If you express $(b - a)$ as $-(a - b)$, you can then factor the expression using the distributive axiom.

$$5(a - b) + 3(b - a) = 5(a - b) - 3(a - b)$$
$$= 2(a - b)$$

In the following example you first group terms and then factor each group of terms.

EXAMPLE 2   Factor $rq - 2rp + 5q - 10p$.

SOLUTION $\underbrace{(rq - 2rp)} + \underbrace{(5q - 10p)} =$
$r(q - 2p) + 5(q - 2p) =$
$(r + 5)(q - 2p)$

The following example applies what you know about factoring trinomial squares and differences of squares.

EXAMPLE 3   Factor $x^2 + 6x + 9 - 9y^2$.

SOLUTION $x^2 + 6x + 9 - 9y^2 = (x + 3)^2 - (3y)^2$
$= (x + 3 - 3y)(x + 3 + 3y)$

Oral Exercises

State a pair of binomial factors whose product is equal to the given expression.

1. $3(a + b) + x(a + b)$

2. $x(y - 7) - 3(y - 7)$

3. $r(p - 2q) - (p - 2q)$

4. $5x(x - 1) + 2(1 - x)$

5. $x(a - 5) - y(5 - a)$

6. $5a(2a - b) + 3b(b - 2a)$

Written Exercises

Factor. Check by multiplying the factors.

A 1. $a(x - 5) + b(x - 5)$

2. $r(2s - 1) + k(2s - 1)$

3. $x^2(5 - r) + (5 - r)$

4. $a(y + 3) - (y + 3)$

5. $2a(4 - y) - b(4 - y)$

6. $(r - 25) + k(r - 25)$

7. $x(a + b) + y(a + b)$

8. $a(k - 3c) - (k - 3c) + b(k - 3c)$

9. $x^2(2d - e + f) + (f - e + 2d)$

10. $a(1 - x) + b(x - 1)$

11. $3a(2 - y) + 7(y - 2)$

12. $x(c - 2d) + 3(2d - c)$

13. $6c(z - 3) - (3 - z)$

14. $5a(p - 5) - 6(5 - p)$

15. $(2a - b + 3c) + x(b - 2a - 3c)$

16. $x^2 + xy + xz + yz$

17. $2p + ap + 2q + aq$

18. $y^2 - 3y + yz - 3z$

19. $pq + 2qr + 2r^2 + pr$

20. $6x - 3y + 2zx - yz$

21. $ab - 2b + ac - 2c$

22. $x^3 - 2x^2 + 3x - 6$

23. $2x^3 + x^2 + 8x + 4$

24. $2ac - 6bc - 3a + 9b$

25. $4x^2 - 8xy - 3x + 6y$

26. $3rs - s + 12r - 4$

27. $4y^2 + 8ay - y - 2a$

28. $2a^3 - a^2 - 10a + 5$

29. $4x^2 - 2xy - 7yz + 14xz$

30. $2x^3 - 6x^2 - 5x + 15$

Factor each expression as a difference of two squares.

B 31. $a^2 - (2b + 3c)^2$

32. $(p - q)^2 - r^2$

33. $36k^2 - (2a - c)^2$

34. $25 - (5x - y)^2$

35. $(x - 4y)^2 - 9$

36. $(a + b)^2 - (c + d)^2$

37. $x^2 + 6x + 9 - y^2$

38. $p^2 - 2pq + q^2 - 4$

39. $h^2 - 12h + 36 - k^2$

40. $a^2 - x^2 - 2x - 1$

41. $25 - a^2 - 4ab - 4b^2$

42. $4a - 4a^2 + 49k^2 - 1$

43. $16y^2 + 8y + 1 - 16z^2$

44. $k^2 + 2kt + t^2 - n^2 - 8n - 16$

Factor.

45. $8b - 4 + a^2 - 4b^2$

46. $x^2 - 16y^2 - 6x + 9$

47. $a^2 - b^2 - 10bc - 25c^2$

48. $8yz - 4y^2 - 4z^2 + x^2$

49. $9a^2 + 9b^2 - 9c^2 - 18ab$

50. $x^4 - 8x^2 + 16 - 16y^2$

51. $a^2 - 2ab + b^2 - 3a + 3b$

52. $x^2 - 16y^2 + 2x + 8y$

C 53. Factor $4x^4 + 1$ by writing it as $4x^4 + 4x^2 + 1 - 4x^2$, a difference of two squares.

54. Factor $64y^4 + 1$.

5-11 *Using More Than One Method of Factoring*

OBJECTIVE   To factor polynomials completely.

A polynomial is said to be **factored completely** when it is expressed as the product of prime polynomials and a monomial. The following guidelines will help you factor polynomials completely.

GUIDELINES FOR FACTORING

1. Always factor out the greatest monomial factor first.
2. Look for a difference of squares.
3. Look for a trinomial square.
4. If a trinomial is not a square, look for a pair of binomial factors.
5. If a polynomial has four or more terms, look for a way to group the terms in pairs or in a group of three terms that is a binomial square.
6. Make sure that each factor is prime. Check your work by multiplying the factors.

In each of the following examples the given polynomial is factored completely.

EXAMPLE 1   Factor $3ax^2 - 27ay^2$.

SOLUTION   First factor out the greatest monomial factor. Then factor the difference of squares.

$$3ax^2 - 27ay^2 = 3a(x^2 - 9y^2)$$
$$= 3a(x + 3y)(x - 3y)$$

EXAMPLE 2   Factor $-x^2 + 8x - 16$.

SOLUTION   First factor out -1. Then factor the trinomial square.

$$-x^2 + 8x - 16 = -1(x^2 - 8x + 16)$$
$$= -(x - 4)^2$$

EXAMPLE 3   Factor $12ax^2 - 14ax - 40a$.

SOLUTION   First factor out the greatest monomial factor. Then find the pair of binomial factors.

$$12ax^2 - 14ax - 40a = 2a(6x^2 - 7x - 20)$$
$$= 2a(3x + 4)(2x - 5)$$

Oral Exercises

State the greatest monomial factor of each polynomial.

1. $3ab^2 - 27a^3$

2. $-a + 4a^3$

3. $-8x + 8x^2 - 2$

4. $12a^2 - 10ab - 8b^2$

5. $4(a - 1)^2 - 36$

6. $30x^2 - 5xy - 5y^2$

Written Exercises

A **1–6.** Factor the polynomials in Oral Exercises 1–6 completely.

Factor completely.

7. $x^4 - y^4$

8. $a^3x - 4ax^3$

9. $2x^4 - 162$

10. $a^2b - 9b + 3a^2 - 27$

11. $a^2 - 1 - 4b^2 - 4b$

12. $9a^2 - b^2 - 4b - 4$

13. $y^4 - 5y^2 + 4$

14. $x^4 - 26x^2 + 25$

15. $b^4 - 18b^2 + 81$

16. $2x^4 - 6x^2 - 8$

17. $10k^3 - 25k - 15k^2$

18. $-x^2 + 6xy - 9y^2$

B **19.** $2x^2 - 8y^2 + 16y - 8$

20. $x^2 - 9y^2 - 2x + 6y$

21. $4(a - 3)^2 - 4$

22. $x^8 - y^8$

23. $x^3 - x^2 - 4x + 4$

24. $a^3 + 2a^2 - 9a - 18$

25. $m^2 + m - k^2 - k$

26. $2pa + 2pr + r^2 - a^2$

27. $a^2c - 4abc - 9c^3 + 4b^2c$

28. $n(n + 1)(n + 2) - 3n(n + 1)$

29. $a(x^2 - a^2) + x(a - x)$

30. $2x^2(x + 1)(x + 3) - 6x^2$

31. $a^2(b - 3c) + 9b^2(3c - b)$

32. $(a - b)^3 + 4(b - a)$

33. $2 - 2y^2 - 8x^2 - 8xy$

34. $a^2 - 2ab + b^2 - 3a + 3b$

35. $x(x^2 - 1) - 2(x + 1)$

36. $x(x - 5)(x - 2) + 6(x - 2)$

37. $ax + 2ay - 3x^2 + 12y^2$

38. $2c^{16} - 2d^{16}$

39. $2p(p + 1)(p - 6) + 16(p + 1)$

40. $4a^2(2a - 1) - 4a(2a - 1) + (2a - 1)$

41. $p^2 - 4pq + 4q^2 - r^2 + 4sr - 4s^2$

42. $16a^2 - 16b^2 - 64bc - 64c^2$

43. $45x^2 - 177xy - 12y^2$

C **44.** $(a^2 - 4)^2 - (a - 2)^2$

45. $4b^2c^2 - (b^2 + c^2 - a^2)^2$

46. $(a^2 - 9)^2 - (3 - a)^2$

47. $(a + 3b)^2 - (a^2 - 9b^2)^2$

48. $x^2(x^2 - 4) + 4x(x^2 - 4) + 4(x^2 - 4)$

49. $x^2 + 4x^2y^2 + y^2 + 2xy - x^4 - 4y^4$

50. $t^3 + t^2 - t - 1$

51. $x^3 - x^2 - 4x + 4$

Self-Test 4

VOCABULARY   factor completely (p. 185)

Factor completely.

1. $xy - 2x + 6y - 12$

2. $n^2 + 8n + 16 - 9m^2$

Obj. 5-10, p. 183

3. $4ax^2 - 16ax + 16a$

4. $4xy^2 - 24xy + 36x$

Obj. 5-11, p. 185

Check your answers with those at the back of the book.

APPLICATIONS OF FACTORING

5-12 *Solving Equations in Factored Form*

OBJECTIVE   To solve equations when one side is in factored form and the other side is 0.

The **converse** of a statement in if-then form is obtained by interchanging the "if" and "then" parts of the statement. The converse of a true statement may be either true or false.

By the multiplicative property of zero you know that for any two real numbers a and b:

$$\text{If } a = 0 \text{ or } b = 0, \text{ then } ab = 0.$$

You can show (see Exercise 13 on page 188) that the converse of the statement above is also true.

$$\text{If } ab = 0, \text{ then } a = 0 \text{ or } b = 0.$$

You can use the words *if and only if* to combine a statement and its converse. The *zero-product property* below combines the multiplicative property of zero and its converse into a single statement.

ZERO-PRODUCT PROPERTY

For all real numbers a and b,

$$ab = 0 \text{ if and only if } a = 0 \text{ or } b = 0.$$

The zero-product property is useful in solving certain equations.

EXAMPLE   Solve $(x + 5)(x - 4) = 0$.

SOLUTION   One of the factors of the left side must be 0. Thus,

$$x + 5 = 0 \qquad \text{or} \qquad x - 4 = 0$$
$$x = -5 \qquad\qquad\qquad x = 4$$

Of course, you might have seen without writing the equations that when $x = -5$ or $x = 4$ one of the factors will be 0. Either method gives the solution set $\{-5, 4\}$.   ***Answer***

The zero-product property is true for any number of factors. *A product of factors is equal to zero if and only if one or more of the factors is zero.*

Oral Exercises

State the values of the variable which make the open sentence a true statement.

1. $x(x - 9) = 0$

2. $y(y + 7) = 0$

3. $(z - 2)(z - 3) = 0$

4. $(k + 4)(k - 5) = 0$

5. $2b(b - 6) = 0$

6. $(c + 8)(c + 1) = 0$

Written Exercises

Solve.

A   **1.** $3k(k - 7) = 0$ **2.** $(x - 8)(x + 8) = 0$ **3.** $(z - 7)(z - 8) = 0$

    4. $(n + 17)(n + 7) = 0$ **5.** $(y - 15)(y - 100) = 0$ **6.** $35n(n - 35) = 0$

Solve.

SAMPLE $(2z - 3)(z - 5) = 0$

SOLUTION $2z - 3 = 0$ or $z - 5 = 0$

$$2z = 3 \qquad\qquad z = 5$$

$$z = \frac{3}{2}$$

$\therefore$ the solution set is $\{\frac{3}{2}, 5\}$.   **_Answer_**

    7. $(3x - 1)(2x + 5) = 0$ **8.** $(4k + 2)(k - 3) = 0$ **9.** $(4z + 5)5z = 0$

B   **10.** $3n(n - 4)(2n + 7) = 0$ **11.** $2x(2x - 5)(5x + 2) = 0$ **12.** $m(3m - 8)(3m + 1) = 0$

C   **13.** Give the missing reasons in the proof of the statement: If $ab = 0$, then $a = 0$ or $b = 0$.

Case 1. If $a = 0$, then there is nothing to prove.

Case 2. If $a \neq 0$:

$ab = 0$	(1) Given
There is a unique real number $\frac{1}{a}$.	(2) _?_
$\frac{1}{a}(ab) = \frac{1}{a}(0)$	(3) _?_
$\frac{1}{a}(ab) = 0$	(4) _?_
$\left(\frac{1}{a} \cdot a\right)b = 0$	(5) _?_
$(1)b = 0$	(6) _?_
$b = 0$	(7) _?_

5-13 *Solving Equations by Factoring*

OBJECTIVE To solve polynomial equations by factoring.

A **polynomial equation** is an equation whose sides are both polynomials. Polynomial equations may be named by the term of highest degree. When $a \neq 0$:

$$ax + b = 0 \quad \textbf{linear equation}$$

$$ax^2 + bx + c = 0 \quad \textbf{quadratic equation}$$

$$ax^3 + bx^2 + cx + d = 0 \quad \textbf{cubic equation}$$

Many polynomial equations can be solved by factoring and then applying the zero-product property. Often, the first step in solving such an equation is to transform it into **standard form** in which one side is 0 and the other side is a simplified polynomial arranged in descending powers of the variable.

EXAMPLE 1 Solve the quadratic equation $2x^2 = x + 1$.

SOLUTION

1. Transform into standard form. $\qquad\qquad\qquad 2x^2 - x - 1 = 0$
2. Factor the left side. $\qquad\qquad\qquad\qquad (x - 1)(2x + 1) = 0$
3. Set each factor equal to zero and solve. $\overline{\quad x - 1 = 0 \;\mid\; 2x + 1 = 0\quad}$
4. Check the solutions in the original $\qquad\qquad x = 1 \;\mid\; \qquad x = -\frac{1}{2}$
   equation $2x^2 = x + 1$.

$$2(-\tfrac{1}{2})^2 \overset{?}{=} -\tfrac{1}{2} + 1 \qquad 2(1)^2 \overset{?}{=} 1 + 1$$

$$2(\tfrac{1}{4}) \overset{?}{=} \quad \tfrac{1}{2} \qquad\qquad\qquad 2 = 2 \;\checkmark$$

$$\tfrac{1}{2} = \quad \tfrac{1}{2} \;\checkmark$$

$\therefore$ the solution set is $\{-\frac{1}{2}, 1\}$. ***Answer***

EXAMPLE 2 Solve the cubic equation $x^3 + 4x = 4x^2$

SOLUTION

1. Transform into standard form. $\qquad\qquad\qquad x^3 - 4x^2 + 4x = 0$
2. Factor completely. $\qquad\qquad\qquad\qquad\quad x(x^2 - 4x + 4) = 0$
3. Solve. $\qquad\qquad\qquad\qquad\qquad\qquad x(x - 2)(x - 2) = 0$
4. The check is left to you. $\qquad\qquad x = 0 \;\mid\; x = 2 \;\mid\; x = 2$

$\therefore$ the solution set is $\{0, 2\}$. ***Answer***

In the last example, 2 is called a *double root* of the equation because the factor $(x - 2)$ occurs twice in the factored form of the equation. Note, however, that 2 is listed only once in the solution set.

Example 2 on page 189 shows the correct way to solve an equation in which a variable or variable expression is a factor of both sides of the equation. CAUTION: Never transform an equation by dividing by an expression containing a variable. If you divide both sides of $x(x^2 - 4x + 4) = 0$ by x in Example 2, you will not be aware that 0 is a solution of the equation.

Written Exercises

Solve.

A
1. $x^2 - 13x + 36 = 0$
2. $y^2 + 2y - 63 = 0$
3. $z^2 + 2z - 8 = 0$

4. $x^2 - 5x + 6 = 0$
5. $x^2 - x - 6 = 0$
6. $x^2 + 25 = 10x$

7. $n^2 - 5n = 24$
8. $k^2 + 9 = 10k$
9. $y^2 - 16y = 0$

10. $y^2 - 16 = 0$
11. $4x^2 - 9 = 0$
12. $a^2 - 4a + 4 = 0$

13. $3x^2 + 2x - 1 = 0$
14. $a^3 - a = 0$
15. $n^3 - 4n = 0$

16. $x^2 - x - 30 = 0$
17. $2x^2 - 5x - 3 = 0$
18. $y^3 - 10y^2 + 25y = 0$

19. $n^2 = 36$
20. $4x^2 = 8x + 5$
21. $3y^2 + 2y = 1$

22. $a^2 = 24 - 5a$
23. $4a^2 = 8a$
24. $6x^2 = x + 1$

25. $6x^2 + x = 77$
26. $3x^2 - 6x = 9$
27. $6x^2 + 17x + 12 = 0$

28. $4y^2 + 7 = 29y$
29. $6y^2 = 22y + 40$
30. $6z^2 + 11z = 72$

B
31. $x^3 - 12x^2 + 32x = 0$
32. $y^3 + 49y = 14y^2$
33. $y^4 - 13y^2 + 36 = 0$

34. $t^3 + t^2 = 4t + 4$
35. $a^4 - 2a^2 + 1 = 0$
36. $2x^4 - 20x^2 + 18 = 0$

37. $9t^3 - 9t^2 - 9t + 9 = 0$
38. $y^3 + 45y = 14y^2$
39. $y^5 = 25y^3$

40. $(x - 2)(x + 3) = 6$
41. $(a - 5)(a - 2) = 28$
42. $4x^4 = 64$

C
43. $x(x - 2)^2 = 16x$
44. $2x(x - 2) = 6(x - 2)$
45. $2(x^2 - 9) = x(3 - x)$

46. $3x(x^2 - 4) = 12(x^2 - 4)$
47. $4(y - 1)^2 = 8(y - 1)$
48. $x(x + 1)(x + 2) = 5x(x + 2)$

Find an equation in standard form having the given solution set.

49. $\{1, 3\}$
50. $\{-7, 4\}$
51. $\{\frac{2}{3}, -\frac{1}{3}\}$

52. $\{-3, 0, 1\}$
53. $\{\frac{4}{5}, -\frac{4}{5}\}$
54. $\{-2, -1, 0, 1, 2\}$

55. What is wrong with the following "proof" that $2 = 1$?

Let a and b be nonzero real numbers such that $a = b$.

$a^2 = ab$	(1) Multiply both sides by a.
$a^2 - b^2 = ab - b^2$	(2) Subtract b^2 from both sides.
$(a - b)(a + b) = b(a - b)$	(3) Factor both sides.
$(a + b) = b$	(4) Divide both sides by $a - b$.
$b + b = b$	(5) Substitute a for b (since $a = b$).
$2b = b$	(6) Combine like terms.
$2 = 1$	(7) Divide both sides by b.

5-14 *Solving Problems by Factoring*

OBJECTIVE To solve problems involving quadratic equations.

The problems in this section all lead to polynomial equations which can be solved by factoring. Sometimes a solution of the equation may not satisfy some of the conditions of the problem. For example, a negative number could not be a length or a width. You simply discard solutions that do not make sense for the problem.

EXAMPLE 1 Jason is mowing a yard 16 m long and 12 m wide. He mows continuously around the yard working toward the center. He wonders how wide a strip must be cut before he is half done.

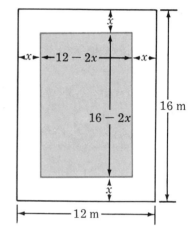

SOLUTION

Step 1 The problem asks for the width of the strip that must be cut in order for half the lawn to be mowed.

Step 2 Let x = width of the strip cut (in meters). Then the length of uncut lawn = $16 - 2x$ and the width of uncut lawn = $12 - 2x$.

Step 3 Area of uncut lawn = $\frac{1}{2}$ the area of the yard.

$$(16 - 2x)(12 - 2x) = \tfrac{1}{2}(16 \cdot 12)$$

Step 4
$$192 - 56x + 4x^2 = 96$$
$$4x^2 - 56x + 96 = 0$$
$$x^2 - 14x + 24 = 0$$
$$(x - 2)(x - 12) = 0$$
$$x - 2 = 0 \quad \bigg| \quad x - 12 = 0$$
$$x = 2 \quad \bigg| \qquad x = 12$$

Step 5 *Check:* When $x = 2$, the area of the uncut lawn is $(16 - 2x) \cdot (12 - 2x) = 12 \cdot 8 = 96$, which is exactly half of $16 \cdot 12 = 192$, the area of the whole yard. When $x = 12$, the width $12 - 2x$ is negative. Because a negative width is meaningless, we must reject $x = 12$ as an answer.

$\therefore$ the width of the strip is 2 m. ***Answer***

You may wonder how the equation in Step 3 can produce a solution, 12, which does not check. The reason is that the equation in Step 3 gives only one of the requirements of the problem. The requirements that the lawn have a positive width ($12 - 2x > 0$) and a positive length ($16 - 2x > 0$) were not written down. Usually, it is easier to write only the equation and then check its solutions against the other conditions stated in the problem.

In the next example, both solutions of the equation satisfy the conditions of the problem.

You can use the formula

$$h = rt - 4.9t^2$$

to obtain a good approximation of the height h in meters that an object will reach in t seconds when it is projected upward with an initial speed of r meters per second (m/s).

EXAMPLE 2

A ball is thrown upward with an initial speed of 34.3 m/s. When is it directly opposite the top of a tower 49 m high?

SOLUTION

Step 1 The problem asks for the time when the ball is opposite the top of the tower.

Step 2 Let $t =$ number of seconds after being thrown that the ball is opposite the top of the tower,

and $h =$ height of ball
$\quad\quad = 49$ (meters),

and $r =$ initial speed
$\quad\quad = 34.3$ (meters per second).

Step 3 $h = rt - 4.9t^2$
$\quad\quad 49 = 34.3t - 4.9t^2$
$\quad\quad \dfrac{49}{4.9} = \dfrac{34.3t}{4.9} - \dfrac{4.9t^2}{4.9}$

Step 4 $10 = 7t - t^2$
$\quad\quad t^2 - 7t + 10 = 0$
$\quad\quad (t - 2)(t - 5) = 0$

Completing the solution and checking the values is left to you.

∴ the ball is opposite the top of the tower both 2 s and 5 s after being thrown. ***Answer***

Problems

Solve.

A   1. The sum of a number and its square is 72. Find the number.

2. The sum of a positive number and its square is 90. Find the number.

3. A negative number is 42 less than its square. Find the number.

4. The square of a number is 20 more than 8 times the number. Find the number.

5. Find two consecutive negative integers whose product is 110.

6. The squares of two consecutive positive even integers total 100. Find the integers.

7. The length of a rectangle is 9 cm more than its width. Its area is 112 cm². Find the dimensions of the rectangle.

8. The length of a rectangle is 4 cm more than twice its width. If the area of the rectangle is 160 cm², find its dimensions.

9. A rectangle has perimeter 42 m and area 104 m². Find the dimensions of the rectangle.

10. The dimensions of a rectangle were 5 cm by 9 cm. When both dimensions were increased by equal amounts, the area of the rectangle increased by 120 cm². Find the dimensions of the new rectangle.

11. A square field has 4 m added to its length and 2 m added to its width, thereby creating a field with an area of 195 m². Find the dimensions of the original field.

12. The sum of two numbers is 20, and the sum of their squares is 218. Find the numbers. (*Hint:* If one number is x, the other will be $20 - x$.)

13. Find two numbers which total 13 and whose squares total 229.

14. I am thinking of three consecutive integers. The square of the largest one equals the sum of the squares of the other two. Find the integers.

In Problems 15–19, use the formula stated on page 192. Notice that all numbers appearing are integral multiples of 4.9.

15. A ball is thrown upward with an initial speed of 24.5 m/s. When is it 29.4 m high? (Two answers)

16. A projectile is fired upward with an initial speed of 2940 m/s. After how many minutes does it hit the ground?

B 17. A cannon ball is fired upward with an initial speed of 245 m/s. A stationary balloonist at a height of 1960 m sees the ball pass on its way up. How long will it be before the ball passes the balloonist again on its way down?

18. A ball is thrown upward from the top of a 98 m tower with an initial speed of 39.2 m/s. When does it hit the ground? (*Hint:* If h is the height of the ball above the top of the tower, then $h = -98$ when the ball hits the ground.)

19. A ball is thrown upward with an initial speed of 29.4 m/s.
   a. When is the ball 44.1 m high?
   b. Explain why 44.1 m is the greatest height attained by the ball.

20. The height of a box is 8 cm, and the total surface area of the box is 114 cm². Find the length of a side of the base of the box if the base is a square.

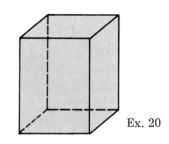

Ex. 20

21. The bottom of a box is a rectangle with dimensions in centimeters of x and $x + 2$. The height of the box is 5 cm and its total surface area is 236 cm². Find x.

22. A rug placed in a room 12 m long and 9 m wide covers half the floor area and leaves a uniform strip of bare floor around the edges. What are the dimensions of the rug?

fence

garden

4 m

12 m

Ex. 23

23. A garden plot 4 m by 12 m has one side along a fence as shown. The area of the garden is to be doubled by digging up a border of uniform width on the other three sides. What should be the width of the border?

fence

x

24. The diagram shows a rectangular enclosure formed by a wall and 20 m of fencing. If the area of the enclosure is 48 m², find its dimensions.

Ex. 24

25. A rectangular garden 40 m by 30 m has two paths crossing through it as shown. If the width of each path in meters is x and the area covered by the paths is 325 m², find x.

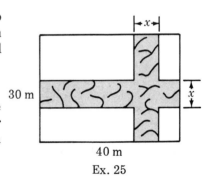

x

30 m

x

40 m

Ex. 25

26. The side of one cube is 2 cm more than the side of another cube. The volumes of the cubes differ by 152 cm³. Find the lengths of the sides of each cube.

C **27.** A rectangular piece of cardboard is 20 cm longer than it is wide. Squares, 10 cm on a side, are cut from the corners of the cardboard, and the sides are folded up to make an open box whose volume is 8 L. Find the dimensions of the original piece of cardboard. (Remember: 1 L = 1000 cm³)

10 cm

10 cm

Ex. 27

Self-Test 5

VOCABULARY   converse of a theorem (p. 187)   quadratic equation (p. 189)
                 polynomial equation (p. 189)   cubic equation (p. 189)
                 linear equation (p. 189)   standard form (p. 189)

Solve.

1. $(x - 5)(x - 9) = 0$
2. $z(z + 5)(z - 2) = 0$
   Obj. 5-12, p. 187
3. $y^2 - 7y + 10 = 0$
4. $n^2 - n - 20 = 0$
   Obj. 5-13, p. 189
5. $v^2 + 8v + 16 = 0$
6. $w^3 + 3w^2 = 28w$

7. The sum of the squares of two consecutive positive integers is
   145. Find the integers.
   Obj. 5-14, p. 191

Check your answers with those at the back of the book.

Chapter Summary

1. The *greatest common factor* of two integers is the greatest integer
   that divides both of them evenly. The *greatest monomial factor* of
   two monomials is the common factor that has the greatest coefficient
   and the greatest degree in each variable.

2. The *cancellation rule for fractions* (page 158) and the *rule of exponents for division* (page 159) can be used to simplify quotients of
   monomials.

3. The following factoring patterns are useful in factoring polynomials:

   $$a^2 + 2ab + b^2 = (a + b)^2 \qquad\qquad a^2 - b^2 = (a + b)(a - b)$$
   $$a^2 - 2ab + b^2 = (a - b)^2$$

4. The guidelines for factoring on page 185 should help you *to factor
   polynomials completely.*

5. The *zero-product property* is useful in solving *polynomial equations*.
   See the examples on pages 187 and 189.

Chapter Review

Give the letter of the correct answer.

1. What is the greatest common factor of 20 and 36?   5-1
   a. 2   **b.** 4   **c.** 180   **d.** 720

2. Find the prime factorization of 495.
   a. $3 \cdot 5 \cdot 11$ **b.** $3 \cdot 5^2 \cdot 11$ **c.** $3^2 \cdot 5 \cdot 11$ **d.** $3^2 \cdot 5^2 \cdot 11$

3. Simplify $\dfrac{3a^2 \cdot 2a^4}{(6a)^2}$. 5-2

    a. a^4 **b.** $\dfrac{a^4}{6}$ **c.** a^6 **d.** $\dfrac{a^6}{6}$

4. What is the greatest monomial factor of $36x^2y - 24xy^2$?

    a. $3x - 2y$ **b.** $6xy$ **c.** $72xy$ **d.** $12xy$

5. Divide: $\dfrac{6a^2b^3 - 12a^3b^2}{3ab^2}$ 5-3

    a. $2ab - 4a^2$ **b.** $2ab - 12a^3b^2$ **c.** $2a^2b - 4a^2$

6. Express the product $(4x - 2)(3x + 8)$ as a polynomial. 5-4

    a. $12x^2 + 26x - 16$ **b.** $12x^2 - 16x - 16$ **c.** $12x^2 - 24x - 16$

7. Express the product $(3k + 9)(3k - 9)$ as a polynomial. 5-5

    a. $9k^2 - 27$ **b.** $9k^2 - 54k + 81$ **c.** $9k^2 - 81$ **d.** $9k^2 - 27$

8. Factor $9x^2 - 64$ completely.

    a. $(9x + 8)(x - 8)$ **b.** $(3x + 8)(3x - 8)$ **c.** $9(x^2 - 6)$

9. Express $(3a^3 - 5)^2$ as a trinomial. 5-6

    a. $9a^6 - 25$ **b.** $9a^6 - 15a^3 + 25$ **c.** $9a^6 - 30a^3 + 25$

10. Factor $c^2 - 13cd + 36d^2$. 5-7

    a. $(c - 3d)(c - 12d)$ **b.** $(c - 4d)(c - 9d)$ **c.** $(c - 6d)^2$

11. Factor $p^2 - 18p - 144$. 5-8

    a. $(p - 12)^2$ **b.** $(p - 24)(p + 6)$ **c.** $(p + 24)(p - 6)$

12. Factor $24x^2 - 23x - 12$. 5-9

    a. $(8x - 3)(3x + 4)$ **b.** $(8x + 3)(3x - 4)$ **c.** $(4x - 3)(6x + 4)$

13. Factor $4a^3 - 2a^2 - 20a + 10$ completely. 5-10

    a. $2(2a^3 - a^2 - 10a + 5)$ **b.** $2a^2(a - 2) - 10(a - 1)$
    c. $(2a^2 - 10)(2a - 1)$ **d.** $2(a^2 - 5)(2a - 1)$

14. Factor $9a^2 - 9b^2 - 6b - 1$ as a difference of squares.

    a. $9(a + b)(a - b) - (6b + 1)$ **b.** $(3a + 1)(3a - 1) - 3b(3b + 2)$
    c. $(3a - 3b - 1)(3a + 3b + 1)$ **d.** $9a^2 - 6b - (3b + 1)(3b - 1)$

15. Factor $2n^3 + 4n^2 - 18n - 36$ completely. 5-11

    a. $2n(n^2 - 9) + 4(n^2 - 9)$ **b.** $2n^2(n + 2) - 18(n + 2)$
    c. $(2n^2 - 18)(n + 2)$ **d.** $2(n + 3)(n - 3)(n + 2)$

16. Solve $3n(n - 5)(3n + 5) = 0$. 5-12

    a. $\{3, 5, -\frac{5}{3}\}$ **b.** $\{0, 3, 5, -\frac{5}{3}\}$ **c.** $\{0, -5, \frac{5}{3}\}$ **d.** $\{0, 5, -\frac{5}{3}\}$

17. Solve $2x^2 + 3x - 14 = 0$. 5-13

    a. $\{\frac{2}{7}, 2\}$ **b.** $\{-2, \frac{7}{2}\}$ **c.** $\{2, -\frac{7}{2}\}$ **d.** $\{7, \frac{2}{3}\}$

18. Solve $9x^2 + 25 = 30x$.

a. $\{\frac{5}{3}\}$ **b.** $\{-\frac{5}{3}, 1\}$ **c.** $\{-\frac{5}{3}\}$ **d.** $\{\frac{5}{3}, -\frac{5}{3}\}$

19. The length of a rectangle is 3 cm more than its width. If the area of the rectangle is 180 cm², find the perimeter.

5-14

     a. 27 cm   **b.** 54 cm   **c.** 72 cm   **d.** 80 cm

Chapter Test ━━━━━━━━━━━━

1. Find the prime factorization of 360.

5-1

2. Find the greatest common factor of 54 and 96.

Simplify.

3. $\dfrac{-24x^5y^3}{8xy^2}$ **4.** $\dfrac{(4a^3)^2}{(2a)(3a^2)}$

5-2

5. Divide: $\dfrac{3a^2b^3 - 9a^3b^2}{3ab^2}$

5-3

6. Factor $10xy^3 - 5xy^2 + 15xy$ as the product of its greatest monomial factor and another polynomial.

Express each product as a polynomial.

7. $(3x - 1)(2x + 4)$ **8.** $(2a^2 - 5)(2a^2 - 3)$

5-4

9. $(3n + 2)(3n - 2)$ **10.** $(4x^2 - 7y)(4x^2 + 7y)$

5-5

11. $(5x + 6)^2$ **12.** $(n^2 - 8)^2$

5-6

Factor if possible. If not possible, write "prime."

13. $9 + 12y + 4y^2$ **14.** $a^2x^2 - 12ax + 36$

15. $x^2 + 12xy + 27y^2$ **16.** $n^2 - 28n + 75$

5-7

17. $p^2 - 9pq - 22q^2$ **18.** $x^2 - 6x - 36$

5-8

19. $3n^2 - 5n - 12$ **20.** $25y^2 + 10y - 3$

5-9

21. $x^2 + 4xy + 4y^2 - 4$ **22.** $4a^2 - 16ab - 3a + 12b$

5-10

23. $3c^2 - 12d^2$ **24.** $x^4 - 16y^4$

5-11

25. $x^4 - 10x^2 + 9$ **26.** $6ax^2 - 7ax - 20a$

27. $x^2(3 - y) + 4(y - 3)$ **28.** $-a^2 - 12a - 36$

Solve.

29. $(3x - 7)(x + 2) = 0$ **30.** $2x(x + 4)(4x + 9) = 0$

5-12

31. $6x^2 - 6 = 5x$ **32.** $2y^4 + 72 = 26y^2$

5-13

33. A border of uniform width surrounds a photograph 15 cm long and 10 cm wide. If the area of the border equals the area of the photograph, what is the width of the border?

5-14

Cumulative Review (Chapters 1-5)

Simplify each expression. Assume that no denominator is zero.

1. $0.3(-1.7) + 0.3(-0.3)$

2. $-4(3n - 2 - 5n + 2)$

3. $(-19 + y) - (-y + 9)$

4. $[-21d \div (-3d)] \div 14$

5. $2(-3)^2 \div 3 - 6$

6. $-2p^2 + 5p - 3p + p^2$

7. $-6b\left(-b^2 + 3b - \dfrac{1}{2}\right)$

8. $\dfrac{(-3xy^2)^3}{-x^2y^4}$

9. $\dfrac{6a^6 - 3a^4 - 9a^3}{3a^3}$

10. $z(3z - 4)(2z + 1)$

11. $(rs - 7t^2)(rs + 7t^2)$

12. $(4d + 5e)^2$

Evaluate if $a = -4$, $b = -1$, $c = 2$, $d = 7$, and $e = \dfrac{3}{2}$.

13. $(2d - c) \div ab$

14. $e(3a + 2c)$

15. $b^3 + 5c^2$

16. Find the prime factorizations of 60 and 75 and find their GCF.

Factor completely, if possible. If not possible, write "prime."

17. $12r^2s^2 - 18rs^3 - 48s$

18. $81k^2 - z^4$

19. $4y^2 + 10y + 25$

20. $p^2 - 16pq + 28q^2$

21. $-14x^2 + 11x + 9$

22. $3t^4 - 6t^3 - 24t^2$

Solve each equation if $y \in \{-3, -1, 0, 1, 3\}$.

23. $5 - 2y = 5$

24. $-y = y - 6$

25. $-2(3y - 1) = -4$

Solve. (The equation may be an identity or have no root.)

26. $-\dfrac{1}{6}r = -\dfrac{1}{2}$

27. $7 = -9 + 4t$

28. $\dfrac{18c - 6}{3} = -2 + 2(3c)$

29. $16 = 2 - 7s$

30. $14b = -4480$

31. $|m| - 2 = -5$

32. $9z - 1 = 5z + 7$

33. $3(6y - 1) = 8y - 28$

34. $(9n - 2)(5n + 4) = 0$

35. $0 = 9x^2 - 3x - 20$

36. $8 + 6a = 2a^2$

37. $4d^3 - 4d^2 = -d$

38. One number is 1 more than twice another number. The sum of the numbers is 46. Find the numbers.

39. At Crossroad Stand, an orange costs 3¢ less than an apple. Myra spent $2.34 for eight apples and six oranges. What is the cost of an orange? of an apple?

40. Find two consecutive integers such that the sum of their squares is 43 more than their product.

41. The dimensions of a rectangle were 5 m by 12 m. When both the length and width were increased by equal amounts, the area of the rectangle increased by 60 m². Find the dimensions of the new rectangle.

Maintaining Skills

Express each fraction as a mixed number.

SAMPLE 1 $\frac{41}{18}$ **SOLUTION** $18\overline{)41}$; $2\frac{5}{18}$ ***Answer***

$\frac{2}{}$

$\frac{36}{5}$

1. $\frac{59}{6}$ **2.** $\frac{113}{5}$ **3.** $\frac{74}{9}$ **4.** $\frac{64}{15}$ **5.** $\frac{163}{12}$ **6.** $\frac{397}{20}$

Express each mixed number as a fraction.

SAMPLE 2 $3\frac{4}{5}$ **SOLUTION** $3\frac{4}{5} = 3 + \frac{4}{5} = \frac{15}{5} + \frac{4}{5} = \frac{19}{5}$

7. $2\frac{5}{8}$ **8.** $7\frac{1}{6}$ **9.** $8\frac{11}{14}$ **10.** $15\frac{2}{3}$ **11.** $1\frac{17}{24}$ **12.** $45\frac{4}{5}$

Express each mixed number as a fraction before performing the indicated operation. Express answers in simplest form. (See page 153 for additional samples.)

SAMPLE 3 $3\frac{5}{12} - 1\frac{2}{3}$ **SOLUTION** $\frac{41}{12} - \frac{5}{3} = \frac{41}{12} - \frac{20}{12} = \frac{21}{12} = \frac{7}{4}$

SAMPLE 4 $2\frac{4}{9} \div 3\frac{2}{3}$ **SOLUTION** $\frac{22}{9} \div \frac{11}{3} = \frac{\overset{2}{\cancel{22}}}{\underset{3}{\cancel{9}}} \times \frac{\overset{1}{\cancel{3}}}{\underset{1}{\cancel{11}}} = \frac{2}{3}$

13. $7\frac{3}{4} + 4\frac{2}{3}$ **14.** $5\frac{8}{15} + 1\frac{4}{5}$ **15.** $2\frac{1}{8} + 2\frac{3}{20}$ **16.** $8\frac{11}{12} - 8\frac{1}{4}$

17. $6\frac{2}{7} - 5\frac{1}{2}$ **18.** $9\frac{3}{8} - 4\frac{5}{6}$ **19.** $2\frac{1}{7} \times 1\frac{5}{9}$ **20.** $2\frac{3}{4} \times 2\frac{2}{5}$

21. $5\frac{1}{7} \times 17\frac{1}{2}$ **22.** $1\frac{5}{12} \div 4\frac{1}{4}$ **23.** $5\frac{5}{8} \div 2\frac{7}{10}$ **24.** $5\frac{3}{5} \div 2\frac{4}{5}$

Simplify.

SAMPLE 5 $\left(-1\frac{1}{2} + 8 - 2\frac{1}{2}\right)\left(-\frac{1}{2}\right)^2 = (4)\left[-\frac{1}{2}\left(-\frac{1}{2}\right)\right] = 4\left(\frac{1}{4}\right) = 1$

25. $3\frac{8}{9} + \left(-\frac{1}{9}\right) + (-2) + 8\frac{2}{9}$ **26.** $\left[-8\frac{2}{5} + \left(5 - 6\frac{1}{5}\right)\right]\left(-2\frac{1}{2}\right)$

27. $\left[1\frac{7}{12} - \left(-\frac{2}{3}\right)\right]\left(-\frac{1}{3}\right)^2$ **28.** $\left[2\left(-3\frac{1}{2}\right) + (-5)\left(-2\frac{1}{5}\right)\right] \div (-4)$

29. $\left|-3\frac{1}{3}\right| - \left[2 + \left(-7\frac{2}{3}\right)\right]$ **30.** $(-7.5)(0.2)(-0.5)$

Lighthouses are designed to project light over great distances. The amount of illumination (E) reaching an object from a light source depends on the power of the light source (I) and its distance (s) from the object according to the formula $E = \dfrac{I}{s^2}$.

6

FRACTIONS

ALGEBRAIC FRACTIONS

6-1 *Simplifying Fractions*

OBJECTIVE   To simplify algebraic fractions.

The procedure for simplifying a quotient of polynomials is the same procedure you learned for simplifying a quotient of monomials. Just factor the numerator and denominator and apply the cancellation rule for fractions. When the numerator and denominator have no common factor other than 1 and -1, the quotient is said to be in *simplest form.*

EXAMPLE 1   Express $\dfrac{a^2 - 4b^2}{a^2 - 4ab + 4b^2}$ in simplest form.

SOLUTION $\dfrac{a^2 - 4b^2}{a^2 - 4ab + 4b^2} = \dfrac{(a + 2b)(a - 2b)}{(a - 2b)(a - 2b)} = \dfrac{a + 2b}{a - 2b} \quad (a \neq 2b)$

Recall that you cannot divide by zero. Thus, you must restrict the variables in a denominator so that the denominator does not equal zero. In Example 1, a cannot equal $2b$.

The next example shows that you must be alert to factors that are opposites of each other.

EXAMPLE 2   Express $\dfrac{2x^2 - 9x + 10}{10 + x - 2x^2}$ in simplest form.

SOLUTION $\dfrac{2x^2 - 9x + 10}{10 + x - 2x^2} = \dfrac{(2x - 5)(x - 2)}{(5 - 2x)(2 + x)} \qquad$ ($2x - 5$ and $5 - 2x$ are opposites.)

$= \dfrac{-(5 - 2x)(x - 2)}{(5 - 2x)(x + 2)}$

$= \dfrac{-(x - 2)}{x + 2} = \dfrac{2 - x}{x + 2} \quad \left(x \neq -2, x \neq \dfrac{5}{2}\right)$

Oral Exercises

Express in simplest form. State the values of the variable for which the fraction is not defined.

1. $\dfrac{x^2 - 1}{x + 1}$

2. $\dfrac{a^2 + 2a + 1}{a + 1}$

3. $\dfrac{x - 5}{x^2 - 25}$

4. $\dfrac{(2a - 9)^2}{(2a - 9)^3}$

5. $\dfrac{3b + 6}{4b + 8}$

6. $\dfrac{2x + 2y}{2x - 2y}$

7. $\dfrac{x^2 - x - 2}{x^2 - 4}$

8. $\dfrac{b^2 - 6b + 9}{b^2 - 9}$

9. $\dfrac{y - 3}{3 - y}$

10. $\dfrac{4c - 14}{7 - 2c}$

11. $\dfrac{(x - 2)^2}{(2 - x)^2}$

12. $\dfrac{(7 - s)(s^2 - 9)}{(s - 7)(s + 3)}$

Written Exercises

Express in simplest form, noting any restrictions on the variable.

A 1. $\dfrac{2x - 4}{x - 2}$

2. $\dfrac{3a + b}{9a + 3b}$

3. $\dfrac{4x - 4y}{4x + 4y}$

4. $\dfrac{y^2 + 3y}{y^2 - 6y}$

5. $\dfrac{x^2 - xy}{x^2 + xy}$

6. $\dfrac{p}{2p^2 - p}$

7. $\dfrac{2ab}{a^2b - b^2a}$

8. $\dfrac{2ab + 2ac}{4ac + 4a^2}$

9. $\dfrac{x^2 - 36}{2x - 12}$

10. $\dfrac{x^2 - 4x + 4}{x - 2}$

11. $\dfrac{4x + 20}{x^2 - 25}$

12. $\dfrac{3x + 4}{9x^2 - 16}$

13. $\dfrac{b^2 + 5b + 6}{b^2 + 6b + 8}$

14. $\dfrac{y^2 - 7y + 6}{y^2 - 1}$

15. $\dfrac{r^2 - 3r}{r^2 - 2r - 3}$

16. $\dfrac{(a - 5)(2a - 7)}{3(5 - a)(7 - 2a)}$

17. $\dfrac{3 - x}{x^2 - 9}$

18. $\dfrac{(s - 6)^2}{36 - s^2}$

19. $\dfrac{(a - b)^7}{(b - a)^8}$

20. $\dfrac{(3x - 8)^5}{(8 - 3x)^5}$

21. $\dfrac{16c^2 + 8c + 1}{1 - 16c^2}$

22. $\dfrac{b^2 + b - 12}{12 - 4b}$

23. $\dfrac{5x - x^2}{x^2 - 6x + 5}$

24. $\dfrac{6x^2 + x}{36x^2 - 1}$

B 25. The width of a rectangle is $(2x - 6)$ cm and its area is $(12x^2 - 44x + 24)$ cm². Find the length.

26. All-natural oatmeal cookies cost $(5n - 3)$ cents each. How many can you buy for $(30n^2 + 2n - 12)$ cents?

Express in simplest form, noting any restrictions on the variable.

27. $\dfrac{2x^2 - 8}{x^2 + 4x - 12}$

28. $\dfrac{c^2 + 10cd + 25d^2}{c^2 - 25d^2}$

29. $\dfrac{16a^2 - 49b^2}{16a^2 - 56ab + 49b^2}$

30. $\dfrac{8c^2a^2 - 32}{c^3a^2 - 4ac^2 + 4c}$

31. $\dfrac{s^2 - 2s - 15}{s^2 + 10s + 21}$

32. $\dfrac{64y^2 - 4x^2}{x^2 + 3xy - 4y^2}$

33. $\dfrac{2a^2 + 2ab - 4b^2}{a^2 + 2ab - 3b^2}$

34. $\dfrac{x^2 - 9y^2}{3x^2 - 15xy + 18y^2}$

35. $\dfrac{4x^2 + 16xy + 15y^2}{2x^2 + xy - 10y^2}$

36. $\dfrac{8x^2 + 6xy - 5y^3}{16x^2 - 25y^2}$

37. $\dfrac{3x^2 - 3y^2}{3x(x - y) + 3y(x - y)}$

38. $\dfrac{x^4 - 4}{x^2(x + 2) + 2(x + 2)}$

First express the fraction in simplest form. Then evaluate it for the given values of the variables. If the original fraction has a zero denominator for these values, indicate that it cannot be evaluated for these values.

39. $\dfrac{4x^2 - y^2}{2x - y};\ x = 4,\ y = 8$

40. $\dfrac{a^2 + 2ab + b^2}{2a + 2b};\ a = -1\dfrac{1}{2},\ b = -\dfrac{1}{2}$

41. $\dfrac{c^2 - 4d^2}{c^2d - 4cd^2 + 4d^3};\ c = \dfrac{1}{2},\ d = \dfrac{3}{4}$

42. $\dfrac{x^3y - xy^3}{x^2y + xy^2};\ x = 6,\ y = -6$

Express in simplest form, noting any restrictions on the variable.

C 43. $\dfrac{2x^3 - 13x^2 + 15x}{15x - 7x^2 - 2x^3}$

44. $\dfrac{x^4 - 10x^2 + 9}{3 - 2x - x^2}$

45. $\dfrac{a^2 - 9b^2 - 2a + 6b}{(a + 3b)^2 - 4}$

46. $\dfrac{x^3 + 6x^2 - 4x - 24}{x^3 - 2x^2 - 36x + 72}$

47. $\dfrac{a^2 - 6ab + 9b^2 - 9}{3a - 9b - 9}$

48. $\dfrac{(a - b)^3 + 4(b - a)}{(a - b)^2 + 4(b - a) + 4}$

Biography Louise Arner Boyd

Louise Arner Boyd (1887–1972) was a geographer and polar explorer. She was born and educated in California. Her first expedition was a trip to Greenland in 1926. On succeeding expeditions she explored East Greenland, Northeast and West Greenland, and eastern arctic Canada. Her research in these areas included the collection of data for maps and studies of the geology, botany, and meteorology of the regions. While preparing for an expedition in 1928, she learned that the explorer Roald Amundsen had disappeared and she joined in the search. Though Amundsen was never found, Louise Boyd was honored by the governments of Norway and France for her efforts.

During World War II, Louise Boyd served as a consultant to the United States government. She studied radio and magnetic phenomena in the ocean surrounding Greenland and other arctic areas, and supplied maps, photographs, and firsthand geographic information about strategic areas of the arctic. In 1955 one of her childhood dreams was realized; she made a successful flight over the North Pole. Among her many honors was her election to the council of the American Geographical Society in 1960.

6-2 *Multiplying Fractions*

OBJECTIVE   To multiply algebraic fractions.

The property of quotients states that

$$\frac{cx}{dy} = \frac{c}{d} \cdot \frac{x}{y}.$$

The symmetric property of equality makes it possible to rewrite this result as the multiplication rule for fractions, shown below. The multiplication rule for fractions enables you to express a product of two fractions as a quotient.

MULTIPLICATION RULE FOR FRACTIONS

If c, d, x, and y are any real numbers such that $d \neq 0$ and $y \neq 0$, then

$$\frac{c}{d} \cdot \frac{x}{y} = \frac{cx}{dy}.$$

EXAMPLE 1   Multiply: $\dfrac{2x}{3} \cdot \dfrac{5}{4y}$

SOLUTION 1 $\dfrac{2x}{3} \cdot \dfrac{5}{4y} = \dfrac{2x \cdot 5}{3 \cdot 4y}$

$$= \frac{\overset{5}{10x}}{\underset{6}{12y}} = \frac{5x}{6y} \quad (y \neq 0)$$

SOLUTION 2 $\dfrac{\overset{1}{2x}}{3} \cdot \dfrac{5}{\underset{2}{4y}} = \dfrac{5x}{6y}$

EXAMPLE 2   Multiply: $\dfrac{x^2 - 3x - 4}{x^2 - 2x} \cdot \dfrac{x^2 - 4}{x - 4}$

SOLUTION

$\dfrac{x^2 - 3x - 4}{x^2 - 2x} \cdot \dfrac{x^2 - 4}{x - 4} = \dfrac{(x+1)(x-4)}{x(x-2)} \cdot \dfrac{(x-2)(x+2)}{(x-4)}$ $\left\{\begin{array}{l}\text{Factor the numerators} \\ \text{and denominators.}\end{array}\right.$

$\qquad\qquad = \dfrac{(x+1)(x\!-\!4)}{x(x\!-\!2)} \cdot \dfrac{(x\!-\!2)(x+2)}{(x\!-\!4)}$ $\left\{\begin{array}{l}\text{Divide by common} \\ \text{factors.}\end{array}\right.$

$\qquad\qquad = \dfrac{(x+1)(x+2)}{x} \quad (x \neq 0,\, x \neq 2,\, x \neq 4)$ *Answer*

Another way to write the answer to Example 2 is $\dfrac{x^2 + 3x + 2}{x}$. The factored form of the answer, as shown in Example 2, will be the one you should use unless otherwise directed.

If you study the denominators in the first step in Example 2, you will see that there will be a zero denominator when x equals 0, 2, or 4. Thus the answer is restricted to values of x other than 0, 2, and 4.

Hereafter, it will be assumed that the domains of the variables include no value for which any denominator is zero. Hence, it will not be necessary to show excluded values of the variables involved.

Oral Exercises

Express each product as a fraction in simplest form.

1. $\dfrac{2}{3} \cdot \dfrac{6}{5}$ **2.** $\dfrac{-3}{4} \cdot \dfrac{1}{9}$ **3.** $\dfrac{-4}{7} \cdot \dfrac{-5}{4}$

4. $\dfrac{3}{8} \cdot \dfrac{4}{15}$ **5.** $\dfrac{1}{x} \cdot \dfrac{2}{y}$ **6.** $\dfrac{x}{2} \cdot \dfrac{4}{y}$

7. $\dfrac{a}{3} \cdot \dfrac{4}{a}$ **8.** $\dfrac{x}{y} \cdot \dfrac{y^2}{2}$ **9.** $\dfrac{3a}{2} \cdot \dfrac{a}{3}$

10. $(3x)^2 \cdot \dfrac{1}{x}$ **11.** $\dfrac{2(x - 3)}{y} \cdot \dfrac{y^2}{x - 3}$ **12.** $\dfrac{2a - 5}{b^2} \cdot \dfrac{b^3}{5 - 2a}$

Written Exercises

Express each product as a fraction in simplest form.

A   **1.** $\dfrac{5}{2} \cdot \dfrac{2}{3}$ **2.** $\dfrac{3}{8} \cdot \dfrac{16}{9}$ **3.** $\dfrac{7}{25} \cdot \dfrac{5}{21}$ **4.** $\dfrac{-8}{15} \cdot \dfrac{3}{40}$

5. $\dfrac{7}{12} \cdot \dfrac{4}{5} \cdot \dfrac{15}{14}$ **6.** $\dfrac{13}{8} \cdot \dfrac{15}{26} \cdot \dfrac{24}{25}$ **7.** $\dfrac{11}{9} \cdot \dfrac{81}{21} \cdot \dfrac{42}{33}$ **8.** $\left(-\dfrac{5}{7}\right)^2 \cdot \dfrac{14}{25}$

9. $\dfrac{a}{b} \cdot \dfrac{b}{c}$ **10.** $\dfrac{3}{xy} \cdot \dfrac{2x^2}{y}$ **11.** $\dfrac{4}{c^2} \cdot \dfrac{3c}{8}$ **12.** $\dfrac{4}{5} \cdot \dfrac{15a^2}{2b}$

13. $\dfrac{p^2}{2q} \cdot \dfrac{6q^2}{p}$ **14.** $\dfrac{5a}{3b^2} \cdot \dfrac{6b^2}{a^2}$ **15.** $\dfrac{34y^4}{x^3} \cdot \dfrac{x}{17y}$

16. $\dfrac{3r^2s}{7t} \cdot \dfrac{14t^2}{9rs^2}$ **17.** $\dfrac{a - 1}{2a - 3} \cdot \dfrac{4a - 6}{1 - a}$ **18.** $\dfrac{x - 1}{3} \cdot \dfrac{12}{x^2 - 1}$

19. $\dfrac{x + 2}{x} \cdot \dfrac{x^2}{x^2 - 4}$ **20.** $\dfrac{a + b}{a - b} \cdot \dfrac{a^2 - b^2}{4a + 4b}$ **21.** $\dfrac{4x - xy}{8x^2y} \cdot \dfrac{4}{16 - y^2}$

22. $\dfrac{y^2 - 5y}{5} \cdot \dfrac{10y}{2y - 10}$ **23.** $\dfrac{(1 - x)^3}{4} \cdot \dfrac{8}{(x - 1)^2}$ **24.** $\dfrac{a^2 - c^2}{a} \cdot \dfrac{4}{2c - 2a}$

Write an expression in simplest form for each of the following.

SAMPLE The distance you go by traveling at $\frac{4v}{5}$ km/h for $\frac{3}{2}$ h.

SOLUTION $\frac{\overset{2}{4v}}{5} \cdot \frac{3}{2} = \frac{6v}{5}; \frac{6v}{5}$ km *Answer*

B 25. The distance you go by traveling at $\frac{3}{4}x$ km/h for $2y$ h.

26. The area of a rectangle with length $\frac{5x - 15}{4}$ cm and width $\frac{4x - 8}{5}$ cm.

27. The total cost of $\frac{3n}{2}$ apples that cost $\frac{8c}{3}$ cents per dozen.

28. The volume of a box with length $\frac{x + 3}{2y}$ cm, width $\frac{x - 3}{2y}$ cm, and height $\frac{8y}{x^2 - 9}$ cm.

Simplify.

SAMPLE $\left(\frac{2}{3c}\right)^4 = \frac{2}{3c} \cdot \frac{2}{3c} \cdot \frac{2}{3c} \cdot \frac{2}{3c} = \frac{2^4}{(3c)^4} = \frac{16}{81c^4}$

29. $\left(\frac{1}{b}\right)^3$ **30.** $\left(\frac{2}{3c}\right)^2$ **31.** $\left(\frac{4d}{5}\right)^3$ **32.** $\left(\frac{5x^2}{2}\right)^3$ **33.** $\left(\frac{d^2}{k}\right)^2$

34. $\left(\frac{4ab^2}{3}\right)^3$ **35.** $\left(\frac{x^2}{y^3}\right)^5$ **36.** $\left(\frac{ay^3}{v^2}\right)^4$ **37.** $\left(\frac{2an}{v^2}\right)^3$ **38.** $\left(\frac{3z^2}{2x^3y}\right)^3$

39. $\frac{x^2 + y^2}{x^2 + 2xy + y^2} \cdot \frac{3x + 3y}{6}$

40. $\frac{a^2 + 5a + 6}{4a - 8} \cdot \frac{a^2 - a}{a + 2}$

41. $\frac{4x^2 - 9y^2}{6x^2 - 9xy} \cdot \frac{6y^2}{4xy + 6y^2}$

42. $\frac{b^2 + b}{b^2 - b} \cdot \frac{3b - 21}{b^2 - 6b - 7}$

43. $\frac{x^2 - 3x + 2}{x^2 + 3x + 2} \cdot \frac{8x + 8}{4x - 8}$

44. $\frac{y^2 + 4y - 21}{y^2 - 6y - 16} \cdot \frac{y^2 - 8y + 15}{y^2 + 9y + 14}$

45. $\frac{4x^2 - 25y^2}{(5y - 2x)^2} \cdot \frac{4}{4x + 10y}$

46. $\frac{3b^2 - 9b + 6}{2b^2 - 10b + 12} \cdot \frac{6 - 2b}{3 - 3b}$

47. $\frac{2x^3 - 5x^2 - 3x}{x^2 - 4x} \cdot \frac{8 - 2x}{x^3 - 3x}$

48. $\frac{4b^2 - 2ab}{b^2 - 4ab + 4a^2} \cdot \frac{(2a - b)^3}{2b - a}$

49. $\frac{8 - 2x^4}{4x^2} \cdot \frac{(4x)^2}{2 + x^2}$

50. $\frac{6a^2b - 4ab^2}{45a^2 - 20b^2} \cdot \frac{30a + 20b}{4a^2b^2}$

C 51. $\frac{4z^2 - 4}{1 + z^2} \cdot \frac{1 - z}{2z} \cdot \frac{1 - 2z^2 + z^4}{2 + 2z}$

52. $\frac{x^2 - x - 2}{x^2} \cdot \frac{x^2 + x - 2}{9x} \cdot \frac{54x^3}{x^4 - 5x^2 + 4}$

53. $\frac{x^3 + 3x^2 - 4x - 12}{2x^2 - 18} \cdot \frac{x^3 - 3x^2 + 3x - 9}{3x^3 - 12x}$

54. $\frac{a^2 - (b - c)^2}{2a - 2b + 2c} \cdot \frac{6a - 6b + 6c}{b^2 - (a - c)^2}$

55. If $s = \dfrac{a + b + c}{2}$, show that

$$2s(2s - 2a)(2s - 2b)(2s - 2c) = (a^2 + 2ac + c^2 - b^2)(b^2 - a^2 + 2ac - c^2).$$

Application Unit Pricing

The **unit price** of an item in a supermarket is its price per unit of measure. The unit price may be expressed per liter, per kilogram, or per dozen, for example.

EXAMPLE   Find the unit price per kilogram for a 350 g jar of marmalade that costs $1.05.

SOLUTION   Express 350 g as 0.35 kg. Then divide.

$$1.05 \div 0.35 = 3.00$$

∴ the unit price is $3.00 per kilogram.

When shopping for a particular product, you can use unit prices to compare the values of containers of different sizes. The container with the lowest unit price is the best buy. It is important to realize that the larger size of an item does not always have the lower unit price.

Although getting the best buy for your money is important, you must use common sense when shopping. It is not economical to buy a larger amount of a product, if you cannot use it up within a reasonable time. The unit price to you is the price per unit used. Another consideration is quality. Will the salad oil with the lowest price make the best salad dressing? Do the potatoes with the lowest unit price have the cooking characteristics you require?

1. What is the unit price per kilogram of a 250 g box of cereal that costs $1.15?

2. Which box of soap powder has a lower unit price: a 1.5 kg box for $1.85 or a 2.5 kg box for $3.15?

3. Which bottle of wine vinegar has the lower unit price: a 700 mL bottle for 63¢ or a 1 L bottle for 88¢?

In many stores unit prices are posted on the shelves where items are kept. Watch for these unit prices as you shop and look to see how they are computed.

6-3 Dividing Fractions

OBJECTIVE To divide algebraic fractions.

The rule for division of real numbers states that to divide by a real number, you multiply by its reciprocal. For example,

$$\frac{3}{5} \div \frac{2}{7} = \frac{3}{5} \cdot \frac{7}{2} = \frac{21}{10}.$$

In algebra division by fractions is defined similarly.

DIVISION RULE FOR FRACTIONS

$$\frac{a}{b} \div \frac{c}{d} = \frac{a}{b} \cdot \frac{d}{c}$$

EXAMPLE 1 Divide: $\dfrac{x^2 + x - 2}{x - 2} \div \dfrac{5x - 5}{x^2 - 4}$.

SOLUTION

$$\frac{x^2 + x - 2}{x - 2} \div \frac{5x - 5}{x^2 - 4} = \frac{x^2 + x - 2}{x - 2} \cdot \frac{x^2 - 4}{5x - 5} \qquad \left|\begin{matrix}\text{Multiply by}\\\text{the reciprocal.}\end{matrix}\right.$$

$$= \frac{(x + 2)(x - 1)}{x - 2} \cdot \frac{(x + 2)(x - 2)}{5(x - 1)} \qquad \left|\text{Factor.}\right.$$

$$= \frac{(x + 2)(x - 1)}{x - 2} \cdot \frac{(x + 2)(x - 2)}{5(x - 1)} \qquad \left|\begin{matrix}\text{Divide by}\\\text{common factors.}\end{matrix}\right.$$

$$= \frac{(x + 2)^2}{5}$$

When simplifying an expression that involves both multiplication and division, do the operations in order from left to right (unless parentheses are used to indicate a different order). Remember that you can change each division sign to a multiplication sign if you also replace the fraction immediately following the division sign by its reciprocal.

EXAMPLE 2 Simplify $\dfrac{y}{y + 1} \div \dfrac{y^2}{6y + 18} \cdot \dfrac{y^3 + y^2}{y^2 - 9}$.

SOLUTION

$$\frac{y}{y + 1} \div \frac{y^2}{6y + 18} \cdot \frac{y^3 + y^2}{y^2 - 9} = \frac{y}{y + 1} \cdot \frac{6y + 18}{y^2} \cdot \frac{y^3 + y^2}{y^2 - 9}$$

$$= \frac{y}{y + 1} \cdot \frac{6(y + 3)}{y^2} \cdot \frac{y^2(y + 1)}{(y + 3)(y - 3)}$$

$$= \frac{y}{y + 1} \cdot \frac{6(y + 3)}{y^2} \cdot \frac{y^2(y + 1)}{(y + 3)(y - 3)}$$

$$= \frac{6y}{y - 3}$$

Oral Exercises

Simplify.

1. $\dfrac{2}{3} \div \dfrac{1}{4}$
2. $\dfrac{1}{5} \div \dfrac{4}{7}$
3. $-\dfrac{5}{8} \div \dfrac{3}{4}$
4. $\dfrac{12}{5} \div \dfrac{3}{10}$

5. $\dfrac{x}{y} \div \dfrac{x}{2}$
6. $\dfrac{a}{b} \div \dfrac{b}{a}$
7. $3a \div \dfrac{a^2}{2}$
8. $1 \div \dfrac{a}{b+c}$

9. $\dfrac{x^3}{4} \div 2x^2$
10. $\dfrac{a}{b^2} \div \dfrac{2}{b}$
11. $\dfrac{1}{4} \div \dfrac{2}{3} \cdot \dfrac{1}{5}$
12. $\dfrac{1}{4} \div \left(\dfrac{2}{3} \cdot \dfrac{1}{5}\right)$

Written Exercises

Divide. Express the answers in simplest form.

A 1. $\dfrac{3}{4} \div \dfrac{1}{2}$
2. $\dfrac{5}{8} \div \dfrac{25}{16}$
3. $\dfrac{3x}{y} \div \dfrac{x}{2}$
4. $\dfrac{a}{b} \div \dfrac{a^2}{2}$

5. $\dfrac{3a^2b}{4} \div \dfrac{6b}{a}$
6. $\dfrac{4x^2}{y} \div \dfrac{-2x}{y^2}$
7. $\dfrac{p^2}{q} \div \dfrac{p}{2q^2}$
8. $\dfrac{-3a^2}{2b} \div \dfrac{2a^2}{3b}$

9. $\dfrac{(2x)^2}{3} \div \dfrac{(4x)^2}{12}$
10. $\left(\dfrac{3a}{2}\right)^2 \div \left(\dfrac{6}{a}\right)^2$
11. $\dfrac{9a^2}{4b} \div 6ab$
12. $1 \div \left(\dfrac{3x^2}{2}\right)^3$

13. $\dfrac{a+b}{5} \div \dfrac{a+b}{10}$
14. $\dfrac{x-1}{2} \div \dfrac{x^2-1}{6}$
15. $\dfrac{y^2-4}{2y} \div (y+2)$

16. $\dfrac{a-b}{cd^2} \div \dfrac{a-b}{cd^3}$
17. $\dfrac{x-y}{x+y} \div \dfrac{1}{(x+y)^2}$
18. $\dfrac{1}{10-2y} \div \dfrac{1}{3y-15}$

19. $\dfrac{2a+2b}{a^2} \div \dfrac{a^2-b^2}{3a}$
20. $\dfrac{x^2+y^2}{a+b} \div \dfrac{7x+7y}{7a+7b}$
21. $1 \div \dfrac{x^2-y^2}{x^2-2xy+y^2}$

22. $\dfrac{3}{a^2-9} \div \dfrac{3a-6}{a-3}$
23. $\dfrac{x^2-36}{6x-36} \div \dfrac{x^2+12x+36}{x^3+6x^2}$
24. $\dfrac{3-3x}{x^2+2x-3} \div (2x-2)$

B 25. $\dfrac{6x^3}{4yz^9} \div \dfrac{10x^7y^4}{15z^3}$
26. $\dfrac{21a^3b^2}{4cd^2} \div \left(\dfrac{5a^2b^5}{8c^3d^2} \cdot \dfrac{3a}{b}\right)$
27. $\dfrac{(4p^2)^2}{2qr^3} \div \left(\dfrac{8p^7}{q^4} \div \dfrac{1}{r^7}\right)$

Simplify.

28. $\dfrac{6x}{6x-14} \cdot \dfrac{9x-21}{21} \div \dfrac{x^2}{35}$
29. $\dfrac{c^2}{c^2-d^2} \cdot \dfrac{c-d}{c+d} \div \dfrac{c}{(c+d)^2}$

30. $\dfrac{x^4-y^4}{2x-2y} \div \dfrac{x^2+y^2}{4}$
31. $\dfrac{(2a-b)^2}{x-2y} \div \dfrac{4ab^2-2b^3}{4y-2x}$

32. $\dfrac{3a^2-9a+6}{2a^2-10a+12} \div \dfrac{3-3a}{6-2a}$
33. $\dfrac{2a^2-13a+15}{a^2-2a} \div \dfrac{10-7a+a^2}{a^2-4a+4}$

34. $\dfrac{3n^2-14n+8}{2n^2-3n-20} \div \dfrac{6-25n+24n^2}{16n^2+34n-15}$
35. $\left(\dfrac{2x-5}{3}\right)^4 \div \left(\dfrac{5-2x}{6}\right)^3$

36. $2x^2 \div 3x^3 \div 4x^4$

Simplify.

C 37. $\dfrac{s^2 - 2s}{s^2 - 3s - 4} \cdot \dfrac{s^2 - 25}{s^2 - 4s - 5} \div \dfrac{s^2 + 5s}{5s^2 + 10s + 5}$

38. $\dfrac{b^2 + 6b - 7}{6b^2 - 7b - 20} \cdot \dfrac{2b^2 + b - 15}{b^2 + 2b - 3} \div \dfrac{b^2 + 5b - 14}{3b^2 - 2b - 8}$

39. $\dfrac{a^3 + 5a^2 - 9a - 45}{2a^2 - 9a + 9} \div \dfrac{a^2 + 10a + 25}{12 - 14a + 4a^2} \cdot \dfrac{a + 5}{a^2 - 4a + 4}$

40. $\dfrac{x^2 - 6xy + 9y^2 - 9}{x^4 - 81y^4} \cdot \dfrac{3x - 9y}{3x - 9y + 9} \div \dfrac{x - 3y - 3}{3x^2 + 27y^2}$

Self-Test 1

Express in simplest form.

1. $\dfrac{k^2 + 6k + 8}{k^2 - 3k - 10}$ **2.** $\dfrac{n^2 + 10n + 25}{n^2 - 25}$ *Obj. 6-1, p. 201*

3. $\dfrac{8a^3}{5b^6} \cdot \dfrac{9b}{10a^2}$ **4.** $\dfrac{z - 1}{9} \cdot \dfrac{12z}{z^2 - 1}$ *Obj. 6-2, p. 204*

5. $\dfrac{3x^3 y}{8} \div \dfrac{6x}{y}$ **6.** $\dfrac{10m^2}{3n^2} \div 5\,mn$ *Obj. 6-3, p. 208*

Check your answers with those at the back of the book.

Just for Fun

Did you ever wonder who drew the first Hindu-Arabic numerals? One theory is that an ancient mathematician first shaped the numerals so that each would contain the corresponding number of angles. For example:

    for one   for seven   for nine

The angles are counted as indicated by the dots:

Can you draw numerals for the other integers between one and nine, each with the appropriate number of angles?

Calculator Key-In

Home Calculators and Computers

Small calculators are operated by tiny electronic circuits. The simplest calculators perform the four arithmetic operations with perhaps a square root key or a percent key also. Most calculators have capabilities far exceeding this.

Calculators designed for business applications can perform such functions as calculating the monthly payment on a mortgage and figuring compound interest. Scientific calculators can find square roots, raise numbers to powers, and calculate trigonometric functions (see Looking Ahead). In addition to their technical functions, calculators can perform social functions, such as keeping time and sounding an alarm beep at a specific time. There are also calculators with constant memories that enable them to remember a number even when the calculator is turned off.

On some calculators, each key can be used for two functions. When the key is pressed directly, it performs the function described by the label printed on it. When a ''shift'' key is pressed before pressing the key, it performs according to the label printed above it.

A ''programmable'' feature is available on some calculators. This enables the user to store sequences of operations for repeated use. This programming is done by means of special ''learning'' keys on the calculator and does not require the use of a special programming language.

Microcomputers for home use are also available. These can be programmed in a version of the BASIC language. They generally use a monitor like a television screen to display what is being done—the program or the results. There are some printing devices that can be added on.

When extensive data, repeated operations, or decision-making steps are involved in the solution of a problem, a computer is better suited for the job than a calculator. Speed of calculation is the major advantage of a computer.

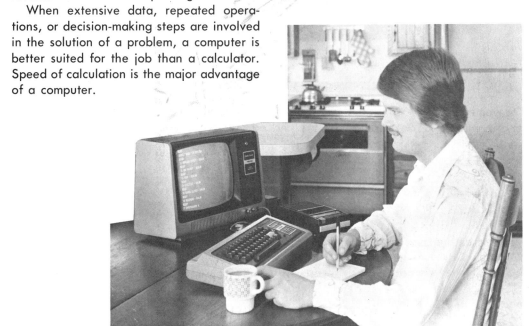

ADDING AND SUBTRACTING FRACTIONS

6-4 *Least Common Denominators*

OBJECTIVE   To express fractions with their least common denominators.

The cancellation rule for fractions states that

$$\frac{cx}{cy} = \frac{x}{y}.$$

It enables you to express a fraction in simpler form by dividing its numerator and denominator by the same nonzero number. You can use the symmetric property of equality to rewrite the rule as

$$\frac{x}{y} = \frac{cx}{cy}.$$

In this form, it enables you to express a fraction in a different form by multiplying its numerator and denominator by the same number.

EXAMPLE 1 $\dfrac{3}{5} = \dfrac{?}{20}$ ⟵—————— 5 must be multiplied by 4 to get 20.

$\dfrac{3}{5} = \dfrac{3 \cdot 4}{5 \cdot 4} = \dfrac{12}{20}$ ⟵————Therefore, multiply 3 by 4 to get 12.

EXAMPLE 2 $\dfrac{6}{5a} = \dfrac{?}{10a^2}$ ⟵—————— $5a$ must be multiplied by $2a$ to get $10a^2$.

$\dfrac{6}{5a} = \dfrac{12a}{10a^2}$ ⟵—————— Therefore, multiply 6 by $2a$ to get $12a$.

EXAMPLE 3 $\dfrac{3}{x+2} = \dfrac{?}{(x+2)(x-1)}$ ⟵——— $(x+2)$ must be multiplied by $(x-1)$ to get $(x+2)(x-1)$.

$\dfrac{3}{x+2} = \dfrac{3(x-1)}{(x+2)(x-1)}$ ⟵——— Therefore, multiply 3 by $(x-1)$.

The technique shown in the last three examples is used to rewrite fractions so that they have equal denominators. For example, you can express $\dfrac{3}{4}$ and $\dfrac{5}{6}$ as fractions having a common denominator of 12, 24, 36, or any other positive **multiple** of 12. (The product of a number and an integer is called a **multiple** of the number.) Usually, it is convenient to use the **least common denominator (LCD)** of two fractions. To determine the LCD of a group of fractions, find the **least common multiple** of the denominators.

EXAMPLE 4   What is the LCD of the fractions $\frac{2}{27}$, $\frac{1}{36}$, and $\frac{7}{30}$?

SOLUTION   1. Factor each denominator into primes.

$$27 = 3^3 \qquad 36 = 2^2 \cdot 3^2 \qquad 30 = 2 \cdot 3 \cdot 5$$

2. Greatest power of 2: 2^2
   Greatest power of 3: 3^3
   Greatest power of 5: 5^1

$$2^2 \cdot 3^3 \cdot 5^1 = 540$$

$\therefore$ the LCD is 540. *Answer*

When the denominators of the fractions contain variables, the LCD will be the simplest of the common multiples of the denominators.

EXAMPLE 5   What is the LCD of $\frac{5}{4x - 20}$ and $\frac{7}{6x - 30}$?

SOLUTION   1. Factor each denominator completely.

$$4x - 20 = 4(x - 5) = 2^2(x - 5)$$
$$6x - 30 = 6(x - 5) = 3 \cdot 2(x - 5)$$

2. Form the product of the greatest power of each prime factor.

$$2^2 \cdot 3(x - 5) = 12(x - 5)$$

$\therefore$ the LCD is $12(x - 5)$. *Answer*

EXAMPLE 6   Express $\frac{4}{a^2 + a - 20}$ and $\frac{3}{a^2 + 10a + 25}$ with their least common denominator.

SOLUTION   Find the LCD: $(a - 4)(a + 5)^2$.

$$\frac{4}{a^2 + a - 20} = \frac{4}{(a - 4)(a + 5)} = \frac{4(a + 5)}{(a - 4)(a + 5)(a + 5)} = \frac{4(a + 5)}{(a - 4)(a + 5)^2}$$

$$\frac{3}{a^2 + 10a + 25} = \frac{3}{(a + 5)^2} = \frac{3(a - 4)}{(a + 5)^2(a - 4)} = \frac{3(a - 4)}{(a - 4)(a + 5)^2}$$

Oral Exercises

Find the missing numerator.

1. $\dfrac{3}{5} = \dfrac{?}{15}$ **2.** $\dfrac{2}{7} = \dfrac{?}{28}$ **3.** $\dfrac{4x}{3} = \dfrac{?}{6}$ **4.** $\dfrac{3}{2y} = \dfrac{?}{10y}$

5. $\dfrac{1}{2} = \dfrac{?}{8(x+1)}$ **6.** $\dfrac{3}{x} = \dfrac{?}{2x^2}$ **7.** $\dfrac{5a}{3b} = \dfrac{?}{9ab}$ **8.** $\dfrac{2}{(x+1)} = \dfrac{?}{(x+1)(x+4)}$

Find the LCD for each group of fractions.

9. $\dfrac{2}{9}, \dfrac{1}{6}$ **10.** $\dfrac{8}{15}, \dfrac{5}{6}$ **11.** $\dfrac{7}{10}, \dfrac{5}{12}, \dfrac{1}{3}$ **12.** $\dfrac{4}{x}, \dfrac{5}{2x^2}$

13. $\dfrac{7}{3xy}, \dfrac{5}{6y^2}$ **14.** $\dfrac{3}{a^2 - b^2}, \dfrac{1}{2(a+b)}$

15. $\dfrac{9}{(x-3)^2}, \dfrac{1}{(x-3)(x-4)}$ **16.** $\dfrac{x}{5x-10}, \dfrac{4}{3x-6}$

Written Exercises

Find the missing numerator.

A   **1.** $\dfrac{2}{5} = \dfrac{?}{15}$ **2.** $\dfrac{3}{8} = \dfrac{?}{32}$ **3.** $\dfrac{4x}{5} = \dfrac{?}{30}$ **4.** $\dfrac{8a}{11} = \dfrac{?}{33}$

5. $\dfrac{2a+3}{8} = \dfrac{?}{24}$ **6.** $\dfrac{3n-5}{2} = \dfrac{?}{10}$ **7.** $\dfrac{1-7x}{4} = \dfrac{?}{24}$ **8.** $\dfrac{3d+2c}{5} = \dfrac{?}{55}$

9. $\dfrac{x}{9} = \dfrac{?}{9x^2}$ **10.** $\dfrac{y}{3} = \dfrac{?}{6xy}$ **11.** $\dfrac{3}{5a} = \dfrac{?}{10a^2}$ **12.** $\dfrac{2}{3ab} = \dfrac{?}{6ab^2}$

13. $\dfrac{2}{3(x+2)} = \dfrac{?}{3(x+2)^2}$ **14.** $\dfrac{4}{(x-3)(x+1)} = \dfrac{?}{(x-3)^2(x+1)}$ **15.** $\dfrac{3}{a-2b} = \dfrac{?}{2b-a}$

16. $\dfrac{7}{5x-3} = \dfrac{?}{2(3-5x)}$ **17.** $\dfrac{1}{x-1} = \dfrac{?}{x^2-1}$ **18.** $\dfrac{3}{x+1} = \dfrac{?}{x^2-1}$

19. $\dfrac{5}{a+3} = \dfrac{?}{2a+6}$ **20.** $\dfrac{4a}{a-2} = \dfrac{?}{3a-6}$ **21.** $\dfrac{2}{x-2} = \dfrac{?}{x^2-2x}$

22. $\dfrac{x}{x-3} = \dfrac{?}{(x-3)(x+4)}$ **23.** $\dfrac{5}{2b-3} = \dfrac{?}{a(3-2b)}$ **24.** $\dfrac{4+x}{4-x} = \dfrac{?}{16-x^2}$

Find the LCD for each group of fractions.

25. $\dfrac{5}{6}, \dfrac{4}{9}$ **26.** $\dfrac{7}{20}, \dfrac{11}{45}$ **27.** $\dfrac{3}{2x}, \dfrac{1}{5y}$ **28.** $\dfrac{1}{4a^2}, \dfrac{5}{6a}$

29. $\dfrac{4}{9c}, \dfrac{5}{3d}, \dfrac{1}{d^2}$ **30.** $\dfrac{5}{16y^3}, \dfrac{-7}{8x}, \dfrac{4}{3y}$

31. $\dfrac{1}{2(x-1)}, \dfrac{3}{x+1}, \dfrac{4}{x^2-1}$ **32.** $\dfrac{1}{2(a-b)}, \dfrac{-3}{4(b-a)}$

Express each group of fractions with their LCD.

B **33.** $\dfrac{5}{18}, \dfrac{3}{8}$
  34. $\dfrac{3}{14}, \dfrac{2}{35}, \dfrac{1}{6}$
  35. $\dfrac{2x-1}{15}, \dfrac{1+x}{20}$
  36. $\dfrac{5x}{12}, \dfrac{x-7}{8}, \dfrac{4x-9}{6}$

37. $\dfrac{2x-3}{6}, \dfrac{7+3y}{9}, \dfrac{x}{16}$
  38. $\dfrac{5}{2y}, \dfrac{2}{3y}$
  39. $\dfrac{1}{4x^2y}, \dfrac{3x}{8y^2}$
  40. $\dfrac{2}{a^2b}, \dfrac{a}{2b^4}$

41. $\dfrac{4}{9-x^2}, \dfrac{3}{x+3}$
  42. $\dfrac{4}{2(x-7)}, \dfrac{5}{3(x-7)}$

43. $\dfrac{1}{x^2-3x}, \dfrac{1}{x^2+2x}$
  44. $\dfrac{2}{a^2-a-2}, \dfrac{1}{a^2-4}$

C **45.** $\dfrac{x}{4x^2-100}, \dfrac{2}{x+5}, \dfrac{-3}{5-x}$
  46. $\dfrac{2}{y^2-4}, \dfrac{3}{y^2-5y+6}, \dfrac{-1}{y^2-y-6}$

47. $\dfrac{2}{3x^2-27}, \dfrac{x}{2x+6}, \dfrac{3+x}{3-x}$
  48. $\dfrac{n+3}{n^2+2n-8}, \dfrac{-4}{3n^2+21n+36}, \dfrac{n}{4n+12}$

ᚻistorical ᚿote Decimals

Computation with fractions has always presented problems. The Babylonians used a place-value system partially based on 60, including fractions with denominators that were powers of 60. This system is reflected in our time measurements of minutes and seconds.

In 1579 Vieta (1540–1603) recommended using fractions with denominators that were powers of 10, but Simon Stevin (see page 177) is usually credited with the invention of the decimal fraction. In 1585 he published a book in which he explained how, by using decimals, all computations could be done as if with whole numbers. In his notation he indicated the decimal places by using small numerals in circles. He showed the addition of the numbers 27⓪8①4②7③, 37⓪6①7②5③, and 875⓪7①8②2③ as follows.

	⓪	①	②	③		
2	7	8	4	7		27.847
3	7	6	7	5	meaning	37.675
8 7	5	7	8	2		875.782
9	4	1	3	0	4	941.304

He wrote the sum as 941⓪3①0②4③

Following Stevin's work, the decimal point and the decimal comma, which is used in some countries today, were soon introduced. Then the small numerals in circles could be omitted.

6-5 *Adding and Subtracting Fractions*

OBJECTIVE   To add and subtract algebraic fractions.

The results proved in Exercises 31 and 32 on page 91 can be used to show how to add and subtract fractions with the same denominator. Rewriting those results using the symmetric property of equality gives the following rules.

ADDITION RULE FOR FRACTIONS

$$\frac{a}{c} + \frac{b}{c} = \frac{a + b}{c}$$

SUBTRACTION RULE FOR FRACTIONS

$$\frac{a}{c} - \frac{b}{c} = \frac{a - b}{c}$$

To add fractions with the same denominator, you add their numerators. To subtract fractions with the same denominator, you subtract their numerators.

EXAMPLE 1 $\dfrac{7x}{5} + \dfrac{2x}{5} = \dfrac{7x + 2x}{5} = \dfrac{9x}{5}$

EXAMPLE 2 $\dfrac{3a}{8} + \dfrac{2a - 3}{8} - \dfrac{3a + 5}{8} = \dfrac{(3a) + (2a - 3) - (3a + 5)}{8}$

$$= \frac{3a + 2a - 3 - 3a - 5}{8}$$

$$= \frac{2a - 8}{8} = \frac{2(a - 4)}{8} = \frac{a - 4}{4}$$

To add or subtract fractions with different denominators, you must first express the fractions with a common denominator. To simplify an expression involving fractions means to express it as a fraction in simplest form.

EXAMPLE 3 $\dfrac{5a}{6} + \dfrac{2a + 2}{9} - \dfrac{a - 4}{2} = \dfrac{15a}{18} + \dfrac{2(2a + 2)}{18} - \dfrac{9(a - 4)}{18}$

$$= \frac{15a + 2(2a + 2) - 9(a - 4)}{18}$$

$$= \frac{15a + 4a + 4 - 9a + 36}{18}$$

$$= \frac{10a + 40}{18} = \frac{10(a + 4)}{18} = \frac{5(a + 4)}{9}$$

EXAMPLE 4 Simplify $\dfrac{1}{x^2 + x} + \dfrac{2x}{x^2 - 1}$.

SOLUTION $\dfrac{1}{x^2 + x} + \dfrac{2x}{x^2 - 1} = \dfrac{1}{x(x + 1)} + \dfrac{2x}{(x + 1)(x - 1)}$

$$= \dfrac{x - 1}{x(x + 1)(x - 1)} + \dfrac{2x^2}{x(x + 1)(x - 1)}$$

$$= \dfrac{x - 1 + 2x^2}{x(x + 1)(x - 1)}$$

$$= \dfrac{(2x - 1)(x + 1)}{x(x + 1)(x - 1)}$$

$$= \dfrac{2x - 1}{x(x - 1)}$$

Oral Exercises

Simplify.

1. $\dfrac{3}{10} + \dfrac{2}{10}$ **2.** $\dfrac{8}{9} - \dfrac{2}{9}$ **3.** $\dfrac{11}{12} + \dfrac{7}{12} - \dfrac{1}{12}$ **4.** $\dfrac{4}{3} - \dfrac{8}{3} - \dfrac{2}{3}$

5. $\dfrac{2}{a} + \dfrac{5}{a}$ **6.** $\dfrac{8}{b} - \dfrac{9}{b}$ **7.** $\dfrac{5}{2x} - \dfrac{3}{2x}$ **8.** $\dfrac{2a}{x + 1} + \dfrac{b}{x + 1}$

9. $\dfrac{2x}{5} + \dfrac{4x}{5}$ **10.** $\dfrac{5n + 8}{6} - \dfrac{1}{6}$ **11.** $\dfrac{2a - 1}{3} + \dfrac{2a - 2}{3}$ **12.** $\dfrac{6n - 3}{4} + \dfrac{3 - 2n}{4}$

13. $\dfrac{x}{2} + \dfrac{x}{6}$ **14.** $\dfrac{3}{a - b} + \dfrac{2}{b - a}$ **15.** $\dfrac{3x}{8} - \dfrac{2x + 1}{8}$ **16.** $\dfrac{2a + 3}{7} - \dfrac{2a - 1}{7}$

Written Exercises

Simplify.

A   **1.** $\dfrac{5}{a} - \dfrac{3}{a} + \dfrac{9}{a}$ **2.** $\dfrac{4}{3b} + \dfrac{5}{3b} + \dfrac{2}{3b}$ **3.** $\dfrac{7}{2c} - \dfrac{8}{2c} + \dfrac{3}{2c}$

4. $\dfrac{x + 2}{3} + \dfrac{2x - 4}{3}$ **5.** $\dfrac{3a + 4}{5} - \dfrac{3a - 1}{5}$ **6.** $\dfrac{5a - 3}{8} - \dfrac{3 - 11a}{8}$

7. $\dfrac{y^2}{y + 2} - \dfrac{4}{y + 2}$ **8.** $\dfrac{b^2}{b - a} - \dfrac{a^2}{b - a}$ **9.** $\dfrac{x^2}{(x + 3)^2} - \dfrac{6x - 9}{(x + 3)^2}$

10. $\dfrac{x}{2} + \dfrac{x}{4}$ **11.** $\dfrac{a}{5} + \dfrac{2a}{15}$ **12.** $\dfrac{5r}{9} - \dfrac{r}{6}$

13. $\dfrac{3}{x} + \dfrac{2}{x^2}$ **14.** $\dfrac{3}{5a} + \dfrac{4}{ab}$ **15.** $\dfrac{5}{2a} - \dfrac{3}{a^2}$

16. $\dfrac{3x - 2}{6} + \dfrac{4x - 1}{4}$ **17.** $\dfrac{4 - 2y}{20} - \dfrac{y + 3}{25}$ **18.** $\dfrac{2a - 2}{15} - \dfrac{3a + 2}{10}$

19. $\dfrac{2n + 4}{5} - \dfrac{n}{6} + \dfrac{3n - 2}{10}$ **20.** $\dfrac{2a - b}{3} - \dfrac{b}{6} - \dfrac{2b - 3a}{4}$ **21.** $\dfrac{2x}{30} - \dfrac{2x - 5y}{45} - \dfrac{x - 3y}{15}$

Simplify.

22. $\dfrac{1}{x-1} + \dfrac{1}{x}$

23. $\dfrac{2}{y-2} + \dfrac{1}{y+2}$

24. $\dfrac{x}{x-5} + \dfrac{4}{5-x}$

25. $\dfrac{7}{3a-b} + \dfrac{5}{b-3a}$

26. $\dfrac{3}{x+5} + \dfrac{2}{x-5}$

27. $\dfrac{2}{2a-3} - \dfrac{1}{a}$

Find the perimeter and area of each figure in terms of the variable.
Assume that the dimensions are given in meters.

28.

$\dfrac{x}{4}$

$\dfrac{x}{6}$

29.

$\dfrac{x-2}{5}$

$\dfrac{x+2}{3}$

30.

$\dfrac{a}{2}$ $\dfrac{a}{2}$

$\dfrac{a}{2}$

$\dfrac{7a}{3}$

Simplify.

B 31. $\dfrac{x+1}{x} - \dfrac{x}{x+1}$

32. $\dfrac{n}{n-1} - \dfrac{2n}{n^2-1}$

33. $\dfrac{1}{4x-4} - \dfrac{1}{2x^2-2}$

34. $\dfrac{3a}{a-2b} + \dfrac{6b}{2b-a}$

35. $\dfrac{x}{x+y} + \dfrac{y}{x-y}$

36. $\dfrac{2}{x^2-2x} - \dfrac{3}{x^2-x-2}$

37. $\dfrac{b}{a^2-ab} - \dfrac{a}{ab-b^2}$

38. $\dfrac{1}{x-5} - \dfrac{x}{(5-x)^2}$

39. $\dfrac{a+2}{a^2+3a} - \dfrac{a-2}{a^2-3a}$

40. $\dfrac{2a}{a^3-5a^2} + \dfrac{2}{a^2+5a}$

41. $\dfrac{2}{c^2-c-2} + \dfrac{1}{c^2-4}$

42. $\dfrac{x}{(1-x)^2} + \dfrac{1}{1-x^2}$

43. $\dfrac{1}{a^2-1} + \dfrac{1}{a^2+2a+1}$

44. $\dfrac{8}{c^2-4} + \dfrac{2}{c^2-5c+6}$

45. $\dfrac{3x}{x^2+3x+2} - \dfrac{3x-6}{x^2+4x+4}$

C 46. $\dfrac{x^2+1}{x^2-1} + \dfrac{1}{x+1} + \dfrac{1}{x-1}$

47. $\dfrac{x}{2x-1} + \dfrac{x-1}{2x+1} - \dfrac{2x}{4x^2-1}$

48. $\dfrac{a+2}{a^2+5a+6} - \dfrac{2+a}{4-a^2} + \dfrac{2-a}{a^2+a-6}$

49. $\dfrac{x-3}{2x+6} - \dfrac{x+3}{3x-9} - \dfrac{5x^2+27}{6x^2-54}$

50. $\dfrac{b+1}{(b-1)^2} + \dfrac{2-2b}{(b-1)^3} + \dfrac{1}{b-1}$

51. $\dfrac{1}{(a-b)(a-c)} + \dfrac{1}{(b-c)(b-a)} + \dfrac{1}{(c-a)(c-b)}$

Self-Test 2

VOCABULARY   multiple (p. 212)   least common denominator
                least common multiple (p. 212)   (p. 212)

Express each group of fractions with their LCD.

1. $\dfrac{5}{16kz^2}, \dfrac{3k}{4}$

2. $\dfrac{1}{3(x-1)}, \dfrac{2}{x^2-1}$ Obj. 6-4, p. 212

Simplify.

3. $\dfrac{8}{3c} - \dfrac{5}{3c} + \dfrac{2}{3c}$

4. $\dfrac{n^2-9}{3} + \dfrac{4}{3}$ Obj. 6-5, p. 216

5. $\dfrac{3}{k^2-4} + \dfrac{1}{k+2}$

6. $\dfrac{7}{2a} - \dfrac{a-2}{4ab}$

Check your answers with those at the back of the book.

Just for Fun

1. a. Find each sum.

$$\frac{1}{1\cdot 2} + \frac{1}{2\cdot 3} = \underline{}$$

$$\frac{1}{1\cdot 2} + \frac{1}{2\cdot 3} + \frac{1}{3\cdot 4} = \underline{}$$

$$\frac{1}{1\cdot 2} + \frac{1}{2\cdot 3} + \frac{1}{3\cdot 4} + \frac{1}{4\cdot 5} = \underline{}$$

b. If this addition pattern were continued for 100 fractions, what would the sum be?

c. If this addition pattern were continued for *n* fractions, what would the sum be?

2. a. Find each sum.

$$\frac{1}{1\cdot 3} + \frac{1}{3\cdot 5} = \underline{}$$

$$\frac{1}{1\cdot 3} + \frac{1}{3\cdot 5} + \frac{1}{5\cdot 7} = \underline{}$$

$$\frac{1}{1\cdot 3} + \frac{1}{3\cdot 5} + \frac{1}{5\cdot 7} + \frac{1}{7\cdot 9} = \underline{}$$

b. If this addition pattern were continued for 50 fractions, what would the sum be?

c. If this addition pattern were continued for *n* fractions, what would the sum be?

POLYNOMIAL DIVISION

6-6 *Mixed Expressions*

OBJECTIVE   To write mixed expressions as fractions in simplest form.

A mixed number like $3\frac{1}{4}$ denotes the sum of an integer and a fraction. Recall that it may be expressed as a fraction as follows:

$$3\frac{1}{4} = \frac{3}{1} + \frac{1}{4} = \frac{12}{4} + \frac{1}{4} = \frac{13}{4}$$

A sum or difference of a polynomial and a fraction is called a **mixed expression.** The following example shows that a mixed expression may be expressed as a fraction in simplest form.

EXAMPLE   Express as a fraction in simplest form.

  a. $k + \dfrac{2}{k}$ **b.** $5 - \dfrac{2x-3}{x+1}$

SOLUTION   **a.** $k + \dfrac{2}{k} = \dfrac{k}{1} + \dfrac{2}{k} = \dfrac{k^2}{k} + \dfrac{2}{k} = \dfrac{k^2+2}{k}$

  b. $5 - \dfrac{2x-3}{x+1} = \dfrac{5}{1} - \dfrac{2x-3}{x+1}$

  $= \dfrac{5(x+1)}{(x+1)} - \dfrac{2x-3}{x+1}$

  $= \dfrac{5x+5-2x+3}{x+1}$

  $= \dfrac{3x+8}{x+1}$

Oral Exercises

State each as a fraction in simplest form.

SAMPLE $-5\frac{2}{3} = -\left(5 + \frac{2}{3}\right) = -\left(\frac{5}{1} + \frac{2}{3}\right) = -\left(\frac{15}{3} + \frac{2}{3}\right) = -\frac{17}{3}$

1. $3\dfrac{1}{5}$ **2.** $4\dfrac{2}{3}$ **3.** $-5\dfrac{3}{8}$ **4.** $-2\dfrac{7}{8}$

5. $1 + \dfrac{1}{a}$ **6.** $3 + \dfrac{2}{c}$ **7.** $x + \dfrac{5}{x}$ **8.** $y - \dfrac{3}{y}$

9. $2 + \dfrac{3}{x+1}$ **10.** $4 - \dfrac{1}{y+3}$ **11.** $\dfrac{2n}{2n+1} - 1$ **12.** $\dfrac{5a}{a-3} + 2$

Written Exercises

Write each expression as a fraction in simplest form.

A **1.** $3\frac{1}{7}$

2. $-4\frac{7}{9}$

3. $5 + \frac{2}{x}$

4. $7 - \frac{1}{n}$

5. $4 + \frac{a}{b}$

6. $\frac{x}{y} - 1$

7. $\frac{3}{2n} + n$

8. $\frac{6}{x+1} - 3$

9. $x - \frac{x-y}{3} + 2y$

10. $\frac{4x-5}{2} - 2 + \frac{3x}{5}$

11. $8 - \frac{x}{2x-3}$

12. $2 + \frac{2a-3b}{a+b}$

13. $\frac{4x}{(x-2)^2} + 1$

14. $\frac{3x}{x^2-9} - 2$

B **15.** $\frac{4}{a} + \frac{1}{b} - 2$

16. $\frac{b}{a+b} + \frac{a}{b-a} + 1$

17. $\frac{x}{x+3} + \frac{x}{x-3} - 2$

18. $4 - \frac{3}{n-1} - \frac{1}{n+1}$

19. $\left(x + \frac{2}{x}\right)\left(x - \frac{3}{x}\right)$

20. $\left(4 - \frac{x}{3}\right)\left(3 - \frac{x}{4}\right)$

21. $\left(\frac{x+y}{x} - 1\right)\left(\frac{x}{y} + 1\right)$

22. $\left(x - \frac{y^2}{x}\right) \div \left(1 + \frac{y}{x}\right)$

23. $\left(x - \frac{2}{x+1}\right)\left(1 - \frac{1}{x+2}\right)$

24. $\left(4 - \frac{1}{b^2}\right) \div (2b+1)$

C **25.** $\left(1 - \frac{b^2+c^2-a^2}{2bc}\right) \div \left(1 - \frac{a^2+b^2-c^2}{2ab}\right)$

26. $\left(2 - \frac{n}{n+1} + \frac{n}{1-n}\right) \div \left(\frac{1}{n-1} - \frac{1}{n+1}\right)$

27. Find constants A and B such that $\frac{4}{x^2-4} = \frac{A}{x+2} + \frac{B}{x-2}$.

28. Find constants C and D such that $\frac{6x}{x^2-x-2} = \frac{C}{x-2} + \frac{D}{x+1}$.

Just for Fun

Diophantus was a famous Greek mathematician, who lived and worked in Alexandria, Egypt, probably in the third century A.D. After he died, someone described his life in this puzzle:

> He was a boy for $\frac{1}{6}$ of his life.
> After $\frac{1}{12}$ more, he acquired a beard.
> After another $\frac{1}{7}$, he married.
> In the fifth year after his marriage
>   his son was born.
> The son lived half as many years as
>   his father.
> Diophantus died 4 years after his son.

How old was Diophantus when he died? Write an equation and solve it.

6-7 Polynomial Long Division

OBJECTIVE To divide polynomials.

Division of one polynomial by another is very much like ordinary long division. Compare the polynomial division and the long division shown below.

$$
\text{Step 1} \quad 31 \overline{)\,658} \atop \begin{array}{r} 2 \\ \hline 62 \\ \hline 38 \end{array}
$$

Step 1 $3x + 1 \overline{)\,6x^2 + 5x + 8}$ quotient $2x$
$$
\begin{array}{r}
2x \\
3x+1\,\overline{)\,6x^2 + 5x + 8} \\
\underline{6x^2 + 2x} \\
3x + 8
\end{array}
$$

Step 2
$$
\begin{array}{r}
21 \\
31\,\overline{)\,658} \\
\underline{62} \\
38 \\
\underline{31} \\
7
\end{array}
$$

Step 2
$$
\begin{array}{r}
2x + 1 \\
3x+1\,\overline{)\,6x^2 + 5x + 8} \\
\underline{6x^2 + 2x} \\
3x + 8 \\
\underline{3x + 1} \\
7
\end{array}
$$

Check: $658 \overset{?}{=} 21 \cdot 31 + 7$
$658 \overset{?}{=} 651 + 7$
$658 = 658$ ✓

Check: $6x^2 + 5x + 8 \overset{?}{=} (2x + 1)(3x + 1) + 7$
$6x^2 + 5x + 8 \overset{?}{=} (6x^2 + 5x + 1) + 7$
$6x^2 + 5x + 8 = 6x^2 + 5x + 8$ ✓

$$\therefore \; \frac{658}{31} = 21\frac{7}{31}$$

$$\therefore \; \frac{6x^2 + 5x + 8}{3x + 1} = (2x + 1) + \frac{7}{3x + 1}$$

In both divisions above, the answer was expressed in the following form:

$$
\frac{\text{Dividend}}{\text{Divisor}} = \text{Quotient} + \frac{\text{Remainder}}{\text{Divisor}}
$$

The following identity was used to check both divisions:

$$
\text{Dividend} = \text{Quotient} \times \text{Divisor} + \text{Remainder}
$$

When you divide polynomials, always make sure that the terms in each polynomial are arranged in order of decreasing degree in the variable.

EXAMPLE 1 Divide $6x^2 + 20 - 23x$ by $2x - 5$.

SOLUTION First rewrite $6x^2 + 20 - 23x$ as $6x^2 - 23x + 20$.

$$3x - 4$$
$$2x - 5 \overline{)6x^2 - 23x + 20}$$
$$\underline{6x^2 - 15x}$$
$$-8x + 20$$
$$\underline{-8x + 20}$$
$$0$$

Check: $(3x - 4)(2x - 5) = 6x^2 - 23x + 20$

$$\therefore \frac{6x^2 - 23x + 20}{2x - 5} = 3x - 4 \quad \textbf{\textit{Answer}}$$

Notice that in Example 1, the remainder is 0. Thus, both $(2x - 5)$ and $(3x - 4)$ are factors of $6x^2 - 23x + 20$.

EXAMPLE 2 Divide $\dfrac{2a^3 - 10}{a - 2}$. Write the answer as a mixed expression.

SOLUTION Rewrite $2a^3 - 10$ in order of decreasing degree in a, inserting 0 coefficients as shown below.

$$2a^2 + 4a + 8$$
$$a - 2 \overline{)2a^3 + 0a^2 + 0a - 10}$$
$$\underline{2a^3 - 4a^2}$$
$$4a^2 + 0a$$
$$\underline{4a^2 - 8a}$$
$$8a - 10$$
$$\underline{8a - 16}$$
$$6$$

Check: It is left to you to verify that
$(2a^2 + 4a + 8)(a - 2) + 6$ equals $2a^3 - 10$.

$$\therefore \frac{2a^3 - 10}{a - 2} = 2a^2 + 4a + 8 + \frac{6}{a - 2} \quad \textbf{\textit{Answer}}$$

The division process ends when the remainder is either 0 or of lesser degree than the divisor.

Written Exercises

Divide. Write your answer as a polynomial or mixed expression. Check.

A

1. $\dfrac{x^2 + 7x + 12}{x + 3}$

2. $\dfrac{k^2 - 4k - 32}{k + 4}$

3. $\dfrac{x^2 - 5x - 36}{x - 9}$

4. $\dfrac{y^2 - 3y - 54}{y - 9}$

5. $\dfrac{a^2 + 4a + 8}{a + 3}$

6. $\dfrac{y^2 + 5y + 9}{y + 2}$

7. $\dfrac{z^2 - 6z + 1}{z - 4}$

8. $\dfrac{x^2 - 1 - 4x}{x + 2}$

Divide. Write your answer as a polynomial or mixed expression. Check.

9. $\dfrac{x^2 - 7 + 9x}{x - 3}$

10. $\dfrac{s - s^2 + 4}{s + 1}$

11. $\dfrac{x^2 + 4}{x + 1}$

12. $\dfrac{y^2 - 3}{y - 2}$

13. $\dfrac{2x^2 - 5x + 3}{2x - 1}$

14. $\dfrac{2v^2 + v - 4}{2v + 1}$

15. $\dfrac{5y^2 - 6y + 7}{5y - 1}$

16. $\dfrac{3y^2 + 8y + 5}{3y + 2}$

17. $\dfrac{6n^2 + 4n + 3}{3n - 1}$

18. $\dfrac{4x^2 + 1}{2x + 1}$

19. $\dfrac{6x^2 + xy - 2y^2}{2x + y}$

20. $\dfrac{6a^2 - ab + b^2}{2a + b}$

B 21. $\dfrac{x^3 + 1}{x + 1}$

22. $\dfrac{a^3 - 1}{a - 1}$

23. $\dfrac{x^3 - 4x^2 + x + 6}{x - 2}$

24. $\dfrac{6a^3 + 5a^2 - 13a + 10}{3a - 5}$

25. $\dfrac{x^3 - 2x^2 - 75}{x - 5}$

26. $\dfrac{2a^4 + 1 - 2a - a^3}{2a - 1}$

27. $\dfrac{a^3 + 7a^2b + 3ab^2 - 14b^3}{a + 2b}$

28. $\dfrac{3x^3 + 5x^2y - xy^2}{3x + 2y}$

29. $\dfrac{3a^3 - 4a^2 + 2a + 4}{a^2 - 2a + 2}$

30. $\dfrac{n^4 + 3n^3 + 3n^2 - 3n - 4}{n^2 - 1}$

31. Factor $3n^3 - 7n^2 + 4$ completely given that $3n + 2$ is one of its factors.

32. Factor $x^3 + 4x^2 + x - 6$ given that $x - 1$ is one of its factors.

33. Factor $4x^3 - 12x^2 - 37x - 15$ given that $2x + 1$ is a factor.

34. Factor $2x^3 - 7x^2 + 4x + 4$ given that $(x - 2)^2$ is a factor.

C 35. Show that $\dfrac{a^4 - 2a^3 + 6a - 4}{a^2 - a - 2} = a^2 - a + 1 + \dfrac{5a - 2}{a^2 - a - 2}$.

36. Divide $n^4 - n^2 - n + 7$ by $n^2 - 4$. Check by multiplying.

37. Find the value of k for which $2x + 3$ is a factor of $6x^2 + 5x + k$.

38. Find the value of k for which $x + 3$ is a factor of $2x^3 + 11x^2 + 13x + k$.

39. Find the value of k for which $y - 2$ is a factor of $y^3 - 4y^2 + ky + 6$.

40. When $6x^4 - 5x^3 - 37x^2 + 46x + n$ is divided by $2x - 5$, the remainder is 5. Find the value of n.

Just for Fun

Two bees leave two locations 180 m apart and fly, without stopping, back and forth between these two places at the rates of 4 m/s and 5 m/s, respectively. When do they meet for the first time? for the second time?

Self-Test 3

VOCABULARY   mixed expression (p. 220)   dividend (p. 222)
quotient (p. 222)   divisor (p. 222)
remainder (p. 222)

Write each expression as a fraction in simplest form.

1. $\dfrac{7}{x+2} - 4$

2. $3 + \dfrac{a-4b}{a+b}$

Obj. 6-6, p. 220

Divide. Write your answer as a polynomial or a mixed expression.

3. $\dfrac{6x^2 - x - 15}{2x + 3}$

4. $\dfrac{8x^2 + 18x - 2}{4x - 1}$

Obj. 6-7, p. 222

Check your answers with those at the back of the book.

EXTRA

Complex Fractions

A complex fraction is a fraction whose numerator or denominator contains one or more fractions. A complex fraction can be expressed as a simple fraction by either of two methods.

>   *Method 1:* Simplify the numerator and denominator. Express the fraction as a quotient using the $\div$ sign, and then divide.

>   *Method 2:* Multiply the numerator and denominator of the complex fraction by the LCD of all the simple fractions within them.

EXAMPLE   Simplify $\dfrac{\dfrac{a}{b} - \dfrac{b}{a}}{\dfrac{1}{2a} - \dfrac{1}{2b}}$.

SOLUTION   Method 1:

$$\frac{\dfrac{a}{b} - \dfrac{b}{a}}{\dfrac{1}{2a} - \dfrac{1}{2b}} = \frac{\dfrac{a^2 - b^2}{ab}}{\dfrac{b - a}{2ab}}$$

$$= \frac{a^2 - b^2}{ab} \div \frac{b - a}{2ab}$$

$$= \frac{(a + b)\overset{-1}{\cancel{(a - b)}}}{\cancel{ab}} \cdot \frac{\cancel{2ab}}{\cancel{b - a}}$$

$$= -2(a + b)$$

Method 2:

The LCD of all the simple fractions is $2ab$.

$$\frac{\dfrac{a}{b} - \dfrac{b}{a}}{\dfrac{1}{2a} - \dfrac{1}{2b}} = \frac{\left(\dfrac{a}{b} - \dfrac{b}{a}\right)2ab}{\left(\dfrac{1}{2a} - \dfrac{1}{2b}\right)2ab}$$

$$= \frac{2a^2 - 2b^2}{b - a}$$

$$= \frac{2(a + b)\overset{}{\cancel{(a - b)}}}{\underset{-1}{\cancel{(b - a)}}}$$

$$= -2(a + b)$$

FRACTIONS   **225**

Exercises

In the following exercises you can use either Method 1 or Method 2 to simplify the fractions. Most people find Method 2 preferable, especially when simplifying more involved complex fractions.

Simplify.

A 1. $\dfrac{\frac{a}{7}}{\frac{3a}{7}}$

2. $\dfrac{\frac{3n}{2}}{\frac{9n}{4}}$

3. $\dfrac{\frac{a}{b}}{\frac{1}{b^2}}$

4. $\dfrac{\frac{3k}{1}}{\frac{1}{6k}}$

5. $\dfrac{\frac{1}{3} - \frac{1}{6}}{\frac{1}{3} + \frac{1}{6}}$

6. $\dfrac{\frac{1}{2} + \frac{1}{8}}{\frac{1}{4} + \frac{1}{3}}$

7. $\dfrac{\frac{3}{4} + \frac{3}{5}}{\frac{3}{4} - \frac{3}{5}}$

8. $\dfrac{\frac{1}{n} - \frac{1}{2n}}{\frac{2}{n}}$

9. $\dfrac{\frac{x}{y^2}}{\frac{x}{y}}$

10. $\dfrac{1 - \frac{4}{x^2}}{x + 2}$

11. $\dfrac{1 + \frac{1}{a}}{1 - \frac{1}{a^2}}$

12. $\dfrac{\frac{3x}{2} + 1}{\frac{3x}{4} - \frac{1}{3x}}$

B 13. $\dfrac{a + \frac{3a}{a - 3}}{a - \frac{3a}{a + 3}}$

14. $\dfrac{1 + \frac{2k}{k^2 + 1}}{1 - \frac{2k + 2}{k^2 + 1}}$

15. $\dfrac{x - \frac{1}{2x + 1}}{1 - \frac{2}{2x + 1}}$

16. $\dfrac{\frac{1}{2b - 2} - \frac{1}{b}}{\frac{2}{b} - \frac{1}{b - 1}}$

17. $\dfrac{\frac{a}{a + b} + \frac{b}{a - b}}{\frac{a}{a - b} - \frac{b}{a + b}}$

18. $\dfrac{1 - \frac{1}{2n}}{1 + 2n} \div \dfrac{1 + \frac{1}{2n}}{1 - 2n}$

19. $\dfrac{2 + \frac{y - 2}{1 - y^2}}{2 - \frac{2}{y + 1}}$

20. $\dfrac{\frac{p}{q} - \frac{p - q}{p + q}}{\frac{q}{p} + \frac{p - q}{p + q}}$

21. If $x = \dfrac{y - 1}{y + 1}$ and $y = \dfrac{1}{1 - t}$, express x in terms of t as simply as possible.

22. If $a = \dfrac{b - c}{1 + bc}$ and $b = \dfrac{1}{t - 1}$ and $c = \dfrac{1}{t + 1}$, find a in terms of t.

23. A car goes d km at 40 km/h and returns the same distance at 60 km/h. Show that the average speed is 48 km/h. (*Hint:* Average speed = total distance divided by total time.)

24. A cyclist travels 10 km on a level road at x km/h and then goes 5 km on a downhill road at 2x km/h. Find her average speed in terms of x. (See Hint for Exercise 23.)

25. If n articles can be purchased for 4 dollars, how many of these articles can be purchased for $4 after the price per article is increased by a half dollar?

26. If $a = \dfrac{1-t}{1+t}$ and $t = \dfrac{1+b}{1-b}$, show that $a + b = 0$.

Simplify.

27. $\left(\dfrac{2}{x} - \dfrac{x}{2}\right) \div \left(\dfrac{x}{2} - 4 + \dfrac{6}{x}\right)$

28. $\left(\dfrac{x}{4 - x^2} + \dfrac{1}{x - 2}\right) \div \left(1 - \dfrac{2}{2 + x}\right)$

29. $\left(\dfrac{1}{a^2 + a} - \dfrac{1}{a - a^2}\right) \div \left(\dfrac{1}{a^2 - 1} - \dfrac{1}{1 + a^2}\right)$

30. $\left(\dfrac{1}{3} - \dfrac{2x^2}{3 - 3x}\right) \div \left(1 - \dfrac{x - 4x^2}{x - 1}\right)$

C 31. $\dfrac{a}{2}\left(\dfrac{1}{a - b} - \dfrac{1}{a + b}\right) \cdot \left(\dfrac{a^2 - b^2}{a^2b + ab^2}\right) \div \dfrac{1}{a + b}$

32. $\dfrac{1}{1 - \dfrac{1}{1 - \dfrac{1}{1 - \dfrac{1}{x}}}}$

Calculator Key-In

You can use a calculator to evaluate algebraic fractions for given values of their variables. First evaluate the denominator and store its value in the calculator's memory. (You may want to review the method for evaluating a polynomial given on page 157.) Then evaluate the numerator and divide by the value of the denominator.

Evaluate each fraction for the given value of the variable.

1. $\dfrac{5}{x + 3}$; $x = 6$

2. $\dfrac{2y + 5}{4}$; $y = 7$

3. $\dfrac{5n - 11}{2n}$; $n = 4$

4. $\dfrac{7a + 15}{3a}$; $a = 2$

5. $\dfrac{7x^2 + 2x + 4}{x}$; $x = 3$

6. $\dfrac{2z^2 + 11z - 30}{2z + 4}$; $z = -3$

7. $\dfrac{a^2 + 5a - 2}{4a}$; $a = 0.5$

8. $\dfrac{5y^2 - 11y + 15}{6y - 5}$; $y = -2$

Chapter Summary

1. A fraction can be simplified by factoring its numerator and its denominator and dividing each by their common factors.

2. The following rules are used for combining fractions.

MULTIPLICATION RULE

$$\frac{c}{d} \cdot \frac{x}{y} = \frac{cx}{dy}$$

DIVISION RULE

$$\frac{a}{b} \div \frac{c}{d} = \frac{a}{b} \cdot \frac{d}{c}$$

ADDITION RULE

$$\frac{a}{c} + \frac{b}{c} = \frac{a+b}{c}$$

SUBTRACTION RULE

$$\frac{a}{c} - \frac{b}{c} = \frac{a-b}{c}$$

3. When adding or subtracting fractions with different denominators, rewrite the fractions using their *least common denominator* (*LCD*). Then apply the appropriate rule. (See the method and the examples on page 213.)

4. A sum or difference of a polynomial and a fraction is called a *mixed expression*. A mixed expression can be expressed as a fraction in simplest form.

5. When dividing polynomials, arrange the terms of the *divisor* and *dividend* in order of decreasing degree in a variable. Insert zero coefficients where the dividend is missing a power.

Chapter Review

Give the letter of the correct answer.

1. Express $\dfrac{3a + 6b}{3a + 3b}$ in simplest form.

6-1

a. 3   **b.** $\dfrac{3}{2}$ **c.** $1 + 2b$ **d.** $\dfrac{a + 2b}{a + b}$

2. Express $\dfrac{5x - x^2}{x^2 - 25}$ in simplest form.

a. $\dfrac{x}{x - 5}$ **b.** $\dfrac{x}{5 - x}$ **c.** $\dfrac{-x}{x + 5}$ **d.** $\dfrac{x}{x + 5}$

3. Express $\dfrac{2n^2 - 8}{n^2 + 4n - 12}$ in simplest form.

a. $\dfrac{2(n + 2)}{n + 6}$ **b.** $\dfrac{2(n - 2)}{n - 6}$ **c.** $2\left(n + \dfrac{1}{3}\right)$ **d.** $2\left(n - \dfrac{1}{3}\right)$

4. Multiply: $\dfrac{3a^2 b}{8ab^3} \cdot \dfrac{40a^3 b}{6b}$

6-2

a. $\dfrac{5a^4}{2b^2}$ **b.** $\dfrac{120a^4}{48b^2}$ **c.** $\dfrac{120a^5 b^2}{48ab^4}$ **d.** $\dfrac{20a^4 b^2}{8}$

5. Express $\left(\dfrac{4x}{y^2}\right)^3$ in simplest form.

a. $\dfrac{12x^3}{y^6}$ **b.** $\dfrac{64x^3}{y^6}$ **c.** $\dfrac{12x^3}{y^5}$ **d.** $\dfrac{64x^3}{y^5}$

6. Multiply: $\dfrac{x^2 - y^2}{(x + y)^2} \cdot \dfrac{x^2 + y^2}{x - y}$

a. $x + y$ **b.** $\dfrac{x^2 + y^2}{x - y}$ **c.** $\dfrac{x^2 + y^2}{x + y}$ **d.** $\dfrac{x + y}{x - y}$

7. Divide: $\dfrac{2n^2}{5} \div \dfrac{(4n)^2}{20}$

6-3

a. $2n$ **b.** 2 **c.** $\dfrac{1}{2n}$ **d.** $\dfrac{1}{2}$

8. Divide: $\dfrac{a^2 - 4b^2}{a^2 - ab - 2b^2} \div \dfrac{a + 2b}{2a + 2b}$

a. 2 **b.** $\dfrac{2}{a + 2b}$ **c.** $\dfrac{a + 2b}{2}$ **d.** $\dfrac{a + 2b}{a - 2b}$

9. Simplify $\dfrac{2x}{3y} \div 4xy$.

a. $\dfrac{8x}{3}$ **b.** $\dfrac{3}{8x^2}$ **c.** $\dfrac{1}{6y^2}$ **d.** $\dfrac{2}{3y^2}$

10. What is the LCD of $\dfrac{3}{10x}$, $\dfrac{5}{12x^2}$, and $\dfrac{1}{4y}$?

6-4

a. $120x^3y$ **b.** $120x^2y$ **c.** $60x^3y$ **d.** $60x^2y$

11. What is the LCD of $\dfrac{2}{a^2 - 4}$ and $\dfrac{3a}{2(a - 2)}$?

a. $2(a - 2)^2(a + 2)$ **b.** $2(a - 2)(a + 2)$

c. $2(a - 2)(a + 2)^2$ **d.** $6a(a - 2)(a + 2)$

12. Simplify $\dfrac{2n + 3}{4} - \dfrac{n - 1}{6}$.

6-5

a. $\dfrac{4n + 11}{12}$ **b.** $\dfrac{4n + 7}{12}$ **c.** $\dfrac{8n + 22}{24}$ **d.** $\dfrac{8n + 14}{24}$

13. Simplify $\dfrac{x}{x - 3} + \dfrac{3}{3 - x}$.

a. $\dfrac{x - 3}{x^2 - 9}$ **b.** $\dfrac{x - 3}{3 - x}$ **c.** 1 **d.** -1

14. Simplify $\dfrac{x}{x - 1} - \dfrac{2x}{x^2 - 1}$.

a. $\dfrac{x}{x + 1}$ **b.** $\dfrac{x^2 - x}{x^2 - 1}$ **c.** $\dfrac{x}{x - 1}$ **d.** $1 - x$

15. Write $2 + \dfrac{7n}{n^2 - 9}$ as a fraction in simplest form. 6-6

a. $\dfrac{2n^2 + 7n - 18}{n^2 - 9}$ **b.** $\dfrac{4 + 7n}{1}$ **c.** $\dfrac{2n + 1}{n + 3}$ **d.** $\dfrac{2n + 1}{n - 3}$

16. Simplify $z + 3 + \dfrac{1}{z - 3}$.

a. $\dfrac{z^2 - 8}{z - 3}$ **b.** $\dfrac{z + 4}{z - 3}$ **c.** $\dfrac{z^2 - 8}{z^2 - 9}$ **d.** $\dfrac{z^2 - 10}{z - 3}$

17. When $x^3 - 3x^2 + 3x + 4$ is divided by $x - 2$, what is the remainder? 6-7

a. 2   **b.** 4   **c.** 6   **d.** 8

18. When $n^3 - 8$ is divided by $n - 2$, what is the quotient?

a. $n^2 + 2n + 4$ **b.** $n^2 - 2n + 4$ **c.** $n^2 + 4$ **d.** $n^2 - 4$

Chapter Test

Simplify.

1. $\dfrac{5n + 25}{n^2 - 25}$ **2.** $\dfrac{(x - 2)^2}{2 - x}$ 6-1

3. $\left(\dfrac{-3}{5}\right)^2 \cdot \dfrac{50}{27}$ **4.** $\left(\dfrac{2x^3}{5y}\right)^2$ 6-2

5. $\dfrac{3}{a^2 - 2a - 15} \cdot \dfrac{a^2 - 9}{6a - 18}$ **6.** $\dfrac{a^2 - b^2}{a^2 + b^2} \cdot \dfrac{a + b}{a - b}$

7. $\dfrac{2a}{3} \div \dfrac{9a^4}{4}$ **8.** $\dfrac{2y^3}{9} \div \dfrac{4y}{3}$ 6-3

9. $\dfrac{1}{10x - 2x^2} \div \dfrac{x}{4x - 20}$ **10.** $\left(\dfrac{y + 2}{y + 1}\right) \div (2y + 4) \cdot (y^2 - 2y - 3)$

What is the LCD for each group of fractions?

11. $\dfrac{3}{4a^2}, \dfrac{5}{2ab}, \dfrac{1}{3b}$ **12.** $\dfrac{5}{x^2 - 1}, \dfrac{2x}{x^2 + 2x + 1}$ 6-4

Simplify.

13. $\dfrac{2x - 1}{3} - \dfrac{4x - 5}{4}$ **14.** $\dfrac{2y}{2y - 3} - \dfrac{3}{2y + 3}$ 6-5

15. $\dfrac{2}{y^2 - 2y} - \dfrac{3}{y^2 - y - 2}$ **16.** $\dfrac{4a}{a - 2b} + \dfrac{8b}{2b - a}$

17. $\dfrac{3}{4 - x} - 2$ **18.** $\dfrac{x}{x + 2} + \dfrac{2}{x - 2} + 1$ 6-6

19. Divide $4x^3 - 2x^2 + 2$ by $2x + 1$. 6-7

20. Use long division to decide whether or not $x - 2$ is a factor of $x^3 + 6x^2 - x - 30$.

Just for Fun

Copy the puzzle and complete it.

ACROSS
1. 7×3^2
2. $2^2 \times 3^2$
4. $3^3 - 2 \times 3$
5. $2^9 + 2^4$
7. $5^2 - 3^2$
8. $(2^3 \times 3)^2 \times 7$
11. $(6 \div 2 \times 3)^2$
13. $5 \times 2 \times 3^2$
14. $12^2 - 10^2 - 2$

DOWN
1. $5^2 \times 5^2$
3. 34×19
4. $3^3 \times 2^3 \times 13$
6. $102 \div 17 \times 2^2$
7. $2^4 \times 3^2 \div 12$
9. $186 \div 12 \times 2$
10. $99^2 - 99 \times 98$
12. $82^2 \div 82$

1				2	3
		4			
5	6			7	
	8		9		
10		11			12
13			14		

Career Note Accountant

A company is considering building a new factory. Before making a decision, the management will discuss the financial position of the company with the chief accountant.

Accountants are responsible for recording and analyzing all financial information of a company. They prepare balance sheets, which indicate the financial position of the company, and income statements, which show profit and loss over a given period. They also prepare inventory analyses and statements for tax purposes.

Every business and government agency needs the services provided by an accountant. Accountants work for banks, department stores, sports arenas, supermarkets, large corporations, and small companies. Accountants may specialize in administrative accounting, cost accounting, managerial accounting, auditing, or budgeting.

To become a certified public accountant, or CPA, it is necessary to pass a standardized examination. Each state has its own requirements for eligibility to take this test. Most states require a bachelor's degree in accounting or a closely related field and three years of experience working for a CPA.

Cumulative Review (Chapters 1-6)

Simplify each expression.

1. $2b - b^2 - 4 + b^2 + 1$
2. $(8c - d) - (9c - 3d)$
3. $(-7j^2k^3)(-3j^3k)$
4. $-3n(3 - 2n - 5n^3)$
5. $(8z + 9)(3z^2 - 2z)$
6. $(3a - 7)(2a + 1)$
7. $-(9rs^2)^2 \div (-3r^2s)^3$
8. $(3d^2 - 2)(3d^2 + 2)$
9. $(7x - 8y)^2$

Evaluate if $q = -7$, $r = -4$, $s = -0.75$, $t = 2$, and $u = 3$.

10. $2rs - qt^2$
11. $(2q + rt + 1) \div q$
12. $2r^2 \div 4 + 3rt$

Factor completely. If the polynomial is not factorable, write "prime."

13. $100a^2 - 4b^4$
14. $16 - 48g + 9g^2$
15. $x^2 - 21xy + 54y^2$
16. $yz + z - 2y - 2y^2$
17. $6k^3 + 7k^2m + 2km^2$
18. $c^2 + 5c - 126$

Solve.

19. $n - 19 = |-2 - 5|$
20. $-15 = -\frac{3}{7}b$
21. $20 - 4x = -8x + 40$
22. $2(k + 8) - 1 = 3$
23. $-7y + 2 = y - 14$
24. $24f = -16$
25. $5(z + 1) - 3z = -9$
26. $(a + 4)(a + 3) = -a$
27. $5m^2 + 38m = 16$

Express in simplest form.

28. $\dfrac{2k^2 - 9k + 7}{3 - 2k - k^2}$
29. $\dfrac{2y^2 + 8y}{y^3 - 16y} \cdot \dfrac{4 - y}{4y^3}$
30. $\dfrac{3z - 2}{4} - \dfrac{6 - z}{4}$
31. $\dfrac{5r^2 + 10r}{r^2 + 4r + 4} \div \dfrac{25}{r + 2}$
32. $\dfrac{5}{3x} + \dfrac{1}{x^2}$
33. $\dfrac{4x}{x + 4} - \dfrac{3}{x + 3}$
34. $\dfrac{2n}{2n + t} + \dfrac{t}{2n - t} - 1$
35. $\dfrac{m^3 - 3m^2 + 20}{m + 2}$
36. $\dfrac{8b^2 + 14b + 6}{4b + 3}$

Solve.

37. Find three consecutive odd integers such that the difference between five times the least and twice the greatest is 61.

38. Su-Chen is 20 years younger than her mother. In 9 years she will be $\frac{3}{5}$ as old as her mother. How old is each now?

39. The length and width of a rectangle are consecutive integers. The area of the rectangle is 132 cm^2. Find the dimensions of the rectangle.

40. While training for a bicycle race, Charles rode up a mountain road at 12 km/h and then back down at 30 km/h. If the round trip took $3\frac{1}{2}$ h, how long did the uphill trip take and how many kilometers was it?

41. A power boat traveled upstream at 24 km/h and downstream at 30 km/h. How far upstream did it go if the round trip took 3 h?

Maintaining Skills

Review the five-step problem solving method described in Section 1-6.

SAMPLE   The length of a rectangle is 55 cm greater than three times the width. If the perimeter is 8.7 m, find the length and the width.

SOLUTION

Step 1   Read the problem carefully. It asks for the length and the width of the rectangle.

Step 2   Choose a variable. If it is helpful, draw a diagram or make a chart of given facts.

Let w = width in centimeters.
Then $3w + 55$ = length in centimeters.

$3w + 55$

Step 3   Write an equation, using the same unit, centimeters:
$$2(3w + 55) + 2w = 870 \leftarrow 8.7 \text{ m} = 870 \text{ cm}$$

Step 4   Solve the equation. $8w + 110 = 870$
$$8w = 760$$
$$w = 95; \quad 3(95) + 55 = 340$$

Step 5   Check your results with the statement of the problem. Give the answer. The check is left to you.

∴ the length is 340 cm and the width is 95 cm.   ***Answer***

Use the five-step method to solve each problem. Making charts and diagrams may help you. Remember to write each expression in terms of the same unit. Reject inappropriate roots.

1. I have $3.65 in dimes and quarters. Thirty cents more than the value of half the dimes is equal to $1. How many of each coin do I have?

2. Trino walked for 75 min. If he had walked for 60 min at a rate 2 km/h faster, he would have gone 1 km farther. Find his average rate of walking.

3. The length of a rectangle is 20 mm greater than its width. The area of the rectangle is 168 cm². Find the length and width in centimeters.

4. Elise is paid twice as much per hour for overtime work as for her usual work. One week she worked 44 h and earned $156. If her usual work week is 40 h, what is her usual rate?

The Toronto metropolitan area is approximately the same size as the Boston and Bogotá, Colombia, metropolitan areas. See the facing page for a discussion of using ratios to compare populations.

7

APPLYING FRACTIONS

RATIO AND PROPORTION

7-1 *Ratios*

OBJECTIVE To solve problems involving ratios.

Recently, the population of the Toronto metropolitan area was 2,800,000, and the population of the Melbourne metropolitan area was 2,600,000. Although the populations of the cities differ by 200,000 people, they are approximately the same size. This relationship is indicated by the quotient, or ratio, of the populations:

$$\frac{2,800,000}{2,600,000} = \frac{14}{13}$$

The **ratio** of one number to another is the quotient of the first number divided by the second. You can express the ratio of 8 to 5 as:

1. an indicated quotient using the division sign ÷ $8 \div 5$

2. an indicated quotient using the ratio sign : $8:5$

3. a fraction $\frac{8}{5}$

4. a decimal numeral 1.6

If you wish to find the ratio of the height of a 4 m tree to the height of a 50 cm sapling, you express 4 m as 400 cm and divide to find the ratio $\frac{400}{50}$ or $8:1$.

> To find the ratio of two quantities of the same kind:
>
> 1. Express the measures in the same unit.
> 2. Then divide them.

The ratio $\frac{10}{4}$ can be expressed in simplest form as $\frac{5}{2}$. When solving certain problems involving ratios, you need to express a ratio in a different form. If you know that two numbers are in the ratio $5:2$, you can represent the numbers as $5x$ and $2x$ for some nonzero x. By the cancellation rule for fractions,

$$\frac{5x}{2x} = \frac{5}{2}.$$

EXAMPLE
Poseidon Fisheries is planning to stock the Olde Mill Pond with bass and trout in the ratio $7:8$. If the pond is to be stocked with 360 fish, how many of each kind will be stocked?

SOLUTION
Step 1 The problem asks for the number of bass and the number of trout to be stocked.

Step 2 Let $7x$ = the number of bass and $8x$ = the number of trout.

Step 3 $7x + 8x = 360$ (the total number of fish)

Step 4 $\qquad 15x = 360$
$\qquad\quad x = 24$
Number of bass $= 7x = 7 \cdot 24 = 168$
Number of trout $= 8x = 8 \cdot 24 = 192$

Step 5 The check is left to you.

$\qquad \therefore$ the pond will be stocked with 168 bass and 192 trout. **Answer**

Saying that three numbers are in the ratio $4:5:8$ means that the ratio of the first to the second is $4:5$ and the ratio of the second to the third is $5:8$.

Oral Exercises

State each ratio in simplest form.

1. $8:24$ **2.** $72:12$ **3.** $20:35$ **4.** $8:12$

5. $8a:4a$ **6.** $32k:40k$ **7.** $10a^3:25a$ **8.** $rst:stu$

9. $\dfrac{3x^2y}{9y^2}$ **10.** $\dfrac{(2a)^2}{4a^2}$ **11.** $\dfrac{(6ks)^2}{9k^2}$ **12.** $\dfrac{pqr}{r^2sq}$

Written Exercises

State each ratio in simplest form.

A **1.** 4 h to 20 min **2.** 8 wk to 16 d **3.** 10 cm to 1 m

4. 175 m to 14 m **5.** 1 kg to 50 g **6.** 80¢ to $4

7. The player-coach ratio in a league with 780 players and 30 coaches.

8. The ratio of new cars to old cars in a fleet of 1200 trolley cars that includes 640 new cars.

9. The ratio of wins to losses in 28 games with 7 losses and no ties.

10. The ratio of copper to total amount of metal in an alloy consisting of 8.4 kg of copper, 1 kg of tungsten, and 2.6 kg of tin.

11. The ratio of the number of guppies to liters of water in a 40 L tank with 24 guppies in it.

12. The ratio of the number of people to the number of apartments in a 84-unit apartment building housing 364 people.

Find the ratio of the areas of each pair of figures.

13. A rectangle with sides 6 cm and 18 cm and one with sides 4 cm and 24 cm.

14. A rectangle with sides 8 cm and 12 cm and one with sides 9 cm and 18 cm.

15. A rectangle with sides 3 m and 4 m and one with sides 75 cm and 80 cm.

16. A rectangle with sides 8 m and 12 m and a square with sides 10 m.

Find the ratio of x to y determined by each equation.

SAMPLE $5x = 8y$ *SOLUTION* $5x = 8y$

$$x = \frac{8}{5}y$$

$$\frac{x}{y} = \frac{8}{5}, \text{ or } x{:}y = 8{:}5 \quad \textbf{\textit{Answer}}$$

B **17.** $4x = 9y$ **18.** $3x = 6y$ **19.** $4y = 10x$

20. $3x - 7y = 0$ **21.** $9y - 12x = 0$ **22.** $-8y + 28x = 0$

23. $4(x + 4y) = 8(x + y)$ **24.** $4(x - 6) = 8(y - 3)$

C **25.** $x^2 + 2y^2 = 2xy + y^2$ **26.** $x^2 + 5y^2 = y^2 - 4xy$

(*Hint:* Collect terms on one side of the equation and factor the resulting polynomial.)

Problems

Solve.

A   **1.** Two numbers are in the ratio 5:3 and their sum is 64. Find the numbers.

    2. Two numbers are in the ratio 6:5 and their sum is 132. Find the numbers.

    3. At Garvey High School, the ratio of students taking driver education to students not taking driver education is 5:12. If there are 1530 students in the school, find the number of students taking driver education.

    4. Three numbers are in the ratio 2:3:4 and their sum is 270. Find the numbers. (*Hint:* Let the numbers be $2x$, $3x$, and $4x$.)

    5. A profit of $1800 is to be divided among three people in the ratio of 8:3:4. How much should each person receive?

    6. The length and width of a rectangle are in a 3:2 ratio and the perimeter of the rectangle is 85 cm. Find its dimensions.

    7. In a small city, five of every eight tax dollars are spent on public education. If $3,840,000 is collected in taxes, find the amount spent on public education.

    8. A flower wholesaler plants gladiola bulbs and expects 4 out of 5 bulbs to produce marketable flowers. Of 24,000 bulbs, how many are expected to produce marketable flowers?

    9. During a typing test Marvin typed 840 words in 21 min, and Barbara typed 750 words in 19 min. Who typed faster during the test?

B **10.** Concrete can be made by mixing cement, sand, and gravel in a 1:4:5 ratio. How many cubic meters of each ingredient are needed to make 220 m^3 of concrete?

   11. Neighboring rectangular lots of the same depth have frontages of 40 m, 50 m, and 70 m. What assessment should be assigned to each lot if the combined lots have an assessment of $19,200?

   12. In a group of nickels and dimes worth $6.80, the ratio of the number of nickels to the number of dimes is 3 to 7. Find the number of dimes.

   13. In a group of dimes and quarters worth $16.10, the ratio of the number of dimes to the number of quarters is 3:8. Find the number of quarters.

   14. A group of nickels, dimes, and quarters is worth $74. The ratio of the numbers of nickels, dimes, and quarters is 6:9:10, respectively. What number of each type of coin is there?

C **15.** I am thinking of three numbers whose sum is 142. The ratio of the first number to the second is $3:8$, and the ratio of the second number to the third is $5:2$. Find the numbers.

16. Find two numbers such that their product, their sum, and their difference have the ratio $5:3:2$.

Computer Key-In

If you have access to a computer that will accept BASIC, try this program for practice in adding, subtracting, and multiplying integers. Try to do the additions and subtractions mentally. This program will keep repeating the exercise until you get the right answer!

Note: Check the use of RND with your own system. INT(101*RND(1)) gives a random selection from the set $\{0, 1, 2, \ldots, 100\}$. INT(101*RND(1)−50) gives a random selection from the set $\{-50, -49, \ldots, 0, 1, 2, \ldots, 50\}$.

```
10   PRINT "HOW MANY EXERCISES WOULD YOU LIKE";
20   INPUT N
30   PRINT
40   FOR I=1 TO N
50   LET A=INT(3*RND(1)+1)
60   LET B=INT(101*RND(1)-50)
70   LET C=INT(101*RND(1)-50)
80   PRINT I;".   ";
90   GOTO A OF 100,150,200
100  PRINT "(";B;") + (";C;") =";
110  INPUT R
120  IF R=B+C THEN 250
130  PRINT "SORRY; TRY AGAIN!"
140  GOTO 100
150  PRINT "(";B;") - (";C;") =";
160  INPUT R
170  IF R=B-C THEN 250
180  PRINT "OOPS; TRY AGAIN!"
190  GOTO 150
200  PRINT "(";B;") × (";C;") = ";
210  INPUT R
220  IF R=B*C THEN 250
230  PRINT "TRY AGAIN--BE CAREFUL!"
240  GOTO 200
250  PRINT
260  NEXT I
270  END
```

7-2 Proportion

OBJECTIVE To solve problems involving proportion.

An equation that states that two ratios are equal is called a **proportion.** You can write proportions in several different ways.

$2\!:\!3 = 4\!:\!6$ read, "2 is to 3 as 4 is to 6."

$\dfrac{x}{12} = \dfrac{9}{4}$ read, "x divided by 12 equals 9 divided by 4."

In the following proportion a and d are the **extremes,** and b and c are the **means.**

$$\frac{a}{b} = \frac{c}{d}$$

You can use the multiplication property of equality to show that in a proportion the product of the extremes equals the product of the means.

$$\frac{a}{b}(bd) = \frac{c}{d}(bd)$$

$$ad = bc$$

EXAMPLE 1 Solve the proportion $\dfrac{5}{x} = \dfrac{7}{3}$.

SOLUTION $5 \cdot 3 = 7x$

$\qquad\qquad 15 = 7x$

$\qquad\qquad \dfrac{15}{7} = x$

$\qquad\qquad \therefore$ the solution is $\dfrac{15}{7}$. ***Answer***

EXAMPLE 2 Solve the proportion $\dfrac{7a - 5}{4} = \dfrac{a + 9}{3}$.

SOLUTION $(7a - 5)3 = 4(a + 9)$

$\qquad\quad 21a - 15 = 4a + 36$

$\qquad\qquad\quad 17a = 51$

$\qquad\qquad\qquad a = 3$

$\qquad\quad \therefore$ the solution is 3. ***Answer***

Proportions may be used to solve word problems.

EXAMPLE 3

The Washington Farm, which has 400 ha (hectares) planted in corn, produces an annual corn harvest of 300 m³. How many additional hectares must be planted in corn to yield an annual crop of 450 m³?

SOLUTION

Step 1 The problem asks for the number of additional hectares to be planted in corn.

Step 2 Let a = number of additional hectares to be planted in corn. Then, $400 + a$ = total number of hectares planted in corn.

Step 3 Because the yield of corn per hectare will remain the same, you can write the following proportion:

$$\frac{300}{400} = \frac{450}{400 + a}$$

Step 4 Solve.

$$\frac{3}{4} = \frac{450}{400 + a}$$

$$3(400 + a) = 4 \cdot 450$$
$$1200 + 3a = 1800$$
$$3a = 600$$
$$a = 200$$

Step 5 The check is left to you.

$\therefore$ an additional 200 ha should be planted in corn. **Answer**

Oral Exercises

State the equation that results when you equate the product of the extremes and the product of the means in each of the following proportions.

1. $\dfrac{2}{3} = \dfrac{14}{x}$ **2.** $\dfrac{y}{6} = \dfrac{6}{4}$ **3.** $\dfrac{3}{5} = \dfrac{6x}{10}$ **4.** $\dfrac{3k}{5} = \dfrac{k + 5}{10}$

5. $\dfrac{a - 5}{8} = -\dfrac{3}{12}$ **6.** $\dfrac{c - 4}{4} = \dfrac{c}{6}$ **7.** $\dfrac{3}{d - 5} = \dfrac{4}{d}$ **8.** $\dfrac{5}{u - 2} = \dfrac{15}{u + 4}$

Written Exercises

Solve.

A 1. $\dfrac{x}{9} = \dfrac{7}{3}$ **2.** $\dfrac{x}{5} = \dfrac{9}{4}$ **3.** $\dfrac{3c}{2} = \dfrac{2}{5}$ **4.** $\dfrac{4}{7} = \dfrac{2b}{3}$

5. $\dfrac{4}{5} = \dfrac{3n}{7}$ **6.** $\dfrac{3}{8c} = \dfrac{4}{5}$ **7.** $\dfrac{2}{9} = \dfrac{3}{x}$ **8.** $\dfrac{9}{4a} = \dfrac{3}{1}$

9. $\dfrac{x}{3} = \dfrac{2x}{5}$ **10.** $\dfrac{15x}{64} = \dfrac{45}{32}$ **11.** $\dfrac{81}{49} = \dfrac{27y}{14}$ **12.** $\dfrac{25}{17a} = \dfrac{125}{51}$

Solve.

SAMPLE $\dfrac{21}{k+1} = 7$ SOLUTION $\dfrac{21}{k+1} = \dfrac{7}{1}$; $21 = 7(k+1)$; $3 = k+1$; $k = 2$

13. $\dfrac{a-4}{6} = 5$

14. $4 = \dfrac{c-2}{7}$

15. $\dfrac{d+9}{2} = 5d$

16. $\dfrac{3z}{2} = z - 4$

17. $\dfrac{x+3}{16} = \dfrac{x}{10}$

18. $\dfrac{x}{3} = \dfrac{2x-1}{5}$

B 19. $\dfrac{2x+1}{18} = \dfrac{4x-3}{21}$

20. $\dfrac{6x-1}{14} = \dfrac{9x+2}{28}$

21. $\dfrac{2x-6}{2} = \dfrac{3x-9}{3}$

22. $\dfrac{4x+2}{18} = \dfrac{6x+3}{17}$

23. $\dfrac{2a+1}{24} = \dfrac{a}{12}$

24. $\dfrac{3x-5}{5} = \dfrac{10-6x}{-10}$

Solve for x in terms of the other variables.

25. $\dfrac{a}{x} = \dfrac{b}{c}$

26. $\dfrac{l}{x} = \dfrac{r}{s}$

27. $\dfrac{x+b}{a} = n$

28. $\dfrac{b}{q} = \dfrac{2}{x}$

Find the ratio of x to y.

29. $\dfrac{2x+3y}{3y} = \dfrac{3}{4}$

30. $\dfrac{5x-y}{y} = \dfrac{4}{3}$

31. $\dfrac{3x-y}{6} = \dfrac{8x-y}{4}$

C 32. Solve the following proportion for x if a is positive: $\dfrac{a}{x} = \dfrac{x}{1}$.

Problems

A 1. A truck can pump 800 L of oil in 25 min. How much oil can it pump in 2 h?

2. A recipe for two dozen bran muffins requires 750 g of bran flour. How much bran flour would be required to make three dozen muffins?

3. The tax on a new car costing $7200 is $504. At the same tax rate, what will the tax be on a new car costing $8000?

4. Lonnie drove 100 km on 12 L of gasohol. How far can he travel on a full tank of 50 L?

5. If 2 g of hydrogen unite with 16 g of oxygen to form water, how much oxygen is required to produce 144 g of water? (Assume that no loss takes place during the reaction.)

6. The owner of a house with an assessment of $62,500 pays real estate taxes of $1250. What is the assessment on a neighboring house whose owner pays $1500 in real estate taxes?

7. If 600 shares of a certain stock earn an annual dividend of $750, how many shares are required to earn an annual dividend of $1200?

8. In a town of 20,000 residences, a survey was taken to determine the number of residences with garbage disposals. Of the 400 residences surveyed, 352 had disposals. Assuming that the residences surveyed are a representative sample, estimate the number of households with garbage disposals.

9. A farm that has 100 ha planted in wheat produces 275 m³ of wheat annually. How many additional hectares should be planted in wheat so that the annual yield will be 385 m³?

B 10. While on a business trip, Julia Wilson decided to test the accuracy of her car's odometer. For the 320 km trip from Oakdale to Alton the odometer registered 324 km. She returned by a different route and noted that the odometer registered 567 km for the round trip. How many kilometers long was the actual return trip?

11. A cubic centimeter of gold has a mass of 19.3 g, while a cubic centimeter of silver has a mass of 10.5 g. Which of the following has the greater mass: a cube of gold 1.2 cm on an edge or a cube of silver 1.4 cm on an edge? By how much? (*Hint:* Use the formula for the volume of a cube.)

12. If 1 cm represents 30 km on a map, and Colorado is shown by a rectangle 20 cm by 15 cm, calculate the area of Colorado in square kilometers.

Self-Test 1

VOCABULARY   ratio (p. 235)   proportion (p. 240)
         means (p. 240)   extremes (p. 240)

State each ratio in simplest form.

1. 8 m to 10 m   2. 3 h to 15 min   Obj. 7-1, p. 235

3. Two numbers are in the ratio of 3 : 7 and their sum is 310. Find the numbers.

4. Solve: $\dfrac{17x}{64} = \dfrac{51}{16}$ Obj. 7-2, p. 240

5. The tax on a new car costing $7600 is $456. At the same tax rate, what will the tax be on a new car costing $8200?

Check your answers with those at the back of the book.

FRACTIONAL EQUATIONS

7-3 *Equations with Fractional Coefficients*

OBJECTIVE To solve equations with fractional coefficients.

You can solve equations with fractional coefficients by using the least common denominator of all the fractions in the equation. Transform the equation by multiplying both sides by the least common denominator. Then solve the transformed equation.

EXAMPLE Solve: $\frac{2x-1}{3} + \frac{x}{5} = 4$.

SOLUTION The LCD of the fractions is 15.

$$15\left[\left(\frac{2x-1}{3}\right) + \left(\frac{x}{5}\right)\right] = 15[4]$$

$$5(2x-1) + 3(x) = 15[4]$$

$$10x - 5 + 3x = 60$$

$$13x - 5 = 60$$

$$13x = 65$$

$$x = 5$$

∴ the solution is 5. *Answer*

Oral Exercises

State the least common denominator of the fractions in each equation. Then tell what equation results when both sides of the equation are multiplied by the LCD.

1. $\frac{x}{2} + \frac{x}{3} = 5$

2. $\frac{3y}{4} + \frac{y}{2} = 5$

3. $\frac{k}{3} + \frac{2k}{5} = \frac{11}{15}$

4. $\frac{a}{3} - \frac{a}{6} = 1$

5. $\frac{5x}{12} - \frac{2x}{9} = 7$

6. $\frac{2b}{5} + \frac{b}{3} = 0$

Written Exercises

A **1–6.** Solve the equations in Oral Exercises 1–6.

Solve.

7. $\frac{n}{3} + \frac{2n}{5} = 11$

8. $\frac{2a}{3} - \frac{a}{2} = 2$

9. $\frac{3-n}{2} = \frac{3}{4}$

Solve.

10. $\frac{3}{8}k - \frac{1}{4}k = 2$ **11.** $\frac{3}{2}x - \frac{1}{6}x + 1 = 0$ **12.** $\frac{6}{7}c - \frac{1}{2}c = 5$

B 13. $\frac{x-7}{5} + 2 = \frac{x+8}{10}$ **14.** $n + \frac{n+2}{4} = 0$ **15.** $\frac{x+8}{16} - \frac{x-4}{12} = 1$

16. $\frac{5x-1}{2} - \frac{3x+1}{4} = \frac{9}{2}$ **17.** $\frac{3x-1}{4} - \frac{9-x}{6} = \frac{14}{3}$ **18.** $\frac{x+1}{5} - \frac{3}{2} = \frac{3x-6}{10}$

19. $\frac{x-5}{8} - \frac{2x+6}{9} + 1 = 0$ **20.** $\frac{x-3}{5} - \frac{x+2}{15} + \frac{2}{3} = 0$

21. $\frac{2a-1}{6} - \frac{1-a}{4} = a$ **22.** $\frac{4n+1}{3} - \frac{2n+1}{5} = \frac{3}{5}$

23. $\frac{x+3}{3} - \frac{x}{4} = \frac{x-2}{5}$ **24.** $\frac{1}{2}(x-5) - (x+1) = \frac{1}{4}(x-12)$

25. $\frac{2}{3}(x-1) - \frac{1}{5}(2x-3) = 1$ **26.** $\frac{1}{3}(x+6) - 1 = \frac{1}{6}(9-x)$

C 27. $\frac{1}{4}\left(y - \frac{1}{3}\right) - \frac{1}{6}(y-3) = \frac{2}{3}$ **28.** $\frac{1}{2}\left(x + \frac{2}{3}\right) - \frac{1}{6}\left(7x - \frac{1}{3}\right) = \frac{1}{6}$

29. $\frac{1}{5}(2x-3) - \frac{2}{3}\left(x - \frac{1}{2}\right) = \frac{7}{15}$ **30.** $\frac{3}{4}(x-2) - \frac{2}{3}\left(x - \frac{1}{2}\right) = \frac{x+1}{2}$

Solve for x in terms of the other variable.

31. $\frac{x+3a}{10} - \frac{x-a}{2} = \frac{x}{5}$ **32.** $\frac{x-n}{5} - \frac{7x-n}{10} = \frac{2n-x}{15}$

33. $\frac{1}{5}(2x-3c) - \frac{1}{3}\left(x - \frac{c}{2}\right) - \frac{x}{6} = 0$

Problems

A 1. One sixth of a number is 5 less than one fourth of the number. Find the number.

2. Two thirds of a number added to three eighths of the number is 25. Find the number.

3. A rectangle is 6 cm longer than it is wide. Its width is one fifth of the perimeter. Find its dimensions.

4. Tom is three years older than Marcia. Three years ago Marcia's age was four fifths of Tom's. What are their present ages?

5. Sam is half as old as Kathy. In two years, he will be two thirds as old as Kathy. How old is each now?

6. David has one third more money than Carl. Together they have $42. How much does each have?

B **7.** Ann had ten dollars more than Beverly. After Ann spent half her money and Beverly spent a quarter of her money, they had equal amounts left. How much money did each have at first?

8. Otis hikes up to the falls at 3 km/h and returns by the same route at 5 km/h. If the entire trip takes him 7.5 h, how far is it to the falls?

9. Sally walks from her home to the recreation center at a rate of 6 km/h, and she jogs home at a rate of 12 km/h. If her jogging time is fifteen minutes less than her walking time, what is the distance to the center?

10. A group of nickels, dimes, and quarters is worth $7.60. There are two thirds as many nickels as dimes and half as many dimes as quarters. How many quarters are there?

11. Three fourths of the coins in a coin bank are dimes and the rest are quarters. The value of the coins is $4.95. How many dimes are there?

12. Ina bought a number of baseballs for her sporting goods store at $2.50 each. She sold four fifths of them at $3.50 each and gave the rest to a team she sponsored. Even so, she made a $9 profit on the baseballs. How many did she buy?

ḫistorical Ոote An Ancient Equation

Equations have been used for thousands of years. Manuscripts that have been preserved since about 1900 B.C. provide some information about the equations used by the ancient Egyptians. Here is one old problem:

> A quantity and its $\frac{1}{5}$ added together become 21.
>
> What is the quantity?

You can write the equation $x + \frac{1}{5}x = 21$ and solve it by the methods you

have studied. The Egyptians used a proportion to solve it (although they did not write it the way we do). Here is their method:

> Let $x = 5$.
> Then $5 + 1 = 6$. But the sum is to be 21.
> Therefore, the correct value of x can be found from:

$$\frac{x}{5} = \frac{21}{6}$$

$$x = \frac{5}{2} \cdot 7 = \frac{35}{2} = 17\frac{1}{2}$$

Compare this method with the one you would use.

7-4 *Fractional Equations*

An equation that has a variable in the denominator of one or more terms is called a **fractional equation.** You can use the multiplication property of equality to solve fractional equations.

EXAMPLE   Solve: $\dfrac{x+1}{2x-2} = \dfrac{x}{6} + \dfrac{1}{x-1}$

SOLUTION   1. Factor all the denominators to determine the LCD.

$$\frac{x+1}{2(x-1)} = \frac{x}{6} + \frac{1}{x-1}$$

The LCD is $6(x-1)$; note that $x \neq 1$.

2. Multiply both sides of the equation by the LCD.

$$6(x-1)\left[\frac{x+1}{2(x-1)}\right] = 6(x-1)\left[\frac{x}{6} + \frac{1}{x-1}\right]$$

$$3(x+1) = (x-1)x + 6$$

$$3x + 3 = x^2 - x + 6$$

$$0 = x^2 - 4x + 3$$

$$0 = (x-1)(x-3)$$

$$x = 1 \text{ or } x = 3$$

3. Recall that 1 is not permissible as a solution to the original equation. Check 3 in the original equation.

$$\frac{3+1}{2\cdot 3 - 2} \overset{?}{=} \frac{3}{6} + \frac{1}{3-1}$$

$$\frac{4}{4} \overset{?}{=} \frac{3}{6} + \frac{1}{2}$$

$$1 = 1 \quad \checkmark$$

∴ the solution is 3.   *Answer*

In the preceding example you saw that 1 was not a solution of the original equation even though it satisfied the transformed equation. Notice that multiplying the equation by $6(x-1)$ led to an equation that was *not equivalent* to the given one. This new equation had the extra root 1, a number for which the multiplier $6(x-1)$ represents *zero*.

In general, multiplying both sides of an equation by a variable expression that can represent zero may produce an equation that is not equivalent to the original equation. Therefore, you must check each root of the resulting equation to see that it satisfies the original equation.

Written Exercises

Solve. If the equation has no solution write "no solution."

A **1.** $\dfrac{1}{5} + \dfrac{1}{x} = \dfrac{6}{5}$

2. $\dfrac{3}{x} - \dfrac{1}{4} = \dfrac{3}{4}$

3. $\dfrac{1}{x} + \dfrac{1}{3} = \dfrac{1}{2}$

4. $\dfrac{1}{a} + \dfrac{1}{3} = \dfrac{8}{15}$

5. $\dfrac{3}{10} = \dfrac{1}{2} - \dfrac{1}{b}$

6. $\dfrac{6}{x} = \dfrac{4}{x-1}$

7. $\dfrac{1+a}{a} = \dfrac{3}{a}$

8. $\dfrac{3n+5}{6} - \dfrac{10}{n} = \dfrac{n}{2}$

9. $\dfrac{y}{y-2} = \dfrac{4}{3}$

10. $\dfrac{x}{x+3} = \dfrac{2x}{x+3} + 3$

11. $\dfrac{a}{2a+4} - \dfrac{1}{a+2} = 1$

12. $\dfrac{1}{x} - \dfrac{2x}{x+1} = 0$

Solve.

B **13.** When 100 is divided by x the quotient is 4 and the remainder is 12. Find x.

14. Julia Ling drove the 200 km to Richmond at a speed 10 km/h faster than usual. If she completed the trip in one hour less than usual, find her usual driving speed.

15. Rodney Smith can bicycle or drive the 30 km from his apartment to the river. If he drives his car, he will travel 25 km/h faster and complete the trip in fifty minutes less time. Find his speed when traveling by bike.

Solve. If the equation has no solution write "no solution."

16. $\dfrac{2}{x^2-x} = \dfrac{2}{x-1} + 1$

17. $\dfrac{1}{2a-1} - \dfrac{3}{4a^2-1} = 0$

18. $\dfrac{y-2}{y} - \dfrac{y-3}{y-6} = \dfrac{1}{y}$

19. $\dfrac{b+4}{2b-6} = \dfrac{b}{b-3} + 2$

20. $\dfrac{2}{x+1} + \dfrac{1}{x-1} = 1$

21. $\dfrac{3}{x-1} + \dfrac{2}{x} = 4$

22. $\dfrac{1}{x-4} = \dfrac{2}{x^2-16}$

23. $\dfrac{a+3}{a-1} + \dfrac{a+1}{a-3} = 2$

24. $\dfrac{1}{y} - \dfrac{1}{y-2} = \dfrac{8}{4y-3}$

25. $\dfrac{2x+1}{3} - \dfrac{3}{2x-1} = -2$

26. $\dfrac{4}{x^2-4x} + \dfrac{1}{4-x} = 0$

27. $\dfrac{1}{x-4} + \dfrac{2}{x^2-16} = \dfrac{3}{x+4}$

28. $\dfrac{3a}{a-1} - \dfrac{4}{a+1} = \dfrac{4}{a^2-1}$

29. $\dfrac{8}{b-1} + \dfrac{30}{1-b^2} = \dfrac{6}{b+1}$

30. $\dfrac{1}{y} - \dfrac{2}{1-y} = \dfrac{8}{y^2-y}$

C **31.** $\dfrac{x-2}{x^2-x-6} = \dfrac{1}{x^2-4} + \dfrac{3}{2x+4}$

32. $\dfrac{x}{x+1} - \dfrac{x+1}{x-4} = \dfrac{5}{x^2-3x-4}$

33. $\dfrac{n-4}{2n^2+5n-3} + \dfrac{2n+7}{8n^2-2n-1} = \dfrac{4n-1}{4n^2+13n+3}$

34. $\dfrac{2x^2}{1-x^2} = \dfrac{x}{x-1} - \dfrac{x}{x+1} - 3$

Application Optics

The curved pieces of glass or plastic in a magnifying glass or a pair of eyeglasses are examples of *lenses.* When light passes through a lens, it is bent. The most common type of lens is the *converging lens,* which is used in cameras, movie projectors, and eyeglasses. Converging lenses cause parallel rays of light to converge to a point, as shown in the photo below.

The point at which the rays converge is called the *principal focus* of the lens. The distance from the principal focus to the center of the lens is called the *focal length* of the lens.

When you look through a converging lens, the size of the image you see will be determined by the distance from the object to the lens (d_o), the distance from the image to the lens (d_i), and the focal length of the lens (f).

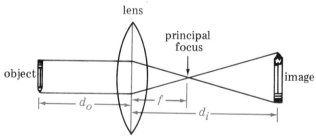

The relationship between d_o, d_i, and f is given by the following formula:

$$\frac{1}{d_o} + \frac{1}{d_i} = \frac{1}{f}$$

The apparent change in the size of an object viewed through a lens is called magnification. The magnification (M) of the image is given by the formula:

$$M = \frac{d_i}{d_o}$$

EXAMPLE

A negative is placed 75 mm from the center of the lens of a photo enlarger. If the focal length of the lens is 50 mm, find the distance from the lens to the image and the magnification of the image.

light source

SOLUTION

1. Substitute in the formula: $\dfrac{1}{75} + \dfrac{1}{d_i} = \dfrac{1}{50}$

2. Solve for d_i.

$$150d_i\left(\frac{1}{75}\right) + 150d_i\left(\frac{1}{d_i}\right) = 150d_i\left(\frac{1}{50}\right)$$

$$2d_i + 150 = 3d_i$$

$$150 = d_i$$

negative

lens

image

$d_o = 75$ mm

d_i

∴ the distance from the lens to the image is 150 mm.

3. Substitute in the formula for magnification.

$$M = \frac{d_i}{d_o} = \frac{150}{75} = 2$$

∴ the magnification of the image will be 2.

In each of the optical relationships described, measurements are given from the center of the converging lens. Find (a) the distance from the lens to the image; (b) the magnification of the image.

1. A slide is placed 90 mm from the converging lens in a slide viewer. The lens has a focal length of 60 mm.

2. A magnifying glass with a focal length of 96 mm is positioned 120 mm above an ant.

3. A slide with a sample of pond water is placed 0.5 cm from the lens of a microscope. The lens has a focal length of 0.49 cm.

4. Opal is taking a picture of James, who is standing 550 mm from her. The lens in her camera has a focal length of 50 mm.

Self-Test 2

VOCABULARY fractional equation (p. 247)

Solve.

1. $\dfrac{5}{8}n - \dfrac{1}{2}n = 6$

2. $\dfrac{2k-3}{4} - \dfrac{k}{8} = \dfrac{1}{4}$

Obj. 7-3, p. 244

3. $\dfrac{2}{y} - \dfrac{1}{3} = \dfrac{1}{6}$

4. $\dfrac{1}{v} - \dfrac{2}{v-2} = \dfrac{3}{v}$

Obj. 7-4, p. 247

Check your answers with those at the back of the book.

PERCENT PROBLEMS

7-5 *Percents*

OBJECTIVE To solve problems involving percents.

The ratio of one number to another can be expressed as a percent. The word **percent** (usually denoted %) means "hundredths" or "divided by 100." For example,

$\frac{13}{100}$ is called "13 percent" and written 13%.

EXAMPLE 1 Express each number as a percent.

        a. $\frac{4}{5}$ **b.** $\frac{2}{3}$ **c.** 2.5

SOLUTION

a. $\frac{x}{100} = \frac{4}{5}$

    $5x = 400$

    $x = 80$

  $\therefore \frac{4}{5} = 80\%$

b. $\frac{x}{100} = \frac{2}{3}$

    $3x = 200$

    $x = 66\frac{2}{3}$

  $\therefore \frac{2}{3} = 66\frac{2}{3}\%$

c. $\frac{x}{100} = 2.5$

    $x = 250$

  $\therefore 2.5 = 250\%$

In problems involving percent, the word "of" indicates multiplication and the word "is" indicates equality. The next three examples illustrate this idea.

EXAMPLE 2 45% of 20 is what number?

SOLUTION $\frac{45}{100} \cdot 20 = x$

                 $9 = x$

    $\therefore$ 45% of 20 is 9.   *Answer*

When finding a percent of a number, it is often convenient to express the percent as a decimal and then multiply. Example 2 can be worked as follows:

       $45\% = 0.45$ 45% of $20 = 0.45 \times 20 = 9$

EXAMPLE 3   98 is 70% of what number?

SOLUTION $98 = \dfrac{70}{100} \cdot x$

$9800 = 70x$

$140 = x$

∴ 98 is 70% of 140. **Answer**

EXAMPLE 4   What percent of 15 is 3?

SOLUTION $\dfrac{x}{100} \cdot 15 = 3$

$15x = 300$

$x = 20$

∴ 20% of 15 is 3. **Answer**

When working investment problems, it is often convenient to express the rate of interest as a decimal. For example, you can find the interest for 1 year on $2000 invested at an $8\frac{1}{2}\%$ annual simple interest as follows:

$8\frac{1}{2}\% = 8.5\% = 0.085$ $8\frac{1}{2}\%$ of $2000 = 0.085 \times 2000 = \$170$

Some investment problems involve an equation with coefficients expressed as decimals. Such an equation can be solved by multiplying both sides of the equation by a power of ten to get an equivalent equation with whole number coefficients.

EXAMPLE 5

Annette Lauphier invests part of $8000 at 9% annual simple interest and the rest at 11% annual simple interest. Her annual income from these investments is $850. How much is invested at each interest rate?

SOLUTION

Step 1   The problem asks for the amount of money invested at 9% and the amount invested at 11%.

Step 2   Let $x =$ amount invested at 9%.
Then $8000 - x =$ amount invested at 11%.

Principal	× Rate	= Interest
x	0.09	$0.09x$
$8000 - x$	0.11	$0.11(8000 - x)$

Step 3   Because the total interest earned is $850, you can write the following equation:

$$0.09x + 0.11(8000 - x) = 850$$

Step 4 $100[0.09x + 0.11(8000 - x)] = 100[850]$ ⟵ Multiply both sides by 100 to eliminate decimals.

$$9x + 11(8000 - x) = 85000$$
$$-2x + 88000 = 85000$$
$$2x = 3000$$
$$x = 1500$$

Step 5   The check is left to you.

∴ $1500 was invested at 9% and $6500 was invested at 11%.   *Answer*

Oral Exercises

Express as a percent.

1. 0.72   **2.** 0.05   **3.** 1.25   **4.** 0.009   **5.** 0.095

6. $\frac{1}{2}$ **7.** $\frac{1}{4}$ **8.** $\frac{3}{5}$ **9.** $1\frac{1}{2}$ **10.** $\frac{7}{50}$

Express as a fraction or mixed number in simplest form.

11. 75%   **12.** 20%   **13.** 8%   **14.** $\frac{1}{2}$%   **15.** 150%

Express as a decimal.

16. 42%   **17.** 3%   **18.** 127%   **19.** 0.2%   **20.** 4.5%

Tell whether you would multiply by 10, 100, or 1000 in order to eliminate the decimals in each equation.

21. $2.4x = 32$ **22.** $0.5x + 0.2 = 1.4$ **23.** $4x - 0.072 = 1.3$

Written Exercises

Solve.

A   **1.** 22% of 400   **2.** 3% of 72   **3.** $5\frac{1}{2}$% of 1000

4. $\frac{1}{2}$% of 36   **5.** 2.75% of 160   **6.** 120% of 45

7. 100% of 91   **8.** 200% of 15.3   **9.** $7\frac{1}{3}$% of 150

10. What percent of 80 is 16?   **11.** What percent of 40 is 30?
12. What percent of 300 is 240?   **13.** What percent of 25 is 16?

14. What percent of 15 is 12?

15. What percent of 12 is 15?

16. What percent of 72 is 24?

17. What percent of 180 is 45?

18. What percent of 450 is 9?

19. What percent of 20 is 2?

20. What percent of 180 is 36?

21. What percent of 36 is 54?

Find the number.

22. 15 is 20% of the number.

23. 18 is 60% of the number.

24. 6.3 is 7% of the number.

25. 63 is 150% of the number.

26. 75% of the number is 270.

27. $1\frac{1}{2}$% of the number is 6.

28. 4% of the number is 3.4.

29. 500% of the number is 90.

Solve.

30. $1.2x = 36$

31. $0.07x = 2.8$

32. $0.2x + 0.4x = 24$

33. $0.4y - 0.7 = 2.9$

34. $1 - 0.3x = 0.4$

35. $0.3a + 0.03a = 9.9$

36. $0.05y = 0.06(110 - y)$

37. $0.025k + 0.05k = 0.3$

38. $0.16(3n - 6) = 4.8$

B **39.** $0.06(1000 - x) + 0.05x = 700$

40. $0.025a - 0.05(20 - 2a) = 0.2$

41. $1.2x + 3.05 = 0.95x - 0.20$

42. $\dfrac{0.3x - 1}{5} = 0.12x + 3.2$

Problems

Solve.

A **1.** One serving of spinach has about 2.6 mg more iron than a piece of chicken. Together they have about 5.4 mg of iron. How much iron is in a serving of spinach?

2. In a country of 225 million people, the urban population is 2.75 times the rural population. Find the urban and rural populations.

3. Find the sales tax on an $8500 automobile if the sales tax rate is 5%.

4. Of the 12,000 votes cast in an election, 55% were for Jefferson. How many votes were cast for the other candidates?

5. In an hour long television biography of a film star, 18% of the time is devoted to film clips from the star's movies. How many minutes are devoted to the film clips?

6. In a small village, 180 people live in wooden structures, 144 live in aluminum-clad structures, and 216 live in brick structures. What percent of the people live in each type of structure?

Solve. Assume that all interest rates indicate annual simple interest.

B 7. Ed Keely invested some money at 6% and an additional $800 at 7%. The money earned $128 interest in a year. How much was invested at 6%?

8. An investment club invested part of a $10,000 amount at $7\frac{1}{2}$% and the rest at $10\frac{1}{2}$%. The interest for one year came to $930. How much money was invested at each rate?

9. An alumni association raised $12,000 in contributions. Each year the money earns $920 interest, which is used for scholarships. Part of the $12,000 is invested at 7% and the rest at 9%. How much is invested at each rate?

10. Nadia Goddard invested $1500 more in tax-free bonds than in stocks. The stocks paid 5% interest and the bonds paid $7\frac{1}{2}$%. If the annual income is $425, find how much she invested in all.

11. Two thirds of a sum of money is invested at 5%, one-sixth at 4%, and the remainder at 6%. If the total income is $450, how much money is invested?

C 12. A woman has d dollars, a part of which is invested at 5% and the rest at $6\frac{1}{2}$%. If she receives k dollars annually in interest, how much is invested at 5%?

Biography Lillian Moller Gilbreth

Lillian Moller Gilbreth (1878–1972) with her husband, Frank Gilbreth, pioneered the field of efficiency engineering. Their story and that of their twelve children was told in the novel *Cheaper by the Dozen*. Their goal was to minimize the time and human motion needed to perform tasks in the home, office, and factory.

After her husband's death in 1924, Lillian Gilbreth continued her study of "time and motion." Some of her motion saving devices are the step-on trash can, shelves in refrigerator doors, and height-adjusted kitchen counters.

Lillian Gilbreth received a master's degree in literature from the University of California and a Ph.D. in industrial psychology from Brown University in 1915. During the Depression and World War II, she served on several presidential committees. In 1936 she was voted one of the ten outstanding women of the year, and throughout her long life she received many awards and honorary degrees for her work.

7-6 *Percent Problems*

OBJECTIVE   To solve problems involving percents.

To find the percent of increase or percent of decrease in a price, measurement, or other quantity, find what percent the change is of the original quantity.

EXAMPLE 1

Arthur Singleton paid $275 per month in rent last year. This year his rent was increased to $286 per month. Find the percent of increase.

SOLUTION

Step 1   The problem asks for the percent of increase.

Step 2   Let $x\%$ = percent of increase.

Step 3   The increase is $286 - 275$, or 11.

$$11 \text{ is what percent of } 275?$$

$$11 = \frac{x}{100} \cdot 275$$

Step 4
$$1100 = 275x$$
$$4 = x$$

Step 5   The check is left to you.

$$\therefore \text{ the percent of increase is } 4\%. \quad \textbf{\textit{Answer}}$$

A discount is an amount that is subtracted from the price of an item to create a new, lower selling price. A 20% discount on an $80 vacuum cleaner is $16; the new selling price is then $80 - 16$, or $64.

EXAMPLE 2

Betty pays $46.75 for an electronic game which is on sale at a 15% discount. What was the original price of the game?

SOLUTION

Step 1   The problem asks for the original price of the game.

Step 2   Let x = original price in dollars.

Step 3   Since the discount is 15%,
the selling price ($46.75) is 85% of the original price.

$$46.75 = \frac{85}{100} \cdot x$$

Step 4
$$4675 = 85x$$
$$55 = x$$

Step 5   The check is left to you.

$$\therefore \text{ the original price was } \$55. \quad \textbf{\textit{Answer}}$$

Oral Exercises

State the amount of the discount and the new selling price.

1. $40 pair of shoes at a 15% discount
2. $35 framed picture at a 20% discount
3. $150 suit at a 30% discount
4. $550 stereo at a 10% discount

Problems

Solve.

A 1. Last year 500 people attended the Senior Citizens Club picnic. This year 565 people attended the picnic. Find the percent of increase in attendance.

2. In February the average price of a dozen eggs was $1.05. In May the average price was 84¢. Find the percent of decrease.

3. A motel manager plans to raise by 22% the current rate of $25 for a room. What will be the new rate for a room?

4. A $180 pair of skis is on sale at a 25% discount. If there is a 5% sales tax, how much do the skis cost in all?

5. The list price of a camera is $150, but a discount of $7.50 is given if you pay cash. What is the percent of discount?

6. At the close of one business day, a company's stock was trading at $24 a share. At the close of the next business day, the stock was trading at $27 a share. Find the percent of increase.

7. In July a newspaper's circulation increased by 6% to a new high of 132,500 subscribers. What was the newspaper's circulation in June?

8. A real estate broker receives a commission of 3% for selling a house. If the commission on a sale was $1560, what was the selling price of the house?

9. The Watanabes received $72,000 for their house after a commission of 4% of the selling price had been paid. What was the selling price?

10. When the United Fund drive in Livonia received $3800, it reached 76% of its goal. What was its goal?

B 11. Shirley Jackson bought some stock valued at $62.50 a share and sold it for $67.50 a share. What was the percent of profit?

12. Three quarters of one percent of the flash bulbs produced by a certain assembly line fail to flash. Of the 1.5 million bulbs produced in one month, about how many will fail to flash?

Solve.

13. After two years a car purchased for $6500 has a book value of only $3900. By what percent has its value decreased?

14. Two years ago Jason Chen bought an antique dresser for $1500. It is now worth $2070. If the value of the dresser increased by 20% during the first year Jason owned it, by what percent did the value of the dresser increase during the second year?

Self-Test 3

VOCABULARY   percent (p. 251)

Solve.

1. What percent of 250 is 75?   Obj. 7-5, p. 251

2. 90 is 45% of what number?

3. What is 55% of 20?

4. The price of a car was raised from $5000 to $5450. What was the   Obj. 7-6, p. 256
   percent of increase?

5. Luis bought a jacket at a sale offering 20% off the original price. If the sale price of the jacket was $60, how much was the original price?

Check your answers with those at the back of the book.

Calculator Key-In

If your calculator does not have a percent key, you can divide by 100 when entering percents. For example, you can find 7.5% of 6000 as follows:

$$7.5 \div 100 \times 6000 = 450.$$

1. Find 6.13% of 23,500.

2. Find 6.6% of 4400.

3. Find 10.5% of 6500.

4. Find 11.84% of 7500.

5. Find $8\frac{1}{2}$% of 15,000.

6. Find $\frac{1}{2}$% of 350.

7. Sue Lee purchased a new car at a sale offering a 15.5% discount off the original price of all new cars. If the original price of the car she bought was $6038 and the sales tax rate was 5.5%, how much did she pay in all?

MIXTURE AND WORK PROBLEMS

7-7 *Mixture Problems*

OBJECTIVE To solve mixture problems.

A merchant often mixes goods of two or more kinds in order to sell a blend at a given price. Similarly, a chemist often mixes solutions of different strengths of a chemical to obtain a solution of desired strength. Charts can be helpful in solving mixture problems.

EXAMPLE 1

The Green Briar Gourmet Shop sells cashews for $6.00 per kilogram and Brazil nuts for $7.50 per kilogram. The store manager wants to mix the nuts to get 15 kg of a mixture worth $6.50 per kilogram. How many kilograms of each kind of nut does the manager need?

SOLUTION

Step 1   The problem asks for the number of kilograms of cashews and the number of kilograms of Brazil nuts needed.

Step 2   Let x = number of kilograms of cashews.
Then $15 - x$ = number of kilograms of Brazil nuts.

	Number of kilograms	$\times$ Price per kilogram	$=$ Total cost
Cashew	x	6.00	$6x$
Brazil	$15 - x$	7.50	$7.5(15 - x)$
Mixture	15	6.50	$6.5(15)$

Step 3   Cost of cashews + Cost of Brazil nuts = Cost of mixture
$$6x + 7.5(15 - x) = 6.5(15)$$

Step 4   Multiply both sides of the equation by 10.
$$60x + 75(15 - x) = 65 \cdot 15$$
$$4x + 5(15 - x) = 65$$
$$4x + 75 - 5x = 65$$
$$-x = -10$$
$$x = 10$$

Step 5   The check is left to you.
$\therefore$ The manager needs 10 kg of cashews and 5 kg of Brazil nuts.   ***Answer***

EXAMPLE 2

A chemist has 60 g of a solution that is 35% acid. How much water should be added to make a solution that is 20% acid?

SOLUTION

Step 1   The problem asks for the number of grams of water to be added.

Step 2   Let x = number of grams of water to be added.

	Total amount	$\times$ % acid =	Amount of acid
Original solution	60	35%	0.35(60)
New solution	60 + x	20%	0.20(60 + x)

Step 3

$$\begin{array}{c}\text{Acid in} \qquad\qquad \text{Acid in} \\ \text{original solution} = \text{final solution} \\ 0.35(60) = 0.20(60 + x)\end{array}$$

Step 4   Multiply both sides of the equation by 100.

$$35(60) = 20(60 + x)$$
$$35(3) = (60 + x)$$
$$105 = 60 + x$$
$$45 = x$$

Step 5   The check is left to you.

$$\therefore 45 \text{ g of water should be added.} \quad \textbf{\textit{Answer}}$$

Oral Exercises

Read each problem. Tell what goes in each blank in the chart. Do not solve the problem.

1. A grocer has two kinds of coffee; one that costs $4.00 per kilogram and another that costs $4.80 per kilogram. How many kilograms of each type of coffee should be mixed in order to have 40 kg of a blend worth $4.50 per kilogram?

	Number of kilograms	$\times$ Price per kilogram =	Total cost
Coffee A	x	4.80	?
Coffee B	?	?	?
Mixture	?	?	?

2. How many kilograms of water must be added to 5 kg of a 20% salt solution in order to produce a 15% salt solution?

	Number of kilograms	× % salt =	Amount of salt
Original solution	5	20%	?
Added water	x	?	?
New solution	?	?	?

Problems

A **1–2.** Solve the problems presented in Oral Exercises 1–2.

Solve.

3. How many kilograms of pure salt must be added to 5 kg of a 20% salt solution in order to produce a 25% solution?

4. A grocer has two varieties of tea, one that costs $3 per kilogram and another that costs $4 per kilogram. How many kilograms of each should the grocer mix in order to get 20 kg of a mixture worth $3.25 per kilogram?

5. A food processing company produces grated cheese made from two types of cheese. One type of cheese costs $2.90 per kilogram, and the other costs $3.10 per kilogram. How much of each type of cheese went into making 200 kg of cheese worth $2.95 per kilogram?

6. How many kilograms of water must be added to 8 kg of a 50% salt solution in order to produce a 10% salt solution?

7. How many grams of water must be added to 120 g of a 30% iodine solution in order to produce a 20% iodine solution?

8. How many kilograms of water must be added to 10 kg of an 80% antifreeze solution in order to produce a 50% solution?

9. Suppose you have 1200 g of a 10% salt solution. How many grams of pure salt must be added to obtain a 20% salt solution?

10. How many kilograms of pure alcohol must be added to 20 kg of 80% pure alcohol to produce an 85% pure alcohol?

B **11.** How many kilograms of water must be *evaporated* from 9 kg of a 50% salt solution to produce a 75% salt solution?

12. How many kilograms of water must be evaporated from 60 kg of a 5% salt solution to produce a 25% salt solution?

Solve.

13. A health food store makes a blend of cereal by mixing oatmeal at $3.60 per kilogram and bran flakes at $4.80 a kilogram. How many kilograms of each should be mixed to obtain 30 kg of cereal worth $4.00 a kilogram?

14. Jack and Louis are making up a snack to take along on a hike. They mix raisins costing $5.00 per kilogram with peanuts costing $3.80 per kilogram. When they finish they will have produced 2 kg of the mixture and spent $8.10. How much of each ingredient did they use?

15. The Town Players received $1150 by selling 640 tickets to the opening night of their play. If full price tickets were $2.50 and discount tickets for students and senior citizens were $1.00, how many discount tickets were sold?

16. In a carnival shooting gallery, you pay a nickel per shot at a very tricky moving target. For every time that you hit the target you are given a dime. If Sheila took 25 shots and lost a quarter, how many times did she hit the target?

17. There are 100 pennies, nickels, dimes, and quarters mixed together in a jar. Together they are worth $8.36. There are nine more dimes than pennies and five times as many nickels as pennies. How many of each kind of coin are in the jar?

18. Tyrone Smith invests $11,000 in a mixed portfolio of investments including stocks that pay 5% annually, tax-free bonds that pay $8\frac{1}{2}\%$ annually, and a savings certificate that pays 10% annually. Twice as much money is invested in bonds as in stocks, and the annual income from the portfolio is $860. How much money is invested in each type of investment?

19. A metallurgist has 40 kg of an alloy that is 65% copper. How many kilograms of a second alloy that is 42% copper should be mixed with the first alloy to get a new alloy that is 50% copper?

C 20. a. If 1 kg is simultaneously taken from each container and dumped into the other, what will the resulting alcohol percentage in each container be?
   b. Answer part (a) if 2 kg is taken from each container and dumped into the other.
   c. Guess the answer to part (a) if 3 kg is taken from each container and dumped into the other.

Container I:
10 kg

Container II:
10 kg

21. In one kind of concrete, the ratio of cement to sand by volume is 3:5. In another kind of concrete, the ratio of cement to sand is 4:3. Find the ratio of the volumes of the two kinds of concrete needed to form a new concrete with equal amounts of cement and sand.

7-8 Work Problems

OBJECTIVE To solve work problems.

The following formula is used to solve work problems.

$$\text{rate} \times \text{time} = \text{work done}$$

$$rt = w$$

Work rates are often expressed in terms of the job to be done. For example, if it takes you 2 days to do a job, then your rate is $\frac{1}{2}$ job per day.

Notice in the following examples that the fractional parts of a job must have a sum of 1.

EXAMPLE 1

It takes you 2 days to paint your garage and it takes your friend 3 days. How long will it take if you both work together?

SOLUTION

Step 1 The problem asks for the number of days it will take if you both work together.

Step 2 Let x = number of days required to do the job together.

	Work rate $\times$	Time =	Work done
You	$\frac{1}{2}$	x	$\frac{x}{2}$
Your friend	$\frac{1}{3}$	x	$\frac{x}{3}$

Step 3

$$\begin{array}{ccccc} \text{Part of job} & + & \text{Part of job} & = & \text{Whole job} \\ \text{you do} & & \text{friend does} & & \end{array}$$

$$\frac{x}{2} \quad + \quad \frac{x}{3} \quad = \quad 1$$

Step 4

$$6\left(\frac{x}{2} + \frac{x}{3}\right) = 6(1)$$

$$3x + 2x = 6$$

$$5x = 6$$

$$x = \frac{6}{5}$$

Step 5 The check is left to you.

$\therefore$ it would take $\frac{6}{5}$, or 1.2, days working together. ***Answer***

EXAMPLE 2

Working alone, Hal can mow a large lawn in 3 hours, and Kevin can mow it in $4\frac{1}{2}$ hours. Suppose that they work together for 1 hour and then Kevin leaves. How long will it take Hal to finish mowing the lawn?

SOLUTION

Step 1 The problem asks for the number of hours it will take Hal to finish mowing the lawn.

Step 2 Let x = number of hours for Hal to finish mowing the lawn. Then find Kevin's work rate and complete the chart.

$$\text{Kevin's work rate: } \frac{1}{4\frac{1}{2}} = \frac{1 \cdot 2}{4\frac{1}{2} \cdot 2} = \frac{2}{9}$$

	Work rate	× Time =	Work done
Hal	$\frac{1}{3}$	$x + 1$	$\frac{1}{3}(x + 1)$
Kevin	$\frac{2}{9}$	1	$\frac{2}{9}$

Step 3

$$\begin{array}{ccc} \text{Part of job} & & \text{Part of job} \\ \text{done by Hal} & + & \text{done by Kevin} \end{array} = \text{Whole job}$$

$$\frac{1}{3}(x + 1) \quad + \quad \frac{2}{9} \quad = \quad 1$$

Step 4

$$3(x + 1) + 2 = 9$$
$$3x + 5 = 9$$
$$3x = 4$$
$$x = \frac{4}{3}$$

Step 5 The check is left to you.

$\therefore$ it would take Hal $\frac{4}{3}$ hours, or 1 h 20 min, to finish the job.   ***Answer***

Oral Exercises

State the work rate.

SAMPLE You can do a job in 5 hours.   **SOLUTION** $\frac{1}{5}$ job per hour

1. Heidi can mow the lawn in 2 hours.

2. Lionel can vacuum his room in 10 minutes.

3. Will can do the whole job in 3 days.

4. A drain pipe can empty the full tank in 4 hours.

Complete the chart. Do not solve the problem.

5. Valve A can drain a swimming pool in 3 hours and Valve B can drain it in 4 hours. Find x, the amount of time it will take to drain the pool using both valves.

	Work rate $\times$	Time =	Work done
Valve A	?	x	?
Valve B	?	x	?

6. Working alone, it will take Pete 8 hours to wallpaper his room. Working with Bernie, Pete takes only 5 hours to wallpaper the room. Find x, the time it will take Bernie working by himself.

	Work rate $\times$	Time =	Work done
Pete	?	5	?
Bernie	$\dfrac{1}{x}$	5	?

Problems

A **1–2.** Solve the problems stated in Oral Exercises 5-6.

Solve.

3. Working alone, Valerie can paint the house in 3 days and Lina can paint it in 4 days. Suppose that Valerie works alone for two days and then is joined by Lina. Find the time it will take the two of them to finish painting the house.

4. It takes Chuck 5 hours to split a cord of wood, and it takes his sister 3 hours. How long will it take them working together?

5. Paula estimates it will take her 4 hours to type a report but only 3 hours for her brother to do it. If they both type at the same time, how long will it take?

6. Ben thinks it will take him 6 hours to replant the window boxes for his apartment, and Rachel thinks it will take her 4 hours. How long will it take them working together?

Solve.

7. The main engine of a rocket fired alone can burn all the fuel in 50 seconds. The secondary engine fired alone can burn all the fuel in 80 seconds. How long can both engines be fired together before all the fuel is consumed?

8. A pump can fill a reservoir tank in 25 minutes. A second pump takes twice as long. How long will it take to fill the tank using both pumps?

9. A heater takes 20 minutes to heat a room from 10° to 20°C. If a second heater is also used, it takes only 12 minutes. How long will it take the second heater working alone to produce this temperature change?

10. Nancy takes an hour and a half to rake the lawn, but it takes her only 40 minutes if her sister rakes, too. How long does it take her sister to rake the lawn alone?

11. One pipe can fill a tank in 15 minutes. If a second pipe is also used, the tank can be filled in 9 minutes. How long will it take the second pipe, by itself, to fill the tank?

12. A battery can operate one radio receiver for four times as long as it can operate another radio receiver. If both receivers are operated together, the battery will last 16 hours. How long will the battery operate each receiver alone?

B 13. Lance can do a job in 30 minutes, Bob in 40 minutes, and Sid in 50 minutes. How long will it take them if they all work together?

14. Lou can plow a field in 5 hours using a tractor, and Verna can plow the field in 6 hours using a tractor. After plowing for 2 hours, Lou is joined by Verna. How long will it take them to finish plowing the field?

15. Mrs. Williams can feed the animals in her pet shop in 30 minutes, and her assistant can feed them in 40 minutes. If Mrs. Williams had been feeding the animals for 15 minutes before she was joined by her assistant, how long did it take them to finish feeding the animals?

16. The fill pipe can fill a tank in 3 hours and the drain pipe can drain the tank in 1 hour. If both pipes are accidentally opened, how long will it take to empty a tank filled with water?

17. Dan and Val addressed all the invitations to the sophomore party in 2 hours. If Dan can write three invitations in the time it takes Val to write two, how long would it have taken Val to address all the invitations by herself?

18. John can type twice as fast as Mitch. Together they can type a report in 30 minutes. How long will it take Mitch by himself?

C 19. Ethan can do a job in 15 hours and Robin can do it in 18 hours. Ethan works for 6 hours alone and then works with Robin for three more hours before quitting. How long does it take Robin to finish the job?

20. A pump can fill an oil tank in 18 hours. Beginning with an empty tank, the pump and a second pump fill $\frac{3}{5}$ of the tank in 6 hours. If the first pump is then shut off, how long will it take the second pump to finish filling the tank?

Career Note Bilingual Math Teacher

Cuarenta y dos obreros construyen en 32 días 1320 m de un camino. ¿Qué longitud construirán 28 obreros en 17 días, trabajando en las mismas condiciones?

Algebra teachers who have Spanish-speaking students in their classes, might assign this problem as homework. Here is a translation.

Forty-two workers construct 1320 m of road in 32 days. How many meters will 28 workers construct in 17 days, working under the same conditions?

Can you follow the solution below?

Solución: 1°   42 obr.   1320 m

           1 obr. $\dfrac{1320 \text{ m}}{42}$

          28 obr. $\dfrac{1320 \text{ m} \times 28}{42} = 880 \text{ m}$

     2°   32 días   880 m

           1 día $\dfrac{880 \text{ m}}{32}$

          17 días $\dfrac{880 \text{ m} \times 17}{32} = 467{,}50 \text{ m}$

Bilingual mathematics teachers must be certified to teach in public schools. For certification a bachelor's degree in mathematics and courses in education are required. In addition, bilingual teachers must be fluent in two languages.

Self-Test 4

Solve.

1. How much water must be added to 20 kg of a 70% antifreeze solution to produce a 50% antifreeze solution? Obj. 7-7, p. 259

2. A test engineer has 200 kg of gasohol that is 10% alcohol. How much alcohol must the engineer add to produce a mixture that is 20% alcohol?

3. John can wash the windows in 40 minutes. Sue can wash the windows in 1 hour. How long will it take them if they work together? Obj. 7-8, p. 263

4. Nate can mow the lawn in 6 hours. Jane can mow the lawn in 4 hours. Jane mows the lawn for 1 hour and then is joined by Nate. How long will it take them to finish mowing the lawn?

Check your answers with those at the back of the book.

Application Gear Ratios

The *crank wheel* on a bicycle has 48 teeth. When the bicycle's *free wheel* with 24 teeth is engaged, the *gear ratio* is said to be 48:24, or 2:1. Shifting to the free wheel with 30 teeth changes the gear ratio to 48:30, or 1.6:1.

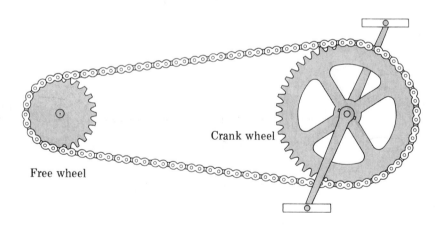

Crank wheel

Free wheel

1. Which gear ratio, 2:1 or 1.6:1, makes it easier to pedal uphill?

2. Find out about the gear ratios in a 10-speed bicycle and in an automobile.

Chapter Summary

1. A *ratio* of two numbers is their quotient. The ratio 6 to 8 can be written as $6:8$ or more simply as $3:4$ or $\frac{3}{4}$ or 0.75. If you are told that the ratio of two numbers is $5:7$, you can represent the numbers as $5x$ and $7x$.

2. A *proportion* is an equation stating that two ratios are equal. Usually the first step in solving a proportion is to equate the product of the means and the product of the extremes. Thus,

$$\text{if } \frac{a}{b} = \frac{c}{d}, \text{ then } ad = bc.$$

3. You can solve equations with fractional coefficients and *fractional equations* by multiplying each term of the equation by the LCD. This step will eliminate all fractions. Similarly, you can eliminate decimals from an equation by multiplying each term by a suitable power of 10.

4. *Percent* means hundredths. Three basic operations with percents are finding a percent of a number, finding what percent one number is of another, and finding a number when a percent of the number is known (see the examples on pages 251–252).

5. When solving word problems involving percents, it is often convenient to express the percent as a decimal. For example:
$$7\tfrac{1}{2}\% = 7.5\% = 0.075$$

6. To solve certain word problems, you need to choose the formula that applies to the problem. For example:
$$\text{Interest} = \text{Principal} \times \text{rate}$$
$$\text{Cost} = \text{Number of kilograms} \times \text{price per kilogram}$$
$$\text{Amount of Salt} = \text{Amount of mixture} \times \% \text{ salt}$$
$$\text{Amount of Work} = \text{Number of hours worked} \times \text{hourly rate}$$

Once you have chosen the appropriate formula, you can use it to make a chart that will help you solve the problem.

Chapter Review

1. State the ratio of $4 to 75 cents in simplest form. 7-1

   a. $4:75$ **b.** $75:4$ **c.** $3:16$ **d.** $16:3$

2. Two numbers are in the ratio of $5:3$ and their sum is 72. Find the smaller number.

   a. 8   **b.** 9   **c.** 27   **d.** 45

3. A pile of nickels and quarters is worth $4.40. There are two more quarters than nickels. How many coins are there?

   a. 13   **b.** 15   **c.** 28   **d.** 32

4. Solve for x: $\dfrac{35}{16} = \dfrac{21x}{32}$ 7-2

   a. $\dfrac{10}{3}$ **b.** $\dfrac{16}{3}$ **c.** $\dfrac{16}{21}$ **d.** $\dfrac{32}{21}$

5. Solve for p: $\dfrac{q}{p} = r$

   a. $p = qr$ **b.** $p = \dfrac{q}{r}$ **c.** $p = \dfrac{r}{q}$ **d.** $p = \dfrac{1}{qr}$

6. If 18 grapefruit cost \$6.30, how much will 24 grapefruit cost?

   a. \$.35   **b.** \$7.20   **c.** \$8.40   **d.** \$9.60

7. Solve for x: $\dfrac{3x}{4} + \dfrac{x}{6} = \dfrac{11}{3}$ 7-3

   a. 4   **b.** 2   **c.** $\dfrac{1}{4}$ **d.** $\dfrac{1}{2}$

8. Solve for n: $\dfrac{3n-1}{5} - \dfrac{2n-4}{3} = 1$

   a. 2   **b.** -2 **c.** 38   **d.** -38

9. Three fourths of a number is 6 less than seven eighths of the number. What is the number?

   a. 8   **b.** 16   **c.** 32   **d.** 48

10. Solve for t: $\dfrac{3}{t} + \dfrac{1}{2} = \dfrac{5}{6}$ 7-4

   a. 3   **b.** 6   **c.** 9   **d.** 12

11. Solve for x: $\dfrac{2}{x^2 - 1} = \dfrac{3}{x+1} + \dfrac{1}{x-1}$

   a. no solutions   **b.** $\{1\}$ **c.** $\{-1\}$ **d.** $\{-1, 1\}$

12. What is 1.5% of 240? 7-5

   a. 0.036   **b.** 0.36   **c.** 3.6   **d.** 36

13. 8% of a number is 120. What is the number?

   a. 9.6   **b.** 960   **c.** 150   **d.** 1500

14. Solve for x: $1.2x - 0.072 = 0.96x$

   a. 0.03   **b.** 0.3   **c.** 3   **d.** 30

15. At a preseason sale, a \$180 bicycle was sold for \$150. What is the percent of discount? 7-6

   a. 15%   **b.** $16\dfrac{2}{3}\%$ **c.** 18%   **d.** 20%

16. A sporting goods store sells a pair of ice skates for 40% more than they cost the store. How much did the skates cost the store if they were sold to a customer for \$70?

   a. \$28   **b.** \$42   **c.** \$50   **d.** \$56

17. How many kilograms of water should be mixed with 60 kg of a 30% acid solution to make a 10% acid solution?

    a. 20 kg   **b.** 90 kg   **c.** 120 kg   **d.** 180 kg

7-7

18. Laura can paint her garage in 12 hours and her sister can do it in 8 hours. How long would it take them working together?

    a. 4 h 48 min   **b.** 5 h   **c.** 5 h 15 min   **d.** 5 h 20 min

7-8

Chapter Test

State each ratio in simplest form.

1. 48 minutes to 2 hours   **2.** $2x^2 : 4x$

7-1

3. Find the ratio of x to y if $9x - 6y = 0$.

4. The ratio of boys to girls in the sophomore class is $7:8$. There are 135 sophomores in all. How many are girls?

Solve for x.

5. $\dfrac{3}{2x} = \dfrac{7}{4}$ **6.** $\dfrac{3x - 5}{4} = \dfrac{5x - 11}{6}$

7-2

7. $\dfrac{1}{x} = \dfrac{a}{b}$ **8.** $\dfrac{4}{3}(x - 2) - \dfrac{1}{2}(2x + 4) = 1$

9. $\dfrac{2x}{3} - \dfrac{x}{5} = \dfrac{1}{10}$ **10.** $\dfrac{x}{2} - \dfrac{5x - 3}{4} = 0$

7-3

11. $\dfrac{3}{x + 2} + \dfrac{2}{x} = 1$ **12.** $2x - 8 = 0.04$

7-4

13. What is 140% of 30?

7-5

14. What percent of 72 is 18?

15. Mrs. Martindale invested part of $6000 at 8% and the rest at 10%. Her investments earn $510 in a year. How much is invested at each rate?

7-6

16. A car dealer receives a 4% commission on each sale. If the commission for selling a new car was $288, how much did the car cost?

17. A $120 surfboard is on sale for $96. What is the percent of the discount?

18. Ted has x nickels and $2x$ dimes worth $4.50. Find x.

19. How many kilograms of pure salt must be added to 8 kg of a 10% salt solution to obtain a 20% salt solution?

7-7

20. Joy can do a job in 2 hours and Mark can do it in 3 hours. How long will it take them if they work together?

7-8

Cumulative Review (Chapters 1-7)

Simplify each expression.

1. $5x - 2y + 3(2y - x)$

2. $(-m^2n)^3(-5mn^3)^2$

3. $7cd(-d^3 + 2cd^2 + 3c)$

4. $(2r + 3st)^2$

5. $(2b^3)^4 \div (4b^2)^3$

6. $(6x^4 - 3x^3 + x) \div x^2$

7. $(8w^2 - z)(2w^2 + 3z)$

8. $(t^5 - 3m)(t^5 + 3m)$

9. $(9g - 5 + h)(g - 4)$

Evaluate if $p = \frac{1}{2}$, $q = 8$, $r = 3$, $s = -5$, and $t = -2$.

10. $2(pqs - rt) + 26$

11. $r^2q - s \div p^2$

12. $7st \div (qt - rs)$

Factor completely if possible. If not possible, write "prime."

13. $3c^2 + 27c - 210$

14. $4h^2 - 20hr^2 + 25r^4$

15. $2d - 2 - cd^2 + cd$

16. $-81xy^2 + 121x^3$

17. $7j^2 + 15jm + 4m^2$

18. $-18 + 33v - 9v^2$

Express in simplest form.

19. $\dfrac{700x}{1.4x}$

20. $\dfrac{2d^2 + 8d - 10}{4d^2 + 20d}$

21. $\dfrac{-40r^3s^2t + 72r^2s^3t}{8r^2s^2t}$

22. $\dfrac{3e^2 - e - 2}{3e^2 + 5e + 2} \cdot \dfrac{e + 1}{2e^2}$

23. $\dfrac{2}{(m + 1)^2} - \dfrac{m}{m + 1}$

24. $\dfrac{8y^2 - 8z^2}{2y + 2z} \div \dfrac{yz - z^2}{y^2z^2}$

25. $\dfrac{8k^2 + 10k + 2}{8k + 2}$

26. $\dfrac{5j^2 - 17j - 40}{j - 5}$

27. $\dfrac{3a}{a - b} + \dfrac{2a}{a + b} + 1$

Solve. (The equation may be an identity or have no root.)

28. $-8a + 7 = 3(a - 5)$

29. $6(5x - 2) = 12 + 30x$

30. $2k + 5 = 0.3k + 0.41$

31. $t(2t - 9) = -7$

32. $m^2 - 14m = 32$

33. $\dfrac{4}{3c - 2} + \dfrac{1}{3c} = \dfrac{1}{c}$

34. $\dfrac{1}{2} = \dfrac{6z + 2}{9z + 5}$

35. $\dfrac{3}{4}n - 8 = 2n - \dfrac{1}{2}$

36. $\dfrac{3w - 2}{w - 3} + \dfrac{16}{w + 6} = 10$

Solve.

37. A copying machine can duplicate a report 50 times in 55 min. An older model takes 70 min. How long would it take the machines to do the job working together?

38. How many liters of water must be added to 5 L of a 24% dextrose solution to produce a 16% solution?

39. A company invested its profits in an account paying $9\frac{1}{2}\%$. If the money had been invested at 9%, the annual interest would have been $30 less. Find the amount invested.

Maintaining Skills

Simplify.

SAMPLE 1 $3(x + 5y) - 2(-x + y) = 3x + 15y + 2x - 2y = 5x + 13y$

1. $-m^2 + 3 - 5m + m^2 + m - 9$
2. $12t + 4s - 13 + 2s - 9t - 4$
3. $-5(x - 2y) + 3x - y$
4. $-(j - 2k - 3) + 4(2j + 7)$
5. $2(w + 3z) - 3(w + 2z)$
6. $-7(-3r^2 - 1) + 9(2r - 5r^2)$
7. $\frac{1}{4}(-12h^2 + 8h) - \frac{1}{2}(6h - 4)$
8. $-\frac{2}{3}(18d + 12e) - 5(2e - d)$

SAMPLE 2 $(-3b^2c^3)(2abc^2) = (-3 \cdot 2)(a)(b^2 \cdot b)(c^3 \cdot c^2) = -6ab^3c^5$

9. $(-7x^2yz^4)(-2x^3y^2z)$
10. $(2m^2n)(-m^3p)(-3n^2p^2)$
11. $3t^n \cdot t^2 \cdot 8t^n$
12. $(-2b)(4b^4) + (13b^3)(b^2)$

SAMPLE 3 $(-5rs^3)^2 = (-5)^2(r^2)(s^3)^2 = 25r^2s^6$

13. $6c^2(-3c^4)^2$
14. $(5t)^2(-2t^3)^3$
15. $(2m^2n)^2(-mn^2)^3$
16. $2rs^2(-r^3s^2)^3 + (-3r^5s^4)^2$
17. $c(2cd^2)^6 - c^3d^4(-cd^2)^4$

Multiply.

SAMPLE 4 $2t^3u(u^2 + 4tu - 5t^2) = 2t^3u^3 + 8t^4u^2 - 10t^5u$

18. $2r(-9r^5 + 7r^3 + 12)$
19. $-8b^3(-3b^2 + b - 6)$
20. $-3m(m^4 - 6m^2t + 9t^2)$
21. $7pq(-2p^2q^3 + pq^4 - 5q^5)$
22. $5j^4k^3(3jk - 2j^3k^4 - 7j^5 + 10k^8)$

SAMPLE 5
$$\begin{aligned}(3c - d)(2c + 7d) &= 3c(2c + 7d) - d(2c + 7d) \\ &= 6c^2 + 21cd - 2cd - 7d^2 \\ &= 6c^2 + 19cd - 7d^2\end{aligned}$$

23. $(y + 9)(y - 5)$
24. $(3v + 2)(v + 1)$
25. $(6k - 7)(k + 4)$
26. $(8b - 3)(8b + 3)$
27. $(2g - 3)^2$
28. $(5x + 2)(3x + 2)$
29. $(r - 5)(2r^2 - r - 9)$
30. $(z^3 + 1)(z^3 - 1)$

The speed of sea gulls relative to the ground depends on their air speed and the speed of the wind. Such relations can be described using systems of equations in more than one variable.

8

LINEAR EQUATIONS AND SYSTEMS

USING TWO VARIABLES

8-1 *Coordinates in a Plane*

OBJECTIVE To graph ordered pairs of numbers in a coordinate plane.

In Section 2-1 you learned to graph a number as a point on a number line. An *ordered pair* of numbers such as (2, −3) can be graphed as a point in a plane. You can construct a "number plane" as follows:

1. Draw a horizontal number line, called the **horizontal axis.**
2. Draw a second number line intersecting the first at right angles so that both number lines have the same zero point, or **origin** (O). The second number line is called the **vertical axis.**
3. Indicate the positive direction on each axis by an arrowhead. The positive direction is usually to the right on the horizontal axis and upward on the vertical axis, as shown in the first diagram.

It is convenient to draw the axes on squared paper, using the length of the side of a square as the unit of each axis. The axes separate the plane into four regions, called **quadrants,** numbered as shown.

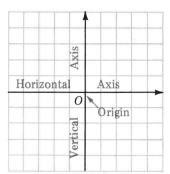

To locate the graph of the ordered pair $(2, -3)$:

1. Find the graph of 2 on the horizontal axis.
2. Find the graph of -3 on the vertical axis.
3. Think of a vertical line through the graph of 2 and a horizontal line through the graph of -3. Draw a dot at the point where these lines intersect. This point is the **graph of $(2, -3)$.**

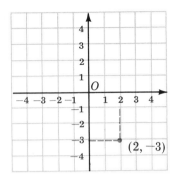

Locating a point in this way is called *plotting* the point. If you label the graph of $(2, -3)$ with the letter P, you can also refer to the point as $P(2, -3)$.

To find the ordered pair of numbers corresponding to point B shown at the right:

1. Think of a vertical line through point B. The coordinate (page 30) of the point where this line meets the horizontal axis is called the **abscissa** of B, namely -3.
2. Think of a horizontal line through B. The coordinate of the point where this line meets the vertical axis is called the **ordinate** of B, namely 4.

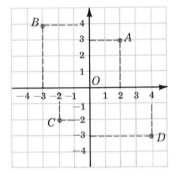

Together, the abscissa and the ordinate of B are called the **coordinates** of B. The coordinates are written as an ordered pair with the abscissa first, $(-3, 4)$. Verify the coordinates of the other points labeled in the diagram above:

$$A(2, 3) \qquad C(-2, -2) \qquad D(4, -3) \qquad O(0, 0)$$

Notice that

in the *first quadrant*, both coordinates are positive;
in the *second quadrant*, the abscissa is negative but the ordinate is positive;
in the *third quadrant*, both coordinates are negative;
in the *fourth quadrant*, the abscissa is positive but the ordinate is negative.

Points on the axes are not considered to be in any quadrant.

When a coordinate system is set up on a plane as shown in this section, the axes are called **coordinate axes** and the plane is called a **coordinate plane.** In working with a coordinate plane, you take the following facts for granted:

1. Each ordered pair of real numbers is paired with exactly one point in the coordinate plane.
2. Each point in the coordinate plane is paired with exactly one ordered pair of real numbers.

Oral Exercises

Exercises 1-44 refer to the diagram below.

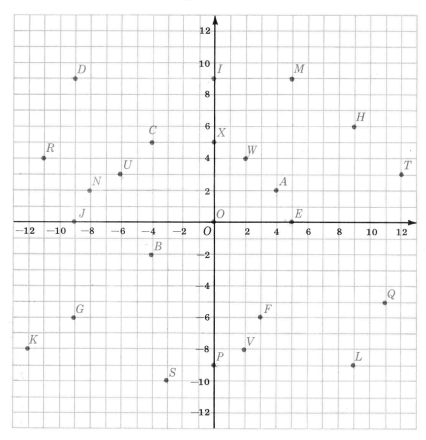

1-24. State the coordinates of each point named by a letter (A-X).

Name the quadrant in which each point is located.

25. A	**26.** F	**27.** N	**28.** S
29. D	**30.** L	**31.** T	**32.** B

Name the point that is the graph of each ordered pair.

33. $(3, -6)$	**34.** $(-6, 3)$	**35.** $(-9, 9)$	**36.** $(9, -9)$
37. $(-8, 2)$	**38.** $(2, -8)$	**39.** $(4, 2)$	**40.** $(2, 4)$
41. $(5, 0)$	**42.** $(0, 5)$	**43.** $(0, 9)$	**44.** $(-9, 0)$

Name the quadrants containing each point described, assuming that the points are not on the axes.

45. The abscissa is 2.
46. The ordinate is -6.
47. The abscissa is -3.
48. The ordinate is 4.
49. The ordinate is negative.
50. The abscissa is positive.
51. The ordinate is positive.
52. The abscissa is negative.
53. The abscissa is 0.5.
54. The ordinate is -0.2.
55. The ordinate equals the abscissa.
56. The ordinate is the opposite of the abscissa.

Written Exercises

Plot the graph of each ordered pair.

A   **1.** $(-3, 4)$ **2.** $(3, -4)$ **3.** $(-3, -4)$ **4.** $(3, 4)$

     5. $(0, -3)$ **6.** $(3, 0)$ **7.** $(0, 3)$ **8.** $(-3, 0)$

     9. $(-1, -1)$ **10.** $(4, 4)$ **11.** $(-4, 6)$ **12.** $(5, -3)$

     13. $\left(2\frac{1}{2}, 3\right)$ **14.** $(5, 2.5)$ **15.** $(-2.5, 6)$ **16.** $(3.5, 3.5)$

In Exercises 17-20, the coordinates of the vertices of a geometric figure are given. Plot the points and name the geometric figures.

17. $A(2, 5)$ $B(8, 5)$ $C(5, -3)$

18. $D(-6, -9)$ $E(-12, -3)$ $F(-6, 3)$ $G(0, -3)$

19. $H(4, 2)$ $I(11, 2)$ $J(11, -2)$ $K(4, -2)$

20. $L(-5, 7)$ $M(1, 10)$ $N(1, 6)$ $P(-5, 3)$

Use the diagram from the Oral Exercises on page 277 to name the point(s) described.

B   **21.** The ordinate equals the abscissa.

     22. The abscissa is the opposite of the ordinate.

     23. The abscissa is 2 more than the ordinate.

     24. The abscissa is 2 less than the ordinate.

     25. The abscissa is half the ordinate.

     26. The abscissa is twice the ordinate.

     27. The sum of the abscissa and the ordinate is 6.

     28. The sum of the abscissa and the ordinate is -3.

     29. The difference between the abscissa and the ordinate is 3.

     30. The ordinate divided by the abscissa is zero.

31. Three vertices of a square are $A(-1, -9)$, $B(3, -1)$, and $C(-5, 3)$. Plot the points. Then find the coordinates of the missing vertex D.

32. Three vertices of a rectangle are $E(2, 8)$, $F(5, 5)$, and $G(-1, -1)$. Plot the points. Then find the coordinates of the missing vertex H.

C **33.** Three vertices of a parallelogram are $A(2, 1)$, $B(1, -2)$, and $C(4, -5)$. Plot the points. Then find the coordinates of the missing vertex D if D is in the fourth quadrant. (Two answers)

34. Three vertices of a parallelogram are $E(2, 4)$, $F(6, -6)$, and $G(0, -4)$. Plot the points. Then find all possible coordinates of the missing vertex H. Sketch the possible parallelograms.

35. Plot any ten points such that the sum of the coordinates of each point is 10. What do you notice about the points?

Career Note Drafter

In constructing a house, a jet plane, an air conditioner, or a television set, workers follow detailed engineering diagrams made by drafters. These drawings, made from several sides of the object, indicate all dimensions. The drafter prepares these drawings from sketches and specifications obtained from the architect and engineer.

Technical institutes, junior colleges, and vocational schools may offer the training required for a career as a drafter. Courses should be taken in mathematics, the physical sciences, and mechanical drawing.

8-2 *Equations in Two Variables*

OBJECTIVE   To solve equations in two variables over given domains of
the variables.

Some equations have only one variable. For example:

$$2x - 7 = -1$$

Any value of x that makes the equation a true statement is a solution of
the equation.

Some equations have two variables. For example:

$$2x + 3y = 8$$

Any *combination* of values of x and y that make the equation a true
statement is a solution of the equation. For example, you can check that
if $x = 1$ and $y = 2$, the preceding equation becomes the true statement

$$2(1) + 3(2) = 2 + 6 = 8.$$

It is customary to write a solution of an equation in the two variables
x and y as an ordered pair (x, y), with the value of x written first. Thus,
$(1, 2)$ is a solution of $2x + 3y = 8$. Here are a few more solutions of this
equation:

$(4, 0)$ is a solution because $2(4) + 3(0) = 8 + 0 = 8.$
$(7, -2)$ is a solution because $2(7) + 3(-2) = 14 - 6 = 8.$
$(-2, 4)$ is a solution because $2(-2) + 3(4) = -4 + 12 = 8.$
$(4, -2)$ is *not* a solution because $2(4) + 3(-2) = 8 - 6 \neq 8.$

Any ordered pair of values that convert an equation in two variables
into a true statement is called a **solution** of the equation. The set of all
solutions is called the **solution set** of the equation. Finding the solution
set is called **solving** the equation.

EXAMPLE   Solve $2x + 3y = 6$ if x and y are whole numbers.

SOLUTION

1. Solve the given equation for y in terms of x.

$$2x + 3y = 6$$
$$3y = 6 - 2x$$
$$y = 2 - \tfrac{2}{3}x$$

x	$y = 2 - \tfrac{2}{3}x$	Solution
0	$2 - \tfrac{2}{3}(0) = 2$	$(0, 2)$
1	$2 - \tfrac{2}{3}(1) = 1\tfrac{1}{3}$	No
2	$2 - \tfrac{2}{3}(2) = \tfrac{2}{3}$	No
3	$2 - \tfrac{2}{3}(3) = 0$	$(3, 0)$
Values of x greater than 3 produce negative values of y.		

2. Replace x with successive whole numbers
and calculate the corresponding values of y.

3. If the value of y found in Step 2 is a whole
number, then the pair of corresponding values is a solution of the equation.

∴ The solution set is $\{(0, 2), (3, 0)\}$. *Answer*

Oral Exercises

Assume that x and y represent real numbers. State whether or not each ordered pair of numbers shown is a solution of the given equation.

1. $x + y = 6$; $(4, 3)$, $(1, 5)$
2. $x - 2y = 10$; $(0, -5)$, $(0, 5)$
3. $2x + y = 4$; $(1, 3)$, $(-1, 3)$
4. $3x + y = 6$; $(1, 3)$, $(2, 0)$
5. $-3x + 2y = 12$; $(0, 6)$, $(-4, 0)$
6. $7x - 5y = -3$; $(4, 5)$, $(-1, -2)$
7. $y = x^2$; $(2, 4)$, $(4, 2)$
8. $y^2 = 2x$; $(2, -2)$, $(-2, 2)$
9. $x^2 + y^2 = 25$; $(-3, -4)$, $(3, 4)$
10. $x^2 - y^2 = 0$; $(1, -1)$, $(2, 2)$
11. $xy = 4$; $\left(\frac{1}{8}, 2\right)$, $(-2, 2)$
12. $4x^2 + 9y^2 = 36$; $(-3, 0)$, $(4, 0)$

Solve each equation for y in terms of x.

13. $x + y = 4$
14. $x - y = 7$
15. $y - x = -6$
16. $3x = 5 + y$
17. $2x = 8 - y$
18. $2x + 2y = 8$

Written Exercises

Complete each ordered pair to form a solution of the given equation. Assume that x and y represent real numbers.

A
1. $y = x - 3$; $(8, ?)$, $(5, ?)$, $(3, ?)$
2. $y = 2x + 1$; $(2, ?)$ $(-1, ?)$ $(0, ?)$
3. $y = \frac{1}{2}x - 2$; $(4, ?)$, $(2, ?)$, $(0, ?)$
4. $y = 3 - 2x$; $(1, ?)$, $(-1, ?)$, $(-2, ?)$
5. $y = \frac{3}{x + 1}$; $(2, ?)$, $(5, ?)$, $(-4, ?)$
6. $y = \frac{1}{1 - 2x}$; $(0, ?)$, $(-1, ?)$, $(2, ?)$
7. $x + y = 8$; $(4, ?)$, $(2, ?)$, $(-3, ?)$
8. $2x + y = 12$; $(1, ?)$, $(-1, ?)$, $(0, ?)$
9. $x - y = 4$; $(-1, ?)$, $(0, ?)$, $(3, ?)$
10. $2x - y = -8$; $(0, ?)$, $(3, ?)$, $(-3, ?)$
11. $2x + 3y = 6$; $(3, ?)$, $(-3, ?)$, $(0, ?)$
12. $2x - 3y = 12$; $(0, ?)$, $(1, ?)$, $(-1, ?)$

Solve each equation for y in terms of x.

13. $x + y = 6$
14. $2x + y = 8$
15. $x - y = 6$
16. $y - x = -4$
17. $2x + 3y = 12$
18. $2x - 3y = 9$

Find the solution set of each equation if both x and y are members of $\{-2, -1, 0, 1, 2\}$.

19. $x + y = 1$ **20.** $x - y = 3$ **21.** $x + 2y = {}^{\vee}-1$

22. $2x + y = 4$ **23.** $3x + y = 5$ **24.** $2x - 3y = -5$

Find the solution set of each equation if both x and y are whole numbers.

B 25. $x + y = 8$ **26.** $x + 2y = 10$

27. $\frac{3}{2}x + y = 5 + x$ **28.** $x + \frac{4}{3}y = y + 10$

Find the solution set of each equation if both x and y are members of $\{0, 1, 2, 3, 4\}$.

29. $y = x^2$ **30.** $y = \frac{1}{2}x^2$ **31.** $y = x^2 - 1$ **32.** $y = x^2 + x$

33. $x^2 + y^2 = 25$ **34.** $xy = 8$ **35.** $x - xy = 4$ **36.** $x - y^2 = 0$

In each exercise, find the ordered pair that is a solution of both equations if x and y are whole numbers.

C 37. $x + y = 5;\ \ x + 2y = 9$ **38.** $x + 2y = 7;\ \ 2x + y = 8$

39. $x + y = 8;\ \ x + \frac{1}{2}y = 5$ **40.** $x + 2y = 7;\ \ x - y = 4$

ℏistorical ℕote Coordinates

Ancient Egyptians and Romans used the idea of coordinates in land surveying. The Egyptian hieroglyphic for surveyed districts was a grid.

In the seventeenth century, two mathematicians, Pierre de Fermat and René Descartes, used a version of coordinates in their work. The plane coordinate system is sometimes called a rectangular Cartesian coordinate system in honor of Descartes.

8-3 *The Graph of a Linear Equation in Two Variables*

OBJECTIVE   To graph a linear equation in two variables.

To graph the solution set of an equation in x and y, it is customary to take the horizontal axis as the **x-axis** and the vertical axis as the **y-axis.** For ordered pairs represented by (x, y), you may call the abscissa the **x-coordinate** and the ordinate the **y-coordinate.**

When x and y are whole numbers, the equation

$$x + 2y = 6$$

has the solution set $\{(0, 3),\ (2, 2),\ (4, 1),\ (6, 0)\}$. Do you see that the graphs of the solutions, shown at the left below, appear to lie on a straight line?

 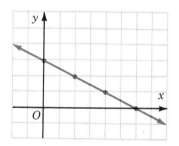

In fact, when x and y are real numbers, each solution of $x + 2y = 6$ gives the coordinates of a point on the line shown above, and the coordinates of each point on the line satisfy the equation. The line is called the **graph of the equation** in the coordinate plane, and the equation is called **an equation of the line.** The equation $x + 2y = 6$ is an example of a *linear equation.*

Any equation which can be written in the form

$$Ax + By = C$$

where A, B, and C are real numbers with A and B not both zero is called a **linear equation in two variables** x and y. If A, B, and C are integers, the equation is said to be in **standard form.**

Note that in a linear equation each term is a constant or a monomial of degree 1.

$x + 2y = 6,\quad 3y - \dfrac{1}{2}x = 3,\quad$ and $\quad x = 5\quad$ are linear equations.

$x^2 + 2y = 6,\quad 3y - \dfrac{2}{x} = 3,\quad$ and $\quad xy = 5\quad$ are *not* linear equations.

You may take the following facts for granted.

> When the variables represent real numbers:
>
> 1. The graph of every linear equation in two variables is a line in a coordinate plane.
> 2. Every line in a coordinate plane is the graph of a linear equation in two variables.

Throughout the rest of this book you may assume, unless otherwise directed, that both variables in an equation in two variables represent real numbers.

Since two points determine a line, you need to find only two solutions to graph a linear equation. As a check it is good practice to find a third solution. It is often convenient to plot the two points where the graph crosses the x-axis ($y = 0$) and the y-axis ($x = 0$).

EXAMPLE 1 Graph $2x - 3y = 6$ in a coordinate plane.

SOLUTION

Let $y = 0$: $\quad 2x - 3(0) = \quad 6$
$$ 2x = \quad 6$$
$$ x = \quad 3; \; Solution \; (3, 0)$$

Let $x = 0$: $\quad 2(0) - 3y = \quad 6$
$$ -3y = \quad 6$$
$$ y = \; -2; \; Solution \; (0, -2)$$

A third solution is $(6, 2)$.

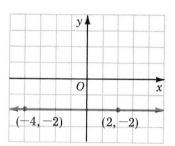

EXAMPLE 2 **a.** Graph $x = 3$ in a coordinate plane.

b. Graph $y = -2$ in a coordinate plane.

SOLUTION

a. The equation places no restriction on y. All points with x-coordinate 3 are graphs of solutions. The graph of $x = 3$ is a vertical line.

b. The equation places no restriction on x. All points with y-coordinate -2 are graphs of solutions. The graph of $y = -2$ is a horizontal line.

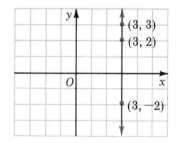

Oral Exercises

State whether or not each equation is linear.

1. $x - 2y = 3$ **2.** $\frac{1}{3}x + \frac{1}{2}y = 6$ **3.** $xy = 8$ **4.** $y = x^2$

5. $y - 3x = 0$ **6.** $y - \frac{3}{x} = 2$ **7.** $y^2 - 3x = 2$ **8.** $y = 6$

9. $x = 3$ **10.** $\frac{1}{x} = y$ **11.** $\frac{2}{x} + \frac{2}{y} = 6$ **12.** $\frac{x}{2} + \frac{y}{2} = 6$

Classify each statement as true or false.

13. A standard form of the equation $x - \frac{1}{2}y = 3$ is $2x - y = 6$.

14. Every equation in two variables x and y is a linear equation.

15. A horizontal line in a coordinate plane is the graph of a linear equation.

16. The graph of $x = 0$ is the y-axis.

17. The graph of $y = -3$ crosses the x-axis at $(-3, 0)$.

18. The point $(0, 0)$ is in the graph of $x - y = 6$.

19. The x-coordinate of every solution of $x = 10$ is 10.

20. The graph of $x + y = 3$ passes through the point $(0, 3)$ and the point $(3, 0)$.

Written Exercises

Complete the coordinates so that each ordered pair is a solution of the given equation.

A **1.** $x + 2y = 8$; $(0, ?), (?, 0), (2, ?)$
   2. $2x + y = 6$; $(0, ?), (?, 0), (?, 2)$
   3. $x - y = 7$; $(0, ?), (?, 0), (?, 1)$
   4. $2x + 3y = 12$; $(0, ?), (?, 0), (3, ?)$

Find the coordinates of the points where the graph of each equation crosses (a) the x-axis and (b) the y-axis.

5. $3x + 4y = 12$ **6.** $4x - 3y = 24$ **7.** $3x + 4y = 0$ **8.** $3x = 4y$

Graph each equation in a coordinate plane.

9. $x = 5$ **10.** $y = -2$ **11.** $x + y = 5$ **12.** $x - y = 5$
13. $y = x + 1$ **14.** $y = 2x - 1$ **15.** $x + 2y = 6$ **16.** $2x - y = 12$
17. $2x - 3y = -6$ **18.** $3x + 2y = -6$ **19.** $2x + 5y = 10$ **20.** $2x + 5y = -10$

Write each equation in standard form. Then graph the equation.

B 21. $3 + x = y + 5$ 22. $2 - y = x - 6$ 23. $9 - y = 8 - x$

     24. $2x - y = 3x + 6$ 25. $2y - 3 - x = 4x$ 26. $2y + 5x = 3x - 2$

Graph each pair of equations on the same set of axes. Write the coordinates of the point where the graphs cross, and show that the coordinates satisfy both equations.

27. $x + y = 7; \quad x - y = 1$ 28. $2x + y = -1; \quad x - 2y = -8$

29. $4x - y = 14; \quad 3x + 2y = 5$ 30. $2x + 3y = y - x; \quad 2x - 3 = 2x + y - 3$

Graph each pair of equations on the same set of axes. How are the lines related to each other?

C 31. $x + y = 2; \quad x + y = 5$ 32. $x - 2y = 6; \quad x - 2y = 1$

     33. $x + 3y = 3; \quad 2x + 6y = 12$ 34. $x + y = 4; \quad x - y = 4$

     35. $2x - y = 6; \quad x + 2y = 6$ 36. $2x - 3y = 12; \quad 3x + 2y = 6$

Self-Test 1

VOCABULARY   horizontal axis (p. 275)   solution of an equation in two
                            origin (p. 275)   variables (p. 280)
                            vertical axis (p. 275) x-axis (p. 283)
                            quadrant (p. 275) y-axis (p. 283)
                            graph of an ordered pair of x-coordinate (p. 283)
                                numbers (p. 276) y-coordinate (p. 283)
                            abscissa (p. 276)   graph of an equation (p. 283)
                            ordinate (p. 276)   equation of a line (p. 283)
                            coordinates (p. 276)   linear equation in two varia-
                            coordinate axes (p. 276)   bles (p. 283)
                            coordinate plane (p. 276)   standard form (p. 283)

Plot the graph of each ordered pair in a coordinate plane.

1. $(2, -2)$ 2. $(-1, 3)$ Obj. 8-1, p. 275

3. Is $(-2, 0)$ a solution of $x - 2y = 4$ if x and y are real   Obj. 8-2, p. 280
    numbers?

4. Find the solution set of $x + y = 3$ if x and y are whole
    numbers.

5. Select the equations which are linear.   Obj. 8-3, p. 283

    a. $5x - y = 2$ **b.** $x = 4$ **c.** $3x^2 + y = 2$

6. Graph the equation $y = x + 3$.

Check your answers with those at the back of the book.

286   *CHAPTER 8*

SOLVING SYSTEMS OF LINEAR EQUATIONS

8-4 *The Graphic Method*

OBJECTIVE   To use graphs to solve systems of linear equations in two variables.

When two lines cross, or *intersect*, they are called **intersecting lines.** The point where they cross is called the **point of intersection.**

You have learned that the graph of a linear equation in two variables is a straight line. The graphs of the linear equations $x - y = 4$ and $2x + y = 5$ are shown. The coordinates of their point of intersection, $(3, -1)$, satisfy the equations of both lines:

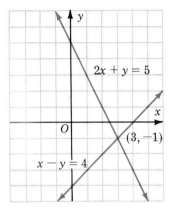

$$x - y = 4 \qquad\qquad 2x + y = 5$$
$$3 - (-1) \stackrel{?}{=} 4 \qquad\qquad 2(3) + (-1) \stackrel{?}{=} 5$$
$$3 + 1 \stackrel{?}{=} 4 \qquad\qquad 6 - 1 \stackrel{?}{=} 5$$
$$4 = 4 \;\checkmark \qquad\qquad 5 = 5 \;\checkmark$$

No other ordered pair satisfies *both* equations, because no point other than the point $(3, -1)$ lies on *both* graphs.

Two equations in the same variables form a **system of equations** or a **system of simultaneous equations.** A **solution of a system** of two equations in two variables is an ordered pair of numbers that satisfy both equations. The set of all solutions is the **solution set of the system.** Finding the solution set is called *solving the system.*

Not all systems of equations have a solution, and some have more than one solution. The diagram at the right shows the graphs of the equations:

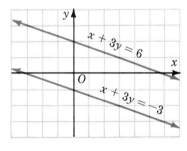

$$x + 3y = 6$$
$$x + 3y = -3$$

The graphs do not intersect. Lines in the same plane which do not intersect are **parallel lines.** This system has *no solution.*

The second diagram shows the graphs of:

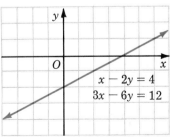

$$x - 2y = 4$$
$$3x - 6y = 12$$

The graphs *coincide.* Every solution of either equation is a solution of the other. The equations are equivalent (divide both sides of the second equation by 3). The coordinates of every point on the line shown form a solution. This system has *an infinite set of solutions.*

> **THE GRAPHIC METHOD**
>
> To solve a system of linear equations in two variables, first graph the equations in the same coordinate plane. Then consider:
>
> If the graphs are parallel, the system has no solution.
> If the graphs coincide, the system has an infinite set of solutions.
> If the graphs intersect, the coordinates of the point of intersection form the solution of the system.

Oral Exercises

State the solution of each system.

1.

2.

3.

4.

5.

6.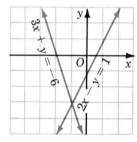

7. Suppose a system of linear equations has no solution. How are the graphs of the equations related?

8. Suppose a system of linear equations has at least two solutions. How are the graphs of the equations related?

9. Suppose the graphs of a pair of linear equations *appear* to intersect in the point $(2, 1)$. How can you check whether or not $(2, 1)$ is a solution of the system?

Written Exercises

Determine whether or not the given ordered pair is a solution of the system.

A **1.** $(3, -5)$; $\begin{aligned} x - y &= 8 \\ x + y &= -2 \end{aligned}$

    2. $(2, -1)$; $\begin{aligned} 2x + y &= 3 \\ x + 2y &= 4 \end{aligned}$

3. $(0, 0)$; $\begin{aligned} y &= 3x \\ x + y &= 3 \end{aligned}$

    4. $(5, 2)$; $\begin{aligned} x - y &= 3 \\ 2x - 2y &= 6 \end{aligned}$

Solve each system by the graphic method.

5. $\begin{aligned} x + y &= 8 \\ x - y &= 4 \end{aligned}$
    6. $\begin{aligned} x - 4y &= 1 \\ x + y &= -4 \end{aligned}$
    7. $\begin{aligned} y - 2 &= 0 \\ x + 3 &= 0 \end{aligned}$

8. $\begin{aligned} 2x - 3y &= 13 \\ x - 2y &= 8 \end{aligned}$
    9. $\begin{aligned} 3x - y &= -8 \\ x + 3y &= -6 \end{aligned}$
    10. $\begin{aligned} y &= 3x \\ x + y &= 4 \end{aligned}$

11. $\begin{aligned} x + 2y &= 4 \\ x + y &= 2 \end{aligned}$
    12. $\begin{aligned} y &= 7 - x \\ x - y &= 3 \end{aligned}$
    13. $\begin{aligned} x - 2y &= 3 \\ 2x - 3y &= 4 \end{aligned}$

14. $\begin{aligned} 2x + y &= 10 \\ 3x - 2y &= 8 \end{aligned}$
    15. $\begin{aligned} 2x + y &= 6 \\ y &= 8 - 2x \end{aligned}$
    16. $\begin{aligned} 3x - y &= 6 \\ 2y &= 6x - 12 \end{aligned}$

Solve each system by the graphic method. Estimate each coordinate of the point of intersection to the nearest integer.

B **17.** $\begin{aligned} x &= y \\ 3x + 3y &= 2 \end{aligned}$
    18. $\begin{aligned} 2x - 4y &= 5 \\ 5x + 12y &= 7 \end{aligned}$

19. $\begin{aligned} 2x + y &= 7 \\ x - 3y &= 5 \end{aligned}$
    20. $\begin{aligned} 8x + 3y &= -14 \\ 7y - 12x &= 21 \end{aligned}$

The solution of each system is $(-2, 3)$. Find the values of A and B.

21. $\begin{aligned} x + By &= -8 \\ Ax + 4y &= 6 \end{aligned}$
    22. $\begin{aligned} 2x + By &= -16 \\ Ax + 3y &= 5 \end{aligned}$

23. $\begin{aligned} Ax + 5y &= 3 \\ 3x + By &= 12 \end{aligned}$
    24. $\begin{aligned} Ax - 7y &= -19 \\ 3x + By &= 9 \end{aligned}$

C **25.** Where on the graph of $x + 3y = 20$ is the x-coordinate equal to the y-coordinate?

26. Where on the graph of $4x + y + 12 = 0$ is the y-coordinate twice the x-coordinate?

27. Find the area of the triangle whose vertices are the points of intersection of the graphs of $2x + y = 5$, $y = x - 4$, and $y = 5$.

28. Find the area of the figure whose vertices are the points of intersection of the graphs of $x = 0$, $y = 0$, $x + 3 = 0$, and $y + 5 = 0$.

8-5 *The Substitution Method*

OBJECTIVE   To use the substitution method to solve systems of linear equations in two variables.

When the solution of a system of equations is an ordered pair of integers, it can usually be found by the graphic method. When the coordinates are fractions, you can use the graphic method to estimate the solution or you can try another method. The following example shows you the *substitution method.*

EXAMPLE   Solve: $x + 4y = 2$
$$2x - 7y = -1$$

SOLUTION

1. Solve for x in the first equation (since its coefficient is 1).

$$x + 4y = 2$$
$$x = 2 - 4y$$

2. Substitute this expression for x in the second equation.

$$2x - 7y = -1$$
$$2(2 - 4y) - 7y = -1$$

3. Solve for y.

$$4 - 8y - 7y = -1$$
$$-15y = -5$$
$$y = \frac{1}{3}$$

4. Find the corresponding value of x (substitute in the expression in Step 1).

$$x = 2 - 4\left(\frac{1}{3}\right)$$
$$x = 2 - \frac{4}{3}$$
$$x = \frac{2}{3}$$

Check:

$$x + 4y = 2 \qquad\qquad 2x - 7y = -1$$

$$\frac{2}{3} + 4\left(\frac{1}{3}\right) \overset{?}{=} 2 \qquad 2\left(\frac{2}{3}\right) - 7\left(\frac{1}{3}\right) \overset{?}{=} -1$$

$$\frac{2}{3} + \frac{4}{3} \overset{?}{=} 2 \qquad\qquad \frac{4}{3} - \frac{7}{3} \overset{?}{=} -1$$

$$\frac{6}{3} \overset{?}{=} 2 \qquad\qquad -\frac{3}{3} \overset{?}{=} -1$$

$$2 = 2 \ \ \checkmark \qquad\qquad -1 = -1 \ \ \checkmark$$

$\therefore$ the solution is $\left(\frac{2}{3}, \frac{1}{3}\right)$.   *Answer*

The systems $\begin{array}{l} x + 4y = 2 \\ 2x - 7y = -1 \end{array}$ and $\begin{array}{l} x = \dfrac{2}{3} \\ y = \dfrac{1}{3} \end{array}$ have the same solution set, $\left\{\left(\dfrac{2}{3}, \dfrac{1}{3}\right)\right\}$.

Systems of equations having the same solution set are called **equivalent systems.**

The substitution method is used to find an equivalent system whose solution can be seen at a glance. The method is most easily applied when the coefficient of one of the variables is 1 or -1.

THE SUBSTITUTION METHOD

To solve a system of linear equations in two variables:

1. Solve *one* equation for *one* of the variables.
2. Substitute the resulting expression in the *other* equation.
3. Solve the resulting equation.
4. Find the corresponding value of the first variable.

In solving equations in two variables other than x and y, it is customary to give the coordinates of a solution in alphabetical order of the variables, unless the conditions of a problem indicate otherwise. Thus, if $(2, 3)$ is a solution of an equation in the two variables r and s, then $r = 2$ and $s = 3$.

Oral Exercises

Solve for y in terms of x.

1. $x + y = 1$ **2.** $x - y = 1$ **3.** $2x + y = -3$

4. $5x + y = 1$ **5.** $4x - y = 6$ **6.** $-2x - y = 8$

Solve for x in terms of y.

7. $x + y = 4$ **8.** $x - y = -2$ **9.** $x + 3y = 7$

10. $-x + 8y = 0$ **11.** $10y - x = 1$ **12.** $-x - 4y = 3$

If you plan to solve the following systems by the substitution method, which equation in each pair is the better choice for Step 1?

13. $2x - 3y = 5$ **14.** $5v + u = -17$ **15.** $4a = 3b + 15$
$\quad\;\; x + 3y = -2$ $\quad\;\;\; 3u = 4v + 6$ $\quad\;\;\; 2b - a = 0$

State the solution of each system.

16. $x = 3$ **17.** $y = x - 8$ **18.** $m = -2$
$\quad\;\; y = x - 2$ $\quad\;\;\; y = 4$ $\quad\;\;\; 2n = m$

19. $b = \frac{1}{2}a - 2$ **20.** $y = 2x + 1$ **21.** $s = -5$
$\quad\;\; a = 2$ $\quad\;\;\;\; x = 3$ $\quad\;\;\; p = 3s - 2$

Written Exercises

Solve each system by the substitution method.

A

1. $y = 2$
$x = 12 - 3y$

2. $b = 3a - 2$
$a = -3$

3. $m = 5$
$n = 6 - m$

4. $g = -2$
$2g + h = 6$

5. $2x - y = -5$
$x = -3$

6. $y = 4$
$3x - y = 2$

7. $y = x$
$2x + 3y = 20$

8. $3a - b = 14$
$a = 2b - 2$

9. $2m - 3n = 6$
$m = 3 - 2n$

10. $x + y = 4$
$2x + 3y = 11$

11. $2a - 3b = -11$
$a - b = -4$

12. $m - 2n = -8$
$n + m = 4$

13. $2x + 3y = 4$
$x - 2y = -5$

14. $3a - b = 11$
$2a + 3b = 0$

15. $x - 2y = 1$
$x + y = 2$

16. $m - 2n = 3$
$5m + 4n = 8$

17. $2x + 3y = 0$
$x - 6y = -5$

18. $4a - b = 5$
$3a - 2b = -6$

B 19. $\frac{x}{2} - y = 1$
$x + y = -7$

20. $\frac{a}{5} - b = -4$
$a - b = 8$

21. $x - y = -15$
$\frac{1}{5}(x + y) = -1$

22. $\frac{1}{3}(x + y) = 6$
$x - y = 4$

23. $\frac{x}{3} + \frac{y}{3} = 2$
$2x + 3y = 10$

24. $\frac{x}{2} + \frac{y}{2} = 7$
$3x + 2y = 48$

In each exercise, two equivalent systems of linear equations are given. Find the values of A and B.

25. $x + y = 14$ $Ax + y = 30$
$x - y = 2$ $2x + By = 10$

26. $2x + y = 6$ $x + By = -4$
$3x - 2y = 2$ $Ax + 3y = 10$

Use the substitution method to solve each system of three equations. Express each solution as an *ordered triple* (x, y, z).

C 27. $x = 3$
$y = 2x - 1$
$x + y + z = 0$

28. $x = 2y + 11$
$y = -3$
$x - 2y - 3z = 5$

29. $x = y + 1$
$z = 2y$
$x + y + z = 9$

30. $x = 2z - 9$
$y = z - 1$
$2x + 3y - z = 3$

31. $x = 2z + 14$
$y = 3z + 15$
$2x - 3 = 3y - z$

32. $4y - 2z = 6x - 4y + 73$
$y = 2 - x$
$z = -\frac{1}{2}(x + 5)$

8-6 *Solving Problems with Two Variables*

OBJECTIVE   To use systems of linear equations in two variables to solve
problems.

You have learned to solve problems using equations in one variable.
Now you can use equations in two variables.

EXAMPLE

Mike and Rose paid a total of $18 for their science
materials. Rose paid $2 more than Mike. How many
dollars did each pay for the materials?

SOLUTION

Step 1   The problem asks for the number of dollars
each paid.

Step 2   Let m = number of dollars Mike paid.
Let r = number of dollars Rose paid.

Step 3 $m + r = 18$ (Total amount paid)
$r - m = 2$ (Difference between amounts paid)

Step 4   Solve the system by the substitution method.

Solve one equation for r: $\qquad\qquad\qquad r = 18 - m$

Substitute in the other: $\qquad\quad (18 - m) - m = 2$

Solve for m: $\qquad\qquad\qquad\quad 18 - 2m = 2$

$$-2m = -16$$

$$m = 8$$

Find the value of r: $\qquad\qquad\qquad r = 18 - m = 18 - 8$

$$r = 10$$

Step 5   Check your results in the statement of the problem, *not* in the
equations you wrote. The check is left to you.

$\therefore$ Mike paid $8 and Rose paid $10.   *Answer*

Oral Exercises

Express each sentence as an equation in m and n.

1. The sum of two numbers m and n is 36.

2. Two numbers m and n differ by 12, and m is the greater.

3. The sum of m and twice n is 48.

4. Twice m exceeds n by 36.

5. m is 1.5 greater than n.

Let s = the number of students at a concert.
Let a = the number of adults at the concert.
Express each sentence as an equation in s and a.

6. The total number of people at the concert is 480.

7. The number of students exceeds the number of adults by 320.

8. Twice the number of adults equals the number of students.

9. Twice the number of students is the same as four times the number of adults.

10. Half the number of students equals the number of adults.

Express the given facts as a system of equations in two variables.

11. The sum of two numbers is 75. Their difference is 25.

12. One number exceeds another by 14. Their sum is 70.

13. The difference between two numbers is 50 and one number is twice the other.

14. Together, Susan and Jill paid $24 for the radio. Susan paid twice as much as Jill.

15. George sold twice as many tickets as Michael. They sold 12 tickets in all.

16. Forty-six trees line the street. There are 14 more oaks than maples.

17. For the fund raising, the students washed 24 more cars than vans. They washed 72 cars and vans in all.

18. Lake Massapoag was stocked with 10,000 fish, all bass and trout. If three times as many bass and four times as many trout are used to stock the lake next year, 36,000 fish will be needed.

Problems

Solve by using a system of two equations in two variables and the substitution method.

A 1. The sum of two whole numbers is 178. They differ by 6. Find the numbers.

2. One whole number exceeds another by 13. The sum is 109. Find the numbers.

3. Lake Lloyd was stocked with 12,000 perch and trout in all. Twice as many perch as trout were used to stock the lake. How many of each fish were used?

4. The total volume of a solution in two laboratory tanks is 568 L. If there are 18 more liters in the larger tank, how many liters are in each tank?

5. Exactly 639 tickets were sold for the school concert. The number of student tickets sold was twice the number of adult tickets sold. How many adult tickets were sold? student tickets?

6. The length of a rectangle is 16 cm longer than twice the width. The perimeter is 122 cm. Find the dimensions of the rectangle.

7. The prices of the tickets for the local rock concert were $6 for Friday night and $8 for Saturday night. The total attendance for the two nights was 1090. If the total receipts were $7856, how many people attended each night?

8. For a part-time job, Jeannie conducted a survey with two questionnaires, Type A and Type B. She chose 500 homes and mailed questionnaires at a cost of 19¢ for Type A and 23¢ for Type B. If the total cost of the mailing was $106.20, how many of each type of questionnaire did she mail?

B 9. In this winter's bird census, the total number of blue jays and chickadees counted was 1216. Last winter 420 more jays and double the number of chickadees were counted, 2024 in all. How many of each type of bird were counted this winter?

10. One number exceeds a second number by 18, and the sum of twice the greater number and three times the smaller number is 86. What are the two numbers?

11. Dave put up a fence around his rectangular garden. Five times the length increased by three times the width is 103 m, and three times the length decreased by 31 m is equal to the width.

a. Find the dimensions of the garden.

b. Find the cost of the fence at $5.60 per meter.

12. At the end of the season, the coach took ten students to Burger Box. The coach and three students each ordered steak-on-a-bun while the other students ordered queen-size burgers. The total bill was $15.15. If steak-on-a-bun costs 90¢ more than a queen-size burger, find the cost of one of each.

For each problem, identify the information that is not needed to solve the problem, and then solve the problem.

C 13. During the week a total of 486 L of gasoline was used by engines A and B of a power launch. Engine A used 74 more liters than engine B. It takes 46 L of gasoline for a round trip to the island. How many liters did each engine use during the week?

14. The total cost of my car insurance and registration is $360. This cost is $60 more than I planned for. If the cost of the insurance is eight times the cost of registration, find the cost of each.

8-7 The Addition-or-Subtraction Method

OBJECTIVE   To use addition or subtraction to solve systems of linear
equations in two variables.

The *addition method* of solving a system of two linear equations in two
variables is useful when a term of one equation, other than a constant
term, is the *opposite* of a term of the other equation.

EXAMPLE 1   Solve: $2x - y = 12$
$\quad\quad\quad\quad\quad\quad\quad x + y = 15$

SOLUTION   The terms in the variable y are opposites.

1. Add similar terms of the two equations to
   obtain an equation in x.

$$2x - y = 12$$
$$\underline{x + y = 15}$$
$$3x \quad\quad = 27$$

2. Solve the resulting equation.

$$x = 9$$

3. Substitute in either of the original equations
   to find the corresponding value of y.

$$x + y = 15$$
$$9 + y = 15$$
$$y = 6$$

Check: $2x - y = 12$ $x + y = 15$
$\quad\quad\quad 2(9) - 6 \stackrel{?}{=} 12$ $9 + 6 \stackrel{?}{=} 15$
$\quad\quad\quad\quad\quad\quad 12 = 12$ ✓ $\quad\quad 15 = 15$ ✓

∴ the solution is $(9, 6)$.   **Answer**

The *subtraction method* is useful when a term of one equation in a
system, other than a constant term, is *the same as* a term of the other
equation.

EXAMPLE 2   Solve: $3t - 4z = -6$
$\quad\quad\quad\quad\quad\quad\quad 3t - 2z = 0$

SOLUTION   The terms in the variable t are the same.

1. Subtract similar terms of the two equations
   to obtain an equation in z.

$$3t - 4z = -6$$
$$\underline{3t - 2z = \quad 0}$$
$$-2z = -6$$

2. Solve the resulting equation.

$$z = 3$$

3. Substitute in either of the original equations
   to find the corresponding value of t.

$$3t - 4z = -6$$
$$3t - 4(3) = -6$$
$$3t - 12 = -6$$
$$3t = 6$$
$$t = 2$$

Checking in both of the original equations is left to you.

∴ the solution is $(2, 3)$.   **Answer**

The *addition-or-subtraction method* is based on the addition property of equality. When a term of one equation in a system has the same absolute value as a term of the other equation, this method can be used to find an equivalent system whose solution can be seen at a glance.

ADDITION-OR-SUBTRACTION METHOD

To solve a system of linear equations in two variables:

1. Eliminate one variable by adding similar terms if two are opposites or by subtracting similar terms if two are the same.
2. Solve the resulting equation for the other variable.
3. Find the corresponding value of the first variable by substitution in either of the original equations.

Written Exercises

A Solve by the addition-or-subtraction method.

1. $x - y = 3$
$x + y = 7$

2. $a - b = 2$
$a + b = 2$

3. $m - 2n = 8$
$m + 2n = -8$

4. $-5 = x - y$
$1 = x + 2y$

5. $a - 2b = 0$
$a + 2b = 12$

6. $3x + y = 8$
$3x - 2y = 2$

7. $3r - \frac{1}{2}s = 7$

$2r - \frac{1}{2}s = 4$

8. $1 = -2m + n$
$1 = 2m - 3n$

9. $3k + 5m = 20$
$2k - 5m = -20$

10. $2p - 3q = 5$
$8 = 3p - 3q$

11. $-10 = m - 3n$
$m + 2n = 20$

12. $2y + x = -7$
$3 = x - 3y$

Express each equation in standard form. Then solve by the addition-or-subtraction method.

B **13.** $2(x - y) = 14$
$x + 2y = -2$

14. $p - 6q = -3$
$3(p + 2q) = 15$

15. $3(r - 2s) = 6$
$r + 6s = 2$

16. $3(p - 2q) = 6$
$2(p + 3q) = -6$

17. $3(4a - 5b) = 27$
$4(3a + 7b) = -16$

18. $2(4m - 5n) = -10$
$-5(6m + 2n) = -10$

19. $\frac{1}{2}(a + b) = -1$

$a - b = 4$

20. $2x + 3y = 2$

$\frac{1}{3}(2x - y) = -2$

21. $\frac{1}{3}(x + 9y) = -4$

$x - 3y = 0$

22. $a + \frac{b}{3} = -3$

$2a - b = -11$

23. $3a - b = 2a - 5$
$3b - a = 5$

24. $2(r - s) = 3 + r$
$r = 3s + 4$

Problems

Solve by using a system of two equations in two variables and the addition-or-subtraction method.

A
1. The sum of two numbers is 170 and their difference is 26. Find the two numbers.

2. There were 200 fans at a game. If the home team's fans outnumbered the visiting team's fans by 96, how many fans were for the home team?

3. To fill two cars at a service station required 100 L of gasoline. The second car took 16 L less than the first. How many liters of gasoline did each car take?

4. Twice the smaller of two numbers is 1 more than the greater. If they differ by 9, find the two numbers.

5. The Rod and Reel Club members caught 13 fish altogether. If they caught four more bass than twice the number of trout, how many of each kind of fish did they catch?

6. The difference between two numbers is 20. The greater exceeds three times the smaller by 10. Find the two numbers.

7. To skate in the Silver Blade Hockey Club, a person must first pay a membership fee and then a fee for each session attended. After attending five sessions, Susan had paid $25 in all. After ten sessions, she has paid $40 in all. What was the membership fee and the fee for each session?

8. Large cans of frozen lemonade sell for 39¢ each and small cans for 20¢ each. Frank bought several cans and paid $2.17. He spent 17¢ less on small cans than on large cans. How many of each size did he buy?

Application A Computation Shortcut

Suppose that you are buying 6 articles costing $0.98 each. Can you find the total cost mentally? Use the distributive property for multiplication with respect to subtraction.

$$6(0.98) = 6(1 - 0.02)$$
$$= 6 - 0.12$$
$$= 5.88$$

∴ the items will cost $5.88.

Find each product.

1. 5(2.96)   2. 4(3.99)   3. 9(1.98)   4. 10(5.94)   5. 7(5.93)   6. 12(3.99)

8-8 *Multiplication with the Addition-or-Subtraction Method*

OBJECTIVE To use multiplication with the addition-or-subtraction method to solve systems of linear equations.

To solve a system such as

$$4x - 6y = 14$$
$$5x + 2y = 8,$$

you cannot apply the addition-or-subtraction method. Neither the terms in x nor the terms in y have the same absolute value. See what happens, however, when you multiply both sides of the second equation by 3:

$$4x - 6y = 14 \longrightarrow 4x - 6y = 14$$
$$3(5x + 2y) = 3(8) \longrightarrow 15x + 6y = 24$$

You now have an equivalent system that can be solved by the addition-or-subtraction method, since the terms in y have the same absolute value.

Sometimes you may need to transform both equations by multiplication before you can apply the addition-or-subtraction method, as shown in Example 1.

EXAMPLE 1 Solve: $2r + 3t = 2$
$$3r - 5t = 22$$

SOLUTION

1. Transform both equations by multiplication so that the terms in r are the same.

$$3(2r + 3t) = 3(2) \longrightarrow 6r + 9t = 6$$
$$2(3r - 5t) = 2(22) \longrightarrow 6r - 10t = 44$$

2. Subtract similar terms.
3. Solve the resulting equation.
$$19t = -38$$
$$t = -2$$

4. Substitute in either of the *original* equations to find the corresponding value of the other variable.

$$2r + 3t = 2$$
$$2r + 3(-2) = 2$$
$$2r - 6 = 2$$
$$2r = 8$$
$$r = 4$$

Checking in *both* of the original equations is left to you.

∴ the solution is $(4, -2)$. ***Answer.***

To solve a system of linear equations involving fractions, it is usually convenient to clear the equations of fractions first, as shown in Example 2.

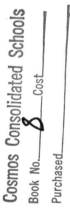

Cosmos Consolidated Schools

Book No. ___ Cost ___

Purchased ___

EXAMPLE 2   Solve: $\dfrac{x}{3} - \dfrac{y}{2} = 7$

$$\dfrac{x}{4} + \dfrac{y}{3} = 1$$

SOLUTION

1. Transform each equation by multiplying by the LCD of its denominators.

$$6\left(\dfrac{x}{3} - \dfrac{y}{2}\right) = 6\,(7) \longrightarrow 2x - 3y = 42$$

$$12\left(\dfrac{x}{4} + \dfrac{y}{3}\right) = 12\,(1) \longrightarrow 3x + 4y = 12$$

2. Transform the resulting equations by multiplication so that the terms in y have the same absolute value.

$$4(2x - 3y) = 4\,(42) \longrightarrow 8x - 12y = 168$$
$$3(3x + 4y) = 3\,(12) \longrightarrow 9x + 12y = 36$$

3. Add similar terms. $17x = 204$
4. Solve the resulting equation. $x = 12$

5. Substitute in either of the original
   equations to find the corresponding
   value of y.

$$\dfrac{x}{3} - \dfrac{y}{2} = 7$$

$$\dfrac{12}{3} - \dfrac{y}{2} = 7$$

$$\dfrac{-y}{2} = 7 - 4 = 3$$

$$y = -6$$

The check is left to you.

$\therefore$ the solution is $(12, -6)$.   **Answer**

Instead of multiplying by the LCD in the first step of Example 2, you can multiply by 24 in the first equation and by 36 in the second equation. Thus, in one step you can clear of fractions and obtain an equivalent system whose terms in y have the same absolute value.

Oral Exercises

Explain how to use multiplication with the addition-or-subtraction method to solve each system by answering these questions:

a. Which equation(s) will you transform by multiplication?

b. By what number(s) will you multiply?

c. Will you then add or subtract similar terms?

1. $x + 2y = 11$
   $5x - y = 11$

2. $2a + 3b = 0$
   $a + 5b = 7$

3. $3r - 8s = 7$
   $r + 2s = -7$

4. $3a + 2b = -12$
$5a - b = -20$

5. $2m + 3n = 4$
$3m - n = 6$

6. $5x - 3y = 29$
$x - 4y = 16$

7. $2p + q = -2$
$4p + 3q = -6$

8. $3u - 4v = 1$
$2u + v = -3$

9. $x - 2y = 3$
$3x + 5y = -2$

10. $2a + 3b = 12$
$3a + 2b = 13$

11. $3p + 2q = -4$
$2p - 3q = -7$

12. $3x + 4y = 0$
$4x + 3y = 7$

13. $2r - 5s = 15$
$3r - 2s = 6$

14. $3x + 7y = -18$
$5x - 2y = -30$

15. $5m - 2n = 7$
$2m + 7n = -5$

16. $3p + 4q = -2$
$2p - 3q = 10$

17. $4a + 3b = -24$
$5a - 2b = -7$

18. $3r - 2s = 20$
$5r - 6s = 36$

Written Exercises

A **1–18.** Solve each system of equations in the Oral Exercises by using multiplication with the addition-or-subtraction method.

Express each equation in standard form. Then solve by the addition-or-subtraction method.

19. $3a + 2b = 4$

$\frac{1}{3}(2a + b) = 1$

20. $\frac{1}{3}(3a - 2b) = -3$

$3(a - b) = -9$

21. $\frac{x}{2} + \frac{y}{3} = -4$

$x + y = -10$

22. $4r - 5s = 26$

$\frac{r}{3} + \frac{s}{5} = \frac{14}{15}$

23. $\frac{x}{6} + \frac{y}{4} = \frac{3}{2}$

$\frac{2x}{3} - \frac{y}{2} = 0$

24. $\frac{m}{15} + \frac{n}{5} = \frac{2}{3}$

$\frac{m}{2} - n = 0$

B **25.** $\frac{x - 1}{2} + \frac{y - 4}{4} = 2$

$x + y = 9$

26. $\frac{3m - 3}{2} + \frac{2n + 5}{3} = 1$

$2m - n = 3$

27. $\frac{a + 1}{3} - \frac{b - 3}{6} = 2$

$3a - b = 9$

28. $\frac{2p + 3}{3} - \frac{3q - 2}{2} = -2$

$2p - 3q = -6$

Solve each system of equations by whatever method you prefer. (*Hint:* These equations are not linear in the given variables. Let $\frac{1}{x} = a$ and $\frac{1}{y} = b$.)

C **29.** $\frac{1}{x} + \frac{1}{y} = 1$

$\frac{3}{x} - \frac{2}{y} = 8$

30. $\frac{2}{x} + \frac{1}{y} = -4$

$\frac{1}{x} - \frac{3}{y} = -9$

31. $\frac{3}{x} + \frac{4}{y} = 1$

$\frac{2}{x} - \frac{2}{y} = 10$

Problems

Solve by using a system of two equations in two variables and whatever method you prefer.

A 1. When the smaller of two numbers is subtracted from the greater, the difference is 14 less than the smaller number. The sum of the two numbers is 1 less than twice the greater number. Find the numbers.

2. Four times the smaller of two numbers is equal to three times the larger. When the larger is doubled, it exceeds their original sum by 5. Find the numbers.

3. The larger of two numbers is 16 more than the smaller. When added together, their sum is 6 less than three times the smaller. What are the numbers?

4. A family has $1200 more invested at 10% than at 8%. They receive $216 more per year from the money invested at the higher rate. How much has been invested at each rate?

5. To join a nature study club, you pay a membership fee and monthly dues. At the end of six months, you will have paid $37 to the club. At the end of ten months, $45 will have been paid. What are the monthly dues and the membership fee?

6. The coach took her basketball team out at the end of the season. If five girls have superburgers and three girls have submarine sandwiches, the bill will be $10.00. If three girls have superburgers and five girls have submarines, the cost will be $10.80. Find the cost of each superburger and each submarine sandwich.

B 7. My mother is four years younger than my father. When they were married, she was five sixths as old as he. How old was each when they were married?

8. The Conrads bought a used car and paid $25 for a safety inspection. An engine overhaul cost three fourths of the price of the car. If the price of the car and the inspection together cost $100 more than the cost of the overhaul, find the cost of the overhaul and the price of the car.

C 9. Creek Farm has 10 more cows than Hill Farm and 20 fewer cows than Dale Farm. If Creek Farm triples its number of cows, it will have 70 less than twice the combined total of cows on Hill and Dale farms. How many cows does Creek Farm have?

10. The average of three numbers is 36. The second is 4 more than the first. The third is twice the first. Find the numbers.

Self-Test 2

VOCABULARY intersecting lines (p. 287)
point of intersection (p. 287)
system of simultaneous equations (p. 287)

solution of a system
(p. 287)
parallel lines (p. 287)
equivalent systems (p. 291)

1. Solve by the graphic method: $y = -2x + 8$
$-2x + y = -4$

Obj. 8-4, p. 287

2. Solve by the substitution method: $d = 2c + 4$
$3c + d = 9$

Obj. 8-5, p. 290

3. Use a system of two equations in two variables and the substitution method to solve this problem:
The perimeter of a rectangular garden is 60 m. The length equals twice the width. Find the length and the width.

Obj. 8-6, p. 293

Solve each system by the addition-or-subtraction method.

4. $2x - 3y = -1$
$2x + 5y = 7$

Obj. 8-7, p. 296

5. $2r - 3s = -2$
$3r + 2s = 10$

Obj. 8-8, p. 299

Check your answers with those at the back of the book.

Calculator Key-In

If you used multiplication with the addition-or-subtraction method to solve the following system of linear equations

$$Ax + By = C$$
$$Dx + Ey = F,$$

you would obtain the following expressions for x and y in terms of A, B, . . . , F:

$$x = \frac{CE - BF}{AE - BD} \qquad y = \frac{CD - AF}{BD - AE}$$

When the values of A, B, . . . , F in such a system are decimal fractions, it is convenient to solve the system by using a calculator to evaluate the expressions for x and y shown above. Use a calculator and this method to solve the following systems.

1. $1.2x + 4.6y = 16.2$
$3.1x + 2.1y = 12.5$

2. $2.3x + 1.6y = 14.9$
$4.1x + 3.2y = 28.3$

APPLICATIONS

8-9 *Puzzle Problems*

OBJECTIVE   To use systems of equations in two variables to solve puzzle problems.

The technique of organizing given facts of a problem in a chart that you learned in Chapter 4 is also helpful when two variables are used.

EXAMPLE 1   (Age problem)

Five years ago Miguel's age was five years less than twice Rachel's age. In three years, one third of Rachel's age will be twelve years less than Miguel's age. How old are they now?

SOLUTION

Step 1   The problem asks for Miguel's age and Rachel's age now.

Step 2   Let m = Miguel's age now and r = Rachel's age now. Make a chart of the given facts.

Age	now	5 years ago	in 3 years
Miguel	m	$m - 5$	$m + 3$
Rachel	r	$r - 5$	$r + 3$

Step 3   Use the facts of the problem to write two equations.

Five years ago: $m - 5 = 2(r - 5) - 5$

In three years: $\frac{1}{3}(r + 3) = (m + 3) - 12$

Step 4   The equations can be simplified:

$$m - 2r = -10$$
$$3m - r = 30$$

The rest of the solution and the check are left to you. You should find that Miguel is now 14 and Rachel is 12.   *Answer*

In the next example, you will use the fact that the value of a two-digit decimal numeral can be written in this general form:

$$10t + u \text{ where } \begin{cases} t \in \{1, 2, 3, 4, 5, 6, 7, 8, 9\} \\ u \in \{0, 1, 2, 3, 4, 5, 6, 7, 8, 9\} \end{cases}$$

Thus, $85 = 10 \cdot 8 + 5$ and $58 = 10 \cdot 5 + 8$

EXAMPLE 2 (Digit problem)

The sum of the digits in a two-digit number is 12. The new number obtained when the digits are reversed is 24 less than three times the original number. Find the original two-digit number.

SOLUTION

Step 1 The problem asks for the original number.

Step 2 Let t = the tens digit of the original number.
Let u = the units digit of the original number.

	tens	units	value
original number	t	u	$10t + u$
new number	u	t	$10u + t$

Step 3 Use the facts of the problem to write two equations.

Sum of the digits of the original number: $t + u = 12$
Value of the new number: $10u + t = 3(10t + u) - 24$

Steps 4 and 5 are left to you. You should find that $t = 3$ and $u = 9$. Thus the original number is 39. *Answer*

EXAMPLE 3 (Fraction problem)

Twice the numerator of a fraction exceeds the denominator by 2. If 1 is added to both the numerator and the denominator, the resulting fraction is equal to $\frac{2}{3}$. Find the original fraction.

SOLUTION

Step 1 The problem asks for the original fraction.

Step 2 Let n = numerator of the original fraction and d = denominator of original fraction. Then $\frac{n}{d}$ = the original fraction.

Step 3 Use the facts of the problem to write two equations.

$$2n = d + 2$$

$$\frac{n + 1}{d + 1} = \frac{2}{3}$$

Step 4 The equations can be simplified:

$$\begin{array}{l} 2n = d + 2 \\ 3(n + 1) = 2(d + 1) \end{array} \quad \text{or} \quad \begin{array}{l} 2n - d = 2 \\ 3n - 2d = -1 \end{array}$$

The rest of the solution and the check are left to you. You should find that $n = 5$ and $d = 8$. Thus the original fraction is $\frac{5}{8}$. *Answer*

Oral Exercises

Let n = Nan's age now and p = Peter's age now. Express the following in terms of n and p.

1. Nan's age in 3 years
2. Peter's age in 3 years
3. Nan's age 4 years ago
4. Peter's age 4 years ago
5. The sum of their ages in 3 years
6. The sum of their ages 4 years ago

A two-digit number is represented by $10t + u$, where t is the tens digit and u is the units digit. Express the following in terms of t and u.

7. The sum of the digits of the number.
8. The new number obtained when the digits are reversed.
9. The new number obtained when the tens digit is increased by 1.
10. The new number obtained when the units digit is decreased by 2.

A fraction is represented by $\frac{n}{d}$. Express in terms of n and d the new fractions obtained by following the given directions.

11. Increase both the numerator and the denominator by 1.
12. Decrease both the numerator and the denominator by 3.
13. Interchange the numerator and the denominator.
14. Increase the numerator by 3 and decrease the denominator by 2.

Problems

Solve by using a system of two equations in two variables.

A
1. Dixie is six years older than her sister. Eight years ago she was four times as old as her sister. How old is each now?

2. Six years ago Cindy was twice as old as Carole. In six years Carole will be as old as Cindy is now. Find their ages now.

3. Joe is three years older than Della. In seven years Joe will be twice as old as Della was five years ago. How old are they now?

4. Five years ago Max was one third as old as his father. In 25 years he will be three fifths as old as his father. Find their ages now.

5. When someone asked Mary her age and the age of her son, she said, "If you subtract 2 from my age and divide this result by 5, you will have my son's age. But in three years his age will be one fourth of mine." Find their ages now.

6. In five years Art will be twice as old as Ben. Five years ago Art was three times as old as Ben. How old is each now?

Solve, assuming that each number is a two-digit number.

7. The sum of the digits of a number is 8. If the digits are reversed, the number is decreased by 54. What is the original number?

8. A number is 6 times the sum of its digits. The units digit is 1 less than the tens digit. Find the number.

9. The units digit of a number is 4 times the tens digit. If 54 is added to the number, the digits will be interchanged. Find the number.

10. The sum of the digits in a number is 15. If the digits are reversed, the number is increased by 27. Find the number.

11. The units digit of a number is 1 more than twice the tens digit. If the digits are reversed, the new number is 8 less than 3 times the original number. What is the original number?

12. The sum of the digits of a number is 6. The number is diminished by 36 when the digits are reversed. What is the original number?

Using two variables, find the original fraction in each exercise.

13. The denominator of a fraction is 7 more than the numerator. If 5 is added to each, the resulting fraction is $\frac{1}{2}$.

14. The numerator of a fraction is 3 less than the denominator. If 1 is subtracted from each, the resulting fraction is $\frac{1}{2}$.

15. The denominator of a fraction is 1 more than the numerator. If the numerator is decreased by 1, the resulting fraction is $\frac{3}{4}$.

16. The numerator of a fraction is $\frac{1}{4}$ the sum of the denominator and 1. If 4 is added to the denominator, the resulting fraction is $\frac{1}{5}$.

17. If 1 is subtracted from the numerator of a fraction, the resulting fraction is $\frac{1}{2}$. If 5 is added to the denominator of the original fraction, the resulting fraction is $\frac{1}{3}$.

18. The denominator of a fraction is 1 less than twice the numerator. If 1 is subtracted from the denominator, the resulting fraction is $\frac{2}{3}$.

Solve by using a system of two equations in two variables.

B 19. Grandmother is three years younger than Grandfather. On their 30th anniversary, she was $\frac{17}{18}$ as old as he. How old were they when they married?

20. When simplified, a fraction has the value $\frac{2}{3}$. If the numerator of the original fraction is increased by 11 and the denominator decreased by 1, the new fraction is equal to the reciprocal of the original fraction. Find the original fraction.

21. The sum of the digits of a three-digit number is 19. The tens digit is 3 times the hundreds digit and 2 more than the units digit. Find the number.

22. A three-digit number is 297 more than the number with the digits reversed. The hundreds digit is 2 more than the tens digit, and the sum of the digits is 13. Find the original number.

C 23. The numerator of a fraction is a three-digit number whose hundreds digit is 4. The denominator is the numerator with the digits reversed. If 31 is subtracted from the numerator, the value of the resulting fraction is $\frac{1}{2}$. If 167 is subtracted from the denominator, the value of the resulting fraction is $\frac{2}{3}$. Find the original fraction.

24. Show that the difference between a three-digit number and the number with the order of the digits reversed is always divisible by 99.

25. Show that if the sum of the digits of a two-digit number is a multiple of 9, then the number itself is a multiple of 9.

26. Mary is twice as old as Jane was at the time when Mary was as old as Jane is now. The sum of the present ages of Mary and Jane is 28 years. How old is each person now?

27. A man is three times as old as his son was at the time when the father was twice as old as his son will be two years from now. Find the present age of each person if the sum of their ages is 55 years.

Computer Key-In

You can also use a computer to solve systems of linear equations by using the formulas given in the Calculator Key-In on page 303. In writing the program in BASIC, you will need to input the six values A, B, C, D, E, F. This can be done in one step by beginning the program as follows:

```
10  PRINT "INPUT A, B, C, D, E, F"
20  INPUT A, B, C, D, E, F
```

Only one question mark will be printed. You type in all six numbers separated by commas.

To complete the program, translate the formulas into BASIC. For example,

```
LET N = A*E - B*D
```

and then write the formulas for X and Y. If N = 0, print:

```
"NO UNIQUE SOLUTION"
```

Use your program to solve the equations at the bottom of page 303.

8-10 *Uniform-Motion Problems*

OBJECTIVE To use systems of equations in two variables to solve uniform-motion problems.

Suppose that you can paddle a canoe at the rate of 7 km/h in still water. If you canoe downstream on a river with a current of 2 km/h, your speed is increased to $7 + 2$, or 9 km/h. If you paddle upstream against the current, your speed is reduced to $7 - 2$, or 5 km/h. In general:

> If r = rate of travel in still water and
> $\quad c$ = rate of current, then:
>
> $r + c$ = rate of travel downstream
> $r - c$ = rate of travel upstream

The next example uses this principle and the basic formula for uniform-motion problems:

$$\text{Distance} = \text{rate} \times \text{time}$$
$$D = rt$$

EXAMPLE

A jet can travel the 3900 km distance from Mexico City to Caracas in three hours with the wind. The return trip of the jet against the same wind takes 4 h 20 min. Find the rate of the jet in still air and the rate of the wind.

SOLUTION

Step 1 The problem asks for the rate of the jet in still air and the rate of the wind.

Step 2 Let j = rate of jet in km/h and w = rate of wind in km/h. (Note that 20 min is a third of an hour.)

	rate	$\times$ time $=$	Distance
with the wind	$j + w$	3	3900
against the wind	$j - w$	$4\frac{1}{3}$	3900

Step 3 Use the given facts to write two equations.

$$3(j + w) = 3900$$
$$4\tfrac{1}{3}(j - w) = 3900$$

Steps 4 and 5 are left to you. You should find that the rate of the jet in still air is 1100 km/h and the rate of the wind is 200 km/h. ***Answer***

Oral Exercises

The rate of a plane is p km/h in still air. The rate of the wind is w km/h. Find the rate of the plane under the conditions described. Express your answers in terms of p and w.

1. Flying with the wind
2. Flying against the wind
3. Flying against the wind if the rate of the wind increases by 15 km/h
4. Flying with the wind if the rate of the wind decreases by 20 km/h

The following rates are given in km/h.
c = rate of a canoe in still water
r = rate of a rowboat in still water
s = rate of a swimmer in still water
a = rate of the Androscoggin River
e = rate of the Eaton River

What rate does each expression represent?

SAMPLE $s + e$ *SOLUTION*   Rate of a swimmer swimming down-stream in the Eaton River

5. $c + a$ 6. $r - e$ 7. $s + a$ 8. $c - e$

9. $r - a$ 10. $s - a$ 11. $c - a$ 12. $r + a$

Problems

Solve by using a system of two equations in two variables.

A

1. A ferry travels upstream against the current at 16 km/h but can travel with the current at 30 km/h. What is the rate of the ferry in still water? What is the rate of the current?

2. A canoeist travels to an outpost 85 km downstream in five hours. Returning upstream, the canoeist travels 10 km in one hour. What is the rate of the canoeist in still water? What is the rate of the current?

3. When a plane flies into the wind, it can travel 2400 km in ten hours. With the wind behind it, the plane can travel a third again as far in the same time. What is the speed of the wind and what is the speed of the plane in still air?

4. Sandy swims at 13 km/h downstream but only 3 km/h upstream. What is the rate of the current? How fast does she swim in still water?

5. A robin flies 1500 m in 5 min with the wind. It would take 25 min to fly this distance against the wind. Find the rate of the wind and the rate of the robin in still air.

6. The nonstop flight of 8400 km from Chicago to Rome takes seven hours with a tail wind. The return flight on the same course but against the wind takes 9 h 20 min. Find the rate of the airplane in calm conditions and find the rate of the wind.

7. A bush plane must return to its hangar in 3 hours for its next job. If it flies at 90 km/h and the wind speed is 20 km/h, how far can the plane fly from the hangar before it must return?

8. On a downstream trip, a boat can be rowed a distance of 66 km in three hours. Upstream, it can be rowed only 33 km in three hours. How fast is the current flowing? What is the rate of rowing in still water?

9. A single-engine plane started out in high tail winds and made a trip of 500 km in two hours. On the return trip, the pilot was forced to land after 45 min, having traveled only 75 km. What was the rate of the plane in still air? What was the rate of the wind?

10. A salmon swims 200 m in 12 min downstream. Swimming in the opposite direction it takes the fish 15 min to travel the same distance. Find the rate of the fish and the rate of the current.

11. The 350 km trip from Paris to London takes two hours on a small aircraft flying with the wind. The return trip against the same wind takes 4 h 40 min. What is the rate of the plane without the wind? What is the rate of the wind?

12. A power boat has a five-hour supply of gasoline. How far can this boat travel from the marina if the rate out with the current is 75 km/h and the rate in against the current is 50 km/h?

13. In three hours a glider can fly 240 km with the wind but only 210 km against the wind. Find the rate of the glider and the rate of the wind.

14. With the wind, a jet can fly a distance of 2800 km in four hours. Against the wind it can go only $\frac{6}{7}$ of the distance in the same time. Find the rate of the plane in still air and the rate of the wind.

B 15. A small craft can fly twice as far with a tail wind as it can with a head wind in the same amount of time. If the rate of the craft is s and the rate of the wind is w, find the relationship between s and w.

16. An air balloon can go four times as far downwind as it can go upwind in the same amount of time. If the rate of the balloon is b and the rate of the wind is w, find the relationship between b and w.

17. A group of campers had to paddle downstream to get fresh supplies. On their return trip the wind had picked up so that the current was twice as strong. If it took twice as long to return to their campsite, find the relationship between their rate, s, and the rate of the current, c.

18. A bird takes 45 min to make a 480 m round trip between two trees. Flying 0.25 m against the wind on the first half of the trip takes the same time as flying 0.5 m with the wind on the return flight. Find the rate of the bird in calm conditions and the rate of the wind.

Self-Test 3

Solve by using a system of two equations in two variables.

1. Uncle Bill is twice as old as his niece Eve. Twelve years ago, he was three times as old as Eve. Find their ages now.

Obj. 8-9, p. 304

2. The sum of the digits of a two-digit number is 10. The number is 16 times the units digit. Find the number.

3. The denominator of a fraction is 9 more than the numerator. If both the numerator and the denominator are increased by 4, the value of the resulting fraction is $\frac{5}{8}$. Find the original fraction.

4. A boat can go downstream at the rate of 25 km/h. It can return against the current at only 8 km/h. Find the rate of the boat in still water and the rate of the current.

Obj. 8-10, p. 309

Check your answers with those at the back of the book.

Biography Wernher von Braun

Wernher von Braun (1912–1977) pioneered the field of rocket engineering. His work on the development of the Jupiter, Redstone, and Saturn rockets contributed in large measure to the success of the American space program in landing men on the moon.

His lifelong interest in space travel began while he was growing up in Germany and was fostered by his mother, who was an amateur astronomer. He received a doctorate in physics from the University of Berlin in 1934 and worked on the German rocket program from 1932 to 1945. After World War II, he moved to the United States and continued his work on rockets.

Wernher von Braun was not only a brilliant scientist but also a persevering leader and champion of space exploration. In 1960 he was named director of the Marshall Space Flight Center of the National Aeronautics and Space Administration at Huntsville, Alabama.

Chapter Summary

1. Ordered pairs of real numbers can be graphed as points in a coordinate plane.

2. The solution set of a linear equation in two variables is a set of ordered pairs of numbers that convert the equation into a true statement. The graph of the solution set in a coordinate plane is a straight line.

3. The solutions of pairs of linear equations in two variables can be estimated by graphing, and computed by substitution or the addition-or-subtraction method.

4. Systems of linear equations in two variables may be used to solve some word problems.

Chapter Review

Give the letter of the correct answer.

1. In which quadrant is the graph of $(3, -2)$? 8-1

     a. I   **b.** II   **c.** III   **d.** IV

2. Where is the graph of $(0, -5)$ in a coordinate plane?

     a. on the x-axis   **b.** on the y-axis

     c. in quadrant II   **d.** at the origin

3. Which ordered pair is a solution of $3x - 2y = -1$? 8-2

     a. $(1, 1)$ **b.** $(2, 1)$ **c.** $(1, 2)$ **d.** $(-1, 2)$

4. Which equation is equivalent to $-x + 3y = -3$?

     a. $y = -1 + x$ **b.** $y = \frac{1}{3}x - 3$

     c. $y = \frac{1}{3}x - 1$ **d.** $y = \frac{1}{3}x + 1$

5. Which equation is *not* linear? 8-3

     a. $4x + 5y^2 = 2$ **b.** $y = -6$

     c. $-3x + 2y = 7$ **d.** $\frac{1}{2}x = y$

6. Which is the best description of the graph of $x - y = 0$?

     a. the origin

     b. a horizontal line

     c. a vertical line

     d. a straight line passing through the points $(0, 0)$ and $(5, 5)$

7. The solution set of the system $\begin{aligned} y &= 2 \\ x + y &= 7 \end{aligned}$ is $\{(5, 2)\}$. 8-4

How are the graphs of the two equations related?

  a. The graphs coincide.

  b. The graphs are parallel lines.

  c. The graphs are lines intersecting in the point $(5, 2)$.

  d. The graphs intersect in the two points $(5, 2)$ and $(0, 2)$.

8. Which expression can be substituted for y in the second equation of the system $\begin{aligned} 2x - y &= 1 \\ 2x + 3y &= 35 \end{aligned}$ in order to solve the system by the substitution method? 8-5

  a. $2x - y$ **b.** $1 - 2x$ **c.** $2x - 1$ **d.** $\dfrac{35}{3} - \dfrac{2}{3}x$

9. Express the given facts as a system of equations in two variables: One number is 5 less than another, and their sum is 23. 8-6

  a. $\begin{aligned} x &= 5 - y \\ x + y &= 23 \end{aligned}$ **b.** $\begin{aligned} x &= y - 5 \\ x + (y - 5) &= 23 \end{aligned}$ **c.** $\begin{aligned} x - y &= 5 \\ x + y &= 23 \end{aligned}$

10. In which system of equations can you eliminate one variable by adding similar terms? 8-7

  a. $\begin{aligned} x + y &= 3 \\ 2x + y &= -3 \end{aligned}$ **b.** $\begin{aligned} 3x - 2y &= 5 \\ 2x + 2y &= -5 \end{aligned}$ **c.** $\begin{aligned} 2x - 3y &= 7 \\ 5x - 3y &= 2 \end{aligned}$

11. To solve the system $\begin{aligned} 7x + 3y &= -1 \\ -9x + 4y &= 1 \end{aligned}$ you plan to transform both equations by multiplication before subtracting to eliminate one of the variables. If you multiply by 4 in the first equation, by which number should you multiply in the second equation? 8-8

  a. 4   **b.** -4 **c.** 7   **d.** 3

12. In five years a girl will be two thirds as old as her aunt. Three years ago she was half as old as the aunt is now. How old is the girl now? 8-9

  a. 11   **b.** 17   **c.** 19   **d.** 28

13. The units digit of a two-digit number is 4 more than the tens digit. If the digits are reversed, the new number is 10 more than twice the original number. What is the original number?

  a. 26   **b.** 37   **c.** 15   **d.** 62

14. The denominator of a fraction exceeds the numerator by 3. If 1 is added to the denominator, a new fraction is obtained whose value is $\frac{2}{3}$. Find the original fraction.

  a. $\dfrac{-4}{-7}$ **b.** $\dfrac{8}{11}$ **c.** $\dfrac{8}{12}$ **d.** $\dfrac{3}{6}$

15. A motorboat went 18 km downstream in one hour. The return trip against the current took three hours. Find the rate of the current.

   a. 18 km/h   **b.** 12 km/h   **c.** 6 km/h   **d.** 3 km/h

8-10

Chapter Test

Plot the graph of each ordered pair in a coordinate plane.

1. $(-2, 4)$ **2.** $(1, -3)$ 8-1

3. Find the solution set of $2x + y = 8$ if both x and y are whole numbers. 8-2

4. Graph $x - y = 2$ in a coordinate plane. 8-3

5. Solve by the graphic method: $x - 2y = 2$ 8-4
$$x + y = 2$$

6. Solve by the substitution method: $a + 2b = 7$ 8-5
$$2a = 3b$$

7. Use a system of two equations in two variables and the substitution method to solve this problem: Meg's bowling score was 12 more than Jan's. Their combined score was 328. Find their scores. 8-6

Solve each system by the addition-or-subtraction method.

8. $3x + 2y = 13$ 8-7
    $3x - 4y = 19$

9. $3a + 4b = -25$ 8-8
    $2a - 3b = 6$

Solve by using a system of two equations in two variables.

10. A clerk mistakenly overcharged a customer 27¢ by reversing the two digits in the price of a marking pen. If the sum of the digits was 15, what was the correct price of the pen? 8-9

11. A salmon swims 24 km downstream from its birthplace to the ocean in three hours. The return trip upstream to spawn takes five hours. How fast does the salmon swim in still water? 8-10

Cumulative Review   (Chapters 1-8)

Simplify each expression.

1. $-2y(y^2 - 8y - 9 + y)$
2. $(-5a^2b^4)^3 \div (2a^7b^6)^2$
3. $(8r^2 - 3s)(8r^2 + 3s)$
4. $(2j - k + 1)^2$
5. $(-8 - d) - (-8d + 4)$
6. $(8x^3 - 4x^2 + 6x) \div 2x$

Factor completely, if possible. If not possible, write "prime."

7. $1 - 18v + 81v^2$
8. $2a^3 + 6a^2b + 4ab^2$
9. $-m^2 - 15n + 5m + 3mn$
10. $40z^2 + z - 6$
11. $5r^2 - r - 7$
12. $9c^2 + 12cd + 4d^2$

Express in simplest form.

13. $\dfrac{4x^2 - 25y^2}{4x^2 - 4xy - 15y^2}$
14. $\dfrac{1}{1 - 4c} + \dfrac{8c}{8c - 2} - 1$
15. $\dfrac{m^2 + m - 30}{m^2 - 6m + 5} \div \dfrac{4m + 24}{m - 1}$

Divide. Express each quotient as a polynomial or a mixed expression.

16. $\dfrac{6v^2 + 7v + 5}{2v + 1}$
17. $\dfrac{n^3 - 5n + 2}{n - 2}$
18. $\dfrac{3x^2 + 7xy + 4y^2 + 2}{3x + 4y}$

Solve. (The equation may be an identity or have no root.)

19. $5z - 1 = 2(z + 4)$
20. $2r^2 + 26r = -72$
21. $0.1x = 0.06x + 0.6$
22. $(5d - 1)(2d + 1) = 6$
23. 2.8% of $k = 63$
24. $|a| - 7 = -3$
25. $\dfrac{1}{t + 1} + \dfrac{1}{5t - 3} = \dfrac{1}{t}$
26. $\dfrac{8s + 2}{6s - 1} = \dfrac{4s - 1}{3s - 2}$
27. $\dfrac{2}{y - 2} = \dfrac{5}{y} + 2$

28. Solve graphically: **a.** $2x - y = 5$
$x + 3y = -1$
b. $y = -4x$
$4x + y = 6$

Solve.

29. $8x - 3 = y$
$5x + 2y = -27$
30. $6a - 7b = 10$
$4a + 7b = 5$
31. $9s + 5t = 2$
$-11s + 2t = 30$

Solve.

32. The sum of two integers is -3 and their product is -40. Find the integers.

33. Half of a two-digit number is 6 less than the number with its digits reversed. If the sum of the digits is 12, find the number.

34. A plane flies 1120 km in 80 min with a tail wind. The return trip with a head wind takes 4 min more. Find the speed of the wind in kilometers per hour.

Maintaining Skills

Factor completely, if possible. If not possible, write "prime."

SAMPLE 1 $15y^2z - 60y = 15y(yz - 4)$

1. $2c^3 + 4c^2d$ **2.** $2\pi rh + 2\pi r^2$ **3.** $9s^2 + 4st^2 - 6t^3$

4. $9p^2 + 36pq - 81q^2$ **5.** $64a^3 - 40a^2 + 72a$ **6.** $8x^3y^3 - 6x^2y^4 - 4xy^5$

SAMPLE 2   **a.** $16x^4 - 4 = 4(4x^4 - 1) = 4[(2x^2)^2 - 1^2] = 4(2x^2 + 1)(2x^2 - 1)$
            b. $49d^2 - 42d + 9 = (7d)^2 - 2(7d \cdot 3) + 3^2 = (7d - 3)^2$

7. $64a - a^3$ **8.** $k^2 + 8k + 2$ **9.** $9p^2 - 6p + 1$

10. $144q^3 - 4qr^2$ **11.** $100w^2 - 30w + 9$ **12.** $100x^2 - 16y^2$

13. $m^4 + 4m^2n + 4n^2$ **14.** $r^6 - 81$ **15.** $3z^2 - 36zt + 108t^2$

SAMPLE 3   **a.** $x^2 - 10xy + 16y^2$ **b.** $n^2 + 3n - 28$

SOLUTION   **a.** Start with $(x - \quad)(x - \quad)$; $(x - 8y)(x - 2y)$.   ***Answer***
            b. Start with $(n + \quad)(n - \quad)$; $(n + 7)(n - 4)$.   ***Answer***

16. $b^2 + 11b + 18$ **17.** $g^2 - 6g - 40$ **18.** $y^2 + 17yz - 38z^2$

19. $5z^2 - 50z + 120$ **20.** $-d^3 - 8d^2 - 7d$ **21.** $s^3 + s^2 - 72s$

22. $m^2 - 18m - 46$ **23.** $c^2 - 14cd + 33d^2$ **24.** $49 + 14k + k^2$

SAMPLE 4 $ac - 3bc - a + 3b = c(a - 3b) - 1(a - 3b) = (c - 1)(a - 3b)$

25. $ar - 5a - 6r + 30$ **26.** $s^3 - 8s^2 + 7s - 56$ **27.** $jx + 3x + 4j + 6$

28. $3d^4 - 6d + 2d^3 - 4$ **29.** $4zm - 6n + 3m - 8zn$ **30.** $12y - 2y^3 + 5y^2 - 30$

SAMPLE 5 $14x^2 - 25x + 6$

SOLUTION   Test the possibilities for the first terms: $14x$ and x; $7x$ and $2x$.
            Test the possibilities for the second terms: 6 and 1; 2 and 3.
            $14x^2 - 25x + 6 = (7x - 2)(2x - 3)$ ***Answer***

31. $12a^2 - 23a + 5$ **32.** $16t^2 + 18t - 9$ **33.** $5r^2 + 19rs + 18s^2$

34. $30y^2 - 19yz - 4z^2$ **35.** $-10z - 3z^2 + 27z^3$ **36.** $-28k^2 - 26k - 6$

37. $15b^2 + 8c^2 - 12bc$ **38.** $35d^2 - 2 + 9d$ **39.** $40x^2 + 46xv + 9v^2$

The steepness of the mountain is one of the factors that influence the skier's speed. Steepness is closely related to the mathematical idea of slope.

9

INTRODUCTION
TO FUNCTIONS

LINEAR EQUATIONS

9-1 *Slope of a Line*

OBJECTIVE   To find the slope of a line.

To describe the steepness, or slope, of a hill, you may determine the vertical *rise* for every 100 m of horizontal *run* and calculate the ratio:

Rise: 75 m

Run: 100 m

$$\frac{\text{rise}}{\text{run}} = \frac{75}{100} = \frac{3}{4}$$

To describe the steepness, or slope, of a straight line, you choose any two points on the line, count the units in the rise and run, and calculate their ratio.

EXAMPLE 1

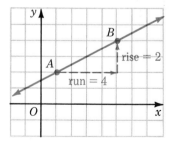

$$\text{slope} = \frac{\text{rise}}{\text{run}} = \frac{2}{4} = \frac{1}{2}$$

EXAMPLE 2

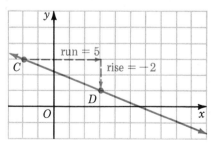

$$\text{slope} = \frac{\text{rise}}{\text{run}} = \frac{-2}{5}$$

In Example 1, the line passes through the points $A(1, 2)$ and $B(5, 4)$. The rise, or *vertical change*, in moving from A to B is the difference between the y-coordinates: $4 - 2 = 2$. The run, or *horizontal change*, in moving from A to B is the difference between the x-coordinates: $5 - 1 = 4$.

Thus, the coordinates of a pair of points on a line can be used to calculate the slope of the line:

$$\textbf{slope} = \frac{\text{rise}}{\text{run}} = \frac{\text{vertical change}}{\text{horizontal change}} = \frac{\text{difference between } y\text{-coordinates}}{\text{difference between } x\text{-coordinates}}$$

EXAMPLE 3 Find the slope of the line whose equation is $2x - 3y = 6$.

SOLUTION Find two points on the line (page 284):

$$(0, -2) \quad \text{and} \quad (3, 0)$$

Then the slope $= \dfrac{0 - (-2)}{3 - 0} = \dfrac{2}{3}$. ***Answer***

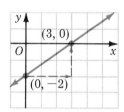

In Example 3, two convenient points were chosen, but the slope calculated using *any* two points on the line would be $\dfrac{2}{3}$.

A basic property of a line is that its slope is constant.

EXAMPLE 4 Determine whether the points whose coordinates are given lie on the same line. If they do, find the slope of the line.

a.
$\begin{matrix} 1 \\ 1 \\ 1 \\ 1 \end{matrix} \begin{matrix} (-1, 8) \\ (0, 6) \\ (1, 4) \\ (2, 2) \end{matrix} \begin{matrix} -2 \\ -2 \\ -2 \end{matrix}$

b.
$\begin{matrix} 1 \\ 1 \\ 1 \\ 1 \end{matrix} \begin{matrix} (0, 0) \\ (1, 1) \\ (2, 3) \\ (3, 6) \end{matrix} \begin{matrix} 1 \\ 2 \\ 3 \end{matrix}$

c.
$\begin{matrix} 2 \\ 6 \\ -4 \end{matrix} \begin{matrix} (0, 3) \\ (2, 4) \\ (8, 7) \\ (4, 5) \end{matrix} \begin{matrix} 1 \\ 3 \\ -2 \end{matrix}$

SOLUTION **a.** As you move from one point to the next, the changes in the x-coordinates and the y-coordinates are shown in color. The ratio of the vertical change to the horizontal change is constant. The points lie on a line. The slope is $\dfrac{-2}{1}$, or -2.

b. The ratio of the vertical change to the horizontal change is *not* constant. The points do *not* lie on a line.

c. The ratio of the vertical change to the horizontal change is constant. The slope is $\dfrac{1}{2}$.

If you use the formula on page 320 to try to compute the "slope" of the vertical line shown at the right, you find that the denominator is zero. Since you cannot divide by zero, the formula does not apply. *Vertical lines have no slope.*

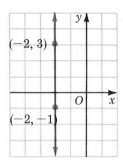

The slope of the horizontal line shown at the right is

$$\frac{-2-(-2)}{1-(-3)} = \frac{0}{4} = 0.$$

The slope of every horizontal line is 0.

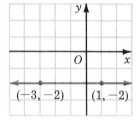

Oral Exercises

Find the slope of each line.

1.

2.

3.

4.

5.

6.

Written Exercises

In each exercise, the coordinates of two points of a line are given. Find the slope of the line.

A **1.** $(7, 3)$ $(5, 4)$ **2.** $(3, -3)$ $(6, -5)$ **3.** $(-6, 3)$ $(-4, 5)$

   4. $(3, 8)$ $(5, 4)$ **5.** $(-4, 5)$ $(5, 4)$ **6.** $(2, -5)$ $(4, 2)$

   7. $(-4, -4)$ $(0, 0)$ **8.** $(8, 3)$ $(-2, 3)$ **9.** $(4, 6)$ $(4, -3)$

  10. $(-4, -5)$ $(-2, -2)$ **11.** $(0, -1)$ $(3, -1)$ **12.** $(0, 0)$ $(4, 3)$

Find the slope of each line whose equation is given.

13. $y = 4x - 3$ **14.** $y = 4x + 5$ **15.** $y = 2x - 3$

16. $2x + y = 6$ **17.** $x - y = 6$ **18.** $4x - y = 16$

19. $2x - 3y = 12$ **20.** $3x + 4y = 24$ **21.** $4x - 5y = 20$

22. $5x + 4y = 20$ **23.** $y = -2$ **24.** $y - 3 = 0$

Determine whether the points in each exercise lie on the same line. If they do, find the slope of the line.

25. $(0, 6)$ **26.** $(3, 5)$ **27.** $(0, -1)$ **28.** $(1, 1)$

     $(1, 4)$ $(4, 7)$ $(1, -2)$ $(0, 4)$

     $(2, 2)$ $(5, 11)$ $(2, -4)$ $(-1, 7)$

     $(3, 0)$ $(6, 14)$ $(3, -8)$ $(-2, 10)$

Through the given point, draw a line with the given slope.

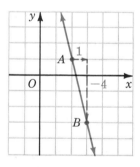

SAMPLE $A(2, 1)$; slope, -4

SOLUTION

First plot point A. Rewrite the slope as the fraction $\dfrac{-4}{1}$.

From point A, measure 1 unit *to the right*, and 4 units *down* to locate a second point, B. Draw the line through A and B.

29. $A(3, 4)$; slope, 3 **30.** $P(-3, 5)$; slope, -2 **31.** $T(2, -8)$; slope, 0

32. $R(-2, 3)$; slope, $\dfrac{2}{3}$ **33.** $K(-4, 5)$; slope, $-\dfrac{1}{2}$ **34.** $N(4, -6)$; slope, $-\dfrac{5}{3}$

B **35.** The vertices of a triangle are $A(-5, 5)$, $B(4, 5)$, and $C(-5, -3)$. Find the slope of each side of the triangle.

   36. The vertices of a rectangle are $D(-4, -2)$, $E(1, 3)$, $F(8, -4)$, and $G(3, -9)$. Find the slope of each side of the rectangle.

37. Do the points $(-2, -4)$, $(2, 8)$, and $(0, 2)$ lie on the same line? How can you use the idea of slope to show this?

38. Determine the slope of the line through the points $(2, 4)$ and $(-2, 2)$. Find the value of y if $(6, y)$ lies on this line.

39. The slope of a line through point $(2, 4)$ is $\frac{3}{2}$. If point $(-2, y)$ lies on this line, find the value of y.

40. A line with slope -3 passes through the points $(-8, p)$ and $(2, 3p)$. Find the value of p.

C **41.** The vertices of a square are $A(1, 7)$, $B(9, 5)$, $C(7, -3)$, and $D(-1, -1)$. Use the idea of slope to show that point $M(4, 2)$ lies on the diagonal joining A and C, and on the diagonal joining B and D.

42. The vertices of a right triangle are $P(-3, 4)$, $Q(-3, -4)$, and $R(7, -4)$. Use the idea of slope to show that point $S(2, 0)$ lies on the triangle.

Career Note Agricultural Engineer

Population experts predict that by the year 2000 there will be six to seven billion people on this planet. All of these people must have food to eat and clothes to wear. Where will it all come from?

Finding the answer to this question is the concern of agricultural engineers. Their primary task is to develop the most efficient techniques for maximizing the amount of food and fiber that can be produced. They are involved in all phases of crop production from planting to processing. Typical tasks might include developing equipment for harvesting or designing systems for the prevention of soil erosion.

A bachelor's degree in agricultural engineering is usually the minimum requirement for a career in this field. Work for the degree includes one to two years of general course work in mathematics, chemistry, physics, basic engineering, and the social sciences.

9-2 *The Slope-Intercept Form of a Linear Equation*

OBJECTIVE **To use the slope-intercept form of a linear equation.**

The table shows the coordinates of a few of the points in the graph of the linear equation $y = 2x$.

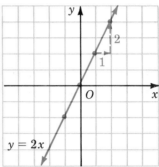

x	y
-1	-2
0	0
1	2
2	4

Notice that the slope of the line whose equation is $y = 2x$ is $\frac{2}{1}$, or 2, and that the line passes through the origin.

The graph of the equation $y = -\frac{1}{3}x$ is a line that has slope $-\frac{1}{3}$ and passes through the origin.

For every real number m, the graph in a coordinate plane of the equation

$$y = mx$$

is the line that has slope m and passes through the origin.

The graphs of the linear equations

$$y = 2x \text{ and } y = 2x + 4$$

have been drawn on the same set of axes. The lines have equal slopes, but they cross the y-axis at different points. The y-coordinate of a point where a graph intersects the y-axis is called the **y-intercept** of the graph.

To determine the y-intercept of a line, replace x with 0 in the equation of the line:

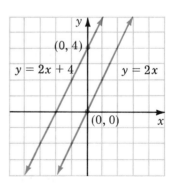

$y = 2x$

$y = 2(0)$

$y = 0$

y-intercept: 0

$y = 2x + 4$

$y = 2(0) + 4$

$y = 4$

y-intercept: 4

If you write $y = 2x$ as $y = 2x + 0$, you can see that the constant term in the following equations is the y-intercept of each graph:

$$y = 2x + 0 \qquad y = 2x + 4$$

For all real numbers m and b, the graph in a coordinate plane of the equation

$$y = mx + b$$

is the line whose slope is m and whose y-intercept is b. This is called the **slope-intercept form** of an equation of a line.

EXAMPLE 1   Write a linear equation in standard form whose graph has the given slope and y-intercept.

      a. $m = -3,\ b = -2$ **b.** $m = \dfrac{1}{2},\ b = 3$

SOLUTION   First write an equation of the form $y = mx + b$. Then transform it into an equivalent equation in the form $Ax + By = C$ where A, B, and C are integers.

    a. $y = -3x + (-2)$ **b.** $y = \dfrac{1}{2}x + 3$

      $3x + y = -2$ ***Answer*** $2y = x + 6$

                                      $-x + 2y = 6$ ***Answer***

EXAMPLE 2   Use only the y-intercept and slope to graph the equation $3x - 2y = 6$.

SOLUTION   Solve for y to transform the equation into the form $y = mx + b$.

$$3x - 2y = 6$$
$$-2y = -3x + 6$$
$$y = \frac{3}{2}x - 3$$

Since the y-intercept is -3, plot $(0, -3)$. Since the slope is $\dfrac{3}{2}$, measure 2 units to the right of $(0, -3)$ and 3 units up to locate a second point. Draw the line through the two points.

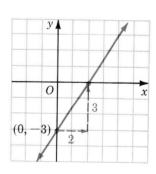

Oral Exercises

State the slope and y-intercept of each line whose equation is given.

1. $y = 3x$ **2.** $y = 3x + 4$ **3.** $y = \frac{1}{2}x + 4$ **4.** $y = -2x$

5. $y = -2x - \frac{1}{2}$ **6.** $y = \frac{3}{2}x - \frac{1}{2}$ **7.** $y = \frac{1}{3}x$ **8.** $y = 4x - \frac{5}{2}$

State an equation of the line that has the given slope and y-intercept.

9. $m = 2,\ b = 3$ **10.** $m = 2,\ b = 0$ **11.** $m = -3,\ b = 4$

Written Exercises

Write in standard form an equation of the line that has the given slope and y-intercept.

A   **1.** $m = 3,\ b = \frac{1}{2}$ **2.** $m = -2,\ b = \frac{2}{3}$ **3.** $m = \frac{1}{4},\ b = 3$

    4. $m = -\frac{2}{3},\ b = 3$ **5.** $m = 5,\ b = -\frac{2}{3}$ **6.** $m = -\frac{2}{5},\ b = -4$

    7. $m = \frac{1}{3},\ b = \frac{2}{3}$ **8.** $m = \frac{3}{2},\ b = -\frac{3}{2}$ **9.** $m = -\frac{4}{5},\ b = \frac{5}{2}$

    10. $m = \frac{2}{3},\ b = -\frac{3}{4}$ **11.** $m = 0,\ b = -3$ **12.** $m = 0,\ b = \frac{3}{2}$

Change each equation to the slope-intercept form and draw the graph using only the y-intercept and the slope.

13. $x + y = 8$ **14.** $2x + y = -4$ **15.** $x - y = 6$

16. $-x + 2y = 8$ **17.** $x - 2y = 8$ **18.** $2y - 3x = 6$

19. $2x + 3y = 0$ **20.** $3x - 4y = 12$ **21.** $-5x + 3y = 20$

22. $3x = 2y$ **23.** $2x - 3y - 12 = 0$ **24.** $3y = 8$

B   **25.** Write an equation of the line that has y-intercept -3 and that has the same slope as the graph of $y = 3x + 2$.

    26. Write an equation of the line that has the same slope as the graph of $y - 2x = 3$ and the same y-intercept as the graph of $3y + 2x = 6$.

    27. In the equation $3y + tx = 2$, for what value of t does the graph of the equation have slope 1? slope -1?

    28. In the equation $ty + 3x = 2$, for what value of t does the graph of the equation have y-intercept 1? y-intercept -1?

C   **29.** Using the standard form of a linear equation, $Ax + By = C$, find a formula for the slope and a formula for the y-intercept in terms of the coefficients, assuming that $B \neq 0$.

Application   Line of Best Fit

Can your adult height be predicted from that of your father or mother? Will your future income be related to the number of years you attend school? When there is a clear relationship between two measurements, researchers can base predictions on data gathered about many, many people. For each person, there must be a pair of measurements.

For example, to predict a person's height at age 24 from the person's height at age 14, researchers can begin by collecting data such as that shown in the chart below for a group of adults. Each pair of heights can then be plotted as a point (x, y) on a graph.

Height at 14	Height at 24
158 cm	185 cm
150 cm	171 cm
148 cm	170 cm
154 cm	178 cm
164 cm	192 cm
152 cm	175 cm

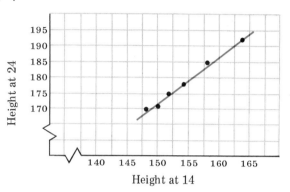

If data were plotted for many more people, the graph would contain many more points. These points would tend to cluster around a line (shown in color) called the *line of best fit*, since it fits closer to the points than all other lines. Mathematicians have derived exact formulas for determining the line of best fit, but you can fit a line quite well "by eye." From graphs based on extensive data gathered over a period of several years, predictions about an individual's growth or income can be made.

Project

a. Gather the following data from your classmates: the height of each girl and her mother; the height of each boy and his father.

b. For each girl, plot a point (x, y) on a graph such that the x-coordinate is the girl's height and the y-coordinate is her mother's height. Make a second graph in the same way using the boys' data.

c. On each graph, draw the line that seems to fit the points of the graph most closely.

d. Determine the heights of other students in the same age group as your class. Estimate the heights of their mothers or fathers from your graphs. Find out how good your estimates are. (*Note:* Your estimates may be inaccurate, but if you based your graph on more data and estimated the heights for a larger group of people, your estimates would be good in a greater percentage of cases.)

9-3 *Determining an Equation of a Line*

OBJECTIVE To find an equation of a line given the slope and one point on the line, or two points on the line.

The line shown below has slope $\frac{2}{3}$ and passes through the point $(-2, -1)$. The slope-intercept form of the equation of this line is

$$y = \frac{2}{3}x + b.$$

Since the point $(-2, -1)$ is on the line, its coordinates satisfy the equation. You can substitute to find the value of b:

$$-1 = \frac{2}{3}(-2) + b$$

$$-1 = -\frac{4}{3} + b$$

$$\frac{1}{3} = b$$

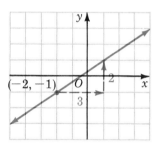

Therefore, an equation of the line with slope $\frac{2}{3}$ and passing through $(-2, -1)$ is

$$y = \frac{2}{3}x + \frac{1}{3}.$$

EXAMPLE Write an equation of the line passing through the points $(-4, 5)$ and $(2, -4)$.

SOLUTION slope $= \dfrac{\text{difference between } y\text{-coordinates}}{\text{difference between } x\text{-coordinates}}$

$$m = \frac{5 - (-4)}{-4 - 2} = \frac{9}{-6} = -\frac{3}{2}$$

Thus, the slope-intercept form of the equation is

$$y = -\frac{3}{2}x + b.$$

Choose one of the given points, say $(-4, 5)$. Since it lies on the line, its coordinates satisfy the equation. Substitute to find the value of b:

$$5 = -\frac{3}{2}(-4) + b$$

$$5 = 6 + b$$

$$-1 = b$$

$\therefore$ an equation of the line is $y = -\frac{3}{2}x - 1$. ***Answer***

As shown on the opposite page, you can find an equation of a line if the slope and one point on the line are known. To determine an equation of a line when two points on the line are known, you first find the slope and then find the y-intercept as shown in the example.

Written Exercises

Each given point is on a line whose equation is $y = \frac{2}{3}x + b$. Find each value of b.

A   **1.** $(3, 4)$ **2.** $(-3, 2)$ **3.** $(-4, -3)$ **4.** $(0, -2)$

Write in standard form an equation of the line that has the given slope and passes through the given point.

   5. $m = 2;\ (3, 1)$ **6.** $m = 3;\ (2, -3)$ **7.** $m = -4;\ (-4, -6)$

   8. $m = -2;\ (-2, 3)$ **9.** $m = \frac{2}{3};\ (3, 0)$ **10.** $m = \frac{5}{4};\ (1, 0)$

   11. $m = \frac{5}{4};\ (-1, -5)$ **12.** $m = -\frac{2}{3};\ (0, 0)$ **13.** $m = -\frac{1}{2};\ (-3, -2)$

   14. $m = -1;\ \left(6, \frac{1}{2}\right)$ **15.** $m = 0;\ \left(\frac{3}{4}, -2\right)$ **16.** $m = 0;\ \left(-2, \frac{3}{4}\right)$

Write in standard form an equation of the line passing through the given points.

   17. $(0, -2)$ $(4, 5)$ **18.** $(3, 0)$ $(-2, 1)$ **19.** $(3, 0)$ $(-4, 0)$

   20. $(-2, 1)$ $(3, 6)$ **21.** $(2, 3)$ $(1, 5)$ **22.** $(6, 0)$ $(2, 1)$

   23. $(2, -2)$ $(5, 6)$ **24.** $(-4, -2)$ $(0, -5)$ **25.** $(-1, -2)$ $(0, 3)$

   26. $(-2, -3)$ $(-1, 2)$ **27.** $(-3, -1)$ $(1, -4)$ **28.** $(2, -1)$ $(-3, 4)$

Write an equation in standard form for each line described.

B   **29.** The line that passes through the point $(-1, 4)$ and has the same slope as the graph of $2x - y = 8$.

   30. The line that passes through the point $(-3, 0)$ and has the same slope as the graph of $x - 3y = 9$.

C   **31.** The line that passes through the point $(-3, -5)$ and has the same y-intercept as the graph of $x + 2y = 8$.

   32. The line that has slope $\frac{1}{2}$ and passes through the point of intersection of the graphs of $x - 6y = 10$ and $x - y = 5$.

   33. The line whose x-intercept is -6 and whose y-intercept is 3. (The *x-intercept* of a line is the x-coordinate of the point where the line crosses the x-axis.)

VOCABULARY slope (p. 320) slope-intercept form of an
 y-intercept (p. 324) equation (p. 325)

1. Find the slope of the line that passes through the points $(1, 2)$ and $(3, 5)$.

Obj. 9-1, p. 319

2. Find the slope of the line $y = 2$.

3. Find the slope and the y-intercept of the line whose equation is $2x - 3y = 1$.

Obj. 9-2, p. 324

4. Write in standard form an equation of the line through point $(-1, 2)$ with slope 2.

Obj. 9-3, p. 328

5. Write in standard form an equation of the line through points $(-3, 0)$ and $(0, 3)$.

Check your answers with those at the back of the book.

Biography Percy Lavon Julian

Percy Lavon Julian (1899–1975), who received a Ph.D. in organic chemistry in Vienna, is sometimes called the "soybean chemist" because of his outstanding work with this bean. Using extracts from the soybean, he was able to produce synthetic cortisone, a drug used in the treatment of arthritis; synthetic physostigmine, a drug used to treat the eye disease glaucoma; and synthetic hormones that are used in the treatment of a variety of disorders. As a result of Percy Julian's work, these drugs can be produced in large quantities, making them available to all.

Julian also used soy protein to make a foam product that was used extensively to fight gasoline and oil fires. In 1950 Percy Julian was voted Chicagoan of the Year.

FUNCTIONS

9-4 *Functions Defined by Equations*

OBJECTIVE **To understand what a function is and how to find its values.**

An equation such as $y = 5x + 2$ assigns to each number in the domain of the variable x another number, the value of y. For example, if the domain of x is $\{2, 4, 6\}$, the equation $y = 5x + 2$ assigns the following values to y:

$$y = 5 \cdot 2 + 2 = 12$$
$$y = 5 \cdot 4 + 2 = 22$$
$$y = 5 \cdot 6 + 2 = 32$$

Thus, the given equation pairs each member of $\{2, 4, 6\}$ with a single member of $\{12, 22, 32\}$, as shown by the diagram. This example illustrates the mathematical idea of a *function*.

A **function** consists of two sets, the **domain** and the **range,** and a *rule* which assigns to each member of the domain *exactly one* member of the range. Each member of the range must be assigned to *at least one* member of the domain.

In the preceding example, the rule that defines the function is the equation $y = 5x + 2$, the domain D is $\{2, 4, 6\}$, and the range R is $\{12, 22, 32\}$.

The rule that defines a function may also be written using an arrow notation and a single letter, such as f, g, F, or H, to name the function. The **arrow notation**

$$f \colon x \to 5x + 2$$

is read "the function f that assigns $5x + 2$ to x" or "the function f that pairs x with $5x + 2$." To specify a function completely, you must also describe the domain of the function. The numbers assigned by the rule then form the range.

EXAMPLE 1 List the members of the range of

$$g \colon x \to 6 + 3x - x^2$$

if the domain $D = \{-1, 0, 1, 2\}$.

SOLUTION In $6 + 3x - x^2$ replace x with each member of D to find the members of the range, R.

$$\therefore R = \{2, 6, 8\} \quad \textit{Answer}$$

x	$6 + 3x - x^2$	
-1	$6 + 3(-1) - (-1)^2 = 2$	
0	$6 + 3 \cdot 0 - 0^2$	$= 6$
1	$6 + 3 \cdot 1 - 1^2$	$= 8$
2	$6 + 3 \cdot 2 - 2^2$	$= 8$

Notice that the function g in Example 1 assigns the number 8 to both 1 and 2. In specifying the range of g, however, you name 8 only once.

Members of the range of a function are called **values of the function.** Thus, in Example 1, the values of the function g are 2, 6, and 8. To indicate that the function g assigns to -1 the value 2, you write

$$g(-1) = 2,$$

which may be read "g of -1 equals 2" or "the value of g at -1 is 2." Notice that $g(-1)$ is not the product of g and -1. It names the number that g assigns to -1.

EXAMPLE 2 Given $F: z \to z^3 - 1$ with the set of real numbers as the domain, find **a.** $F(1)$ **b.** $F(-1)$ **c.** $F(2)$.

SOLUTION First write the equation: $F(z) = z^3 - 1$

Then: **a.** $F(1) = 1^3 - 1 = 0$

  b. $F(-1) = (-1)^3 - 1 = -2$

  c. $F(2) = 2^3 - 1 = 7$

You may use whatever variable you choose to define a function. For example, $G: t \to t^3 - 1$ with the set of real numbers as the domain is the same function as F in Example 2. Both F and G assign to each real number its cube decreased by 1.

Unless otherwise stated, you may assume in this text that each domain is the set of real numbers.

Oral Exercises

Given the function $g: x \to 3 - 2x$, find the following values of g.

1. $g(0)$ **2.** $g(-1)$ **3.** $g(1)$ **4.** $g(2)$

5. $g(-2)$ **6.** $g(5)$ **7.** $g(8)$ **8.** $g(-8)$

State the range of each function.

9. $f: u \to u + 2$, $D = \{0, 1, 2\}$ **10.** $g: m \to 3 - m$, $D = \{-1, 0, 1\}$

11. $F: t \to t^2$, $D = \left\{\frac{1}{2}, 0, -\frac{1}{2}\right\}$ **12.** $G: x \to x^2 + 1$, $D = \{-1, 0, 1\}$

13. $h: k \to 3k^2$, $D = \{0, 1, 2\}$ **14.** $H: x \to x^2 + 3$, $D = \{-1, 0, 1\}$

Complete the following statements about the function $g: x \to x^2 - 1$.

15. The value of g at -2 is __?__. **16.** The value of g at 2 is __?__.

17. The value of g at __?__ is -1. **18.** The value of g at both __?__ and __?__ is 0.

Written Exercises

Given $f: x \to 4 - 3x$, find the following values of f.

A **1.** $f(0)$ **2.** $f(-1)$ **3.** $f(1)$ **4.** $f(-2)$

     5. $f(3)$ **6.** $f(-4)$ **7.** $f(\frac{1}{3})$ **8.** $f(-\frac{1}{3})$

Given $G(t) = t^2 + 2t$, find the following values of G.

     9. $G(0)$ **10.** $G(1)$ **11.** $G(2)$ **12.** $G(-1)$

    13. $G(-2)$ **14.** $G(3)$ **15.** $G(\frac{1}{2})$ **16.** $G(-\frac{2}{3})$

Find all the values of each function.

    17. $g(x) = 3x + 2$, $D = \{-1, 0, 1\}$ **18.** $f(x) = 2x - 5$, $D = \{1, 2, 3\}$

    19. $f(x) = 3 - 4x^2$, $D = \{0, 1, 2\}$ **20.** $h(x) = x^2 - 3x + 1$, $D = \{-1, 0, 1\}$

    21. $G(m) = \dfrac{6}{3m - 1}$, $D = \{-1, 0, 1\}$ **22.** $F(t) = 8 + \dfrac{1}{t + 3}$, $D = \{-2, -1, 0\}$

Find the range of each function.

    23. $h: t \to 3 - 2t$, $D = \{-2, 0, 2\}$ **24.** $g: t \to -1 - 3t$, $D = \{-3, -1, 1\}$

    25. $r: x \to \dfrac{6}{x}$, $D = \{1, 2, 3\}$ **26.** $k: t \to \dfrac{12}{t + 1}$, $D = \{1, 2, 3\}$

    27. $g: x \to \dfrac{x^2 + 3}{3x + 1}$, $D = \{-1, 0, 1\}$ **28.** $h: v \to \dfrac{v^2 + v}{v - 1}$, $D = \{-3, 0, 3\}$

B **29.** $f: t \to (3t - 1)(3t + 1)$, $D = \{-1, 0, 1\}$ **30.** $F: z \to (z - 2)^2$, $D = \{0, 2, 4\}$

    31. $f: z \to z^2 - 3z + 2$, $D = \{1, 2, 3\}$ **32.** $h: x \to x^3 - 3x^2 + 2x$, $D = \{0, 1, 2\}$

    33. $G: u \to (1 - u^2)^3$, $D = \{-2, -1, 0, 1\}$

    34. $H: x \to (x^2 - 2x)^2$, $D = \{-2, 0, 1, 2\}$

    35. $f: z \to 3(z - 1)^2 - 8$, $D = \{-1, 0, 1, 2, 3\}$

    36. $g: t \to (t - 2)(t - 1)$, $D = \{\frac{1}{2}, 1, 1\frac{1}{2}, 2, 2\frac{1}{2}\}$

Given that $f(x) = 3x^2$ and $g(x) = -2x^2$, find each of the following.

    37. $\frac{1}{2}f(4)$ **38.** $2g(-2)$ **39.** $f(1) + g(1)$ **40.** $f(2) - g(2)$

Given that $f(x) = 2x^2$ and $g(x) = 3x$, find each of the following. (*Hint:* To find $g[f(2)]$, first find $f(2)$.)

C **41. a.** $g(1)$ **b.** $f(1)$ **c.** $g[f(1)]$ **d.** $f[g(1)]$

    42. a. $g(-2)$ **b.** $f(-2)$ **c.** $g[f(-2)]$ **d.** $f[g(-2)]$

    43. a. Is it true that $g[f(x)] = f[g(x)]$ for all real values of x? Base your answer on your results for Exercises 41 and 42.

       b. Find a value of x for which $g[f(x)] = f[g(x)]$.

9-5 Functions Described by Tables and Graphs

OBJECTIVE To define functions in other ways.

In Section 9-4 the rules for functions were given as equations or with arrow notation. There are many numerical relationships in the world around you which illustrate the idea of a function but which cannot be defined by such rules. For example, the radius of each growth ring of a tree is related to the amount of rainfall in each year of the tree's life. Also, you can relate the attendance at a movie theater to the day of the week.

Sometimes functions are defined by giving a table of corresponding values. The table below shows the attendance at the first four games the Eagles played this year. The contents of the table can also be presented as a *correspondence* and as a set of ordered pairs.

Table	Correspondence	Ordered Pairs

Opponent	Attendance
Jetters	43,521
Stars	32,789
Hotshots	56,561
Falcons	28,456

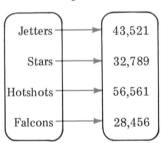

(Jetters,   43,521)
(Stars,   32,789)
(Hotshots, 56,561)
(Falcons,   28,456)

Corresponding to each team listed in the table there is one and only one attendance figure. Therefore, the table describes a function with domain

$$D = \{\text{Jetters, Stars, Hotshots, Falcons}\}$$

and range

$$R = \{43{,}521,\ 32{,}789,\ 56{,}561,\ 28{,}456\}.$$

It is easier to compare the attendance figures if the facts are shown in a *bar graph*. In the following graph, the members of the domain are listed down the left side. For each member of the domain a horizontal bar is drawn to represent the corresponding value in the range of the function. It is clear from the graph that the game with the greatest attendance was played against the Hotshots.

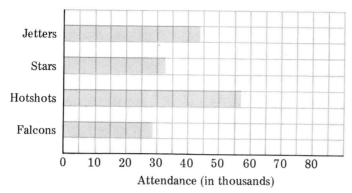

Attendance (in thousands)

When the members of the domain of a function are in a numerical succession, you may use a *broken-line graph*. The one at the right shows the number of people immigrating to the Yukon in each year from 1972 through 1977. Note that in this graph the members of the domain are listed across the bottom.

The line segments do *not* show the number of immigrants for the months in between each year marked. They do, however, help you see the trends from year to year.

The paired numbers in the function pictured by the graph above can be displayed as the set of ordered pairs.

$\{(1972, 305), (1973, 268), (1974, 300), (1975, 290), (1976, 250), (1977, 174)\}$.

The domain of the function consists of the first coordinates of the ordered pairs, and the range consists of the second coordinates.

Oral Exercises

State the domain and range of the function shown by each table.

1.

Student	Height
Arlene	172 cm
Ben	185 cm
Carla	150 cm
Denise	163 cm
Ed	180 cm
Frank	150 cm

2.

Month	Rainfall
May	50 mm
June	92 mm
July	68 mm
August	56 mm
September	35 mm
October	19 mm

State the domain and range of the function shown by each table.

3.

Building	Stories
Erieview Plaza	40
Iolani Towers	38
John Hancock	60
Main Tower	26
Place Victoria	47
Sears Tower	110

4.

Year	World Population (millions)
1800	910
1850	1,130
1900	1,600
1950	2,510
1970	3,575
1978	4,219
1979	4,321

5.

World Cotton Production						
Year	1967	1969	1971	1973	1975	1977
Millions of bales	49.7	53.2	59.8	63.2	54.3	63.7

6.

Highest Individual NBA Scores								
Year	1950	1954	1958	1962	1966	1970	1974	1978
Points	1865	1759	2001	4029	2649	2309	2261	2232

Written Exercises

A **1-3.** Make a bar graph for the facts shown in each table in Oral Exercises 1-3.

4-6. Display the function specified by each table in Oral Exercises 4-6 as a set of ordered pairs. Then make a broken-line graph for each function.

Application   Histograms

A *histogram* is a bar graph used to summarize a large set of data. The horizontal axis of a histogram represents ranges of observed values, and the vertical axis indicates their frequencies.

EXAMPLE

The points scored in each game played by the Conestoga High School basketball team are listed on the following page.

Draw a histogram presenting these scores in ten-point intervals.

63 67 82 87 60 53
68 79 74 79 93 71
61 59 67 48 68 73

SOLUTION

1. Use tally marks to count the number of scores within each ten-point interval. A measurement occurring on a boundary is included in the interval that will be to the measurement's left on the graph. For example, the score of 60 is counted in the interval from 50 to 60.

2. Draw the histogram.

Range	Frequency	
40–50	|	1
50–60	|||	3
60–70	|||||	6
70–80	||||	5
80–90	||	2
90–100	|	1

Points per game

Exercises

The following pulse rates (expressed in beats per minute) were recorded for a group of 40 people.

58 86 101 73 96 81 94 61 103 76
81 77   66 82 79 64 84 90   98 71
74 88   76 59 87 63 82 93   88 106
69 78   77 67 83 89 72 73   68 66

1. Draw a histogram for these data. Use intervals of width 10, such as 50–60 and 60–70, on the horizontal axis.

2. Which ten-unit interval represents the greatest number of people?

3. How many of the people have pulse rates between 60 and 70?

4. How many of the people have pulse rates greater than 80?

5. How many of the people have pulse rates no greater than 90?

9-6 *Quadratic Functions*

OBJECTIVE To graph quadratic functions.

You have seen a function presented as a set of ordered pairs and shown in a bar graph or a broken-line graph. A function defined by an equation in two variables can be presented as the set of ordered pairs that is the solution set of the equation. The graph of such a function in a coordinate plane is the graph of the defining equation. For example:

The function $f: x \rightarrow 2x - 8$ can be defined by $y = 2x - 8$.
The graph of f is the straight line with slope 2 and
y-intercept -8.

A **linear function** is a function that can be defined by a linear equation. The graph of every linear function is a straight line.

Now consider the function defined by the quadratic equation

$$y = x^2 - 2x - 3.$$

You can graph this function by first finding the coordinates of selected points, as shown in the table at the right. Then plot the points and connect them with a smooth curve.

x	$x^2 - 2x - 3 = y$
-2	$(-2)^2 - 2(-2) - 3 = \quad 5$
-1	$(-1)^2 - 2(-1) - 3 = \quad 0$
0	$0^2 - \quad 2(0) - 3 = -3$
1	$1^2 - \quad 2(1) - 3 = -4$
2	$2^2 - \quad 2(2) - 3 = -3$
3	$3^2 - \quad 2(3) - 3 = \quad 0$
4	$4^2 - \quad 2(4) - 3 = \quad 5$

The curve shown at the right is a **parabola.** This parabola opens upward and has a **minimum point** (lowest point): $(1, -4)$. The y-coordinate of this point is the least value of the function.

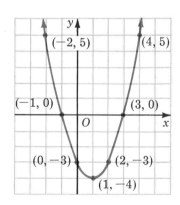

338   CHAPTER 9

Compare the parabola just seen with the graph of the function defined by the quadratic equation

$$y = -x^2 + 2x + 3.$$

x	$-x^2 + 2x + 3 = y$
-2	$-(-2)^2 + 2(-2) + 3 = -5$
-1	$-(-1)^2 + 2(-1) + 3 = 0$
0	$-0^2 + 2(0) + 3 = 3$
1	$-1^2 + 2(1) + 3 = 4$
2	$-2^2 + 2(2) + 3 = 3$
3	$-3^2 + 2(3) + 3 = 0$
4	$-4^2 + 2(4) + 3 = -5$

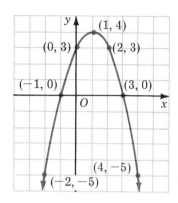

This graph is a parabola that opens downward and has a **maximum point** (highest point): $(1, 4)$. The y-coordinate of this point is the greatest value of the function.

A **quadratic function** is a function that can be defined by a quadratic equation of the form

$$y = ax^2 + bx + c \quad (a \neq 0).$$

The graph of every quadratic function is a parabola.

The minimum or maximum point of a parabola is called the **vertex**. Notice that in each example shown, the points except the vertex occur in *pairs that have the same y-coordinate*. Also, the average of the x-coordinates of any such pair is the x-coordinate of the vertex. For the parabola above:

Pairs of points		x-coordinate of vertex
$(-2, -5)$	$(4, -5)$	Average: $\dfrac{-2 + 4}{2} = 1$
$(-1, 0)$	$(3, 0)$	Average: $\dfrac{-1 + 3}{2} = 1$
$(0, 3)$	$(2, 3)$	Average: $\dfrac{0 + 2}{2} = 1$

To graph an equation of the form $y = ax^2 + bx + c$ $(a \neq 0)$, it is helpful to find the x-coordinate of the vertex and then plot enough points on both sides of the vertex to enable you to draw a smooth curve.

The graphs at the right illustrate that the x-coordinate of the vertex is the same for equations that differ only in the constant term. Therefore, a formula for the x-coordinate of the vertex of $y = ax^2 + bx + c$ can be found using the two points where the graph of $y = ax^2 + bx$ crosses the x-axis:

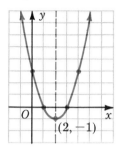

$$y = x^2 - 4x + 3$$

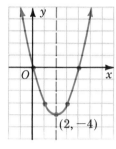

$$y = x^2 - 4x$$

Let $y = 0$:
$$0 = ax^2 + bx$$
$$0 = x(ax + b)$$
$$x = 0 \quad \text{or} \quad ax + b = 0$$

$$\therefore x = 0 \quad \text{or} \quad x = -\frac{b}{a}$$

The average of these x-coordinates is $\dfrac{0 + \left(-\dfrac{b}{a}\right)}{2}$, or $-\dfrac{b}{2a}$.

In general:

THE GRAPH OF $y = ax^2 + bx + c$ $(a \neq 0)$

If a is positive, the parabola opens upward.

If a is negative, the parabola opens downward.

The x-coordinate of the vertex is $-\dfrac{b}{2a}$.

Oral Exercises

State whether the graph of each quadratic equation opens upward or downward.

1. $y = x^2 - 5x - 4$ **2.** $y = -2x^2 + x + 1$ **3.** $y = 9 - x^2$

4. $x^2 - 9 = y$ **5.** $5x^2 + 5x = y$ **6.** $y = -\frac{1}{2}x^2$

State whether the graph of each quadratic function has a minimum or a maximum point.

7. $f: x \rightarrow x^2 - 2x + 1$

8. $g: x \rightarrow -4 - 4x - x^2$

9. $h: x \rightarrow 5x^2 - 3x$

10. $T: x \rightarrow 1 - x^2$

11. $S: x \rightarrow -10x^2 + x + 5$

12. $p: x \rightarrow \frac{3}{4}x^2$

Written Exercises

Find the coordinates of the vertex of the graph of each equation. Use the vertex and six other points to graph the equation.

A   **1.** $y = x^2$

2. $y = 3x^2$

3. $y = -2x^2$

4. $y = -4x^2$

5. $y = \frac{1}{2}x^2$

6. $y = -\frac{1}{2}x^2$

7. $y = x^2 + 4x$

8. $y = -x^2 + 2x$

9. $y = -x^2 - 2x + 1$

10. $y = x^2 - 3x - 4$

11. $y = \frac{1}{2}x^2 - 2$

12. $y = -\frac{1}{2}x^2 + 4x + 8$

Find the least value of each function.

13. $f: x \rightarrow x^2 + 3x$

14. $g: x \rightarrow x^2 + 4$

15. $h: x \rightarrow x^2 - x - 6$

16. $r: x \rightarrow 4 - 6x + 3x^2$

17. $F: x \rightarrow 4x^2 - 6$

18. $G: x \rightarrow \frac{1}{2}x^2$

Find the greatest value of each function.

19. $f: x \rightarrow -x^2 - 3x$

20. $F: x \rightarrow -2x^2 + 4x$

21. $g: x \rightarrow -x^2 - 6x - 10$

22. $G: x \rightarrow 9 - 7x - 14x^2$

23. $H: x \rightarrow -2x^2 + x$

24. $h: x \rightarrow -\frac{1}{3}x^2$

B   **25. a.** On the same set of axes draw the graphs of $y = x^2$, $y = x^2 + 1$, and $y = x^2 - 2$.

     b. Use your results in part (a) to describe the changes in the graph of $y = x^2 + c$ as the value of c increases; as c decreases.

26. a. On the same set of axes draw the graphs of $y = \frac{1}{2}x^2$, $y = x^2$, and $y = 2x^2$.

     b. On the same set of axes draw the graphs of $y = -\frac{1}{2}x^2$, $y = -x^2$, and $y = -2x^2$.

     c. Use your results in parts (a) and (b) to describe the change in the graph of $y = ax^2$ as $|a|$ increases.

Computer Key-In

The following computer program in BASIC will compute coordinates for use in graphing quadratic functions. The program will compute the coordinates of the vertex and five points on each side of it. When you use the program, you input the values A, B, C of

$$y = Ax^2 + Bx + C.$$

```
10   PRINT "INPUT A (NOT ZERO), B, C";
20   INPUT A,B,C
30   IF A=0 THEN 10
40   LET X1=-B/(2*A)
50   LET Y1=A*X1*X1+B*X1+C
60   PRINT "VERTEX AT (";X1;",";Y1;")"
70   LET X1=INT(X1)
80   PRINT "X", "Y"
90   FOR X=X1-5 TO X1+5
100  PRINT X,A*X*X+B*X+C
110  NEXT X
120  END
```

Self-Test 2

VOCABULARY function (p. 331)
domain of a function (p. 331)
range of a function (p. 331)
arrow notation (p. 331)
value of a function (p. 332)
linear function (p. 338)

parabola (p. 338)
minimum point (p. 338)
maximum point (p. 339)
quadratic function (p. 339)
vertex (p. 339)

1. Given $f(x) = 2x - 1$, find $f(3)$. Obj. 9-4, p. 331

2. Find the range of the given function:
   $g: t \rightarrow t^2 - 2t - 3 \quad D = \{-1, 0, 1, 2, 3\}$

3. The table shows a function. Obj. 9-5, p. 334

   a. State the domain and range of the function.

   b. Display the function as a set of ordered pairs.

Stock number	Price
N7621	$12.88
N6523	$ 9.85
V2231	$ 3.39
V2232	$ 3.39

4. Find the coordinates of the vertex of the graph of $y = 2x^2 + 4x - 1$. Obj. 9-6, p. 338

5. Find the greatest value of the function
   $f: x \rightarrow -\frac{1}{5}x^2$.

Check your answers with those at the back of the book.

9-7 *Direct Variation*

OBJECTIVE To use the concept of direct variation to solve problems.

The table below shows the distance, y, that a group of hikers will walk in x hours if they maintain a steady pace of 6 km/h.

Time in hours: x	Distance in kilometers: y
1	6
2	12
3	18
4	24
5	30

You can see that

$$y = 6x$$

and that this equation defines a function. Notice that if the hikers double the hiking time, the distance covered is doubled; if they triple the time, the distance is tripled. You can say that the distance *varies directly as* the time. This function is an example of a *direct variation*.

A **linear direct variation** (or simply, a **direct variation**) is a function defined by an equation of the form

$$y = kx, \text{ where } k \text{ is a nonzero constant.}$$

You can say that y *varies directly as* x, or y *varies with* x. The constant k is called the **constant of variation.**

When the domain is the set of real numbers, the graph of a direct variation is a straight line through the origin.

EXAMPLE 1 Given that d varies directly as t, and that $d = 110$ when $t = 2$, find the following:

    a. the constant of variation

    b. the value of d when $t = 3$

SOLUTION Let $d = kt$.

    a. Substitute $d = 110$ and $t = 2$: $110 = k \cdot 2$

                                           $55 = k$ *Answer*

    b. Substitute $k = 55$ and $t = 3$: $d = 55 \cdot 3 = 165$ *Answer*

If two ordered pairs of a direct variation defined by $y = kx$ are

$$(x_1, y_1), \quad \text{read "} x \text{ sub 1, } y \text{ sub 1," and}$$

$$(x_2, y_2), \quad \text{read "} x \text{ sub 2, } y \text{ sub 2,"}$$

and if neither pair is $(0, 0)$, then the coordinates satisfy $y = kx$:

$$y_1 = kx_1 \quad \text{and} \quad y_2 = kx_2.$$

From these equations you can write the ratios

$$\frac{y_1}{x_1} = k \quad \text{and} \quad \frac{y_2}{x_2} = k.$$

Since each ratio equals k, the ratios are equal:

$$\frac{y_1}{x_1} = \frac{y_2}{x_2}, \quad \text{read "} y_1 \text{ is to } x_1 \text{ as } y_2 \text{ is to } x_2.\text{"}$$

Since the equality of two ratios is a proportion (page 240), k is sometimes called the **constant of proportionality,** and y is said to be *directly proportional to x.*

When you use a proportion to solve a problem, you will find it helpful to recall that the product of the extremes equals the product of the means.

EXAMPLE 2

The amount of interest earned on savings is directly proportional to the amount of money saved. If $20 interest is earned on $250, how much interest will be earned on $700 in the same period of time?

SOLUTION

Step 1 The problem asks for the interest on $700.

Step 2 Let i, in dollars, be the interest on d dollars.

$$i_1 = 20 \qquad i_2 = \underline{\quad ? \quad}$$
$$d_1 = 250 \qquad d_2 = 700$$

Step 3 An equation can be written in the form $\dfrac{i_1}{d_1} = \dfrac{i_2}{d_2}$:

$$\frac{20}{250} = \frac{i_2}{700}$$

Step 4 $\quad 20(700) = 250i_2$
$$14{,}000 = 250i_2$$
$$56 = i_2$$

Step 5 The check is left to you.

$$\therefore \text{ the interest earned on \$700 is \$56.} \quad \textit{Answer}$$

Examples 1 and 2 illustrate two methods of solving problems involving direct variation. To solve Example 2 by the method shown in Example 1, first write the equation $i = kd$ and solve for the constant of variation, k, by using the fact that $i = 20$ when $d = 250$. Then use the resulting value of k to find the value of i when $d = 700$. Complete the problem this way for yourself. You will find the exercises and problems of this section easier if you understand *both* methods.

Oral Exercises

State whether or not the equation defines a direct variation. For each direct variation, state the constant of variation.

1. $y = 2x$

2. $p = 6s$

3. $xy = 8$

4. $d = 2.6t$

5. $\frac{1}{2}x = y$

6. $\frac{y}{x} = 3$

7. $p = \frac{12}{q}$

8. $C = 2\pi r$

9. $A = \pi r^2$

10. $\frac{b}{a} = 1$

11. $y = 2x^2$

12. $\frac{x}{y} = \frac{2}{3}$

State whether or not each set of ordered pairs is a direct variation.

SAMPLE $\{(8, 6), (12, 9), (24, 18)\}$

SOLUTION $\frac{6}{8} = \frac{3}{4}, \frac{9}{12} = \frac{3}{4}, \frac{18}{24} = \frac{3}{4}$; since the ratios are equal, the function is a direct variation.

13. $\{(2, 4), (3, 6), (4, 8)\}$

14. $\{(1, 3), (4, 12), (-3, -9)\}$

15. $\{(0, 1), (1, 2), (2, 3)\}$

16. $\{(-1, 2), (3, -6), (5, -10)\}$

17. $\{(-1, 7), (2, -14), (-3, 21)\}$

18. $\{(-2, 4), (4, -8), (-6, -12)\}$

Written Exercises

In Exercises 1-6, find the constant of variation.

A **1.** y varies directly as x, and $y = 12$ when $x = 72$.

2. y varies directly as x, and $y = 2$ when $x = 6$.

3. n varies directly as m, and $n = -10$ when $m = -2$.

4. t varies directly as s, and $t = 168$ when $s = 14$.

5. w is directly proportional to y, and $w = 150$ when $y = 6$.

6. p is directly proportional to q, and $p = 225$ when $q = 15$.

7. If y varies directly as x, and $y = 300$ when $x = 3$, find y when $x = 10$.

8. If w varies directly as z, and $w = 6$ when $z = 12$, find w when $z = 15$.

9. If h is directly proportional to t, and $h = 325$ when $t = 6.5$, find h when $t = 12$.

10. If a is directly proportional to b, and $a = 8$ when $b = 288$, find a when $b = 20$.

Find the missing value in each exercise if (x_1, y_1) and (x_2, y_2) are ordered pairs of the same direct variation.

11. $x_1 = 12,\ y_1 = 9$
    $x_2 = 28,\ y_2 = \underline{\ ?\ }$

12. $x_1 = 25,\ y_1 = \underline{\ ?\ }$
    $x_2 = 20,\ y_2 = 100$

13. $x_1 = 4.8,\quad y_1 = 2$
    $x_2 = \underline{\ ?\ },\ y_2 = 1$

14. $x_1 = \underline{\ ?\ },\ y_1 = 5$
    $x_2 = 6.75,\ y_2 = 9$

15. $x_1 = \dfrac{1}{6},\ y_1 = \dfrac{1}{8}$
    $x_2 = \dfrac{2}{3},\ y_2 = \underline{\ ?\ }$

16. $x_1 = \dfrac{4}{5},\ y_1 = \underline{\ ?\ }$
    $x_2 = \dfrac{2}{3},\ y_2 = \dfrac{1}{6}$

Translate each statement into *two* formulas expressing direct variation. Use k as the constant of variation.

SAMPLE   The velocity, v, of a freely falling object varies directly as the length of time, t, that it falls.

SOLUTION $v = kt$ or $\dfrac{v_1}{t_1} = \dfrac{v_2}{t_2}$

B 17. The weight, M, of a person on the moon is directly proportional to the person's weight, E, on earth.

18. The perimeter, P, of a square varies directly as the length, s, of a side.

19. The amount of money, m, earned on a job varies with the number of hours, h, of work.

20. The amount of interest, I, paid on a bank account varies directly as the amount of money, p, in the account.

21. The amount of pressure, P, on the inner wall of a tire is directly proportional to the temperature, T, of the air in the tire.

22. The distance, d, traveled at a fixed rate of speed varies with the time of travel, t.

23. The income, i, from the Varsity Club car wash is directly proportional to the number, n, of cars washed.

Problems

Solve.

A 1. A worker's wages are directly proportional to the number of hours worked. If $26 is earned for eight hours of work, how much is earned for forty hours of work?

2. The distance traveled by a truck driver at a constant rate varies with the length of time she travels. If she travels 168 km in two hours, how far will she travel in three hours?

3. The number of words typed is directly proportional to the time spent typing. If Jim can type 225 words in five minutes, how long will it take him to type a 675-word essay?

4. An estimate of the number of hot dogs that will be sold at a baseball game varies directly as the number of people expected to attend. If it is estimated that 60,000 hot dogs will be sold when 45,000 people attend, how many hot dogs are estimated to be sold when 30,000 people attend?

B 5. The amount of oats required in a cookie recipe is directly proportional to the amount of flour required. If the recipe calls for three measuring cups of oats and one measuring cup of flour, how many cups of oats should be used with one and one half cups of flour?

6. The amount of bend of a diving board varies directly as the mass of the diver. If a 30 kg diver causes the board to bend 1.5 cm, how much will the board bend if the diver is 65 kg?

7. The amount of chlorine needed for a pool varies as the size of the pool. If 5 units of chlorine is the amount needed for 2500 L of water, how much chlorine is required for 3750 L of water?

8. When an electric current is 35 A (amperes), the electromotive force is 315 V (volts). Find the force when the current is 50 A if the force varies directly as the current.

9. The odometer on the Santanas' car was not measuring distance correctly. For the 220 km trip from home to the grandparents' home, the odometer registered only 216.7 km. On the return trip, the Santanas had to detour for road repairs. If the odometer registered 453.1 km for the round trip, how many actual kilometers was the detour?

10. Two thermometers are exactly the same except that thermometer F is marked off into 180 equal units and thermometer C is marked off into 100 equal units. A length equal to 66.6 units on thermometer F is equal to a length of how many units on thermometer C?

Calculator Key-In

The *light year* is a unit used for describing very great distances, such as the distance to a neighboring star. The distance that light travels in one year is one light year. If the speed of light is about 2.9979×10^8 m/s, about how many meters is one light year?

9-8 *Inverse Variation*

OBJECTIVE   **To use the concept of inverse variation to solve problems.**

The table shows the time, t, that it takes a car to cover a distance of 40 km traveling at the rate of r km/h. You can see that

$$rt = 40$$

Rate in km/h: r	Time in hours: t
20	2
40	1
60	$\frac{2}{3}$
80	$\frac{1}{2}$

and that this equation defines a function. Notice that if the rate of travel is increased, the time required is decreased so that the product is always 40. You can say that the time *varies inversely as* the rate. This example illustrates an *inverse variation*.

An **inverse variation** is a function defined by an equation of the form

$xy = k$, when k is a nonzero constant.

$y = \frac{k}{x}$ for all ordered pairs other than $(0, 0)$.

You can say that y *varies inversely as* x or y *is inversely proportional to* x. The constant k is the **constant of variation.**

The graph of an inverse function is not a straight line since the defining equation

$$xy = k$$

is not linear; the term xy is of degree 2. The graph of $xy = 1$ is shown below.

$xy = 1$

x	y
-4	$-\frac{1}{4}$
-2	$-\frac{1}{2}$
-1	-1
$-\frac{1}{2}$	-2
$-\frac{1}{4}$	-4

x	y
$\frac{1}{4}$	4
$\frac{1}{2}$	2
1	1
2	$\frac{1}{2}$
4	$\frac{1}{4}$

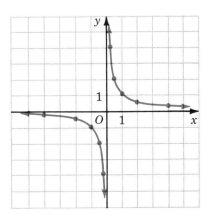

Neither x nor y can have the value 0. This graph is called a **hyperbola.** It consists of two branches neither of which intersects an axis.

For every nonzero value of k, the graph of $xy = k$ is a hyperbola. When k is positive, the branches of the graph are in Quadrants I and III. When k is negative, the graph is in Quadrants II and IV.

In some practical problems involving inverse variation, negative answers are meaningless, and the domain and the range are limited to positive numbers. The graph of such an inverse variation has only the branch in Quadrant I.

If (x_1, y_1) and (x_2, y_2) are ordered pairs of the same inverse variation, then the coordinates satisfy the equation $xy = k$:

$$x_1 y_1 = k \quad \text{and} \quad x_2 y_2 = k.$$

Therefore,

$$x_1 y_1 = x_2 y_2.$$

Compare:

DIRECT VARIATION	INVERSE VARIATION
$y = kx$	$xy = k$
$\dfrac{y_1}{x_1} = \dfrac{y_2}{x_2}$	$x_1 y_1 = x_2 y_2$

These equations can be written in other equivalent forms, but the forms shown are the easiest to remember. For direct variation the quotients of coordinates are constant, and for inverse variation the products are constant.

One example of inverse variation is the law of the lever. A lever is a bar pivoted at a point called the fulcrum. If masses m_1 and m_2 are placed at distances d_1 and d_2 from the fulcrum, and the lever is at balance, then

$$m_1 d_1 = m_2 d_2.$$

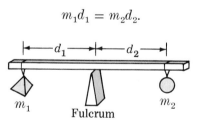

EXAMPLE If a 10 g mass is 75 cm from the fulcrum of a lever, how far from the fulcrum is a 30 g mass which balances it?

SOLUTION Let $m_1 = 10$, $d_1 = 75$, and $m_2 = 30$. $d_2 = \underline{\ ?\ }$

Use $m_1 d_1 = m_2 d_2$.
$$10(75) = 30 d_2$$
$$25 = d_2$$

∴ the distance of the 30 g mass from the fulcrum is 25 cm. **Answer**

Oral Exercises

State whether each equation defines an inverse variation or a direct variation. (k is a constant.)

1. $y = \dfrac{k}{x}$

2. $\dfrac{y}{x} = k$

3. $z = \dfrac{k}{p}$

4. $xy = 64$

5. $d = 4.8t$

6. $s = \dfrac{1}{r}$

7. $\dfrac{p_1}{t_1} = \dfrac{p_2}{t_2}$

8. $a_1 b_1 = a_2 b_2$

9. $\dfrac{1}{2} = rt$

10. $\dfrac{2}{3} = \dfrac{r}{s}$

11. $\dfrac{x}{y} = \dfrac{1}{k}$

12. $kxy = 1$

Complete the ordered pairs so that they belong to the given function.

13. $xy = 12$: $(2, \underline{\ ?\ })$ $(\underline{\ ?\ }, 12)$ $(4, \underline{\ ?\ })$

14. $m = \dfrac{50}{n}$: $(2, \underline{\ ?\ })$ $(\underline{\ ?\ }, 50)$ $(25, \underline{\ ?\ })$

15. $200 = rt$: $(8, \underline{\ ?\ })$ $(1, \underline{\ ?\ })$ $(\underline{\ ?\ }, 50)$

16. $xy = -1$: $(-1, \underline{\ ?\ })$ $\left(\dfrac{1}{2}, \underline{\ ?\ }\right)$ $(\underline{\ ?\ }, 4)$

17. If $yz = k$ and y is tripled while k remains constant, how does z change?

18. If $D = rt$ and r is halved while D remains constant, how does t change?

Written Exercises

Graph each equation if the domain and the range are both limited to the set of positive numbers.

A　**1.** $xy = 4$

2. $2xy = 1$

3. $x = \dfrac{3}{y}$

4. $\dfrac{x}{3} = \dfrac{4}{y}$

Find the missing value in each exercise if (x_1, y_1) and (x_2, y_2) are ordered pairs of the same inverse variation.

5. $x_1 = 5,\ y_1 = 100,\ x_2 = 4,\ y_2 = \underline{\ ?\ }$

6. $x_1 = 20,\ y_1 = 5,\ x_2 = \underline{\ ?\ },\ y_2 = 50$

7. $x_1 = \underline{\ ?\ },\ y_1 = 6.5,\ x_2 = 3.9,\ y_2 = 3.5$

8. $x_1 = 64,\ y_1 = \underline{\ ?\ },\ x_2 = 16,\ y_2 = \dfrac{1}{2}$

Translate each statement into *two* formulas expressing inverse variation. Use k as the constant of variation.

SAMPLE　　The length, l, of a rectangle of constant area varies inversely as the width, w.

SOLUTION　$lw = k$　or　$l_1 w_1 = l_2 w_2$

B **9.** The amount of information retained, i, is inversely proportional to the number of hours, h, that have passed since the information was studied.

10. The time, t, required to drive between two cities varies inversely as the rate, r, of the bus.

11. The force, f, needed to shift a heavy log varies inversely as the length, l, of the crowbar used.

12. At a fixed temperature the volume, V, of a gas varies inversely as the pressure, P.

13. The frequency, f, of a sound wave is inversely proportional to the wavelength, l.

14. The amount of current, I, flowing through a circuit is inversely proportional to the amount of resistance, R, of the circuit.

Problems

Solve. In Exercises 1 and 2, apply the law of the lever.

A **1.** If Susie is 30 kg and her mother is 60 kg, how far from the seesaw support must Susie sit to balance her mother who is 1 m from it?

2. Jimmy sits 1.5 m from the seesaw support to balance a friend who is 24 kg and sits 2 m from the support. How many kilograms is Jimmy?

3. The number of days needed to finish a quilt varies inversely as the number of people working on it. It takes 14 days for two people to finish a quilt. If the job has to be finished in four days, how many people are needed?

4. Three friends on a fishing trip pay $100 each to share the rent of a cottage. The cost per person varies inversely as the number of people sharing the rent. How many people would have to share the rent of the cottage to make the cost $60 per person?

5. A jet traveling at 2400 km/h takes three hours to make a New York-to-London crossing. If another jet makes the same trip in nine hours, how fast does it fly?

6. A rectangle has length 36 cm and width 14 cm. Find the width of another rectangle of equal area whose length is 42 cm.

7. The number of chairs on a ski lift varies inversely as the distance between them. When they are 10 m apart, the ski lift can accommodate 32 chairs. If 40 evenly spaced chairs are used on the lift, what space is left between them?

8. The number of plants used to fill a row of given length in a garden varies inversely as the distance between the plants. If 75 plants are used to fill the row when planted 20 cm apart, how many plants are used to fill the row when planted 15 cm apart?

B **9.** The rate of travel varies inversely as the time of travel. On a holiday weekend the Lee family drove to Montreal in 7.5 h at the rate of 88 km/h. How much longer would it have taken them if they had driven at 80 km/h?

10. When the tension on a piano wire is kept constant, the number of vibrations per second varies inversely as the length of the wire. A wire 200 cm long vibrates at 320 vibrations per second. By how much should the wire be shortened to vibrate at 520 vibrations per second? Give the answer to the nearest centimeter.

For the wave motion of sound, the following formula holds:

$$fl = v,$$

where f is the frequency (number of waves per second), l is the wavelength (in meters), and v is the speed of sound (about 335 meters per second in air). Use this information in the following problems.

C **11.** The frequency of a note an octave above a given note is twice that of the given note. How does the wavelength of the higher note compare with that of the lower note?

12. If the wavelength of a note is $\frac{3}{2}$ that of a given note, how do the frequencies compare?

13. An open organ pipe produces a sound wave that has a length that is twice the length of the pipe. Find the length of an open pipe that will produce the note A with the frequency 440. Give the answer to the nearest tenth of a meter.

14. A stopped organ pipe produces a sound wave that has a length that is four times the length of the pipe. What is the frequency of the sound produced by a stopped organ pipe 2 meters long?

ḫistorical Ռote Function Notation

Leonhard Euler (1707–1783) was a Swiss mathematician who taught and wrote about mathematics in both St. Petersburg, Russia, and Berlin, Germany. He made contributions to many branches of mathematics and was particularly successful in devising useful notations. Among his notations was the symbol $f(x)$ to represent the value of a function. Other mathematicians before him had denoted functions with Greek letters.

9-9 *Direct and Inverse Variation Involving Squares*

OBJECTIVE To use quadratic direct variation and variation inversely as a square in problem solving.

In the world around you, there are many examples in which a quantity varies either directly or inversely *as the square* of another quantity. For example, the area of a circle varies directly as the square of the radius: $A = \pi r^2$. This is an example of a *quadratic direct variation*.

A **quadratic direct variation** is a function defined by an equation of the form

$$y = kx^2, \text{ where } k \text{ is a nonzero constant.}$$

If (x_1, y_1) and (x_2, y_2) are ordered pairs of the same quadratic direct variation, and neither pair is $(0, 0)$, then:

$$\frac{y_1}{x_1{}^2} = \frac{y_2}{x_2{}^2}$$

You say that *y varies directly as x^2 or y is directly proportional to x^2.*

EXAMPLE 1 Given that z varies directly as the square of w, and $z = 4$ when $w = 2$, find the value of z when $w = 8$.

SOLUTION

Method 1

Use $z = kw^2$.
$$4 = k(2)^2$$
$$\therefore 1 = k$$

$$z = 1(8)^2$$
$$\therefore z = 64 \quad \textbf{\textit{Answer}}$$

Method 2

Use $\dfrac{z_1}{w_1{}^2} = \dfrac{z_2}{w_2{}^2}$.
$$\frac{4}{2^2} = \frac{z_2}{8^2}$$

$$1 = \frac{z_2}{64}$$

$$\therefore z_2 = 64 \quad \textbf{\textit{Answer}}$$

The intensity of sound *varies inversely as the square* of the distance of a listener from the source of sound. That is, if you halve the distance between yourself and a drummer, the intensity of the sound that reaches your ears will be quadrupled.

An **inverse variation as the square** is a function defined by an equation of the form

$$x^2y = k, \text{ where } k \text{ is a nonzero constant.}$$
$$y = \frac{k}{x^2} \text{ for all ordered pairs other than } (0, 0).$$

You say that *y varies inversely as x^2 or y is inversely proportional to x^2.*

If (x_1, y_1) and (x_2, y_2) are ordered pairs of the function defined by $x^2 y = k$, then

$$x_1{}^2 y_1 = x_2{}^2 y_2.$$

EXAMPLE 2 Given that y varies inversely as the square of x, and $y = 4$ when $x = 2$, find the value of y when $x = 8$.

SOLUTION Method 1   Method 2

Use $x^2 y = k$.   Use $x_1{}^2 y_1 = x_2{}^2 y_2$.
$2^2(4) = k$ $2^2(4) = 8^2(y_2)$
$\therefore 16 = k$ $16 = 64 y_2$

$8^2 y = 16$ $\therefore y_2 = \dfrac{1}{4}$ **Answer**

$\therefore y = \dfrac{16}{64} = \dfrac{1}{4}$ **Answer**

Oral Exercises

Translate each statement into a formula. Use k as a constant where needed.

1. The surface area, A, of a sphere varies directly as the square of the diameter, d, of the sphere.

2. The force of attraction, f, between two magnets is inversely proportional to the square of the distance, d, between them.

3. The distance, d, that a ball rolls down a hill is directly proportional to the square of the time, t, that the ball rolls.

4. The time, t, required to fill a gasoline tank varies inversely as the square of the diameter, d, of the hose.

5. The area, A, of a circular irrigation field varies directly as the square of the radius, r, of the field.

6. The intensity, i, of the sound of a parade that you hear varies inversely as the square of your distance, d, from the parade.

Problems

Solve.

A 1. The area of a square varies directly as the square of a side. If the area of a square 2 cm on a side is 4 cm², what is the area of a square 5 cm on a side?

2. The amount of material needed to cover a ball is directly proportional to the square of the radius. A ball with radius 4 cm requires 256 cm² of material to cover it. How much material is needed to cover a ball with radius 20 cm?

3. The time needed to fill the gasoline tank of a car varies inversely as the square of the diameter of the hose. If a hose of diameter 2 cm takes 10 minutes to fill the tank, how long will it take to fill the same tank using a hose with diameter 5 cm?

4. The height of a cylinder of a given volume is inversely proportional to the square of the radius. If a cylinder of radius 2 cm has a height of 9 cm, what is the height of a cylinder of equal volume that has radius 3 cm?

5. The distance the signal from an FM radio station travels is directly proportional to the square of the number of kilowatts (kW) it produces. A 50 kW station can broadcast a distance of 100 km. How far could the station broadcast if it produced 60 kW?

6. The distance required for a car to come to a stop varies directly as the square of the speed of the car. If the stopping distance for a car traveling 16 km/h is 7 m, what is the distance required for a car traveling 48 km/h to stop?

B **7.** The exposure time required for a photograph is inversely proportional to the square of the diameter of the camera lens. If the lens diameter is 2 cm, the exposure time needed is 0.01 s. Find the diameter of the lens if an exposure time of 0.0016 s is needed.

8. The distance an object falls varies directly as the square of the time of fall. If an object falls 78 m in 4 s, how far will it fall in 4.8 s?

9. The force between two magnets varies inversely as the square of the distance between them. If the magnets are initially 8 cm apart and then the distance is decreased to 0.5 cm, what is the effect on the force between them?

10. The brightness of the illumination of an object varies inversely as the square of the distance of the object from the source of illumination. If you move a book from a position 25 cm from a light to a position 50 cm from the light, what part of the original illumination will you get?

C **11.** The volume of a sphere varies directly as the cube of the radius.
    a. If the volume of a sphere of radius 5 cm is 125 times that of another sphere, what is the radius of the second sphere?
    b. If the ratio of the radii of two spheres is 3:2, what is the ratio of the volumes of the spheres?

9-10 *Joint and Combined Variation*

OBJECTIVE   To solve problems involving joint variation and combined variation.

If Susan earns $300 next summer and puts her earnings into a savings account, the amount of simple interest she receives depends on her bank's interest rate and on the length of time that she leaves the money in the account:

$$I = 300rt$$

The interest is directly proportional to the product of the rate and the time. You say that the interest *varies jointly as* the rate and the time.

In general, if a variable varies directly as the product of two or more other variables, the resulting relationship is called a **joint variation.** If z varies jointly as x and y, you can express the relationship in the following equations. For a nonzero constant k:

$$z = kxy \quad \text{and} \quad \frac{z_1}{x_1 y_1} = \frac{z_2}{x_2 y_2}$$

EXAMPLE 1   The volume of a cylinder, V, varies jointly as the height, h, and the square of the radius, r. If $V = 160\pi$ when $h = 10$ and $r = 4$, find V when $h = 8$ and $r = 3$.

SOLUTION   Let $V_1 = 160\pi$, $h_1 = 10$, $r_1 = 4$, $h_2 = 8$, and $r_2 = 3$. $V_2 = \underline{\ \ ?\ \ }$

$$\frac{V_1}{h_1 r_1{}^2} = \frac{V_2}{h_2 r_2{}^2}$$

$$\frac{160\pi}{10(4)^2} = \frac{V_2}{8(3)^2}$$

$$160 V_2 = 72 \cdot 160\pi$$

$$V_2 = 72\pi \quad \textbf{\textit{Answer}}$$

If a variable varies *directly* as one variable and *inversely* as another, the resulting relationship is called a **combined variation.** For example, if z varies directly as x and inversely as y, you can express the relationship in the following equations. For a nonzero constant k:

$$zy = kx \left(\text{or } z = \frac{kx}{y}\right) \quad \text{and} \quad \frac{z_1 y_1}{x_1} = \frac{z_2 y_2}{x_2}$$

EXAMPLE 2 p varies directly as q and inversely as r^2.
If $p = 1$ when $q = 6$ and $r = 2$,
find p when $q = 9$ and $r = 3$.

SOLUTION Let $p_1 = 1$, $q_1 = 6$, $r_1 = 2$, $q_2 = 9$, and $r_2 = 3$. $p_2 = \underline{\ ?\ }$

$$\frac{r_1{}^2 p_1}{q_1} = \frac{r_2{}^2 p_2}{q_2}$$

$$\frac{2^2 \cdot 1}{6} = \frac{3^2 \cdot p_2}{9}$$

$$54 p_2 = 36$$

$$p_2 = \frac{2}{3} \quad \textit{Answer}$$

Oral Exercises

Translate each statement into a formula. Use k where needed.

1. p varies jointly as q and r.

2. r varies directly as d and inversely as t.

3. z varies directly as the square of x and inversely as y.

4. i varies directly as m and inversely as the square of d.

5. u varies directly as the square of v and inversely as the square of w.

6. I varies jointly as P, r, and t.

7. The area, A, of a triangle varies jointly as the base, b, and the altitude, h.

8. The mass, m, of a rectangular metal block varies jointly as the length, l, width, w, and thickness, t, of the block.

9. The volume, V, of a gas varies directly as the temperature, T, and inversely as the pressure, P.

10. The power, P, of an electric circuit varies directly as the square of the voltage, V, and inversely as the resistance, R.

11. The lateral surface, S, of a cylinder varies jointly as the radius, r, and the height, h, of the cylinder.

12. The heat, H, generated by an electric stove element varies jointly as the resistance, R, and the square of the current, C.

Problems

Solve.

A **1.** The area of a triangle varies jointly as the base and altitude. A triangle with base 6 cm and altitude 4 cm has an area of 12 cm². What is the area if the base is 19 cm and the altitude is 6 cm?

2. The lateral surface area of a motor cylinder varies jointly as the radius and the height of the cylinder. For radius 5 cm and height 10 cm, the surface area is 300 cm². What is the radius if the surface area is 720 cm² and the height is 40 cm?

Solve.

3. The volume of a motor cylinder of a truck varies jointly as the height of the cylinder and the square of the radius. A cylinder of radius 25 cm has height 8 cm and volume 15,000 cm³. What is the radius of a cylinder whose volume is 21,384 cm³ and whose height is 5.5 cm?

4. The distance a car travels from rest varies jointly as its acceleration and the square of the time of motion. If a car travels 500 m from rest in 5 s at an acceleration of 40 m/s², how far will the car travel from rest in 10 s with an acceleration of 3 m/s²?

In Exercises 5 and 6, apply the statement: The number of persons needed to do a job varies directly as the amount of work to be done and inversely as the time in which the job must be done.

5. If 2 students in the typing pool can type 210 pages in 3 days, how many students will be needed to type 700 pages in 2 days?

6. If 2 workers can erect 400 m of fence in 10 h, how long will it take 5 workers to erect 600 m of fence?

B 7. The resistance of a wire to an electrical current varies directly as the length of the wire and inversely as the square of the diameter. 4.8 km of wire with diameter 6 mm has a resistance of 21 ohms. Find the resistance for 1.2 km of the wire with diameter 3 mm.

8. The area of a trapezoid varies jointly as the sum of the two parallel sides and the distance between the parallel sides. When the lengths of the parallel sides are 7 cm and 9 cm and the distance between them is 4 cm, the area is 32 cm². If the area is to remain constant and the height is reduced to 0.5 cm, what is the sum of the parallel sides?

C 9. The heat generated by a stove element varies jointly as the resistance and the square of the current. What is the effect on the heat generated in the following cases?

   a. The current is unchanged but the resistance is doubled.

   b. The resistance is unchanged but the current is doubled.

   c. The current is tripled and the resistance is doubled.

10. The power in an electric circuit varies directly as the square of the voltage and inversely as the resistance. What is the effect on the power in the following cases?

   a. The resistance is constant and the voltage is doubled.

   b. The voltage is constant and the resistance is doubled.

   c. The voltage is doubled and the resistance is quadrupled.

Self-Test 3

Solve.

1. Jan's earnings vary directly as the number of hours she works. If she earns $5.50 for two hours of work, how many hours does she work to earn $8.25?

    Obj. 9-7, p. 343

2. The time it takes Milo to walk to school varies inversely as the rate at which he walks. If it takes him a quarter of an hour to walk to school at 6.4 km/h, how long will it take him at 4.8 km/h?

    Obj. 9-8, p. 348

3. Given that y varies inversely as the square of x, and $y = 45$ when $x = 2$, find the value of y when $x = 3$.

    Obj. 9-9, p. 353

4. The surface area of a sphere varies directly as the square of the radius. A tennis ball has a radius $\frac{1}{4}$ times that of a basketball. Find the surface area of the tennis ball if the surface area of the basketball is 144π cm².

5. The area of a trapezoid varies jointly as the height of the trapezoid and the sum of the bases. The area of a trapezoid is 24 cm² when the height is 4 cm and the sum of the bases is 12 cm. Find the area of another trapezoid if the height is 6 cm and the sum of the bases is 10 cm.

    Obj. 9-10, p. 356

Check your answers with those at the back of the book.

Chapter Summary

1. An equation of a straight line can be found from: (a) the slope and the y-intercept; (b) the slope and any point on the line; (c) two points on the line.

2. A function can be defined by an equation, a table, a correspondence, or a set of ordered pairs.

3. The value of the function $f: x \rightarrow 5x + 2$ when $x = 6$ is denoted by $f(6)$. Thus, $f(6) = 5(6) + 2 = 32$.

4. A linear function is defined by a linear equation. Its graph is a straight line.

5. A quadratic function is defined by an equation of the form $y = ax^2 + bx + c = 0$, $a \neq 0$. Its graph is a parabola (see page 338).

6. Several kinds of variation have been described (k is a nonzero constant):

    a. A linear direct variation is a linear function defined by an equation of the form $y = kx$.

    b. An inverse variation is a function defined by an equation of the form $xy = k$ $\left(\text{or } y = \dfrac{k}{x}\right)$.

    c. A quadratic direct variation is a quadratic function defined by an equation of the form $y = kx^2$.

    d. An inverse variation as the square is a function defined by an equation of the form $x^2y = k$ $\left(\text{or } y = \dfrac{k}{x^2}\right)$.

Chapter Review

Give the letter of the correct answer.

1. Find the slope of the line that passes through the points $(-2, 4)$ and $(3, -1)$.   9-1

    a. $-\dfrac{3}{5}$ **b.** -1 **c.** 0 **d.** $\dfrac{1}{3}$

2. Find the slope of the line $y = -8$.

    a. -8 **b.** 1 **c.** 0 **d.** no slope

3. Find the slope of the line whose equation is $2x - 3y = 6$.   9-2

    a. 2 **b.** -2 **c.** $-\dfrac{2}{3}$ **d.** $\dfrac{2}{3}$

4. Find the y-intercept of the line whose equation is $x + 2y = 6$.

    a. 6 **b.** -6 **c.** 3 **d.** -3

5. Write an equation of the line through point $(2, 5)$ with slope 1.   9-3

    a. $x - y = -3$ **b.** $2x + 5y = 0$ **c.** $y = x - 3$ **d.** $x + y = 7$

6. Given $f(x) = -3x + 5$, find $f(-2)$.   9-4

    a. 11 **b.** 10 **c.** 1 **d.** 0

7. Find the range of the function $\{(\text{F}, 9), (\text{Cl}, 17), (\text{Br}, 35), (\text{I}, 53)\}$.   9-5

    a. $(\text{I}, 53)$ **b.** $\{9, 17, 35, 53\}$ **c.** $\{\text{F, Cl, Br, I}\}$ **d.** 53

8. Find the coordinates of the vertex of the graph of $y = x^2 + 6x + 5$.   9-6

    a. $(0, 5)$ **b.** $(-6, 5)$ **c.** $(3, 32)$ **d.** $(-3, -4)$

9. If p varies directly as q, and $p = 3$ when $q = 6$, find the value of p when $q = 18$.   9-7

    a. 36 **b.** 6 **c.** 9 **d.** 27

10. If y varies inversely as x, and x is doubled, then y is __?__.   9-8

    a. doubled   **b.** halved   **c.** quadrupled   **d.** unchanged

11. The area, A, of a circle is directly proportional to the square of the radius, r. If $A = \pi$ when $r = 1$, find A where $r = 2$.

9-9

    a. $A = 4$ **b.** $\dfrac{1}{4}\pi$ **c.** 4π **d.** 2π

12. Which equation describes "y varies inversely as the square of x"?

    a. $x^2 y = k$ **b.** $y = \dfrac{k}{x}$ **c.** $y^2 = \dfrac{k}{x}$ **d.** $y = kx^2$

13. y varies jointly as w and x. If $y = 144$ when $w = 12$ and $x = 6$, find y when $w = 10$ and $x = 3$.

9-10

    a. 345.6   **b.** 240   **c.** 100   **d.** 60

Chapter Test

1. Find the slope of the line through the points $(2, 1)$ and $(6, 7)$.

9-1

2. Find the slope and y-intercept of the line whose equation is $2x + 4y = 1$.

9-2

3. Write an equation of the line that passes through the points $(-2, -3)$ and $(0, 0)$.

9-3

4. Given that $f(t) = t^2 - 2t + 3$, find $f(-1)$.

9-4

5. $\{(1, 2), (2, 4), (3, 6), (4, 8), (5, 10)\}$ expresses a function.

9-5

    a. Give the domain.   **b.** Give the range.

6. Find the coordinates of the vertex of the graph of $y = -2x^2 + 8x - 9$.

9-6

7. The number of doughnuts a machine can make varies directly as the running time of the machine. If a machine can make 1000 doughnuts in six hours, in how many hours can it make 300 doughnuts?

9-7

8. The number of chairs in a row varies inversely as the distance between them. When they are 10 cm apart, 27 chairs fit in a row. If 45 chairs are needed in a row, how far apart should they be placed?

9-8

9. In the design of a building, the height is directly proportional to the square of the length of the base. A building 400 m high has a base length of 100 m. If the base length is 110 m, what should the height be?

9-9

10. Translate the statement into a formula, using k as the constant of variation if needed: The force of gravity, g, between two planets is inversely proportional to the square of the distance, d, between them.

11. The volume of a pyramid varies jointly as the altitude of the pyramid and the area of the base. A pyramid whose altitude is 6 cm and whose base area is 16 cm^2 has a volume of 32 cm^3. Find the volume of a pyramid with altitude 8 cm and base area 9 cm^2.

9-10

Cumulative Review   (Chapters 1-9)

Simplify each expression.

1. $(-7 + 3x) - (9 - 2x)$ **2.** $3ab(7a^2 + 5ab - ab^3)$ **3.** $(p + 2q)(3p - q - 1)$

4. $(2r^3s^2t)^3 \div (-6r^9t^2)$ **5.** $(-9x^2y + 3xy^2) \div 3xy$ **6.** $(2cd - 3g)^2$

Factor completely.

7. $25a^3 - 20a^2 - 60a$ **8.** $-36y^2 + 31yz - 3z^2$ **9.** $16t^4 - 9v^2$

Express in simplest form.

10. $\dfrac{9m^2 + 30m + 25}{6m^2 + 10m}$ **11.** $\dfrac{2b}{b^2 - 1} + \dfrac{b}{b + 1} + 1$ **12.** $\dfrac{a^3 - 4a}{3a^2 + 9a} \cdot \dfrac{9 - a^2}{a^2 - a - 6}$

13. $\dfrac{3}{c - 2d} - \dfrac{2}{c + d} + \dfrac{1}{c}$ **14.** $\dfrac{g^4 - 81}{g^2 + 3g} \div \dfrac{2g^3 + 18g}{4g^2}$ **15.** $\dfrac{35r^3 + 55r^2 + 20r}{5r + 5}$

16. Find an equation of the line: **a.** with slope -3 and passing through $(9, -8)$ **b.** that contains $(2, 7)$ and $(-3, 12)$

17. If $f(x) = -2x^2 - x + 3$ and $D = \{-2, -1, 0, 1, 2\}$, find the range of the function.

18. Graph: **a.** $y = -4x$ **b.** $5x - 3y = 9$ **c.** $y = x^2 - x - 12$

19. Solve graphically: **a.** $\begin{aligned} x + y &= 3 \\ 2x + y &= 1 \end{aligned}$ **b.** $\begin{aligned} 4x - y &= 4 \\ 3x + 2y &= -8 \end{aligned}$

Solve each equation or system.

20. $-(3 - 2x) = 5(2x + 1)$ **21.** $-3|n| = -84$ **22.** $p\%$ of $32 = 6$

23. $0.3v + 7 = -1.37$ **24.** $8r^2 = 13r + 6$ **25.** $(a - 1)(3a - 2) = 4$

26. $\dfrac{y - 9}{y + 4} = \dfrac{y + 3}{y + 7}$ **27.** $\dfrac{3z}{7} + \dfrac{z}{2} = \dfrac{13}{28}$ **28.** $\dfrac{b}{b + 3} - \dfrac{3}{b - 1} = -\dfrac{1}{8}$

29. $\begin{aligned} y &= 7x - 16 \\ 3x + 2y &= 2 \end{aligned}$ **30.** $\begin{aligned} 4x - 5y &= 0 \\ 8x + 5y &= -60 \end{aligned}$ **31.** $\begin{aligned} 6x + 2y &= 3 \\ -9x + 8y &= 1 \end{aligned}$

32. The denominator of a fraction is 3 more than the numerator. If 25 is added to each, the resulting fraction is equivalent to 0.9. Find the original fraction.

33. The volume of a sphere varies directly as the cube of the radius. If the volume of a sphere with radius 6 cm is 288π cm³, find the volume of a sphere with radius 3 cm.

Maintaining Skills

Simplify.

SAMPLE 1 $\dfrac{2z-8}{2z^2} \cdot \dfrac{z^3}{z^2-16} = \dfrac{2(z-4)\cdot z^3}{2z^2(z+4)(z-4)} = \dfrac{z}{z+4}$

1. $\dfrac{y-2}{21y^2} \cdot \dfrac{7y}{2-y}$

2. $\dfrac{qr^2st}{-3s^2t^2} \cdot \dfrac{2rt^3}{r^3t^2}$

3. $\dfrac{a^2+2ab}{ab-b^2} \cdot \dfrac{5a-5b}{2b+a}$

4. $\dfrac{50-2k^2}{15+3k} \cdot \dfrac{12-3k}{5k-k^2}$

5. $\dfrac{8t+8}{(t-1)^2} \cdot \dfrac{7t-7}{6+6t}$

6. $\dfrac{m^2+m-12}{m^2+4m} \cdot \dfrac{m^3}{m-3}$

SAMPLE 2 $\dfrac{a^2+ab-2b^2}{a^2-3ab+2b^2} \div \dfrac{a+2b}{a-2b} = \dfrac{(a+2b)(a-b)}{(a-2b)(a-b)} \cdot \dfrac{a-2b}{a+2b} = 1$

7. $-\dfrac{8t^4u}{15zt^3} \div \dfrac{2tuz^2}{3z^5}$

8. $2j \div \dfrac{j-5j^2}{5j-1}$

9. $\dfrac{d^3-4d}{d^2-7d} \div (d-2)$

10. $\dfrac{3rq+3q^2}{r^2-rq} \div \dfrac{3r^2-3q^2}{r}$

11. $\dfrac{m^2-2m-8}{m^2-3m-10} \div \dfrac{m^2-3m-4}{m^2-6m+5}$

12. $\dfrac{9b^2+12b+4}{3b^2-b-2} \div \dfrac{9b^2-4}{3b^2-2b}$

13. $\dfrac{x^3+2x^2y}{xy+4y^2} \div \dfrac{x^2+6xy+8y^2}{x^2y-2xy^2}$

SAMPLE 3 $\dfrac{x-1}{2x-1} + 3 = \dfrac{x-1}{2x-1} + \dfrac{3(2x-1)}{2x-1} = \dfrac{x-1+6x-3}{2x-1} = \dfrac{7x-4}{2x-1}$

14. $\dfrac{z+4}{2z} + \dfrac{3z-4}{2z}$

15. $\dfrac{16}{g+4} - \dfrac{g^2}{g+4}$

16. $\dfrac{a+3b}{a^2b^2} - \dfrac{3b+a}{a^2b^2}$

17. $\dfrac{8}{3r+1} - 2r$

18. $d-1+\dfrac{1}{d+1}$

19. $5 - x^2 + \dfrac{3}{2x}$

SAMPLE 4 $\dfrac{y}{y-4} - \dfrac{y}{y+3} = \dfrac{y(y+3)-y(y-4)}{(y-4)(y+3)} = \dfrac{y^2+3y-y^2+4y}{(y-4)(y+3)} = \dfrac{7y}{(y-4)(y+3)}$

20. $\dfrac{5}{t} - \dfrac{1}{t^2} + \dfrac{3}{2t}$

21. $\dfrac{1}{6a} + \dfrac{4}{9a^2}$

22. $\dfrac{t+5}{t+2} - \dfrac{t}{t-1}$

23. $\dfrac{1-x}{x} - \dfrac{4}{x^2+4x}$

24. $\dfrac{2}{x^2+x} + \dfrac{1}{x^2-x}$

25. $\dfrac{p+2}{p-3} - \dfrac{p+3}{p-4}$

These cakes are being produced by a large-scale commercial baking process. To help make production decisions, the branch of mathematics called linear programming can be used. Linear programming makes use of systems of inequalities related to quantities of materials.

10
INEQUALITIES

INEQUALITIES IN ONE VARIABLE

10-1 *Order of Real Numbers*

OBJECTIVE   To review the concept of order of real numbers and to solve inequalities by substitution.

The horizontal number line below pictures the order (page 33) of real numbers.

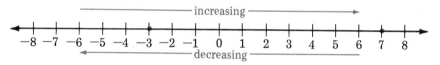

You recall that any number n is greater than every number whose graph is to the left of the graph of n, and less than every number whose graph is to the right.

Negative three is less than seven.   Seven is greater than negative three.

$$-3 < 7 \qquad\qquad\qquad 7 > -3$$

The sentence

$$-3 < x < 7$$

means "-3 is less than x and x is less than 7." Thus x represents a number *between* -3 and 7 on the number line. The sentence above may also be read as "x is greater than -3 and less than 7." (The same relationship is shown by the sentence $7 > x > -3$.)

The statement

$$-3 < 1 < 7$$

is true, but the statement

$$-3 < 8 < 7$$

is false, since 8 is not less than 7 (although -3 is less than 8).

For a statement like $-3 < 8 < 7$ to be true, *both* "less than" relationships must be true.

Sometimes it is convenient to indicate that one number is greater than or equal to another number. This can be written

$x \geq 5$, read "x is greater than or equal to 5."

Similarly, you can write $x \leq 5$ for "x is less than or equal to 5." The statements

$$6 \geq 5 \quad \text{and} \quad 5 \geq 5$$

are both true since such statements are true *either* if the first number is greater than the second *or* if the first number equals the second.

Here are three *inequalities:*

$$-2 < 0 \qquad 4x - 3 > 2 \qquad y + 8 \leq 12$$
$$\text{the sides}$$

An **inequality** is formed by placing an inequality symbol ($>, <, \geq, \leq$) between numerical or variable expressions, called the **sides** of the inequality.

As in the case of equations, an inequality containing a variable is called an *open sentence* (page 9). You solve such an inequality by finding the values of the variable for which the inequality is a true statement. Such values are called **solutions of the inequality;** they make up the **solution set of the inequality.**

EXAMPLE 1 If $y \in \{1, 2, 3, 4, 5, 6\}$ what is the solution set of $y + 8 \leq 12$?

SOLUTION Replace y with each of its values in turn.

$$y + 8 \leq 12$$
$$1 + 8 \leq 12 \qquad \text{True}$$
$$2 + 8 \leq 12 \qquad \text{True}$$
$$3 + 8 \leq 12 \qquad \text{True}$$
$$4 + 8 \leq 12 \qquad \text{True}$$
$$5 + 8 \leq 12 \qquad \text{False}$$
$$6 + 8 \leq 12 \qquad \text{False}$$

$\therefore$ the solution set is $\{1, 2, 3, 4\}$. ***Answer***

When you show the graphs of the numbers in the solution set of an open sentence on a number line, you say that you have drawn the **graph of the open sentence.** The graph of the inequality $y + 8 \leq 12$ in Example 1 is shown below.

EXAMPLE 2 Draw the graph of $-2 \leq x < 3$ if the domain of x is the set of real numbers.

SOLUTION x represents a number between -2 and 3. The solution set includes -2, but not 3.

  Answer

Notice that the graph includes all the points on the number line from the graph of -2 up to, but not including, the graph of 3. The open circle shows that 3 is not a solution.

Oral Exercises

Classify each statement as true or false.

1. $8 \geq -3$ **2.** $19 \leq 21$ **3.** $-15 \leq -21$ **4.** $-1 \geq -4$

5. $-9 < 8 < 10$ **6.** $3 > -3 > -2$ **7.** $6 > 0 > -11$ **8.** $-2.5 < 0.5 < 1.5$

9. $|-8| \geq 0$ **10.** $|-3| > |-10|$ **11.** $2^3 < 3^2$ **12.** $\left(\frac{1}{2}\right)^2 \geq \frac{1}{2}$

Describe the numbers whose graphs appear in color. There may be more than one correct description.

SAMPLE 1

SOLUTION The real numbers between -1 and 2, or greater than -1 and less than 2

SAMPLE 2

SOLUTION The real numbers less than or equal to 1

13.

14.

15.

16.

17.

18.

19.

20.

Written Exercises

Translate the statements into symbols.

A **1.** 5 is greater than -2. **2.** -7 is less than -3.

3. -15 is less than or equal to -10. **4.** 9 is greater than or equal to 6.

Translate the statements into symbols.

5. 4 is greater than 2 and less than 4.5.

6. 0 is greater than -0.5 and less than 1.

7. -12 is between -10 and -20.

8. 4 is between 7 and -7.

9. 8 is greater than 1 and 1 is greater than -2.

10. -2 is less than -1 and -1 is less than $-\frac{1}{3}$.

Classify each statement as true or false.

11. $|-0.6| < -0.5$

12. $|-\frac{1}{2}| \geq 0$

13. $|-8| < |-21|$

14. $|3 - 2| \leq |2 - 3|$

15. $-5 < 2 < 8$

16. $7 > 0 > 2$

Solve each inequality if $x \in \{-4, -3, -2, -1, 0, 1, 2, 3, 4\}$.

17. $3x < 9$

18. $2x \geq 6$

19. $-4x > 8$

20. $x + 2 < 3$

21. $\frac{1}{2}x \geq -3$

22. $-12 - x > 9$

23. $1 - x \geq 0$

24. $2x + 1 \leq -4$

Solve each inequality over the given domain and draw its graph.

B 25. $28 < 7x$; {the positive numbers}

26. $3y < 15$; {the positive numbers}

27. $-4 \leq x < 2$; {the integers}

28. $3 \geq y \geq -1$; {the integers}

29. $5 > u \geq 0$; {the real numbers}

30. $-2 < m < 4$; {the real numbers}

31. $-6 \leq k < 1$; {the negative integers}

32. $4 \geq t > -7$; {the negative integers}

For each statement in Exercises 33–35:

a. Find a pair of values of x and y for which the statement is true.

b. Find a pair of values of x and y for which the statement is false.

C 33. If $x \geq y$, then $|x| \geq |y|$.

34. If $x \geq 0$ and $y < 0$, then $xy \geq 0$.

35. If $x > y$, then $xy > y^2$.

Calculator Key-In _____

You can compare two fractions with the aid of a calculator. First change each fraction to a decimal by dividing numerator by denominator. Then compare the decimals.

True or false?

1. $\frac{3}{8} > \frac{7}{20} > \frac{4}{13}$

2. $\frac{21}{23} < \frac{22}{24} < \frac{23}{25}$

3. $\frac{98}{101} > \frac{99}{102} > \frac{100}{103}$

10-2 *Solving Inequalities*

OBJECTIVE   To transform inequalities to find their solution sets.

Only the first of the following statements is true:

$$-5 < 2 \qquad -5 = 2 \qquad -5 > 2$$
$$\text{(true)} \qquad \text{(false)} \qquad \text{(false)}$$

In comparing real numbers, you make the following basic assumption:

AXIOM OF COMPARISON

For all real numbers a and b, one and only one of the following statements is true:

$$a < b, \qquad a = b, \quad \text{or} \quad a > b.$$

Now suppose you know two facts about the graphs of three numbers a, b, and c.

1. The graph of a is to the left of the graph of b: $a < b$.
2. The graph of b is to the left of the graph of c: $b < c$.

Where is the graph of a relative to the graph of c? You can see that it is to the left of c: $a < c$.

In general the following assumption is made:

TRANSITIVE AXIOM OF ORDER

For all real numbers a, b, and c:

1. If $a < b$ and $b < c$, then $a < c$;
2. If $c > b$ and $b > a$, then $c > a$.

What happens when the same number is added to each side of an inequality?

$$
\begin{array}{ccc}
3 & < & 6 \\
\downarrow & & \downarrow \\
3 + 2 & & 6 + 2 \\
\downarrow & & \downarrow \\
5 & < & 8
\end{array}
\qquad\qquad
\begin{array}{ccc}
3 & < & 6 \\
\downarrow & & \downarrow \\
3 - 2 & & 6 - 2 \\
\downarrow & & \downarrow \\
1 & < & 4
\end{array}
$$

These numerical examples suggest another axiom of order. (Recall that subtracting a number is the same as adding the opposite of that number.)

ADDITION AXIOM OF ORDER

For all real numbers a, b, and c:

1. If $a < b$, then $a + c < b + c$;

2. If $a > b$, then $a + c > b + c$.

What happens when each side of the inequality $-3 < 2$ is multiplied by a nonzero real number?

Multiply by 5: Is it true that $5(-3) < 5(2)$?

Yes, $-15 < 10$.

Multiply by -5: Is it true that $-5(-3) < -5(2)$?

No, $15 > -10$.

This example suggests that multiplying each side of an inequality by a negative number *reverses the direction*, or order, of the inequality.

In general, the following assumption is made:

MULTIPLICATION AXIOM OF ORDER

For all real numbers a, b, and c such that

$c > 0$:

1. If $a < b$, then $ac < bc$;

2. If $a > b$, then $ac > bc$.

$c < 0$:

1. If $a < b$, then $ac > bc$;

2. If $a > b$, then $ac < bc$.

Multiplying both sides of an inequality by zero does not produce an inequality; the result is the identity $0 = 0$.

The axioms that have been stated guarantee that the following transformations of a given inequality always produce an **equivalent inequality,** that is, one with the same solution set.

TRANSFORMATIONS THAT PRODUCE AN EQUIVALENT INEQUALITY

1. Substituting for either side of the inequality an expression equivalent to that side.

2. Adding to (or subtracting from) each side the same real number.

3. Multiplying (or dividing) each side by the same positive number.

4. Multiplying (or dividing) each side by the same negative number and reversing the direction of the inequality.

To solve an inequality, you usually try to transform it into a simple equivalent inequality whose solution or solutions can be seen at a glance.

You may assume that the domain of all variables is the set of real numbers unless otherwise mentioned.

EXAMPLE 1 Solve $4x - 3 < 7 + 2x$ over the set of real numbers and draw its graph.

SOLUTION

$$4x - 3 < 7 + 2x$$

$$4x - 3 + 3 < 7 + 2x + 3 \qquad \text{Add 3 to each side.}$$

$$4x < 10 + 2x$$

$$4x - 2x < 10 + 2x - 2x \qquad \text{Subtract } 2x \text{ from each side.}$$

$$2x < 10$$

$$\frac{2x}{2} < \frac{10}{2} \qquad \text{Divide each side by 2.}$$

$$x < 5$$

∴ the solution set is {the real numbers less than 5}. The graph of the solution set is:

To solve an inequality, you take the same steps used to solve equations:

---

1. Simplify each side of the inequality.
2. Use the inverse operations to undo any indicated additions or subtractions.
3. Use the inverse operations to undo any indicated multiplications or divisions.

EXAMPLE 2 Solve and graph $2(x - 3) + 6 \geq 3(4 - x) - 2$.

SOLUTION

$$2(x - 3) + 6 \geq 3(4 - x) - 2$$

$$2x - 6 + 6 \geq 12 - 3x - 2$$

$$2x \geq 10 - 3x$$

$$5x \geq 10$$

$$x \geq 2$$

∴ the solution set is {the real numbers greater than or equal to 2}. The graph is:

Oral Exercises

Tell how to transform the first inequality to obtain the second one.

1. $y + 2 < 6$
$y < 4$

2. $m - 3 > 5$
$m > 8$

3. $-3 < k - 6$
$3 < k$

4. $s + 8 < 0$
$s < -8$

5. $3k < 9$
$k < 3$

6. $2n < -18$
$n < -9$

7. $-4p < 16$
$p > -4$

8. $\frac{k}{3} > 2$
$k > 6$

9. $2 > \frac{v}{5}$
$10 > v$

10. $\frac{x}{-2} < -4$
$x > 8$

11. $2y < \frac{1}{3}$
$y < \frac{1}{6}$

12. $\frac{t}{-2} > 0$
$t < 0$

Explain how to transform each inequality in order to solve it. Then
state the transformed inequality.

13. $y - 3 < 8$

14. $6 < x + 2$

15. $3k > 9$

16. $-8 < -2m$

17. $\frac{y}{2} \geq 9$

18. $-3 \leq \frac{y}{-2}$

Written Exercises

Match each inequality in Exercises 1–8 with its solution set in a–h.

A **1.** $x - 3 \geq 6$

`2.** $4 > y + 4$

3. $2m \neq 8$

4. $6 < 3p$

5. $-16 > -4k$

6. $\frac{m}{5} < -4$

7. $2 - x > 0$

8. $3 \leq \frac{y}{-2}$

a.

b.

c.

d.

e.

f.

g.

h.

Solve each inequality and draw its graph.

9. $m - 3 > 12$

10. $y + 3 < 12$

11. $-\frac{x}{2} > 12$

12. $3p < 12$

13. $12 < \frac{x}{-4}$

14. $-12 < \frac{y}{3}$

15. $-2k \geq 2$

16. $-3p \leq 9$

17. $\frac{x}{2} - 2 > -4$

18. $3k + 1 > 7$

19. $\frac{y}{-2} \geq 10$

20. $5 \geq 2y - 3$

21. $\frac{3}{2}p - 5 < 4$

22. $-2 \leq 2 - \frac{k}{3}$

23. $-3 < 7 + \frac{2}{3}m$

24. $3 + \frac{y}{4} \leq 6$

25. $9 - \frac{3}{2}y > 0$

26. $0 > 6 - \frac{3}{4}s$

Solve each inequality.

27. $3y < 2y + 8$

28. $4m - 3 > 3m + 6$

29. $2x - 3 < 4x + 5$

30. $1 + 3r > 5 - r$

31. $6 - 2p \geq 3 - p$

32. $3(x - 5) \leq 6$

33. $8 < 4(2 - y)$

34. $2(k - 6) < 3(k - 2)$

35. $4(1 - t) \geq 2(3 - t)$

Solve each inequality and draw its **graph**.

B **36.** $\frac{m}{3} - 2 \geq \frac{2}{3}$

37. $\frac{1}{8} < 2 - \frac{3}{4}p$

38. $3(y - 1) \geq \frac{3}{4}y$

39. $\frac{2}{3}m \leq 4(m - 5)$

40. $k + \frac{1}{2} > \frac{3}{4}(k - 2)$

41. $3p - \frac{1}{2}(p + 10) \geq 0$

42. $3(3 - m) - 5(5 + m) < 0$

43. $2(k - 3) > 3(k + 2) - 3$

44. $2(y - 2) - 4 \leq 3(y + 1) + 3$

45. $2(x - 1) - 3(x + 2) \leq 3 - 2x$

46. $3 - t + 2(t - 3) \geq 3(t + 1)$

47. $3(2x - 1) - 2(x + 1) > 3x + 8$

Given that a and b are real numbers such that $a > b$, describe the real numbers c for which each statement is true.

C **48.** $ac > bc$

49. $ac < bc$

50. $ac = bc$

51. $\frac{a}{c} > \frac{b}{c}$

52. $\frac{a}{c} < \frac{b}{c}$

53. $ac^2 > bc^2$

54. $\frac{a}{c^2} < \frac{b}{c^2}$

55. $ac^2 = bc^2$

Classify each statement as true or false for all real numbers a and b such that $a > b > 0$.

56. $a > 0$

57. $a^2 > a$

58. $ab > 0$

59. $a + b > a$

60. $a^2 > b$

61. $a^2 > ab$

62. $ab > b^2$

63. $a^2 > b^2$

10-3 *Solving Problems Involving Inequalities*

OBJECTIVE To solve problems involving inequalities.

EXAMPLE 1

The width of a rectangle is 26 cm less than twice the length. The perimeter is less than 74 cm. Find the maximum dimensions of the rectangle if each dimension, in centimeters, is an integer.

SOLUTION

Step 1 The problem asks for the maximum length and width in centimeters. The measures must be integers. (Such measures must also be positive.)

Step 2 Let x = length in centimeters.
Then $2x - 26$ = width in centimeters.

Step 3

The perimeter	is less than	74 cm.
$2x + 2(2x - 26)$	$<$	74

Step 4

$2x + 4x - 52$	$<$	74
$6x - 52$	$<$	74
$6x$	$<$	126
x	$<$	21

$\therefore$ the greatest length that the rectangle can have is 20 cm. The greatest width is $(2 \times 20) - 26$, or 14 cm.

Step 5 *Check:* (1) Is the width 26 cm less than twice the length?

$$14 \overset{?}{=} (2 \times 20) - 26$$
$$14 = 14 \quad \sqrt{}$$

(2) Is the perimeter less than 74 cm?

$$(2 \times 20) + (2 \times 14) = 40 + 28 = 68; \ 68 < 74 \quad \sqrt{}$$

(3) Are the dimensions the greatest possible? Suppose the length were the next larger integer, 21 cm. Then the width would be $(2 \times 21) - 26$, or 16 cm. The perimeter would be $(2 \times 21) + (2 \times 16)$, or 74 cm, which is *not* less than 74 cm.

$\therefore$ the dimensions are 14 cm and 20 cm. ***Answer***

EXAMPLE 2

The average of three consecutive integers is greater than 9. Find the smallest possible values for the integers.

SOLUTION

Step 1 The problem asks for the three smallest consecutive integers whose average is greater than 9.

Step 2 Let n = the least integer.
Then $n + 1$ and $n + 2$ are the next consecutive integers.

Step 3

The average of three consecutive integers	is greater than	9
		↓

$$\frac{n + (n + 1) + (n + 2)}{3} \qquad > \qquad 9$$

Steps 4, 5 Solving the inequality and checking that the three required consecutive integers are 9, 10, and 11 are left to you.

To translate phrases such as "is at least" and "is no less than" or "is at most" and "is no more than" into mathematical terms, you use the symbols $\geq$ or $\leq$. For example:

My grandfather's age is at least 65: $a \geq 65$

The rent is no less than \$300 per month: $r \geq 300$

The price of the paperback book is at most \$3.95: $p \leq 3.95$

Her time in the 10 km race was no more than 40 min: $t \leq 40$

Written Exercises

For each of the following:

a. Choose a variable to represent the number indicated in color.

b. Use the variable to write an inequality based on the given information. (Do not solve.)

A **1.** After selling a dozen copies of the *Bulletin*, a newsdealer had fewer than 75 copies left. (The number of copies the dealer had originally)

2. Jim, who is over 21, is three years older than his cousin Bob. (Bob's age)

3. A businesswoman traveled a certain number of kilometers by automobile, and then ten times as far by airplane. Her total trip was more than 2800 km.

4. The number of State College students studying mathematics is one third the number studying computer science. The total number of students enrolled in these subjects is at least 9500.

5. Mary's bowling score was 12 more than half Ann's score. Mary's bowling score was less than 100.

6. A house and lot together cost more than \$90,000. The cost of the house was \$1000 more than seven times the cost of the lot.

7. The sum of two consecutive odd integers is less than 25 and greater than 9. (The smaller integer)

8. The product of two consecutive integers is a positive number less than 60. (The greater integer)

For each of the following:

a. Choose a variable to represent the number indicated in color.

b. Use the variable to write an inequality based on the given information.

B   **9.** The smaller of two consecutive even integers is less than or equal to 4 more than twice the larger.

    10. The larger of two consecutive integers is greater than 4 more than half the smaller.

    11. There are three consecutive integers such that four times the greatest diminished by twice the second is at least one more than three times the least.

    12. Three consecutive even integers are such that their sum is more than 24 decreased by twice the greatest of the three integers.

Problems

Solve.

A   **1.** Two integers are in the ratio $3:7$. If their sum is less than 60, what is the greatest possible value of the smaller integer?

    2. Of all pairs of consecutive even integers whose sum is less than 50, find the pair whose sum is the greatest.

    3. The sum of two consecutive integers is less than 25. Find the pair of integers with the greatest sum.

    4. The sum of two consecutive even integers is less than 100. Find the pair with the greatest sum.

    5. The sum of two consecutive integers is greater than 75. Find the pair with the smallest sum.

    6. Of all pairs of consecutive odd integers whose sum is greater than 45, find the pair whose sum is the least.

    7. Two trucks start from the same point going in opposite directions. One truck travels at 88 km/h, the other at 72 km/h. How long must they travel to be at least 672 km apart?

    8. Between them, Al and Ben have 48 dimes. If Al has more than three fifths as many dimes as Ben, at least how many dimes does Al have? At most how many does Ben have?

    9. Marie Simone said, "Three fourths of my age two years ago is greater than or equal to two thirds of my age three years from now." At least how old is she now?

    10. Milly is two thirds as old as Marcia. Four years from now she will be at most five sevenths as old as Marcia. At least how old is Milly?

11. A purse contains 22 coins, some of which are dimes and the rest, quarters. Altogether, the coins are worth more than \$3.40. At least how many of the coins are quarters? At most how many are dimes?

12. Ken has more than \$10 in dimes, quarters, and half dollars. There are five times as many quarters as half dollars, and one and one half times as many dimes as quarters. At least how many of each kind of coin does Ken have?

B 13. A pair of consecutive even integers has the property that five times the smaller is less than 4 times the greater. Find the greatest pair of integers with this property.

14. The average of four consecutive even integers is greater than 6. Find the smallest possible values for the integers.

15. The average of four consecutive odd integers is less than 8. Find the greatest possible values for the integers.

16. The sum of three consecutive integers decreased by 6 is greater than twice the smallest of the three. What are the three smallest possible integers?

17. The units digit of a certain two-digit number is one more than the tens digit. Sixteen times the tens digit is greater than the number with the digits reversed. Find the least possible value of the original number.

18. If the digits of a certain two-digit number are reversed, the resulting number is 6 less than twice the original number. The sum of the digits is less than 8. Find the greatest possible value of the original number.

C 19. A family sold $2 \, \text{km}^2$ more than three fifths of their farm and had more than $4 \, \text{km}^2$ less than half of it left. If the farm originally contained an integral number of square kilometers, what was the greatest possible area it could have had?

20. Two consecutive odd integers have the property that their product exceeds the square of the greater integer. Find the greatest pair of integers that have this property.

21. Three consecutive integers have the property that the square of the second integer decreased by the square of the smallest integer is less than the third integer. Find the integers that have this property and have a positive sum.

22. Scott has saved quarters in a bank. On Monday he took out 2 quarters, and one sixth of what was left. On Tuesday he took out 3 quarters, and one sixth of what then remained. If he took out more on Monday than on Tuesday, what was the least possible number of quarters originally in the bank?

Self-Test 1

VOCABULARY   inequality (p. 366)   graph of an open sentence
                  solutions of an inequality   (p. 366)
                      (p. 366)   equivalent inequalities (p. 370)
                  solution set of an inequality
                      (p. 366)

1. Translate the statement "-3 is between -6 and 0"   Obj. 10-1, p. 365
into symbols.

2. Solve $3x + 7 \leq 13$ if the domain of x is   Obj. 10-2, p. 369
$\{-4, -3, -2, -1, 0, 1, 2, 3, 4\}$.

Solve and graph.

3. $a - 7 < -3$ **4.** $5 - 2r \leq 6$

Solve.

5. The sum of two consecutive even integers is greater   Obj. 10-3, p. 374
than 88. Find the pair with the smallest sum.

Check your answers with those at the back of the book.

Biography Ada Byron Lovelace

Lady Ada Byron Lovelace (1815–1852) was the daughter of Lord Byron, the famous English poet, and Annabella Milbanke. Encouraged by her mother and friends, she studied mathematics enthusiastically. For 18 years she worked with Charles Babbage, the acknowledged father of the computer. In 1842 she began work on translating and annotating a paper detailing Babbage's Analytical Engine. Her descriptions of the way in which instructions and information were given to this precursor of the modern computer make her the first computer programmer. In recognition of her contribution to mathematics, a computer language developed in the 1970's was named after her and called ADA.

Computer Key-In

Computers and Words

Computers can handle words as well as numbers. You have already seen (page 46) that a simple PRINT statement will cause the computer to print back anything that is enclosed within quotation marks. Moreover, computers can store words in "files" and then later search for and find (retrieve) words and expressions that are asked for. Thus, if the texts of books and magazines have been copied into computer files, the statements about a chosen subject can be located and printed out.

Small computers can be combined with electric typewriters to make *word processors*. Generally, on one of these machines, whatever is typed is shown on a screen like a television screen and is recorded on a tape or a diskette. By using a program stored in the machine, changes can easily be made without retyping the whole page. The finished copy can then be printed out. The tapes or diskettes can be kept and changed later. Thus, a directory can be stored and updated from time to time by simply making the necessary changes. Some word processors can merge two files so that what is essentially a form letter can be addressed to individuals and contain individual details of information.

Several word processors can be connected to a central computer and storage unit. For example, in a newspaper office, one person can type in a story and store it, and then another person can call it up and edit it.

Some computers can be connected to several terminals and used on a "time-sharing" basis. When the terminals are at a distance, the connections are made over the telephone. Similarly, word processors can be set up to communicate with a central computer over the telephone, making an extensive word processing network.

EXTRA

Intersection and Union of Sets

The diagram shows the relationship among the sets:

$$A = \{1, 2, 3, 4, 5\}$$
$$B = \{2, 4, 6\}$$
$$C = \{7, 8\}$$

The set represented by shading consists of those members and only those members *common to both* set A and set B. You call $\{2, 4\}$ the **intersection** of $\{1, 2, 3, 4, 5\}$ and $\{2, 4, 6\}$ and write

$$\{1, 2, 3, 4, 5\} \cap \{2, 4, 6\} = \{2, 4\}$$

or

$$A \cap B = \{2, 4\}.$$

The latter is read, "The intersection of A and B is $\{2, 4\}$."

Notice in the diagram above that the regions A and C do not overlap. Two sets, such as A and C, that have no members in common are called **disjoint sets.** Their intersection is the empty set: $A \cap C = \emptyset$.

The diagram at the right again shows the sets A, B, and C. Here, the set represented by the shaded region,

$$\{1, 2, 3, 4, 5, 6\},$$

consists of the members that belong to *at least one* of the sets A and B. You call this set the **union** of A and B and write

$$\{1, 2, 3, 4, 5\} \cup \{2, 4, 6\} = \{1, 2, 3, 4, 5, 6\}$$

or

$$A \cup B = \{1, 2, 3, 4, 5, 6\}.$$

The latter is read, "The union of A and B is $\{1, 2, 3, 4, 5, 6\}$."

Exercises

Refer to the diagram and list the members of each of the following sets.

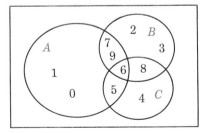

1. $A \cup B$
2. $A \cap B$
3. $B \cap C$
4. $B \cup C$
5. $A \cap (B \cap C)$
6. $(A \cap B) \cup C$
7. $(A \cup B) \cap C$
8. $(A \cup B) \cup C$
9. $(A \cap B) \cup (A \cap C)$

10. Express $\{6, 7, 8, 9\}$ in terms of A, B, and C.

Specify the union and the intersection of the given sets. If the sets are disjoint, say so.

11. $\{0, 1, 2, 3\}, \{2, 3, 4\}$

12. $\{-3, -2, -1, 0\}, \{-1, 0, 1\}$

13. $\{2, 4, 6\}, \{1, 3, 5\}$

14. $\{2, 4\}, \{1, 2, 3, 4, 5\}$

15. $\{2, 3, 5, 7, 11\}, \{1, 3, 5, 7, 9\}$

16. $\{-6, -5, -4\}, \{-3, -2, -1\}$

In Exercises 17–24, refer to the number lines shown and describe each set.

$D = \{$the real numbers greater than $-2\}$
$E = \{$the real numbers between -3 and $3\}$
$F = \{$the real numbers less than $1\}$

17. $D \cup F$ 18. $D \cup E$ 19. $D \cap E$ 20. $D \cap F$

21. $E \cup F$ 22. $E \cap F$ 23. $D \cap (E \cap F)$ 24. $(D \cap E) \cup F$

For each of Exercises 25 and 26, make two copies of the diagram shown at the right. On your copies shade the regions representing the sets named.

25. $A \cap (B \cup C); (A \cap B) \cup (A \cap C)$

26. $A \cup (B \cap C); (A \cup B) \cap (A \cup C)$

27. State a "distributive axiom" that appears to be true on the basis of Exercise 25.

28. State a "distributive axiom" that appears to be true on the basis of Exercise 26.

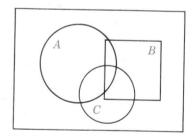

29. Copy the diagram at the right and write in the remaining members of these sets:

$A = \{1, 2, 3, 4, 5, 6, 7\}$
$B = \{1, 3, 5, 7, 9\}$
$C = \{3, 4, 5, 6, 7\}$
$D = \{-3, -1, 1, 3, 4\}$

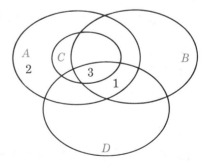

COMBINING OPEN SENTENCES

10-4 *Solving Combined Inequalities*

OBJECTIVE   To find the solution sets of combined inequalities.

In (a) and (b) below, two inequalities and their graphs are shown. In (c) the two inequalities have been joined by the word "and." A sentence formed by joining two sentences by the word *and* is called a **conjunction.** To **solve a conjunction** of open sentences, you find the values of the variable for which *both* sentences are true. Note that the conjunction in part (c) can be written in the form $-2 < x < 3$. The graph consists of the points that belong to *both* the graph of $-2 < x$ and the graph of $x < 3$.

(a) $-2 < x$

(b) $x < 3$

(c) $-2 < x$ and $x < 3$

(d) $-2 < x$ or $x < 3$

In (d) above, the inequalities in (a) and (b) have been joined by the word "or." A sentence formed by joining two sentences by the word *or* is called a **disjunction.** To **solve a disjunction** of open sentences, you find the values of the variable for which *at least one* of the sentences is true (that is, one or the other or both are true). Notice that *every* real number is a solution of the disjunction in (d).

Recall that the disjunction "$y > 2$ or $y = 2$" is written $y \geq 2$. Similarly, $y \leq 2$ means "$y < 2$ or $y = 2$."

EXAMPLE 1   The solution set of "$x < 2$ and $x \geq 2$" is the empty set.

EXAMPLE 2   The solution set of "$x < 2$ or $x \geq 2$" is the set of all real numbers.

To solve conjunctions and disjunctions of inequalities, you can use the transformations listed on page 370.

EXAMPLE 3   Find the solution set of $-3 \leq x - 1 < 4$, and draw its graph.

SOLUTION   To solve the inequality $-3 \le x - 1 < 4$, you solve the conjunction:

$$-3 \le x - 1 \quad \text{and} \quad x - 1 < 4$$
$$-2 \le x \quad \text{and} \quad x < 5$$
$$\underbrace{\phantom{-2 \le x \quad \text{and} \quad x < 5}}$$
$$-2 \le x < 5$$

∴ the solution set is $\{-2,$ and the real numbers between -2 and $5\}$. The graph is:

EXAMPLE 4   Solve the disjunction and draw its graph: $3y - 1 < 5$ or $3y \ge y + 6$.

SOLUTION
$$3y - 1 < 5 \quad \text{or} \quad 3y \ge y + 6$$
$$3y < 6 \quad \text{or} \quad 2y \ge 6$$
$$y < 2 \quad \text{or} \quad y \ge 3$$

∴ the solution set is $\{3,$ and the real numbers greater than 3 or less than $2\}$. The graph is:

Oral Exercises

In Exercises 1–7, match each graph with one of the open sentences in a–g.

1.

2.

3.

4.

5.

6.

7.

a. $y > 2$

b. $y \ge 2$ or $y < -2$

c. $-2 < y < 2$

d. $y \le 2$

e. $y \le -2$ or $y > 2$

f. $y < 2$

g. $-2 \le y \le 2$

In Exercises 8–12, match each open sentence with an equivalent inequality in a–e.

8. $y < 2$ and $y > -3$ **a.** $y \geq 2$

9. $y = 2$ or $y < 2$ **b.** $-3 \leq y \leq 2$

10. $y \leq 2$ and $y > -3$ **c.** $y \leq 2$

11. $y = 2$ or $y > 2$ **d.** $-3 < y \leq 2$

12. $y \leq 2$ and $y \geq -3$ **e.** $-3 < y < 2$

Written Exercises

Draw the graph of each open sentence.

A   **1.** $-3 < y \leq 2$ **2.** $x > 2$ or $x \leq -3$

   3. $4 \leq m \leq 8$ **4.** $k < -3$ or $k \geq 0$

Solve each open sentence and graph each solution set which is not empty.

5. $-2 < y + 1 < 3$ **6.** $-1 < x - 1 \leq 2$

7. $-3 < -3 + y \leq 2$ **8.** $-1 \leq 2 + y < 4$

9. $-1 \leq 2y + 1 < 5$ **10.** $-3 \leq 2y - 1 \leq 9$

11. $-5 \leq 3x + 1 < 4$ **12.** $-5 < 3x - 2 \leq 7$

13. $y - 1 < -2$ or $y - 1 \geq 2$ **14.** $k + 5 \leq -3$ or $k + 5 \geq 3$

15. $3m + 1 \leq -5$ or $3m - 1 \geq 5$ **16.** $1 + 2y < -5$ or $1 + 2y > 5$

17. $2y - 1 \leq -3$ or $3 \leq 2y - 1$ **18.** $1 + 2k < -7$ or $7 < 1 + 2k$

B   **19.** $-3 < -x \leq 5$ **20.** $-5 \leq -x + 1 < 3$

   21. $-6 \leq -2x \leq 4$ **22.** $-5 < -2x + 1 \leq 3$

   23. $-2y < -4$ or $-2y > 4$ **24.** $-2y + 1 \leq -5$ or $-2y + 1 \geq 5$

   25. $-3m < 6$ and $4 < -2m$ **26.** $-8 < -4k$ or $2k - 1 > -3$

   27. $-3 \leq 2 - y < 4$ **28.** $-2 < -3 - y \leq 3$

   29. $3 - m > 4$ or $m - 3 > 4$ **30.** $t - 4 \geq 3$ or $4 - t \geq 3$

   31. $3 - 2p > 5$ or $3 - 2p < -7$

   32. $5 - 3k \geq 8$ or $-4 \geq 5 - 3k$

   33. $2y + 1 \geq -3$ and $2y + 1 \leq y + 3$

   34. $8 - 2y \leq 2 - y$ and $1 - 2y \geq -3$

C   **35.** $2 - y < 2y - 1 \leq 3 + y$

   36. $3 - t \leq 1 - 2t$ or $t + 3 > 3t - 1$

   37. $2(1 - t) \geq 4$ or $3t - 1 \leq 2t + 5$

   38. $1 - 3t \leq 3 - 4t \leq 2t - 3$

39. Find the value of a so that the solution set of

$$a - 3 \leq y - 4 \leq 5$$

will be the same as the solution set of

$$2y - 3 \leq 6 + y \quad \text{and} \quad y - 2 \geq 4.$$

40. Find an example of real values of $a, b, c,$ and d for which the following statement is *false:* If $a < b$ and $c < d$, then $ac < bd$.

Historical Note Greater Than—Less Than

The symbols $>$ and $<$ for "is greater than" and "is less than" were invented by Thomas Harriot, an English mathematician and astronomer. The symbols appeared in his algebra book, published in 1631, ten years after his death. At that time many mathematicians were using the symbols shown below.

The Frenchman Pierre Bouguer is credited with inventing the symbols $\geqq$ and $\leqq$ in 1734. The symbols $\gg$ and $\ll$, which are used for "is much greater than" and "is much less than," and the symbols $\not>$ and $\not<$ are all modern inventions.

Career Note Darkroom Technician

Unless you use a camera which develops film instantly, taking a picture is only part of the art of photography. An equally important part is the processing of the film.

It is the task of the darkroom technician to develop and print the film for snapshots, slides, and movies, whether in black-and-white or color. Special tasks also include cropping, enlarging, and restoring photographs.

If the photographic lab is small, darkroom technicians do these jobs manually. In a large lab they operate the machinery which processes the film automatically.

Most darkroom technicians acquire their skills informally by assisting experienced people in the trade. In general, a high school diploma is required of applicants in this field. Courses in chemistry and mathematics are desirable.

10-5 *Equations and Inequalities Involving Absolute Value*

OBJECTIVE   To solve equations and inequalities involving absolute value.

You may use absolute value (page 44) to write certain open sentences in more compact form.

SENTENCE	COMPACT FORM	GRAPH
$x = 2$ or $x = -2$	$\lvert x \rvert = 2$	
$x < -2$ or $x > 2$	$\lvert x \rvert > 2$	
$x > -2$ and $x < 2$; that is, $-2 < x < 2$	$\lvert x \rvert < 2$	

EXAMPLE 1   Solve $\lvert 3y - 2 \rvert = 4$.

SOLUTION $\lvert 3y - 2 \rvert = 4$ is a compact form of the disjunction:

$$3y - 2 = 4 \quad \text{or} \quad 3y - 2 = -4$$
$$3y = 6 \quad \text{or} \quad 3y = -2$$
$$y = 2 \quad \text{or} \quad y = -\frac{2}{3}$$

$\therefore$ the solution set is $\{-\frac{2}{3}, 2\}$.

EXAMPLE 2   Draw the graph of $\lvert 2m - 3 \rvert \geq 1$.

SOLUTION $\lvert 2m - 3 \rvert \geq 1$ is a compact form of the disjunction:

$$2m - 3 \leq -1 \quad \text{or} \quad 2m - 3 \geq 1$$
$$2m \leq 2 \quad \text{or} \quad 2m \geq 4$$
$$m \leq 1 \quad \text{or} \quad m \geq 2$$

$\therefore$ the graph is:

EXAMPLE 3   Solve $\lvert 3x + 1 \rvert \leq 4$.

SOLUTION $\lvert 3x + 1 \rvert \leq 4$ is a compact form of the conjunction:

$$-4 \leq 3x + 1 \leq 4$$
$$-5 \leq 3x \quad\ \leq 3$$
$$-\frac{5}{3} \leq x \quad\ \leq 1$$

$\therefore$ the solution set is $\{-\frac{5}{3}, 1,$ and the real numbers between $-\frac{5}{3}$ and $1\}$. ***Answer***

Oral Exercises

State a conjunction or a disjunction that is equivalent to the given open sentence.

1. $|y| = 3$ **2.** $|y| > 3$ **3.** $|y| < 3$

4. $|y| \geq 3$ **5.** $|x - 1| = 2$ **6.** $|x - 1| > 2$

7. $|x - 1| < 2$ **8.** $|x - 1| \leq 2$ **9.** $|2m| < 4$

10. $\left|\dfrac{m}{2}\right| > 1$ **11.** $|3k| = 6$ **12.** $\left|\dfrac{k}{3}\right| \geq 2$

13. $|m - 3| < 2$ **14.** $|2 - y| = 3$ **15.** $|2k - 1| \leq 1$

16. $|8 - 2k| \geq 4$ **17.** $2 < |2k - 1|$ **18.** $5 \geq |3 - m|$

In Exercises 19–23, match each open sentence with its graph in a–e.

19. $|x| = 1$

20. $|x| \leq 1$

21. $|x| > 1$

22. $|x| \geq 1$

23. $|x| < 1$

Written Exercises

Write an equation or an inequality involving absolute value to describe each graph. Use x as the variable.

A   **1.**   **2.**

3.   **4.**

5.   **6.**

Solve each open sentence and draw its graph.

7. $|m - 1| = 2$ **8.** $|k + 1| = 3$ **9.** $|1 - y| = 1$

10. $|3 - x| = 4$ **11.** $|k| < 2$ **12.** $|p| \geq 1$

13. $|t| \leq 4$ **14.** $|s| > 3$ **15.** $|2x| = 4$

16. $\left|\dfrac{y}{3}\right| = 2$ **17.** $|3k| \leq 6$ **18.** $\left|\dfrac{s}{4}\right| > 1$

B **19.** $|y + 1| < 2$ **20.** $|m - 1| > 3$ **21.** $|t - 3| \leq 4$

     22. $|6 - y| \geq 0$ **23.** $|2m - 1| = 5$ **24.** $|1 - 2a| < 3$

     25. $|2p - 4| = 0$ **26.** $|6 - 2x| \leq 4$ **27.** $|p| - 2 < 5$

     28. $3|y| - 4 \geq 5$ **29.** $|1 - 2a| - 2 > 5$ **30.** $|3 - 2x| - 2 < |8 - 3|$

     31. $3(2|y| - 1) \geq 6$ **32.** $\dfrac{5 - 3|m|}{2} < 1$ **33.** $\left|\dfrac{y}{3} - 2\right| = 3$

C **34.** $|2x - 3| = x$ **35.** $|2y - 1| = y + 4$

     36. $|y - 2| = y - 2$ **37.** $|t - 2| > t - 2$

     38. $|m - 2| < m - 2$ **39.** $|-1 - 2m| < m$

40. The solution set of $|x - a| < b$ can be interpreted geometrically as the set of real numbers whose distance from the graph of a on a number line is less than b. Using this interpretation, solve the following inequalities mentally.

     a. $|x - 2| < 1$ **b.** $|x - 7| < 2$

     c. $|x + 2| < 1$ **d.** $|x + 7| < 2$

Self-Test 2

VOCABULARY   conjunction (p. 382)
                       solve a conjunction (p. 382)
                       disjunction (p. 382)
                       solve a disjunction (p. 382)

Solve each open sentence and graph its solution set.

1. $2x - 1 > 5$ or $1 - x > 0$ **2.** $-3 < y - 3 \leq 4$ Obj. 10-4, p. 382

3. $|x - 3| = 2$ **4.** $|2 - t| \geq 3$ Obj. 10-5, p. 386

Check your answers with those at the back of the book.

INEQUALITIES IN TWO VARIABLES

10-6 *Graphing Linear Inequalities*

OBJECTIVE   To graph linear inequalities in two variables.

The graph of the linear equation

$$y = x + 2$$

separates the coordinate plane into three sets of points:

the points *on* the line,
the points *above* the line,
the points *below* the line.

Each of the regions above and below the line is called an **open half-plane,** and the line is the **boundary** of each half-plane.

If you start at any point on the line, say $P(2, 4)$, and move upward from P, the y-coordinate increases. If you move downward from P, the y-coordinate decreases.

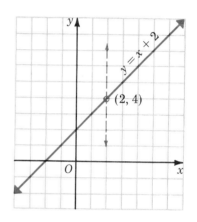

Thus, the upper open half-plane is the graph of

$$y > x + 2$$

and the lower open half-plane is the graph of

$$y < x + 2.$$

The graphs of

$$y > x + 2, \quad y = x + 2, \quad \text{and} \quad y < x + 2$$

completely cover the coordinate plane. The upper half-plane and the boundary line together form the graph of

$$y \geq x + 2.$$

The lower half-plane and the boundary line together form the graph of

$$y \leq x + 2.$$

The graph of an open half-plane and its boundary is called a **closed half-plane.**

The graphs of inequalities are shown by shading. If the boundary line is part of a graph, it is drawn as a solid line. If the boundary line is *not* part of the graph, it is drawn as a dashed line.

(a) $y > x + 2$

(b) $y \geq x + 2$

(c) $y < x + 2$

(d) $y \leq x + 2$

   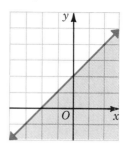

In general, to graph a linear inequality in the variables x and y, when the coefficient of y is not zero, you follow these steps:

1. Transform the given inequality into an equivalent inequality that has y alone as one side.
2. Graph the equation of the boundary. Use a solid line if the symbols $\geq$ or $\leq$ are used in the inequality; use a dashed line if $>$ or $<$ are used.
3. Shade the appropriate region.

EXAMPLE 1 Graph $2x - y \geq -4$.

SOLUTION

1. Transform the inequality:
$$2x - y \geq -4$$
$$-y \geq -4 - 2x$$
$$y \leq 4 + 2x$$

2. Draw the boundary line $y = 4 + 2x$ as a *solid* line, since the symbol $\leq$ is used in the transformed inequality.

3. Shade the region *below* the line, since $y \leq 4 + 2x$.

Check: Choose a point of the graph not on the boundary, say $(0, 0)$. See whether its coordinates satisfy the given inequality:

$$2x - y \geq -4$$
$$2(0) - 0 \overset{?}{\geq} -4$$
$$0 \geq -4 \quad \checkmark$$

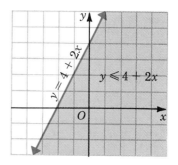

Thus $(0, 0)$ is in the solution set, and the correct region has been shaded.

EXAMPLE 2 Graph $y > 2$.

SOLUTION Graph $y = 2$ as a dashed line. Shade the region *above* the line, since $y > 2$.

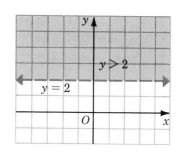

The next example shows how to graph a linear inequality in x and y when the coefficient of y is zero.

EXAMPLE 3 Graph $x > 4$.

SOLUTION

Draw the vertical line that is the graph of $x = 4$. The coordinates of any point *to the right* of that vertical line satisfy $x > 4$. Hence the graph of $x > 4$ is the open half-plane to the right of the graph of $x = 4$.

Oral Exercises

State whether or not the given points belong to the graph of the given inequality.

1. $x \geq 3$; $(3, 2)$, $(-3, 4)$, $(0, 0)$

2. $y < -2$; $(3, -2)$, $(4, -3)$, $(0, 0)$

3. $y < x + 2$; $(2, 3)$, $(-2, 3)$, $(0, 0)$

4. $y \leq 2x - 3$; $(3, 0)$, $(2, 1)$, $(0, 0)$

5. $x + y < 0$; $(-3, 2)$, $(3, -2)$, $(0, 0)$

6. $x - 3y \geq -1$; $(1, -1)$, $(-1, 1)$, $(0, 0)$

Transform each inequality into an equivalent inequality having y alone as one side. Then state the equation of the boundary of the graph.

7. $x + y < 2$

8. $-x + y > 2$

9. $2x + y \geq 6$

10. $3x + y \leq -1$

11. $2x + 3y > 0$

12. $9x + 3y < 0$

13. $4y < x$

14. $3x > 2y$

15. $x - y \leq 1$

16. $10x - 5y \leq 0$

17. $x - 2y > 4$

18. $7 < x - y$

Written Exercises

Graph each inequality.

A **1.** $y \geq 2$

2. $y > 2$

3. $x \leq 3$

4. $x < 3$

5. $x > 0$

6. $y < 0$

7. $y \geq -1$

8. $x \leq -3$

9. $y < x + 1$

10. $y > -x + 1$

11. $y \leq 3 - x$

12. $y \geq 1 - 2x$

Transform each inequality into an equivalent inequality with y as one side. Then graph the inequality.

13. $x + y < 3$
14. $x - y \geq 2$
15. $x - 2y \leq -5$
16. $2x + y > -3$
17. $3x - y > 6$
18. $y - 2x \leq -2$
19. $3x - 2y \geq 8$
20. $2y - 3x < 0$
21. $2x - 3y \leq x - 2$
22. $3y - 4 > 2x - 5$
23. $2(x - y) \geq 3x + 5$
24. $2y - 6 < 2(x + 2y)$

In each of Exercises 25–33, write an inequality whose graph is shown.

B 25.

26.

27.

28.

29.

30.

31.

32.

33.

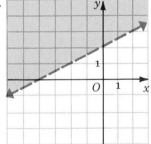

C 34. a. If $|y| > 1$ is graphed in a coordinate plane, which of the following points belong to the graph?

$(0, 0)$ $(3, 0)$ $(-2, \frac{1}{2})$ $(0, 1)$ $(0, -1)$ $(\frac{1}{2}, -2)$ $(-3, 2)$

b. Graph $|y| > 1$ in a coordinate plane.

35. Graph $|x| \geq 2$ in a coordinate plane.

10-7 *Systems of Linear Inequalities*

OBJECTIVE To graph the solution set of a system of two linear inequalities in two variables.

You can use graphs to find the solution set of a system of linear inequalities in two variables.

EXAMPLE Graph the solution set of the system:

$$x + y \le 4$$
$$x - 2y \le 4$$

SOLUTION
1. First transform each inequality into an equivalent one with y as one side.

$$x + y \le 4 \rightarrow y \le -x + 4$$
$$x - 2y \le 4 \rightarrow y \ge \tfrac{1}{2}x - 2$$

2. Draw the graph of $y = -x + 4$, the boundary of the first inequality. Use a solid line, and shade the region below this line to show the graph of $y \le -x + 4$ (colored shading).

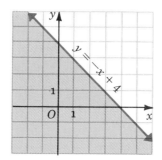

3. In the same coordinate system, draw the graph of $y = \tfrac{1}{2}x - 2$, the boundary of the second inequality. Use a solid line, and shade the region above this line to show the graph of $y \ge \tfrac{1}{2}x - 2$ (gray shading).

4. The doubly shaded region resulting from Steps 2 and 3 is the graph of the solution set of the given system.

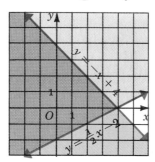

Oral Exercises

Give a system of two linear inequalities whose solution set is shown by the shaded region in each graph.

1. **2.**

3.

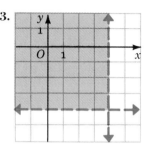

State whether or not each ordered pair is a solution of the system:

$$y \geq 5$$
$$x < 3$$

4. $(0, 0)$ **5.** $(3, 5)$ **6.** $(2, 5)$ **7.** $(-3, 5)$ **8.** $(-3, -5)$

State whether or not each point belongs to the graph of the solution set of the system:

$$y \leq 2$$
$$x - y \leq 6$$

9. $(0, -6)$ **10.** $(8, 2)$ **11.** $(9, 2)$ **12.** $(-10, 2)$ **13.** $(-10, 3)$

Written Exercises

Graph each pair of inequalities and indicate the solution set of the system with crosshatching or shading.

A **1.** $y \geq 0$
      $x \geq 0$

2. $y \leq 6$
   $x \geq 3$

3. $y > 4$
   $x < -2$

4. $y < -3$
   $x > 3$

5. $y < x$
   $x > 3$

6. $y > 2x$
   $x < 3$

7. $x \leq 5$
   $y > 6 - x$

8. $x > -3$
   $y \leq 2x + 5$

9. $y \leq x - 1$
   $y \geq 1 - x$

10. $y < 3x + 3$
    $y > -3x + 3$

11. $y > 2x - 3$
    $y < 2x + 4$

12. $y < 2x + 2$
    $y > 2 - 2x$

B **13.** $x + y \leq 9$
       $x - y \geq 3$

14. $x + y \geq 3$
    $2x - y > 9$

15. $3x - y > -2$
    $x - y \leq -6$

16. $x - y < 5$
    $x - 3y > 9$

17. $2x - 3y < -12$
    $2x + 3y > 0$

18. $2x - 3y > 0$
    $x - 6y \leq -5$

Write a system of linear inequalities whose solution set is shown by the shaded region in each graph.

19.

20.

21.

22.

SAMPLE

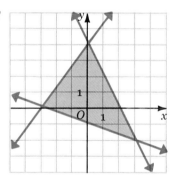

SOLUTION $y \leq \frac{4}{3}x + 4$

$$y \geq -\frac{1}{3}x - 1$$

$$y \leq -2x + 4$$

C 23.

24.

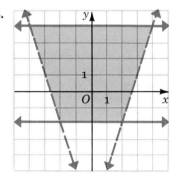

Graph each system of inequalities. Determine exactly the *corner points* of the graph of the solution set of the system, that is, the points where boundary lines intersect.

25. $y \leq -x$
$y \leq x$
$y \geq -1$

26. $3x - y \leq 3$
$x \geq 0$
$y < 3$

27. $x + 2y < 6$
$y \geq 0$
$2x - y + 3 > 0$

Self-Test 3

VOCABULARY   open half-plane (p. 389)   closed half-plane (p. 389)
boundary (p. 389)

Graph each inequality in a coordinate plane.

1. $y < 1$ **2.** $2x + y \geq 4$ Obj. 10-6, p. 389

3. Graph the solution set of the system: Obj. 10-7, p. 393

$$x + y > 3$$
$$2x - y > 2$$

Check your answers with those at the back of the book.

Just for Fun

1. On the same set of axes, graph the following line segments to draw a picture.

$x = 0, 2 \leq y \leq 7$
$x = 18, 4 \leq y \leq 9$
$x + 3y = 21, 0 \leq x \leq 6$
$x - 3y = 6, 6 \leq x \leq 18$
$x - 3y = -27, 3 \leq x \leq 15$
$5x + 3y = 117, 15 \leq x \leq 18$

$x = 6, 0 \leq y \leq 5$
$x + 3y = 6, 0 \leq x \leq 6$
$x - y = -7, 0 \leq x \leq 3$
$x - 3y = -9, 6 \leq x \leq 18$
$5x + 3y = 45, 3 \leq x \leq 6$

2. Draw a picture on graph paper using line segments. Write a set of equations and inequalities to describe your picture as in Exercise 1.

Application Nutrition Labeling

Have you noticed the nutrition information that is printed on the labels of many canned foods? For example, a can of corn has:

Nutrition Information per Serving

Calories 230	Carbohydrates 50 grams
Protein 4 grams	Fat 2 grams

Percentage of U.S. Recommended Daily Allowance (U.S. RDA) per Serving

Protein	6	Riboflavin (B_2)	6
Vitamin A	4	Niacin	8
Vitamin C	20	Calcium	Less than 2
Thiamin (B_1)	2	Iron	4

What percent of the U.S. RDA of vitamin C would be provided by a meal that included two servings of corn along with other foods that provided 15% of the U.S. RDA of vitamin C? The label indicates that one serving should provide 20% of the U.S RDA of vitamin C. Thus,

$$2 \cdot 20 + 15 = 55.$$

Therefore, the meal would provide 55% of the U.S. RDA of vitamin C.

Refer to the following table to answer the questions below.

Percentage of U.S. Recommended Daily Allowance (U.S. RDA) per Serving				
	Beans	Zucchini	Vegetable Juice	Grade A Milk
Protein	4	2	2	20
Vitamin A	15	20	40	10
Vitamin C	40	4	45	4
Thiamin (B_1)	4	6	4	6
Riboflavin (B_2)	10	4	2	25
Niacin	4	4	6	0
Calcium	4	2	2	30
Iron	8	8	2	0

1. Find the percent of the U.S. RDA of vitamin C that one would get from a serving of corn, a serving of beans, and a serving of vegetable juice.

2. Find the percent of the U.S. RDA of niacin that one would get from the servings described in Exercise 1.

3. A serving each of corn and zucchini would provide what percent of the U.S. RDA of iron?

4. A serving each of corn, beans, and milk would provide what percent of the U.S. RDA of riboflavin (B_2)?

Chapter Summary

1. The symbols $>$, $<$, $\geq$, and $\leq$ are used to express inequalities. $-3 < 1 < 7$ (or $7 > 1 > -3$) means that 1 is between -3 and 7.

2. Open inequalities can be solved by transformations to obtain simple equivalent inequalities whose solution sets can be seen at a glance. The graph of the solution set of an inequality in one variable can be shown on a number line.

3. Sentences joined by "and" are conjunctions. A conjunction is true if and only if it is formed of true statements. Sentences joined by "or" are disjunctions. A disjunction of statements is true if at least one of the statements is true.

4. Open sentences involving the absolute value of a variable may be written as equivalent conjunctions or disjunctions.

5. The solution set of a linear inequality in two variables is graphed in a coordinate plane.

6. The graph of the solution set of a system of inequalities consists of the points common to the graphs of all the inequalities in the system.

Chapter Review

Give the letter of the correct answer.

1. Which statement is true? 10-1

   a. $1 < -2 < 5$ **b.** $5 > -2 > 1$ **c.** $-2 < 1 < 5$ **d.** $-2 > 1 < 5$

2. Find the solution set of $2x - 3 \leq 4$ if the domain of x is $\{-4, -2, 0, 2, 4\}$.

   a. $\{-4, -2, 0, 2, 4\}$ **b.** $\{-4, -2, 0, 2\}$ **c.** $\{-2, 0, 2\}$ **d.** $\{0\}$

3. Find an inequality equivalent to $\frac{x}{-2} < -6$. 10-2

   a. $x > 12$ **b.** $x < 12$ **c.** $x > 3$ **d.** $x < 3$

4. Find an inequality equivalent to $4x - 2y \leq 3$.

   a. $2y \leq 4x - 3$ **b.** $y \geq 2x - 3$ **c.** $2y - 4x \geq 3$ **d.** $y \geq 2x - \frac{3}{2}$

5. Represent the statement "The sum of two consecutive even integers is at most 60" as an inequality. 10-3

   a. $n + (n + 1) \geq 60$ **b.** $n + (n + 1) \leq 60$

   c. $n + (n + 2) \geq 60$ **d.** $n + (n + 2) \leq 60$

6. Which is the graph of the solution set of the disjunction "$x < 2$ or $x > 2$"?   10-4

7. Which is the graph of the conjunction "$-3 \leq x$ and $x < 2$"?

8. Which is a compact form for the disjunction "$y < -3$ or $y > 3$"?   10-5

    a. $-3 > y > 3$ **b.** $|y| > 3$ **c.** $|y| = 3$ **d.** $|y| < 3$

9. What is the equation of the boundary of the graph of the inequality   10-6
$3x - 2y \leq 6$?

    a. $3x - 2y = 6$ **b.** $-2y = 6$ **c.** $y \leq \frac{3}{2}x - 3$ **d.** $y = 0$

10. Which point belongs to the graph of the solution set of the system: 10-7

$$y \geq 3$$
$$x - y > 3?$$

    a. $(0,0)$ **b.** $(6,3)$ **c.** $(10,4)$ **d.** $(6,-3)$

Chapter Test

1. Classify the statement as true or false: $-4 < \frac{1}{4} < 1$ 10-1

2. Find the solution set of $2y + 2 \leq 5$ if $y \in \{-2, -1, 0, 1, 2\}$.

3. Solve the inequality $2 - \frac{1}{2}x \geq 3$ and graph the solution set on a num-   10-2
ber line.

4. Of all pairs of consecutive odd integers whose sum is less than 20,   10-3
find the pair whose sum is the greatest.

Solve each open sentence and graph its solution set.

5. $-5 < 2x - 1 < 3$ 10-4

6. $|y + 3| > 2$ 10-5

Graph each inequality in a coordinate plane.

7. $x > -3$ **8.** $3x + y \leq -3$ 10-6

9. Graph the solution set of the system: $\quad 2x - y \geq 2$ 10-7
$$x - y < 2$$

Cumulative Review (Chapters 1-10)

Factor completely.

1. $15u^2 - 44uv + 21v^2$ **2.** $48d^2 - 144d - 4d^3$ **3.** $2g - 3gh + 3h - 2$

Simplify. In Exercise 14, divide.

4. $-3t(rt - t^2 + 4rt^2)$ **5.** $6 + 5y - 3(7y + 2)$ **6.** $2h(h + 8)(7h - 2)$

7. $(-6m^5 + 9m^2) \div 1.5m^2$ **8.** $(3a^4b^2)^3 \div (-9ab^4)^2$ **9.** $(c + d - 1)^2$

10. $\dfrac{200j^2 - 2k^2}{k^2 + 7kj - 30j^2}$ **11.** $\dfrac{5x}{12} - \dfrac{x}{8} - \dfrac{14}{3x}$ **12.** $\dfrac{4r^2 - 6r}{r^2 - r} \div \dfrac{9 - 4r^2}{18 - 12r}$

13. $\dfrac{-28 + 7c}{(c - 4)^2} + \dfrac{c + 1}{4 - c}$ **14.** $\dfrac{8y^4 + 6y^3 - 25y^2 + 9}{-4y + 3}$ **15.** $\dfrac{z^4 - 81}{2z - 4} \cdot \dfrac{z^2 + 2z - 8}{z^2 + z - 12}$

16. Find an equation of the line: **a.** with slope 4 and passing through $(-2, -5)$ **b.** containing $(-3, 0)$ and $(7, -6)$.

17. If $g(x) = 2x^2 - x - 3$, find $g(2)$ and $g(-4)$, and graph $g(x)$.

18. Graph: **a.** $-3 < 2x + 1 \le 7$ **b.** $5 - y < -1$ or $5 - y > 1$

19. Solve graphically: **a.** $4x + 3y = -3$ **b.** $x < 3$
                             $5x + 2y = 5$ $2x - y \le 4$

Solve each equation, inequality, or system.

20. $4(8 - 3p) = 3(p - 1)$ **21.** $8 - |k| = -1$ **22.** $1.3d = 1.9d - 0.03$

23. 1.8% of $150 = t$ **24.** $1 = 12g^2 - 4g$ **25.** $(s - 4)(s + 6) = 7s$

26. $7 - 9b < 34$ **27.** $3(n - 4) \ge 2(n + 1)$ **28.** $-88 \ne -18w + 2$

29. $\dfrac{m}{2} - \dfrac{4}{m + 2} = \dfrac{5}{2}$ **30.** $\dfrac{3q - 2}{5q + 6} = \dfrac{q + 1}{q}$ **31.** $\dfrac{g - 2}{3} + 1 \le \dfrac{g + 7}{5}$

32. $x = 3y + 4$ **33.** $4x + 9y = 14$ **34.** $5a + 3b = 31$
      $3x - 7y = 6$ $-7x + 9y = -8$ $2a - 5b = 62$

Solve.

35. Bob and Jenny took as long to row 15 km downstream as they did to row 9 km upstream. If their rate in still water was 6 km/h faster than the speed of the current, find the speed of the current.

36. A pouch contains 19 coins, some of which are dimes and some of which are nickels. The total value of the coins is more than $1.15. At least how many of the coins are dimes and at most how many are nickels?

Maintaining Skills

Divide. Write your answer as a polynomial or a mixed expression.

SAMPLE 1 $\dfrac{2a^2 - 3}{a + 3}$ **SOLUTION**

$$a + 3 \overline{)2a^2 + 0a - 3}$$

$$\begin{array}{r} 2a - 6 \\ \underline{2a^2 + 6a} \\ -6a - 3 \\ \underline{-6a - 18} \\ 15 \end{array}$$

$2a - 6 + \dfrac{15}{a + 3}$ ***Answer***

1. $\dfrac{n^2 + 6n - 1}{n + 4}$

2. $\dfrac{6x^2 + 7x - 5}{2x - 1}$

3. $\dfrac{r^2 + 8r + 18}{r + 5}$

4. $\dfrac{12p^2 - p - 6}{4p - 3}$

5. $\dfrac{12s^2 - 20}{2s + 3}$

6. $\dfrac{2a^2 - 7ab + b^2}{a - 3b}$

7. $\dfrac{c^3 - c^2 + 1}{c + 1}$

8. $\dfrac{t^4 - 1}{t + 1}$

Solve.

SAMPLE 2 $\dfrac{2}{3}x - \dfrac{5}{12}x = -\dfrac{3}{2}$

SOLUTION $12\left(\dfrac{2}{3}x - \dfrac{5}{12}x\right) = 12\left(-\dfrac{3}{2}\right);$

$8x - 5x = -18;\ 3x = -18;\ x = -6$ ***Answer***

9. $\dfrac{6r - 1}{5} = \dfrac{4r + 1}{3}$

10. $0.15x = 0.2x - 0.9$

11. $\dfrac{20d - 8}{9} = \dfrac{2}{3}(4d + 2)$

12. $\dfrac{7m}{4} = \dfrac{m + 5}{6} + \dfrac{m}{8}$

13. $\dfrac{z}{7} - 3 = \dfrac{z + 3}{16} - \dfrac{3}{2}$

14. $3t + \dfrac{6 - t}{3} = \dfrac{t}{2} + 2$

15. $\dfrac{5y}{6} = \dfrac{3y}{5} + \dfrac{7}{3}$

16. $\dfrac{3a + 5}{2} = -\dfrac{4 - 9a}{25}$

17. $\dfrac{3k}{7} - \dfrac{k - 1}{3} = \dfrac{3 - 4k}{21}$

Solve, and check each root.

SAMPLE 3 $\dfrac{2x + 3}{x} = \dfrac{1}{2}$

SOLUTION $2x\left(\dfrac{2x + 3}{x}\right) = 2x\left(\dfrac{1}{2}\right);\ 4x + 6 = x;\ 3x = -6;\ x = -2$ ***Answer***

18. $\dfrac{z - 3}{z} = \dfrac{4}{z}$

19. $\dfrac{b + 2}{b + 3} - \dfrac{8}{b} = 1$

20. $\dfrac{4g - 3}{2g + 1} = \dfrac{2g - 9}{g - 2}$

21. $\dfrac{r^2}{r + 2} + \dfrac{2r}{r + 2} = -r$

22. $\dfrac{m + 2}{4m} = \dfrac{m}{m + 2}$

23. $\dfrac{3}{y - 1} - \dfrac{7}{2y} = \dfrac{11}{40}$

24. $\dfrac{3}{v} + \dfrac{1}{v + 1} = \dfrac{4}{v - 1}$

25. $\dfrac{3 - x}{2x - 8} + 6 = \dfrac{28x}{x - 4}$

26. $\dfrac{2}{3c + 2} - \dfrac{1}{5c - 2} = \dfrac{1}{4c}$

The boom of this self-propelled center-post irrigation system in Nevada sweeps out a circle. If r is the length of the boom, then πr^2 will be the area of the land that is irrigated.

11

RATIONAL AND
IRRATIONAL NUMBERS

RATIONAL NUMBERS

11-1 *Properties of Rational Numbers*

OBJECTIVE   To learn and apply some properties of real numbers.

A real number that is a quotient of two integers is called a **rational number.** Thus, the following numbers are rational numbers:

$$0 = \frac{0}{1} \qquad 2 = \frac{2}{1} \qquad 5\frac{1}{2} = \frac{11}{2} \qquad 0.37 = \frac{37}{100} \qquad -\frac{2}{3} = \frac{-2}{3}$$

Using the properties of fractions, a rational number can be expressed as a quotient of integers in an unlimited number of ways:

$$1 = \frac{4}{4} = \frac{-8}{-8} = \frac{37}{37} = \cdots \qquad -2\frac{1}{2} = \frac{-5}{2} = \frac{10}{-4} = \cdots \qquad 24\% = \frac{24}{100} = \frac{12}{50} = \cdots$$

To determine the greater of two rational numbers, you can write them with the same positive denominator and compare their numerators.

EXAMPLE 1   Compare $\frac{9}{4}$ and $\frac{15}{7}$.

SOLUTION   The LCD is 28.

$$\frac{9}{4} = \frac{63}{28} \qquad \frac{15}{7} = \frac{60}{28}$$

Because $63 > 60$, $\frac{63}{28} > \frac{60}{28}$.

Thus, $\frac{9}{4} > \frac{15}{7}$.   *Answer*

The procedure shown in Example 1 may be generalized as shown below. (See Exercise 35 on page 407 for a proof.)

For all integers a and b and all positive integers c and d:

$$\frac{a}{c} > \frac{b}{d} \text{ if and only if } ad > bc.$$

Similarly, $\frac{a}{c} < \frac{b}{d}$ if and only if $ad < bc$.

Thus, $\frac{5}{7} > \frac{2}{3}$ because $5(3) > 2(7)$;

$-\frac{3}{8} > -\frac{4}{5}$ because $-3(5) > -4(8)$.

EXAMPLE 2 Compare $-\frac{5}{8}$ and $-\frac{7}{12}$.

SOLUTION   Write $-\frac{5}{8}$ as $\frac{-5}{8}$ and $-\frac{7}{12}$ as $\frac{-7}{12}$. Then use the technique shown above to compare $\frac{-5}{8}$ and $\frac{-7}{12}$.

$(-5)(12) < (-7)(8)$ because $-60 < -56$.

Thus, $-\frac{5}{8} < -\frac{7}{12}$. **Answer**

Rational numbers differ from integers in several ways: For each integer, there is a next larger integer. For example, -3 follows -4, 1 follows 0, and 8 follows 7. There is, however, no "next larger" rational number after a given rational number. One property that the set of rationals has that the set of integers does not have is the following:

THE BETWEENNESS PROPERTY

Between every pair of different rational numbers there is another rational number.

If a and b are rational numbers, and $a < b$, then:

the number halfway from a to b is $a + \frac{1}{2}(b - a)$;

the number one third of the way from a to b is $a + \frac{1}{3}(b - a)$;

and so on.

Thus, it is possible to find an endless number of rational numbers between two given rational numbers.

EXAMPLE 3 Find a rational number between $\frac{7}{5}$ and $\frac{13}{8}$.

SOLUTION The number halfway between $\frac{7}{5}$ and $\frac{13}{8}$ will be $\frac{7}{5} + \frac{1}{2}\left(\frac{13}{8} - \frac{7}{5}\right)$.

$$\frac{13}{8} - \frac{7}{5} = \frac{65}{40} - \frac{56}{40} = \frac{9}{40}$$

$$\frac{7}{5} + \frac{1}{2}\left(\frac{9}{40}\right) = \frac{7}{5} + \frac{9}{80} = \frac{112}{80} + \frac{9}{80} = \frac{121}{80}$$

Check: Is $\frac{7}{5} < \frac{121}{80} < \frac{13}{8}$?

$$7(80) \overset{?}{<} 5(121) \qquad 8(121) \overset{?}{<} 80(13)$$
$$560 \ < \ 605 \ \checkmark \qquad\qquad 968 \ < \ 1040 \ \checkmark$$

$\therefore$ a rational number between $\frac{7}{5}$ and $\frac{13}{8}$ is $\frac{121}{80}$. *Answer.*

(In fact, $\frac{121}{80}$ is halfway between the two numbers.)

In the last example, observe that $\frac{121}{80}$ is also the average of $\frac{7}{5}$ and $\frac{13}{8}$. In general, the number halfway between two numbers is the average of the two numbers because

$$a + \frac{1}{2}(b - a) = \frac{2a}{2} + \frac{b - a}{2} = \frac{a + b}{2}.$$

Oral Exercises

Express each number as a quotient of integers.

SAMPLE 2.9 **ONE SOLUTION** $\frac{29}{10}$

1. 4.8 **2.** $-\frac{1}{8}$ **3.** $-2\frac{1}{5}$ **4.** 31%

5. -5 **6.** 18 **7.** 0 **8.** $\frac{4}{6} + \left(-\frac{5}{6}\right)$

Which rational number in each pair is greater?

9. $\frac{5}{9}, \frac{7}{9}$ **10.** $-3, \frac{1}{2}$ **11.** $-\frac{2}{5}, -\frac{4}{5}$

12. $7, \frac{46}{7}$ **13.** $\frac{5}{8}, \frac{3}{4}$ **14.** $-\frac{9}{2}, -\frac{13}{3}$

Written Exercises

Replace the __?__ with $<$, $=$, or $>$ to make a true statement.

A 1. $\dfrac{1}{8}$ __?__ $\dfrac{5}{32}$

2. $\dfrac{3}{4}$ __?__ $\dfrac{9}{13}$

3. $-\dfrac{11}{14}$ __?__ $-\dfrac{19}{25}$

4. $\dfrac{22}{27}$ __?__ $\dfrac{31}{38}$

5. $\dfrac{123}{47}$ __?__ $\dfrac{190}{82}$

6. $\dfrac{25}{95}$ __?__ $\dfrac{55}{209}$

7. $-12\dfrac{1}{4}$ __?__ $-\dfrac{149}{12}$

8. $21\dfrac{3}{5}$ __?__ $\dfrac{131}{6}$

9. $\dfrac{423}{8}$ __?__ $52\dfrac{5}{7}$

Arrange each group of numbers in order from least to greatest.

10. $\dfrac{1}{4}, -\dfrac{2}{3}, \dfrac{5}{8}$

11. $-\dfrac{5}{7}, -\dfrac{3}{5}, \dfrac{2}{9}$

12. $-4.2, -\dfrac{38}{9}, -4$

13. $2.3, \dfrac{57}{25}, \dfrac{91}{40}$

14. $\dfrac{7}{24}, \dfrac{4}{15}, \dfrac{5}{16}, \dfrac{1}{2}$

15. $\dfrac{3}{7}, \dfrac{5}{6}, \dfrac{3}{5}, \dfrac{7}{9}$

Find the number halfway between the given numbers.

16. $\dfrac{4}{7}, \dfrac{5}{6}$

17. $\dfrac{2}{3}, \dfrac{5}{12}$

18. $-\dfrac{4}{25}, -\dfrac{9}{50}$

19. $-\dfrac{7}{35}, -\dfrac{26}{140}$

20. $-2\dfrac{2}{3}, -3\dfrac{3}{4}$

21. $-5\dfrac{1}{5}, 6\dfrac{4}{9}$

If $x \in \{0, 1, 2, 3\}$ state whether each fraction increases or decreases in value as x takes on its values in increasing order.

22. $\dfrac{x}{4}$

23. $\dfrac{7}{x+1}$

24. $\dfrac{x+1}{5}$

25. $\dfrac{7-2x}{9}$

26. $\dfrac{7}{6-x}$

B 27. Find the number one fourth of the way from $\dfrac{5}{8}$ to $1\dfrac{1}{2}$.

28. Find the number one third of the way from $-\dfrac{1}{5}$ to $-\dfrac{5}{6}$.

29. Find the number one sixth of the way from $-\dfrac{3}{4}$ to $\dfrac{1}{3}$.

30. Find the number three fourths of the way from $\dfrac{1}{2}$ to $\dfrac{8}{9}$.

31. Find a rational number between $\dfrac{1}{2}$ and $\dfrac{1}{3}$.

32. Find a rational number between $-\dfrac{1}{5}$ and $-\dfrac{1}{4}$.

33. Write an expression for the number halfway between $\dfrac{5a}{6}$ and $-\dfrac{a}{7}$.

34. Write an expression for the number one third of the way from $-\dfrac{6b}{5}$ to $-\dfrac{2b}{9}$.

C **35.** Give the reason for each statement in the proof of the following theorem: For all integers a and b and all positive integers c and d,

$$\frac{a}{c} > \frac{b}{d} \text{ if and only if } ad > bc.$$

1. $\dfrac{a}{c} > \dfrac{b}{d}$ 1. given

2. $\dfrac{ad}{cd} > \dfrac{bc}{cd}$ 2. __?__

3. $ad > bc$ 3. __?__

$\therefore$ if $\dfrac{a}{c} > \dfrac{b}{d}$, then $ad > bc$.

4. $ad > bc$ 4. given

5. $\dfrac{ad}{cd} > \dfrac{bc}{cd}$ (since $cd > 0$)   5. __?__

6. $\dfrac{a}{c} > \dfrac{b}{d}$ 6. __?__

$\therefore$ if $ad > bc$, then $\dfrac{a}{c} > \dfrac{b}{d}$.

$\therefore$ $\dfrac{a}{c} > \dfrac{b}{d}$ if and only if $ad > bc$.

Biography Pierre de Fermat

Pierre de Fermat (1601–1665) was a lawyer and legislator by profession in Toulouse, France. He achieved some fame as a poet and scholar, but his primary contribution was made in the field of pure mathematics. In the theory of numbers there are two theorems which bear his name. One of these, Fermat's Last Theorem, states that if x, y, and z are integers, then the equation $x^n + y^n = z^n$ has no solution when $n > 2$ and $xyz \neq 0$. To this day the truth of this theorem remains an open question. Fermat also contributed to the foundations of differential calculus, integral calculus, and probability.

11-2 *Decimal Forms for Rational Numbers*

OBJECTIVE To express rational numbers as decimals or fractions.

To change a common fraction to a decimal, you divide the numerator by the denominator. If there is a remainder of zero, the decimal is called a **terminating, ending,** or **finite decimal.** The division at the right shows that $\frac{5}{32}$ can be expressed as the terminating decimal 0.15625.

$$\frac{5}{32} = 5 \div 32 = 0.15625$$

```
        0.15625
32)5.00000
   3 2
   1 80
   1 60
     200
     192
      80
      64
     160
     160
       0
```

If there is no zero remainder, you continue dividing until the remainders start to repeat.

$$\frac{11}{18} \longrightarrow$$
```
      0.611
18)11.000
   10 8
     20
     18
     20
     18
      2
```

$$\frac{9}{11} \longrightarrow$$
```
     0.8181
11)9.0000
   8 8
    20
    11
    90
    88
    20
    11
     9
```

$$\frac{7}{13} \longrightarrow$$
```
       0.5384615
13)7.0000000
   6 5
    50
    39
   110
   104
    60
    52
    80
    78
    20
    13
    70
    65
     5
```

The decimal quotients shown above are **nonterminating, unending,** or **infinite.** They are also called **repeating** or **periodic** because the same digit (or block of digits) repeats unendingly.

$$\frac{11}{18} = 0.611 \ldots \qquad \frac{9}{11} = 0.8181 \ldots \qquad \frac{7}{13} = 0.538461538 \ldots$$

The dots indicate that the decimals continue unendingly. A bar is used to indicate the block of digits that repeat, as shown below.

$$\frac{11}{18} = 0.6\overline{1} \qquad \frac{9}{11} = 0.\overline{81} \qquad \frac{7}{13} = 0.\overline{538461}$$

When you divide a positive integer n by a positive integer d, the remainder r at each step must be zero or a positive integer less than d. If the divisor is 7, the remainders will be 0, 1, 2, 3, 4, 5, or 6, and the division will terminate or begin repeating within 6 steps after only zeros remain to be brought down. In general:

> For every integer n and every positive integer d, the decimal numeral of the rational number $\frac{n}{d}$ either terminates or eventually repeats in a block of fewer than d digits.

To express a terminating decimal as a common fraction, express the decimal as a common fraction with a power of ten as the denominator. It is usual to express the fraction in simplest form.

$$0.83 = \frac{83}{100} \qquad 0.328 = \frac{328}{1000} = \frac{41}{125}$$

To express a repeating decimal as a common fraction you may use the method shown in the following examples.

EXAMPLE 1   Express $0.2\overline{45}$ as a common fraction.

SOLUTION   Let $N =$ the number. Multiply the given number N by 10^n where n is the number of digits in the block of repeating digits. Because $n = 2$ for $0.2\overline{45}$, you multiply by 10^2, or 100.

$$100N = 24.5\overline{45}$$
Subtract $\underline{\quad N = 0.2\overline{45}}$
$$99N = 24.300$$
$$N = \frac{24.3}{99} = \frac{243}{990} = \frac{27}{110}$$

$\therefore 0.2\overline{45} = \frac{27}{110}$.   *Answer*

EXAMPLE 2   Express $0.\overline{528}$ as a common fraction.

SOLUTION   Let $N =$ the number.

$$1000N = 528.\overline{528}$$
Subtract $\underline{\quad N = 0.\overline{528}}$
$$999N = 528$$
$$N = \frac{528}{999} = \frac{176}{333}$$

$\therefore 0.\overline{528} = \frac{176}{333}$.   *Answer*

All terminating decimals and all repeating decimals represent rational numbers that can be written in the form $\frac{n}{d}$ where n is an integer and d is a positive integer.

It is often convenient to use an approximation of a lengthy decimal. For example, you may approximate $\frac{5}{12}$ as

$$0.41667 \quad \text{or} \quad 0.417 \quad \text{or} \quad 0.42.$$

To round a decimal:
1. If the first digit dropped is 5 or more, add 1 to the last digit retained;
2. If the first digit dropped is less than 5, leave the retained digits unchanged.

The following examples show approximations of nonterminating decimals. The symbol $\approx$ is read, "is approximately equal to."

$\frac{13}{30} = 0.433\ldots \approx 0.43$ to the nearest hundredth
≈ 0.4 to the nearest tenth

$\frac{23}{33} = 0.\overline{69}$ ≈ 0.70 to the nearest hundredth
≈ 0.7 to the nearest tenth

$\frac{196}{111} = 1.\overline{765}$ ≈ 1.8 to the nearest tenth
≈ 2 to the nearest unit

Oral Exercises

Round each number to the nearest tenth.

1. 4.893   **2.** -0.249 **3.** $3.\overline{5}$ **4.** $2.96\overline{7}$ **5.** $0.1\overline{4}$

6–10. Round the numbers in Exercises 1–5 to the nearest hundredth.

Written Exercises

Express each rational number as a terminating or repeating decimal.

A **1.** $\frac{4}{9}$ **2.** $\frac{15}{4}$ **3.** $\frac{5}{8}$ **4.** $\frac{7}{12}$

5. $\frac{3}{5}$ **6.** $-\frac{9}{25}$ **7.** $\frac{69}{50}$ **8.** $\frac{11}{9}$

9. $\frac{9}{16}$ **10.** $-\frac{7}{18}$ **11.** $-\frac{11}{20}$ **12.** $\frac{5}{7}$

13. $-\frac{5}{11}$ **14.** $\frac{27}{32}$ **15.** $-3\frac{7}{8}$ **16.** $2\frac{22}{99}$

Express each rational number as a fraction in simplest form.

17. 0.33 **18.** 0.6 **19.** $0.222\ldots$ **20.** 0.58

21. $0.6\overline{3}$ **22.** 0.725 **23.** $-0.41\overline{6}$ **24.** 3.9

25. $1.4\overline{6}$ **26.** $4.\overline{18}$ **27.** $-3.0\overline{8}$ **28.** $0.\overline{428571}$

Express both numbers as fractions and find their product.

B 29. $\frac{1}{4}$ and 0.5 **30.** 0.375 and $\frac{4}{5}$ **31.** $0.444\ldots$ and $\frac{3}{4}$

32. $-4.333\ldots$ and $1.\overline{6}$ **33.** $0.\overline{81}$ and $0.\overline{814}$ **34.** $0.36\overline{3}$ and -0.3

Find the difference of the given numbers. Then find a number between them.

35. $\frac{3}{4}$ and 0.758 **36.** $\frac{1}{8}$ and 0.123 **37.** 0.66 and $0.\overline{6}$

38. 0.29 and $0.\overline{29}$ **39.** $\frac{5}{44}$ and $0.11\overline{38}$ **40.** $\frac{5}{6}$ and 0.84

C 41. a. Express $\frac{1}{7}$ and $\frac{3}{7}$ as repeating decimals.

b. In the decimals that you found in part (a), what is the relationship between the blocks of digits that repeat?

c. Express $\frac{2}{7}$, $\frac{4}{7}$, and $\frac{6}{7}$ as decimals.

42. a. Express $\frac{1}{9}$, $\frac{5}{9}$, and $\frac{7}{9}$ as repeating decimals.

b. Express $\frac{1}{18}$, $\frac{5}{18}$, and $\frac{7}{18}$ as repeating decimals.

c. What is the relationship between the decimals in part (a) and part (b)?

43. Since $\frac{1}{99} = 0.\overline{01}$, then $\frac{n}{99} = n(0.\overline{01})$ for $n < 100$.

a. Confirm the fact stated above by expressing $\frac{7}{99}$, $\frac{15}{99}$ and $\frac{86}{99}$ as decimals.

b. Express 1 as $\frac{99}{99}$ to show that $0.\overline{9} = 1$.

11-3 *Rational Square Roots*

OBJECTIVE   To find the square roots of numbers and quotients that
have rational square roots.

Recall that subtracting a number is the inverse of adding that number,
and dividing by a (nonzero) number is the inverse of multiplying by
that number. The inverse of squaring a number is finding a square root.
If $a^2 = b$ then a is called a **square root** of b. Because $6^2 = 36$ and
$(-6)^2 = 36$, both 6 and -6 are square roots of 36.

The symbol $\sqrt{}$ is used to denote the **principal,** or positive, square
root of a positive number. Thus,

$$\sqrt{36} = 6 \quad \text{and} \quad -\sqrt{36} = -6.$$

The symbol $\sqrt{}$ is called the **radical sign,** and $\sqrt{36}$ is an example of a
radical. An expression written beneath the radical sign, such as 36, is
called the **radicand.** Often it is convenient to use *plus-or-minus* notation with radicals, for example:

$$\pm\sqrt{36}, \text{ read "positive or negative square root of 36."}$$

> For all positive real numbers c, the symbol $\sqrt{c}$ denotes the princi-
> pal square root of c.

It follows from the definition of square root that $(\sqrt{c})^2 = c$.

Zero has only one square root, namely zero itself: $\sqrt{0} = 0$

Because the square of every real number is either positive or zero, *negative numbers do not have square roots in the set of real numbers.*

The values of certain square roots are easy to find, for example
$\sqrt{25} = 5$. To find other square roots, it is often helpful to factor the
radicand.

Notice that

$$\sqrt{4 \cdot 25} = \sqrt{100} = 10$$

and

$$\sqrt{4} \cdot \sqrt{25} = 2 \cdot 5 = 10.$$

This relationship suggests the following fact about square roots.

> PRODUCT PROPERTY OF SQUARE ROOTS
>
> For any nonnegative real numbers a and b:
>
> $$\sqrt{ab} = \sqrt{a} \cdot \sqrt{b}$$

EXAMPLE 1 Find $\sqrt{225}$.

SOLUTION $\sqrt{225} = \sqrt{9} \cdot \sqrt{25} = 3 \cdot 5 = 15.$

If you cannot see any squares that divide the radicand, you can begin by factoring the radicand. (See the material on factoring integers on page 156.)

EXAMPLE 2 Find $\sqrt{1764}$.

SOLUTION $\sqrt{1764} = \sqrt{2^2 \cdot 3^2 \cdot 7^2}$

$= \sqrt{2^2} \cdot \sqrt{3^2} \cdot \sqrt{7^2}$

$= 2 \cdot 3 \cdot 7 = 42$

The examples

$$\sqrt{\frac{36}{9}} = \sqrt{4} = 2 \quad \text{and} \quad \frac{\sqrt{36}}{\sqrt{9}} = \frac{6}{3} = 2$$

suggest another property of square roots.

QUOTIENT PROPERTY OF SQUARE ROOTS

For any nonnegative real number a and any positive real number b:

$$\sqrt{\frac{a}{b}} = \frac{\sqrt{a}}{\sqrt{b}}$$

EXAMPLE 3 Find $\sqrt{\dfrac{81}{676}}$.

SOLUTION $\sqrt{\dfrac{81}{676}} = \dfrac{\sqrt{81}}{\sqrt{676}} = \dfrac{9}{\sqrt{2^2 \cdot 13^2}} = \dfrac{9}{2 \cdot 13} = \dfrac{9}{26}$

Oral Exercises

Find the indicated square roots.

1. $\sqrt{4}$ **2.** $\sqrt{1}$ **3.** $\sqrt{100}$ **4.** $\sqrt{7^2}$ **5.** $\sqrt{33^2}$

6. $(\sqrt{6})^2$ **7.** $(\sqrt{19})^2$ **8.** $\sqrt{\dfrac{1}{9}}$ **9.** $\sqrt{5^2 - 3^2}$ **10.** $\sqrt{5^2} - \sqrt{3^2}$

11. $\sqrt{\dfrac{1}{64}}$ **12.** $\sqrt{\dfrac{100}{9}}$ **13.** $\left(\sqrt{\dfrac{7}{12}}\right)^2$ **14.** $\sqrt{\left(\dfrac{3}{5}\right)^2}$ **15.** $\sqrt{\dfrac{81}{25}}$

Written Exercises

Find the indicated square roots.

A
1. $\sqrt{256}$
2. $\sqrt{900}$
3. $\sqrt{225}$
4. $\sqrt{625}$
5. $\sqrt{361}$

6. $-\sqrt{1849}$
7. $-\sqrt{2704}$
8. $\sqrt{2401}$
9. $\sqrt{5184}$
10. $\pm\sqrt{44100}$

11. $\sqrt{\dfrac{49}{3600}}$
12. $\sqrt{\dfrac{1}{196}}$
13. $\sqrt{\dfrac{169}{64}}$
14. $\sqrt{\dfrac{16}{729}}$
15. $\sqrt{\dfrac{121}{625}}$

16. $-\sqrt{\dfrac{324}{529}}$
17. $\sqrt{\dfrac{49}{1225}}$
18. $\pm\sqrt{\dfrac{25}{784}}$
19. $-\sqrt{\dfrac{484}{289}}$
20. $\pm\sqrt{\dfrac{529}{10000}}$

SAMPLE $\sqrt{0.49} = \sqrt{\dfrac{49}{100}}$

$$= \frac{\sqrt{49}}{\sqrt{100}} = \frac{7}{10} = 0.7$$

21. $\sqrt{0.04}$
22. $\sqrt{0.81}$
23. $-\sqrt{1.44}$
24. $\sqrt{2.56}$
25. $\sqrt{5.29}$

26. $-\sqrt{0.0121}$
27. $\pm\sqrt{0.0729}$
28. $\sqrt{0.1225}$
29. $\pm\sqrt{0.0049}$
30. $\sqrt{0.0324}$

Evaluate the expression $(\sqrt{a})^2 - \sqrt{a^2 + b^2}$ for the given values of a and b.

31. $a = 3, b = 4$
32. $a = 8, b = 6$
33. $a = 5, b = 12$
34. $a = 7, b = 24$

Find the indicated square roots.

SAMPLE $\sqrt{\dfrac{48}{75}} = \sqrt{\dfrac{3\cdot 16}{3\cdot 25}} = \sqrt{\dfrac{16}{25}} = \dfrac{4}{5}$

B
35. $\sqrt{\dfrac{12}{75}}$
36. $\sqrt{\dfrac{98}{32}}$
37. $-\sqrt{\dfrac{33}{132}}$
38. $\pm\sqrt{\dfrac{108}{147}}$
39. $\sqrt{\dfrac{243}{300}}$

40. $\pm\sqrt{\dfrac{400}{484}}$
41. $\sqrt{\dfrac{18}{338}}$
42. $-\sqrt{\dfrac{80}{1125}}$
43. $\pm\sqrt{\dfrac{507}{1200}}$
44. $\sqrt{\dfrac{1458}{20000}}$

Calculator Key-In _____

Use a calculator to approximate each square root to the indicated decimal place.

To the nearest thousandth:

1. $\sqrt{5}$
2. $\sqrt{2}$
3. $\sqrt{3.15}$
4. $\sqrt{0.625}$
5. $\sqrt{0.453}$

To the nearest ten thousandth:

6. $\sqrt{4000}$
7. $\sqrt{3533}$
8. $\sqrt{2175}$
9. $\sqrt{3750}$
10. $\sqrt{8145}$

Self-Test 1

VOCABULARY   rational number (p. 403)   square root (p. 412)
terminating decimal (p. 408)   principal square root (p. 412)
repeating decimal (p. 408)   radicand (p. 412)

Find a rational number halfway between the given numbers.

1. $\frac{2}{3}$ and $\frac{3}{4}$

2. $1\frac{1}{5}$ and $1\frac{1}{3}$ Obj. 11-1, p. 403

Which rational number is greater?

3. $\frac{4}{5}$ or $\frac{5}{7}$

4. $\frac{3}{4}$ or $\frac{8}{11}$

5. Express $\frac{37}{50}$ as a decimal.   Obj. 11-2, p. 408

6. Express $\frac{7}{44}$ as a decimal.

7. Express $2.\overline{13}$ as a fraction in simplest form.

Find the indicated square roots.

8. $\sqrt{729}$ **9.** $\sqrt{\dfrac{441}{1024}}$ **10.** $\sqrt{1.44}$ Obj. 11-3, p. 412

Check your answers with those at the back of the book.

ḣistorical Ṅote π

An English writer, William Jones, in 1706 was the first person to use the Greek letter π to stand for the ratio of the circumference of a circle to the diameter.

The value $\frac{22}{7}$, which is used today as an approximation for π, was used as early as the first century. By the sixteenth century, the value of π correct to thirty-five decimal places was known, and by the mid-nineteenth century, its value had been calculated to over seven hundred places.

It wasn't until the late nineteenth century, however, that it was first proved that π cannot be expressed as a ratio of integers and is thus *not* a rational number.

11-4 *Irrational Square Roots*

OBJECTIVE   **To find decimal approximations to irrational square roots.**

In this section you will see that those integers that are not squares of integers do not have rational square roots. The following proof shows that if an integer has a rational square root, then the integer is equal to the square of an integer.

1. Let n be a positive integer that has a rational square root.

2. Then $\sqrt{n} = \frac{a}{b}$, where a and b are positive integers that have no common prime factors.

3. If $\sqrt{n} = \frac{a}{b}$, then $n = \frac{a^2}{b^2}$. Since a^2 has the same prime factors as a, and b^2 has the same prime factors as b, a^2 and b^2 have no common prime factors. Thus, $\frac{a^2}{b^2}$ is in simplest form.

4. If a fraction in simplest form is equal to an integer, the denominator of the fraction must be 1. From Step 3 you know that $\frac{a^2}{b^2}$ is equal to the integer n and that $\frac{a^2}{b^2}$ is in simplest form. Thus, $b^2 = 1$.

5. Therefore, $n = \frac{a^2}{b^2} = \frac{a^2}{1} = a^2$. Thus, n is the square of an integer.

Since integers like 2, 5, and 6 are not squares of integers, the numbers $\sqrt{2}$, $\sqrt{5}$, and $\sqrt{6}$ are not in the set of rational numbers. These numbers are in another major subset of the real numbers called the set of *irrational numbers*.

Irrational numbers are real numbers that cannot be expressed in the form $\frac{a}{b}$, where a and b are integers.

Irrational square roots are not the only irrational numbers, however. For example, π is an irrational number.

The set of real numbers is made up of the rational numbers and the irrational numbers. By advanced methods, it can be shown that there are both rational and irrational numbers between any two real numbers. The set of real numbers has the *property of completeness*, which is stated at the top of the next page.

> PROPERTY OF COMPLETENESS
>
> Every decimal represents a real number, and every real number can be represented as a decimal.

Terminating and repeating decimals represent rational numbers. Therefore, the decimals for irrational numbers neither terminate nor repeat. You can use a calculator or a table of square roots to get a decimal approximation of an irrational square root. For example, the Table of Square Roots on page 526 indicates that $\sqrt{73} \approx 8.544$. The product and quotient properties of square roots can be used with the table to approximate irrational square roots.

EXAMPLE 1 Approximate $\sqrt{1224}$ to the nearest hundredth.

SOLUTION $\sqrt{1224} = \sqrt{2^2 \cdot 3^2 \cdot 34} = \sqrt{2^2} \cdot \sqrt{3^2} \cdot \sqrt{34} = 6\sqrt{34}$

From the table: $\sqrt{34} \approx 5.831$

$6\sqrt{34} \approx 6 \cdot 5.831 = 34.986$

$\therefore \sqrt{1224} \approx 34.99$ *Answer*

EXAMPLE 2 Approximate $\sqrt{0.93}$ to the nearest ten thousandth.

SOLUTION $\sqrt{0.93} = \sqrt{\dfrac{93}{100}} = \dfrac{\sqrt{93}}{\sqrt{100}} \approx \dfrac{9.644}{10} = 0.9644$

$\therefore \sqrt{0.93} \approx 0.9644$ *Answer*

If you divide a positive number by a positive divisor which is smaller than the square root of that number, the quotient will be larger than the square root. This property forms the basis for the *divide-and-average method* of approximating a square root.

EXAMPLE 3 Approximate $\sqrt{38}$ to the nearest ten thousandth using the divide-and-average method.

SOLUTION
1. Select the integer whose square is nearest 38 as your first approximation, a. Since $6^2 = 36$, let $a = 6$.

2. Divide 38 by a, carrying out the division to two more digits than are in the divisor.

$$38 \div 6 \approx 6.33$$

3. Find the average of a and $\dfrac{38}{a}$.

$$\frac{1}{2}(6 + 6.33) \approx 6.17$$

(*Solution continued on page 418.*)

4. Use the average as the new value for a. Continue repeating steps 2 and 3 as often as necessary.

(Step 2)   (Step 3)

$$38 \div 6.17 = 6.1588 \longrightarrow \frac{1}{2}(6.17 + 6.1588) \approx 6.1644$$

$$38 \div 6.1644 = 6.164428$$

5. The approximation is accurate to at least as many digits as match in a and $38 \div a$.

$$\therefore \ \sqrt{38} \approx 6.1644 \quad \textit{Answer}$$

Oral Exercises

State whether the following represent rational or irrational numbers.

1. $\sqrt{11}$ **2.** $\sqrt{64}$ **3.** $\sqrt{15}$ **4.** $\sqrt{61.8}$ **5.** $\sqrt{0.81}$

Express as a product of a number between 1 and 100 and a power of 100.

SAMPLE $437 = 4.37 \times 100$

6. 600   **7.** 7200   **8.** 5103   **9.** 80,000   **10.** 134,000

Express as a quotient of a number between 1 and 100 and a power of 100.

SAMPLE $0.07 = \dfrac{7}{100}$

11. 0.04   **12.** 0.063   **13.** 0.305   **14.** 0.0067   **15.** 0.0185

Written Exercises

In Exercises 1–15, use the table on page 526 as necessary. In Exercises 1–5, approximate each square root to the nearest tenth.

A   **1.** $-\sqrt{500}$ **2.** $\sqrt{5300}$ **3.** $\sqrt{800}$ **4.** $-\sqrt{3700}$ **5.** $\sqrt{9900}$

Approximate each square root to the nearest hundredth.

6. $\sqrt{43}$ **7.** $\sqrt{89}$ **8.** $\sqrt{0.26}$ **9.** $\sqrt{0.58}$ **10.** $\sqrt{0.07}$

Approximate each square root to the nearest unit.

11. $\sqrt{730,000}$ **12.** $\sqrt{170,000}$ **13.** $\sqrt{260,000}$ **14.** $\sqrt{390,000}$ **15.** $\sqrt{940,000}$

Approximate each square root to the nearest hundredth using the divide-and-average method.

16. $\sqrt{29}$ **17.** $\sqrt{13}$ **18.** $\sqrt{42.3}$ **19.** $-\sqrt{350}$ **20.** $\sqrt{23.8}$

11-5 *Square Roots of Variable Expressions*

OBJECTIVE   To find square roots of variable expressions and to use them to solve equations and problems.

Does $\sqrt{y^2} = y$? Not necessarily. Recall that the square root symbol, $\sqrt{}$, stands for the nonnegative square root of a number. For example, when $y = -6$:

$$\sqrt{(-6)^2} = -(-6) = 6$$

If there are variables in the radicand, you must be careful to use absolute value signs when needed, as shown below:

$$\sqrt{y^2} = |y|$$

EXAMPLE 1   Simplify: **a.** $\sqrt{64x^2}$ **b.** $\sqrt{25a^8}$ **c.** $\sqrt{x^2 + 6x + 9}$

SOLUTION   **a.** $\sqrt{64x^2} = 8|x|$

b. $\sqrt{25a^8} = 5a^4$ (a^4 is always nonnegative)

c. $\sqrt{x^2 + 6x + 9} = \sqrt{(x + 3)^2} = |x + 3|$

EXAMPLE 2   Solve $x^2 = 49$

SOLUTION 1
$$\begin{aligned} x^2 &= 49 \\ x^2 - 49 &= 0 \\ (x - 7)(x + 7) &= 0 \\ x = 7 \text{ or } x &= -7 \end{aligned}$$

SOLUTION 2 $x^2 = 49$
$$x = \pm\sqrt{49} = \pm 7$$

Check: $7^2 = 49$ and $(-7)^2 = 49$ $\checkmark$

$\therefore$ the solution set is $\{7, -7\}$.   **Answer**

Solution 2 is based upon the following:

PROPERTY OF SQUARE ROOTS OF EQUAL NUMBERS

If r and s are any real numbers,

$r^2 = s^2$ if and only if $r = s$ or $r = -s$.

Oral Exercises

Simplify.

1. $\sqrt{81x^2}$ **2.** $\sqrt{121b^2}$ **3.** $\sqrt{64a^4}$ **4.** $\sqrt{100x^2y^2}$ **5.** $\sqrt{0.09y^8}$

6. $\sqrt{\dfrac{c^2}{25}}$ **7.** $\pm\sqrt{\dfrac{d^4}{49}}$ **8.** $-\sqrt{\dfrac{x^2y^2}{9}}$ **9.** $\sqrt{\dfrac{m^3n^3}{81}}$ **10.** $\sqrt{\dfrac{r^{12}}{36n^6}}$

Written Exercises

Simplify.

A **1.** $-\sqrt{0.36t^6}$ **2.** $-\sqrt{1.96x^2y^4}$ **3.** $\sqrt{2.25a^4b^2}$ **4.** $\sqrt{625z^6}$ **5.** $\sqrt{3.61k^6n^2}$

  6. $\sqrt{\dfrac{4}{144}}$ **7.** $\sqrt{\dfrac{n^6}{169}}$ **8.** $\sqrt{\dfrac{n^{72}}{6400}}$ **9.** $\sqrt{\dfrac{8100}{k^{10}}}$ **10.** $\sqrt{\dfrac{144k^8}{25x^6}}$

11. $\sqrt{x^2 + 10x + 25}$ **12.** $\sqrt{y^2 - 8y + 16}$ **13.** $\sqrt{81 + 18k + k^2}$

Solve.

14. $m^2 = 36$ **15.** $r^2 - 81 = 0$ **16.** $b^2 - 49 = 0$

17. $25x^2 - 9 = 0$ **18.** $16x^2 - 81 = 0$ **19.** $6y^2 - 24 = 0$

20. $2b^2 - 50 = 0$ **21.** $18t^2 - 2 = 0$ **22.** $4n^2 - 36 = 0$

Find both roots of each equation to the nearest tenth.

B **23.** $x^2 = 748$ **24.** $a^2 = 381$ **25.** $m^2 = 6.8$

  26. $y^2 - 14.2 = 0$ **27.** $b^2 - 131 = 0$ **28.** $c^2 - 28.4 = 0$

  29. $5x^2 = 620$ **30.** $8m^2 - 1000 = 0$ **31.** $3s^2 - 0.66 = 0$

C **32.** $0.7x^2 = 5.11$ **33.** $17x^2 = 120$

  34. $(y - 3)^2 + (y + 3)^2 = 152$ **35.** $(a + 2)^2 + (a - 2)^2 = 86$

Problems

Solve. Find each answer to the nearest tenth. (Use $\pi \approx 3.14$.)

A **1.** Find the side of a square whose area is 300 cm².

  2. The area of a square is 72 cm². How long is its side?

  3. The length of a rectangle is 4 times its width. Find the dimensions of the rectangle if its area is 204 cm².

  4. The altitude of a triangle is 6 times its base. Find the altitude if the area of the triangle is 36 m².

  5. Find the radius of a circle whose area is 66 cm².

  6. Find the diameter of a circle with the same area as a rectangle that is 33 cm by 40 cm.

B **7.** A water pipe is 30 cm in diameter. What is the diameter of a new pipe if the cross-sectional area of the new pipe is to be twice that of the old?

  8. The search for a missing airplane covered a circular region with an area of 154 km². What was the radius of the search area?

9. The formula $s = 4.9t^2$ gives the approximate distance traveled in t seconds by an object falling from rest. How long does it take a rock falling from rest to travel 610 m?

Let a, b, and c represent the lengths of the sides of a triangle, and let $s = \frac{1}{2}(a + b + c)$. Then the area (A) of the triangle is given by the formula $A = \sqrt{s(s - a)(s - b)(s - c)}$. Use the formula to answer the following questions. Find each answer to the nearest tenth.

C 10. What is the area of a triangle whose sides are 5 cm, 7 cm, and 10 cm long?

11. What is the area of a triangle whose sides are 8 cm, 9 cm, and 11 cm long?

Computer Key-In

If you have access to a computer that will accept BASIC, you can use the program below to print successive stages of the divide-and-average method of computing the square root of a positive integer. BASIC also has a built-in square root function which will give a positive square root directly. Before running the long program, try this:

```
10  PRINT SQR(16), SQR(17), SQR(18)
20  END
```

The last line of the following program prints the positive square root as given by the built-in function for comparison.

```
10  PRINT "INPUT A POSITIVE INTEGER";
20  INPUT N
30  IF N <= 0 THEN 10
40  PRINT "WHAT FACTOR WOULD YOU LIKE TO TRY";
50  INPUT F
60  IF F <= 0 THEN 40
70  LET Q=N/F
80  PRINT F,Q
90  IF ABS(F-Q)<.00001 THEN 120
100 LET F=(F+Q)/2
110 GOTO 70
120 PRINT "CHECK:";SQR(N)
130 END
```

1. Run the program to find $\sqrt{15}$ by trying 1 as the factor. (Note: Input 15 as the positive integer.) Repeat, trying 2, 3, 4, and then 5 as factors.

2. Compare the print-out for the five parts of Exercise 1.

Experiment with other numbers and factors.

11-6 *The Pythagorean Theorem*

OBJECTIVE   To use the Pythagorean theorem and its converse to construct lengths corresponding to irrational numbers and to solve geometric problems.

In this section you will see how the Pythagorean theorem can be used to find lengths corresponding to irrational numbers.

THE PYTHAGOREAN THEOREM

In any right triangle, the square of the length of the hypotenuse equals the sum of the squares of the lengths of the other two sides. For the triangle shown,

$$a^2 + b^2 = c^2.$$

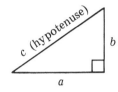

The following two diagrams suggest a proof of the theorem. Each diagram shows a square, $(a + b)$ units on a side, divided into other figures. Each diagram suggests a different expression for the area of a square $(a + b)$ units on a side. Equating these expressions leads to the equation $a^2 + b^2 = c^2$.

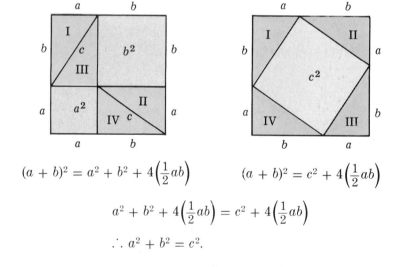

$$(a + b)^2 = a^2 + b^2 + 4\left(\frac{1}{2}ab\right) \qquad (a + b)^2 = c^2 + 4\left(\frac{1}{2}ab\right)$$

$$a^2 + b^2 + 4\left(\frac{1}{2}ab\right) = c^2 + 4\left(\frac{1}{2}ab\right)$$

$$\therefore a^2 + b^2 = c^2.$$

To draw a line segment with a length of $\sqrt{2}$ units, draw a right triangle whose two shorter sides are 1 unit long, as shown in the diagram at the top of the next page.

Then:

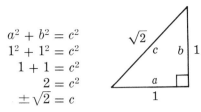

$$a^2 + b^2 = c^2$$
$$1^2 + 1^2 = c^2$$
$$1 + 1 = c^2$$
$$2 = c^2$$
$$\pm\sqrt{2} = c$$

∴ the length of the hypotenuse is $\sqrt{2}$ units.

The following diagrams show that a segment $\sqrt{2}$ units long can be used to construct a segment $\sqrt{3}$ units long, a segment $\sqrt{3}$ units long can be used to construct a segment $\sqrt{4}$ units long, and so on.

  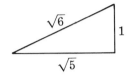

A series of such triangles can be used to locate irrational square roots such as $\sqrt{2}$, $\sqrt{3}$, and $\sqrt{5}$ on the number line. The arcs are drawn to transfer the length of the hypotenuse of each triangle to the x-axis. Note below that $-\sqrt{2}$ is located $\sqrt{2}$ units to the left of 0.

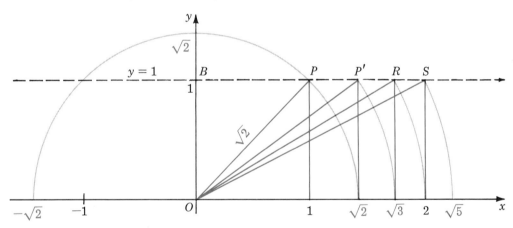

The converse of the Pythagorean theorem is also true. It can be used to test whether or not a triangle is a right triangle.

CONVERSE OF THE PYTHAGOREAN THEOREM

If the sum of the squares of the lengths of the two shorter sides of a triangle is equal to the square of the length of the longest side, then the triangle is a right triangle. The right angle will be opposite the longest side.

EXAMPLE   Is a triangle whose sides are 5, 12, and 13 units long a right triangle?

SOLUTION
$$a^2 + b^2 = c^2$$
$$5^2 + 12^2 \overset{?}{=} 13^2$$
$$169 = 169 \quad \sqrt{}$$

∴ a triangle whose sides are 5, 12, and 13 units long is a right triangle.   *Answer*

Oral Exercises

State and solve an equation for the length of the unknown side.

1.

2.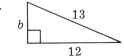

Written Exercises

In Exercises 1-10, refer to the right triangle drawn at the right. Find the missing length correct to the nearest hundredth.

A   1. $a = 6$, $b = 8$, $c = $ _?_

3. $a = 5$, $b = 9$, $c = $ _?_

5. $a = 13$, $b = 13$, $c = $ _?_

7. $a = $ _?_ , $b = 5$, $c = 13$

9. $a = 5$, $b = $ _?_ , $c = \sqrt{30}$

2. $a = 10$, $b = 24$, $c = $ _?_

4. $a = 12$, $b = 7$, $c = $ _?_

6. $a = 24$, $b = $ _?_ , $c = 25$

8. $a = 11$, $b = $ _?_ , $c = 15$

10. $a = $ _?_ , $b = \sqrt{11}$, $c = \sqrt{27}$

State whether or not the three numbers given are the lengths of the sides of a right triangle.

11. 4, 9, 12

12. 7, 24, 25

13. 8, 10, 13

14. 15, 20, 25

15. 18, 24, 28

16. 12, 15, 18

In Exercises 17-22, refer to the diagram for Exercises 1-10. Find the missing length correct to the nearest hundredth.

B 17. $a = b = 11$, $c = $ _?_

18. $a = 8$, $b = \frac{1}{2}a$, $c = $ _?_

19. $a = 12$, $b = \frac{1}{4}a$, $c = $ _?_

20. $a = 15$, $b = \frac{1}{3}a$, $c = $ _?_

21. $a = \frac{2}{3}b$, $b = 18$, $c = $ _?_

22. $a = \frac{4}{5}b$, $b = 20$, $c = $ _?_

In Exercises 23–26, refer to the diagram for Exercises 1–10 on the previous page. Find a and b correct to the nearest hundredth.

C **23.** $c = 12$, $a = b$ **24.** $c = 20$, $a = 2b$

25. $c = 20$, $a = \frac{1}{2}b$ **26.** $c = 39$, $a = \frac{2}{3}b$

Problems

Make a sketch for each problem. Approximate each square root to the nearest hundredth.

A **1.** Find the length of a diagonal of a rectangle whose dimensions are 5 cm by 8 cm.

2. A rope 13 m long is attached to the top of a flagpole. The rope is just able to reach a point on the ground 5 m from the base of the pole. Find the height of the flagpole.

3. The diagonal of a square measures $5\sqrt{2}$ m. Find the length of a side of the square.

4. The base of an isosceles triangle is 18 cm long. The equal sides are 20 cm long. Find the altitude (a) of the triangle.

B **5.** A right triangle has sides whose lengths can be expressed by consecutive even integers. Determine the length of each side.

6. The dimensions of a rectangular doorway are 200 cm by 80 cm. Can a circular mirror with a diameter of 220 cm be carried through the doorway?

C **7.** What is the length of the diagonal of a cube that is 20 cm on each side?

8. What is the length of the diagonal of a rectangular box with a length of 40 cm, a width of 30 cm, and a height of 80 cm? Would a meter stick fit in the box?

9. Robin is standing on a dock 1.5 m above the water. She is drawing in a boat that is attached to the end of a 3.9 m rope. If she pulls in 1.4 m of rope, how far did she move the boat?

Just for Jun

An elephant ate 100 peanuts in four days, each day eating eight more than on the day before. How many peanuts did the elephant eat on the first of the four days?

Self-Test 2

VOCABULARY   irrational numbers (p. 416)   Pythagorean theorem (p. 422)
divide-and-average method
(p. 417)

Approximate each square root to the nearest hundredth using the Table of Square Roots.

1. $\sqrt{6500}$

2. $-\sqrt{0.83}$ Obj. 11-4, p. 416

Simplify.

3. $\sqrt{49m^2n^6}$

4. $\sqrt{169x^5y^4}$ Obj. 11-5, p. 419

Solve.

5. $9x^2 = 36$

6. $4x^2 - 49 = 0$

7. Find c correct to the nearest hundredth if $a = 5$ and $b = 9$.

8. Is a triangle with sides 10, 22, and 26 units long a right triangle?

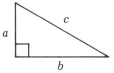

Obj. 11-6, p. 422

Check your answers with those at the back of the book.

EXTRA

The Distance Formula

The distance between two points on the x-axis or on a line parallel to that axis is the absolute value of the difference between their abscissas. Using the notation A′B′ to denote the distance from A′ to B′, you can write the following:

$$A'B' = |3 - 8| = |8 - 3| = 5$$

$$AB = |3 - 8| = |8 - 3| = 5$$

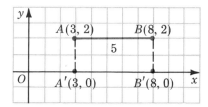

The distance between two points on the y-axis or on a line parallel to that axis is the absolute value of the difference between their ordinates:

$$A'C' = |2 - 5| = |5 - 2| = 3$$

$$AC = |2 - 5| = |5 - 2| = 3$$

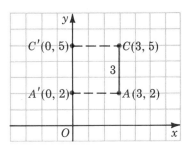

To find the distance between two points not on an axis or a line parallel to an axis, use the Pythagorean theorem (page 422):

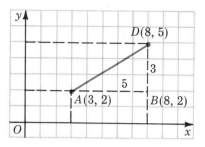

$$AD = \sqrt{(AB)^2 + (BD)^2} = \sqrt{(8-3)^2 + (5-2)^2}$$
$$= \sqrt{5^2 + 3^2} = \sqrt{25 + 9} = \sqrt{34}$$

To find the distance between any two points, use the following:

THE DISTANCE FORMULA

For any points $P_1(x_1, y_1)$ and $P_2(x_2, y_2)$

$$P_1P_2 = \sqrt{(x_2 - x_1)^2 + (y_2 - y_1)^2}$$

EXAMPLE   Find the distance between points $M(-3, 8)$ and $N(5, 2)$.

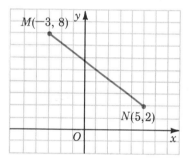

SOLUTION 1 $MN = \sqrt{(-3-5)^2 + (8-2)^2}$
$$= \sqrt{(-8)^2 + 6^2} = \sqrt{64 + 36}$$
$$= \sqrt{100} = 10$$

SOLUTION 2 $MN = \sqrt{(5 - (-3))^2 + (2-8)^2}$
$$= \sqrt{8^2 + (-6)^2} = \sqrt{64 + 36}$$
$$= \sqrt{100} = 10$$

Exercises

Use the distance formula to find the distance to the nearest tenth between the points.

1. $(-2, 0), (7, 0)$ **2.** $(0, -4), (0, 12)$ **3.** $(1, 1), (7, 9)$

4. $(-1, 2), (-8, 6)$ **5.** $(-1, -3), (-6, -9)$ **6.** $(2, -7), (5, -2)$

7. $(3, 1), (-3, 7)$ **8.** $(-2, 1), (-8, -5)$ **9.** $(-7, -2), (2, -2)$

10. $(4, -3), (9, -8)$ **11.** $(2, 3), (-7, -8)$ **12.** $(-8, 5), (7, -2)$

13. Show that points $(0, 3)$, $(3, 9)$, $(6, 0)$, $(9, 6)$ are the vertices of an equal-sided quadrilateral.

14. Show that point $(-2, 2)$ is the midpoint of the segment joining $(-7, 0)$ and $(3, 4)$.

RADICAL EXPRESSIONS

11-7 *Multiplication, Division, and Simplification of Radicals*

OBJECTIVE   To simplify products and quotients of radicals.

You can use the product and quotient properties of square roots together with the commutative and associative axioms to multiply, divide, and simplify square-root radicals.

An expression having a square-root radical is in **simplest form** when
1. no integral radicand has a square factor other than 1,
2. no fractions are under a radical sign, and
3. no radicals are in a denominator.

EXAMPLE 1   Simplify: **a.** $\sqrt{45}$ **b.** $5\sqrt{24}$

SOLUTION   **a.** $\sqrt{45} = \sqrt{9} \cdot \sqrt{5} = 3\sqrt{5}$

   b. $5\sqrt{24} = 5\sqrt{4 \cdot 6} = 5 \cdot 2\sqrt{6} = 10\sqrt{6}$

EXAMPLE 2   Simplify: **a.** $\sqrt{\dfrac{3}{7}}$ **b.** $\dfrac{4}{\sqrt{5}}$ **c.** $\dfrac{3\sqrt{13}}{4\sqrt{32}}$

SOLUTION   **a.** $\sqrt{\dfrac{3}{7}} = \dfrac{\sqrt{3}}{\sqrt{7}} = \dfrac{\sqrt{3} \cdot \sqrt{7}}{\sqrt{7} \cdot \sqrt{7}} = \dfrac{\sqrt{21}}{(\sqrt{7})^2} = \dfrac{\sqrt{21}}{7}$

   b. $\dfrac{4}{\sqrt{5}} = \dfrac{4 \cdot \sqrt{5}}{\sqrt{5} \cdot \sqrt{5}} = \dfrac{4\sqrt{5}}{5}$

   c. $\dfrac{3\sqrt{13}}{4\sqrt{32}} = \dfrac{3\sqrt{13} \cdot \sqrt{2}}{4\sqrt{32} \cdot \sqrt{2}} = \dfrac{3\sqrt{26}}{4\sqrt{64}} = \dfrac{3\sqrt{26}}{4 \cdot 8} = \dfrac{3\sqrt{26}}{32}$

The process of expressing a fraction with an irrational denominator such as $\dfrac{4}{\sqrt{5}}$ as a fraction with a rational denominator such as $\dfrac{4\sqrt{5}}{5}$ is called **rationalizing the denominator.**

EXAMPLE 3   Approximate $\dfrac{4}{\sqrt{5}}$ to the nearest thousandth.

SOLUTION   From Example 2(b), $\dfrac{4}{\sqrt{5}} = \dfrac{4\sqrt{5}}{5}$. From the table on page 526, $\sqrt{5} \approx 2.236$. Substitute this value for $\sqrt{5}$, as shown at the top of the next page.

$$\frac{4\sqrt{5}}{5} \approx \frac{4(2.236)}{5} = \frac{8.944}{5} = 1.7888 \qquad \therefore \frac{4}{\sqrt{5}} \approx 1.789 \quad \textbf{\textit{Answer}}$$

In Example 3 rationalizing the denominator made it possible to avoid dividing by a decimal. When approximating the value of a radical expression, it is not always necessary to rationalize the denominator. When using a calculator, it is better to approximate the value of the original expression directly.

Oral Exercises

Express in simplest form.

1. $\sqrt{3} \cdot \sqrt{5}$ 2. $\dfrac{\sqrt{21}}{\sqrt{3}}$ 3. $\dfrac{\sqrt{18}}{\sqrt{2}}$ 4. $\sqrt{7} \cdot 3\sqrt{2}$ 5. $\sqrt{12}$

6. $\sqrt{18}$ 7. $\sqrt{75}$ 8. $\sqrt{48}$ 9. $\dfrac{2}{\sqrt{7}}$ 10. $\sqrt{\dfrac{3}{5}}$

Written Exercises

Express in simplest form.

A 1. $\sqrt{3} \cdot 2\sqrt{3}$ 2. $4\sqrt{8} \cdot 3\sqrt{8}$ 3. $\sqrt{3} \cdot \sqrt{2} \cdot \sqrt{6}$

4. $\sqrt{4} \cdot \sqrt{2} \cdot \sqrt{2}$ 5. $3\sqrt{3} \cdot \sqrt{2} \cdot \sqrt{7}$ 6. $3\sqrt{5} \cdot \sqrt{2} \cdot \sqrt{3}$

7. $4\sqrt{18}$ 8. $6\sqrt{50}$ 9. $4\sqrt{243}$

10. $\sqrt{\dfrac{3}{5}} \cdot \sqrt{\dfrac{5}{3}}$ 11. $\sqrt{\dfrac{3}{5}} \cdot \sqrt{\dfrac{10}{3}}$ 12. $\sqrt{\dfrac{10}{9}} \cdot \sqrt{\dfrac{27}{5}}$

13. $\sqrt{\dfrac{7}{9}} \cdot \sqrt{\dfrac{27}{21}}$ 14. $\sqrt{\dfrac{5}{3}} \cdot \sqrt{\dfrac{3}{20}}$ 15. $\sqrt{\dfrac{3}{2}} \cdot \sqrt{\dfrac{2}{27}}$

16. $\sqrt{3\dfrac{1}{3}} \sqrt{1\dfrac{1}{8}}$ 17. $\dfrac{1}{4}\sqrt{\dfrac{8}{5}} \cdot \dfrac{1}{3}\sqrt{\dfrac{5}{4}}$ 18. $\dfrac{18\sqrt{12}}{9\sqrt{3}}$

19. $4\sqrt{108}$ 20. $11\sqrt{\dfrac{64}{8}}$ 21. $7\sqrt{\dfrac{32}{9}}$

22. $\dfrac{12\sqrt{147}}{4\sqrt{9}}$ 23. $\dfrac{5\sqrt{10}}{10\sqrt{5}}$ 24. $\dfrac{4\sqrt{5}}{3\sqrt{72}}$

Simplify. Assume the radicands are nonnegative real numbers.

B 25. $(-3\sqrt{a^2b})(2\sqrt{b})$ 26. $(-\sqrt{x^2y}\sqrt{xy^3})$ 27. $\sqrt{m}(5 + \sqrt{m})$

28. $\sqrt{c}(\sqrt{c^3} - 3)$ 29. $(4\sqrt{3})(-\sqrt{9})(\sqrt{27})$ 30. $(3\sqrt{2})(-\sqrt{6})(\sqrt{3})$

31. $(\sqrt{11x})(\sqrt{2x})(4\sqrt{x^3})$ 32. $(\sqrt{2x})(\sqrt{8x})(\sqrt{3})$ 33. $(3\sqrt{5x})^2$

34. $5y(\sqrt{3y})^2$ 35. $-6\sqrt{2\dfrac{4}{9}}$ 36. $4\sqrt{2\dfrac{1}{2}}$

C 37. $\sqrt{6m}(\sqrt{2m} - 3\sqrt{8m^2})$ 38. $2\sqrt{10x^3}(3\sqrt{2x} - 5\sqrt{8x^4})$

39. $(2\sqrt{3y^3})^3$ 40. $(\sqrt{12xy})^3(x\sqrt{5x^2y} + y\sqrt{6xy^2})$

11-8 *Addition and Subtraction of Radicals*

OBJECTIVE To simplify sums and differences of radicals.

You can use the distributive axiom to simplify the sum of $4\sqrt{5}$ and $3\sqrt{5}$ because they have $\sqrt{5}$ as a common factor.

$$4\sqrt{5} + 3\sqrt{5} = (4+3)\sqrt{5} = 7\sqrt{5}$$

On the other hand, terms that have unlike radicands cannot be combined.

$$2\sqrt{6} - 7\sqrt{13} + 3\sqrt{6} = 5\sqrt{6} - 7\sqrt{13}$$

By expressing each radical in simplest form, you can sometimes combine terms in sums and differences of radicals.

EXAMPLE Simplify $3\sqrt{5} - 2\sqrt{3} + 3\sqrt{20} - \sqrt{12}$.

SOLUTION $\begin{aligned}
3\sqrt{5} - 2\sqrt{3} + 3\sqrt{20} - \sqrt{12} &= 3\sqrt{5} - 2\sqrt{3} + 3\sqrt{4\cdot 5} - \sqrt{4\cdot 3} \\
&= 3\sqrt{5} - 2\sqrt{3} + 3(2\sqrt{5}) - 2\sqrt{3} \\
&= 3\sqrt{5} - 2\sqrt{3} + 6\sqrt{5} - 2\sqrt{3} \\
&= 9\sqrt{5} - 4\sqrt{3} \quad \textbf{\textit{Answer}}
\end{aligned}$$

To simplify sums or differences of square-root radicals:
1. Express each radical in simplest form.
2. Use the distributive axiom to add or subtract radicals with like radicands.

Oral Exercises

Indicate the terms in each expression that can be expressed with the same radicand. Then state the expression in simplest form.

1. $5\sqrt{2} + 3\sqrt{2}$ **2.** $7\sqrt{3} - 5\sqrt{3}$ **3.** $\sqrt{11} - 8\sqrt{11}$

4. $3\sqrt{5} + 5\sqrt{3} + \sqrt{5}$ **5.** $3\sqrt{11} - 2\sqrt{11} + \sqrt{6}$ **6.** $\sqrt{15} - 3\sqrt{5} + 5\sqrt{3}$

7. $7\sqrt{7} - 4\sqrt{7}$ **8.** $5\sqrt{3} - 4\sqrt{13} + 8\sqrt{13}$ **9.** $7\sqrt{15} - 4\sqrt{15} + 5\sqrt{15}$

10. $\sqrt{8} + \sqrt{2}$ **11.** $\sqrt{50} + \sqrt{2}$ **12.** $\sqrt{12} + \sqrt{3}$

Written Exercises

Simplify.

A   **1.** $5\sqrt{3} - 2\sqrt{3}$ **2.** $7\sqrt{5} + 11\sqrt{5}$ **3.** $-4\sqrt{21} - 7\sqrt{21}$

     4. $5\sqrt{2} + \sqrt{72}$ **5.** $2\sqrt{75} - \sqrt{3}$ **6.** $-4\sqrt{5} + \sqrt{45}$

7. $3\sqrt{12} - \sqrt{50}$ **8.** $\sqrt{81} - \sqrt{36}$ **9.** $\sqrt{32} + 4\sqrt{8}$

10. $-2\sqrt{147} - \sqrt{27}$ **11.** $\sqrt{125} + \sqrt{405}$ **12.** $\sqrt{144} - \sqrt{54}$

13. $5\sqrt{17} + 7\sqrt{6} - \sqrt{17}$ **14.** $4\sqrt{28} + 2\sqrt{7} - \sqrt{14}$

15. $-3\sqrt{5} + 4\sqrt{180} + 2\sqrt{27}$ **16.** $\sqrt{48} - \sqrt{192} + \sqrt{12}$

Simplify.

$$SAMPLE \quad \sqrt{15} - \sqrt{\frac{3}{5}} = \sqrt{15} - \frac{\sqrt{3}}{\sqrt{5}} = \sqrt{15} - \frac{\sqrt{3}}{\sqrt{5}} \cdot \frac{\sqrt{5}}{\sqrt{5}}$$

$$= \sqrt{15} - \frac{\sqrt{15}}{5}$$

$$= \frac{5\sqrt{15}}{5} - \frac{\sqrt{15}}{5} = \frac{4\sqrt{15}}{5}$$

17. $\sqrt{3} - \sqrt{\frac{1}{3}}$ **18.** $\sqrt{21} - \sqrt{\frac{5}{7}}$ **19.** $4\sqrt{32} - \sqrt{\frac{2}{9}}$

20. $\sqrt{\frac{5}{11}} - \sqrt{\frac{11}{5}}$ **21.** $\sqrt{\frac{2}{3}} - \sqrt{\frac{3}{8}}$ **22.** $5\sqrt{\frac{16}{5}} - \sqrt{\frac{5}{18}}$

B 23. $7\sqrt{10} - 4\sqrt{90} + 4\sqrt{\frac{1}{10}}$ **24.** $11\sqrt{\frac{2}{7}} + 5\sqrt{\frac{7}{2}} - \sqrt{56}$

25. $\sqrt{\frac{2}{3}} + 6\sqrt{\frac{3}{8}} - \frac{1}{5}\sqrt{48}$ **26.** $3\sqrt{\frac{3}{7}} + \sqrt{\frac{7}{3}} + \frac{1}{2}\sqrt{84}$

27. $4\sqrt{2}(\sqrt{6} + 3\sqrt{8})$ **28.** $2\sqrt{3}(5\sqrt{3} - 2\sqrt{6})$

Simplify. Assume that all variables represent nonnegative real numbers.

C 29. $\sqrt{\frac{x^2}{64} + \frac{x^2}{36}}$ **30.** $\sqrt{\frac{x^2}{9} - \frac{x^2}{25}}$ **31.** $\sqrt{\frac{x^2}{a^2} + \frac{x^2}{b^2}}$ **32.** $\sqrt{\frac{x}{a}} + \sqrt{\frac{a}{x}}$

Solve each equation.

33. $3x\sqrt{3} + 2\sqrt{15} = 8\sqrt{60} + x\sqrt{3}$ **34.** $a\sqrt{112} + \sqrt{63} = \sqrt{448} - a\sqrt{343}$

Just for Fun

An ant is at the foot of a flight of ten steps. Every day it will climb up three steps and climb back down two steps. When will it reach the top?

11-9 *Multiplication of Binomials Containing Radicals*

OBJECTIVE   To multiply binomials containing square-root radicals.

When working with radicals, you sometimes need to use the special methods of multiplying binomials you learned in Chapter 5.

EXAMPLE 1   Simplify $(8 + \sqrt{5})(8 - \sqrt{5})$.

SOLUTION   The pattern is $(a + b)(a - b) = a^2 - b^2$.
$$(8 + \sqrt{5})(8 - \sqrt{5}) = 8^2 - (\sqrt{5})^2$$
$$= 64 - 5 = 59$$

EXAMPLE 2   Simplify $(3 + \sqrt{5})^2$

SOLUTION   The pattern is $(a + b)^2 = a^2 + 2ab + b^2$.
$$(3 + \sqrt{5})^2 = (3)^2 + 2(3)(\sqrt{5}) + (\sqrt{5})^2$$
$$= 9 + 6\sqrt{5} + 5 = 14 + 6\sqrt{5}$$

If b and d are both nonnegative, then the binomials
$$a\sqrt{b} + c\sqrt{d} \quad \text{and} \quad a\sqrt{b} - c\sqrt{d}$$
are called **conjugates** of one another. Conjugates differ only in the sign of one term.

If a, b, c, and d are all integers, then the product
$$(a\sqrt{b} + c\sqrt{d})(a\sqrt{b} - c\sqrt{d})$$
will be an integer (see Example 1 above). Conjugates can be used to rationalize binomial denominators that contain radicals.

EXAMPLE 3   Rationalize the denominator of the fraction $\dfrac{3}{5 - 2\sqrt{7}}$.

SOLUTION $\dfrac{3}{5 - 2\sqrt{7}} = \dfrac{3}{5 - 2\sqrt{7}} \cdot \dfrac{5 + 2\sqrt{7}}{5 + 2\sqrt{7}} = \dfrac{15 + 6\sqrt{7}}{5^2 - (2\sqrt{7})^2}$

$\qquad\qquad = \dfrac{15 + 6\sqrt{7}}{25 - 28} = \dfrac{15 + 6\sqrt{7}}{-3} = -5 - 2\sqrt{7}$

Written Exercises

Express in simplest form.

A   **1.** $(4 - \sqrt{3})(4 + \sqrt{3})$

3. $(7 + \sqrt{7})(7 - \sqrt{7})$

2. $(\sqrt{2} + 5)(\sqrt{2} - 5)$

4. $(\sqrt{13} - 7)(\sqrt{13} + 7)$

5. $(\sqrt{13} - \sqrt{7})(\sqrt{13} + \sqrt{7})$

6. $(\sqrt{2} - \sqrt{6})(\sqrt{2} + \sqrt{6})$

7. $(4 + \sqrt{3})^2$

8. $(2 - \sqrt{5})^2$

9. $(\sqrt{3} + 8)^2$

10. $(3\sqrt{2} - 5)^2$

11. $(4\sqrt{10} + 3)^2$

12. $(\sqrt{7} - \sqrt{3})^2$

13. $3\sqrt{7}(\sqrt{21} + \sqrt{7})$

14. $7\sqrt{5}(2\sqrt{10} - 3\sqrt{15})$

15. $6\sqrt{3}(5\sqrt{6} - 3\sqrt{10})$

16. $2\sqrt{6}(5\sqrt{2} - 4\sqrt{14})$

B 17. $(4\sqrt{7} - 2)(2\sqrt{7} + 3)$

18. $(\sqrt{3} + 3\sqrt{5})(\sqrt{3} + 4\sqrt{5})$

19. $(4\sqrt{11} - 3\sqrt{5})(2\sqrt{11} - 5\sqrt{5})$

20. $(6\sqrt{10} + 2\sqrt{2})(5\sqrt{10} - 5\sqrt{2})$

21. $(9\sqrt{7} + 8\sqrt{11})(2\sqrt{7} + 7\sqrt{11})$

22. $(2\sqrt{10} - 3\sqrt{5})(3\sqrt{10} + 4\sqrt{5})$

Rationalize the denominator of each fraction.

23. $\dfrac{3}{1 + \sqrt{3}}$

24. $\dfrac{4}{\sqrt{7} - 2}$

25. $\dfrac{5}{3 + \sqrt{5}}$

26. $\dfrac{1 + \sqrt{2}}{3 - \sqrt{2}}$

27. $\dfrac{2 + \sqrt{5}}{\sqrt{3} - 2}$

28. $\dfrac{\sqrt{3} + 5}{2 + \sqrt{7}}$

29. $\dfrac{6}{3\sqrt{5} - 2}$

30. $\dfrac{4 + \sqrt{3}}{2\sqrt{2} + 1}$

If $f(x) = x^2 - 2x + 2$, find these function values.

31. $f(\sqrt{2})$ **32.** $f(\sqrt{3} + 1)$ **33.** $f(1 - \sqrt{7})$ **34.** $f(3 + \sqrt{5})$

35. Show that $(1 + \sqrt{2})$ and $(1 - \sqrt{2})$ are roots of the equation $x^2 - 2x - 1 = 0$.

36. Show that $(4 + \sqrt{3})$ and $(4 - \sqrt{3})$ are roots of the equation $x^2 - 8x + 13 = 0$.

37. Show that $\left(\dfrac{1}{2} + \dfrac{\sqrt{3}}{2}\right)$ and $\left(\dfrac{1}{2} - \dfrac{\sqrt{3}}{2}\right)$ are roots of the equation $2x^2 - 2x - 1 = 0$.

C 38. Write an expression in simplest form for the area of a square whose perimeter is $(9\sqrt{2} + 4)$ cm.

Simplify each expression, assuming that the value of each variable is nonnegative.

39. $(x - \sqrt{y})(x + \sqrt{y})$

40. $(x - 3\sqrt{2})^2$

41. $(3m\sqrt{n} - p)(4m\sqrt{n} - 5p)$

42. $\sqrt{\dfrac{a}{b}} - 3\sqrt{\dfrac{b}{a}} + \sqrt{ab}$

11-10 *Simple Radical Equations*

OBJECTIVE To solve simple radical equations.

An equation that has a variable in the radicand is called a **radical equation**. Simple radical equations are solved in Examples 1 and 2.

EXAMPLE 1 Solve $\sqrt{x} = 9$

SOLUTION $(\sqrt{x})^2 = 81 \longleftarrow$ Square both members.

$$x = 81$$

$$\textit{Check: } \sqrt{81} \overset{?}{=} 9$$
$$9 = 9 \; \sqrt{}$$

$\therefore$ the solution is 81. **Answer**

EXAMPLE 2 Solve $\sqrt{3x - 2} = 5$

SOLUTION

$$3x - 2 = 25 \qquad \textit{Check: } \sqrt{3(9) - 2} \overset{?}{=} 5$$
$$3x = 27 \qquad\qquad\qquad \sqrt{27 - 2} \overset{?}{=} 5$$
$$x = 9 \qquad\qquad\qquad\quad \sqrt{25} \overset{?}{=} 5$$
$$5 = 5 \; \sqrt{}$$

$\therefore$ the solution is 9. **Answer**

When you square both members of an equation, the new equation is not necessarily equivalent to the original equation. Therefore, you must check every apparent root in the original equation to see whether it is, in fact, a root. By the multiplication property of equality, any root of the original equation is also a root of the squared equation. Thus, you are sure to find all roots of the original equation among the roots of the squared equation.

EXAMPLE 3 Solve $\sqrt{5x^2 - 36} - x = 0$

SOLUTION $\sqrt{5x^2 - 36} - x = 0$

$$\sqrt{5x^2 - 36} = x \longleftarrow \text{ Isolate the radical.}$$
$$5x^2 - 36 = x^2$$
$$4x^2 = 36$$
$$x^2 = 9$$
$$x = 3 \text{ or } x = -3$$

$$\textit{Check: } \sqrt{5(3)^2 - 36} - 3 \overset{?}{=} 0 \qquad \sqrt{5(-3)^2 - 36} - (-3) \overset{?}{=} 0$$
$$\sqrt{9} - 3 \overset{?}{=} 0 \qquad\qquad\qquad \sqrt{9} + 3 \overset{?}{=} 0$$
$$0 = 0 \; \sqrt{} \qquad\qquad\qquad\qquad 6 \neq 0$$

$\therefore$ the solution is 3. **Answer**

Oral Exercises

Solve.

1. $\sqrt{x} = 3$

2. $\sqrt{y} = 7$

3. $\sqrt{k} = 12$

State the first step in the solution of each equation.

4. $\sqrt{2x} = 9$

5. $\sqrt{3x - 8} = 5$

6. $\sqrt{5a - 7} = a$

Written Exercises

Solve.

A 1. $\sqrt{y} = 20$

2. $\sqrt{x} = 5$

3. $\sqrt{3m} = 9$

4. $\sqrt{4a} = 10$

5. $\sqrt{3r} = \frac{1}{4}$

6. $\sqrt{7x} = \frac{3}{5}$

7. $\sqrt{x} + 5 = 8$

8. $\sqrt{z} - 4 = 7$

9. $\frac{2}{3} + \sqrt{a} = 2$

10. $\sqrt{\frac{a}{3}} = 2$

11. $\sqrt{\frac{x}{4}} = 5$

12. $\sqrt{x + 2} = 5$

13. $\sqrt{z - 7} = 8$

14. $2\sqrt{3b} = 4$

15. $5\sqrt{2c} = 8$

16. $\sqrt{3s} + 4 = 7$

17. $\sqrt{5x} - 3 = 12$

18. $\sqrt{6a} + 9 = 11$

19. $\sqrt{3x + 2} - 1 = 3$

20. $\sqrt{8x - 1} + 2 = 9$

21. $\sqrt{5a - 3} + 8 = 11$

22. $\sqrt{\frac{5b}{4}} - 2 = 8$

23. $\sqrt{\frac{9a}{7}} + 3 = 10$

24. $\sqrt{\frac{5m}{6}} - 2 = 11$

B 25. $\sqrt{\frac{3x + 1}{4}} = 5$

26. $\sqrt{\frac{4t - 3}{5}} = 5$

27. $\sqrt{\frac{3y - 7}{11}} = 4$

28. $\sqrt{s} = 5\sqrt{3}$

29. $7\sqrt{t} = 14\sqrt{5}$

30. $8\sqrt{x} = 3\sqrt{6}$

31. $\sqrt{3a^2 - 4} = 11$

32. $4\sqrt{2r^2 - 20} = 8$

33. $3\sqrt{5x^2 - 4} = 27$

34. $\sqrt{x^2 + 1} = 1 - x$

35. $\sqrt{3a^2 - 32} = a$

36. $\sqrt{7b^2 + 14} = 3b$

C 37. $\sqrt{a^2 + 3a} = 2$

38. $\sqrt{10a^2 - 16a} = 4a$

39. $\sqrt{s} + 1 = \sqrt{4s}$

Problems

Solve.

A 1. Twice the square root of a number is 18. Find the number.

2. The square root of twice a number is 18. Find the number.

3. The square root of one fifth of a number is 4. Find the number.

4. One fifth of the square root of a number is 4. Find the number.

5. When 5 is subtracted from 3 times a number, the square root of the result is 8. Find the number.

6. Find the length of the hypotenuse of a right triangle whose shorter sides are $(\sqrt{6} + 2)$ m and $(\sqrt{6} - 2)$ m long.

B 7. The diameter of a circle is related to the area in the formula $d = \sqrt{\dfrac{4A}{\pi}}$. Find the area of the circle whose diameter is 20 cm. Express your answer in terms of π.

8. The current I that flows through an electrical appliance is determined by

$$I = \sqrt{\frac{P}{R}},$$

where P is the power required and R is the resistance of the appliance. To use this formula, express the current in amperes (A), the power in watts (W), and the resistance in ohms (Ω). If an electric hair dryer has a resistance of 60 Ω and draws 4.5 A of current, how much power does it use?

9. The geometric mean of two numbers is the positive square root of their product. Find two consecutive, positive even integers whose geometric mean is $12\sqrt{21}$.

10. The period of a pendulum (T) is the amount of time in seconds it takes the pendulum to make a complete swing back and forth. The period is determined by the formula

$$T = 2\pi \sqrt{\frac{l}{9.8}}$$

where l is the length of the pendulum in meters. Find the length of a pendulum with a period of 5 s. Express your answer to the nearest tenth. (Use $\pi \approx 3.14$.)

Calculator Key-In

Use a calculator to approximate the value of each expression to the nearest thousandth. (Recall that it is *not* necessary to rationalize the denominator first.)

1. $\dfrac{2}{1 + \sqrt{5}}$

2. $\dfrac{5}{\sqrt{6} - 1}$

3. $\dfrac{\sqrt{7}}{\sqrt{10} + 3}$

4. $\dfrac{2 + \sqrt{11}}{2\sqrt{3}}$

5. $\dfrac{2\sqrt{10}}{\sqrt{13}}$

6. $\dfrac{\sqrt{2} + \sqrt{13}}{\sqrt{7} + \sqrt{5}}$

7. $\dfrac{\sqrt{7} + \sqrt{11}}{\sqrt{14} - \sqrt{6}}$

8. $\dfrac{3\sqrt{8} + \sqrt{2}}{5\sqrt{2} - \sqrt{3}}$

Self-Test 3

VOCABULARY   simplest form of a radical (p. 428)

rationalizing the denominator (p. 428)

conjugate (p. 432)

radical equation (p. 434)

Express in simplest form.

1. $5\sqrt{80}$

2. $\sqrt{32x^2y^4}$

3. $3\sqrt{5} - \sqrt{3} + 2\sqrt{5}$

4. $\sqrt{50} - 3\sqrt{2}$

5. $(2 + \sqrt{5})^2$

6. $(4 - \sqrt{7})(4 + \sqrt{7})$

Obj. 11-7, p. 428

Obj. 11-8, p. 430

Obj. 11-9, p. 432

Rationalize the denominator.

7. $\dfrac{3}{2 - \sqrt{3}}$

8. $\dfrac{\sqrt{5}}{4 + \sqrt{5}}$

Solve.

9. $\sqrt{x} - 2 = 3$

10. $\sqrt{\dfrac{x + 1}{2}} = 5$

Obj. 11-10, p. 434

Check your answers with those at the back of the book.

Chapter Summary

1. A rational number can be expressed as a fraction in simplest form, $\frac{a}{b}$, where a and b are integers and $b > 0$. Rational numbers in fractional form can be expressed as either terminating or repeating decimals by dividing.

2. Irrational numbers are represented by nonterminating, nonrepeating decimals which may be rounded to a convenient number of places for use in computation. These numbers cannot be represented in fractional form.

3. Square roots may be rational or irrational. Irrational square roots may be approximated using a table of square roots or a calculator.

4. Some quadratic equations can be solved using the property of square roots of equal numbers (page 419).

5. Many problems involving right triangles can be solved using the Pythagorean theorem:
$$a^2 + b^2 = c^2$$

6. Radical expressions can be added, subtracted, multiplied, and divided. The product and quotient properties of square roots (pages 412, 413) are useful in simplifying expressions involving radicals. Divisions can often be simplified by rationalizing the denominator.

Chapter Review

1. Find the rational number halfway between $\frac{5}{8}$ and $\frac{3}{4}$.

   11-1

   a. $\frac{1}{2}$
   b. $\frac{11}{16}$
   c. $\frac{2}{3}$
   d. $\frac{11}{8}$

2. Compare $\frac{7}{12}$ and $\frac{11}{18}$.

   a. $\frac{7}{12} > \frac{11}{18}$
   b. $\frac{11}{18} > \frac{7}{12}$
   c. $\frac{7}{12} = \frac{11}{18}$

3. Express $\frac{47}{99}$ as a decimal.

   11-2

   a. 0.47
   b. $0.\overline{474}$
   c. $0.\overline{47}$
   d. $0.0\overline{47}$

4. Express 0.035 as a fraction in simplest form.

   a. $\frac{7}{2000}$
   b. $\frac{35}{1000}$
   c. $\frac{3.5}{100}$
   d. $\frac{7}{200}$

5. Find $\sqrt{2.89}$.

   11-3

   a. 1.7
   b. 0.17
   c. 17
   d. 0.017

6. Find $\sqrt{\dfrac{529}{900}}$.

   a. $\frac{29}{30}$
   b. $\frac{23}{30}$
   c. $\frac{17}{30}$
   d. $\frac{7}{9}$

7. Approximate $\sqrt{3400}$ to the nearest hundredth using the Table of Square Roots on page 526.

   11-4

   a. 538.10
   b. 5.83
   c. 5.831
   d. 58.31

8. Simplify $\sqrt{121a^3b^4c^5}$.

   11-5

   a. $11|a|b^2c^2\sqrt{ac}$
   b. $11a^2b^2c^2$
   c. $11|a|b^2c^2\sqrt{11ac}$

9. Solve $9x^2 = 144$.

   a. $\{4\}$
   b. $\left\{\frac{1}{4}, -\frac{1}{4}\right\}$
   c. $\{16\}$
   d. $\{4, -4\}$

10. The shorter sides of a right triangle are 10 cm and 24 cm long. Find the length of the hypotenuse.

    11-6

    a. 25 cm
    b. 26 cm
    c. 34 cm
    d. 676 cm

11. Can a right triangle have sides 8 m, 15 m, and 17 m long?

    a. yes
    b. no

12. Simplify $\sqrt{96x^4y^6}$.

    11-7

    a. $16x^2|y^3|\sqrt{6}$
    b. $x^2|y^3|\sqrt{96}$
    c. $4x^2|y^3|\sqrt{6}$

13. Simplify $4\sqrt{2} + \sqrt{32} - \sqrt{16}$.

    11-8

    a. $4\sqrt{2} + \sqrt{32} - 4$
    b. $8\sqrt{2} - 4$
    c. $9\sqrt{2} - 4$
    d. $4\sqrt{2}$

14. Multiply $(2 - \sqrt{5})(2 + \sqrt{5})$.

11-9

    a. -1 **b.** $4 - \sqrt{5}$ **c.** $4 - 4\sqrt{5}$ **d.** -21

15. Rationalize the denominator of $\dfrac{\sqrt{7}}{3 - \sqrt{3}}$.

    a. $\dfrac{3\sqrt{7} + \sqrt{21}}{6}$ **b.** $\dfrac{2\sqrt{21}}{3}$ **c.** $2\sqrt{7}$ **d.** $\sqrt{7} + \sqrt{21}$

16. Solve $\sqrt{\dfrac{x - 4}{9}} = 7$.

11-10

    a. 5 **b.** 445 **c.** 437 **d.** 67

Chapter Test

1. Find the rational number halfway between $\dfrac{5}{6}$ and $\dfrac{7}{8}$.

11-1

2. Arrange $\dfrac{7}{12}, \dfrac{9}{24}, \dfrac{19}{48}, \dfrac{2}{3}$ in order from least to greatest.

3. Express $\dfrac{11}{12}$ as a decimal.

11-2

4. Express $3.0\overline{4}$ as a fraction in simplest form.

5. Find the indicated square roots.

11-3

    a. $\sqrt{\dfrac{729}{1764}}$ **b.** $\sqrt{0.0025}$

6. Use the Table of Square Roots on page 526 to approximate $\sqrt{8700}$ to the nearest tenth.

11-4

7. Simplify $\sqrt{625r^4s^3t^2}$.   **8.** Solve $49x^2 = 1225$.

11-5

9. In a right triangle, the hypotenuse is 17 cm long, and one of the shorter sides is 6 cm long. Find the length of the other side to the nearest hundredth.

11-6

10. Is a triangle with sides 9 units, 16 units, and 25 units long a right triangle?

Express in simplest form.

11. $3\sqrt{180}$ **12.** $\sqrt{108x^4y^3}$

11-7

13. $6\sqrt{2} + \sqrt{32} - \sqrt{128}$ **14.** $\sqrt{20} - \sqrt{64} + \sqrt{125}$

11-8

15. $(4 + \sqrt{3})^2$ **16.** $(6 - \sqrt{7})(6 + \sqrt{7})$

11-9

17. Rationalize the denominator of $\dfrac{\sqrt{6}}{3 - \sqrt{5}}$.

18. Solve $\sqrt{\dfrac{x + 12}{3}} = 5$.

11-10

RATIONAL AND IRRATIONAL NUMBERS   **439**

Cumulative Review (Chapters 1-11)

Factor completely.

1. $h^4 - 81r^8$

2. $80p + 110p^2 - 15p^3$

3. $12z^2 - 47z + 45$

Simplify. In Exercise 14, divide.

4. $-[1 - 2q - (-3q)]$

5. $x^2y(x^3y^2 - xy^2 + 9x)$

6. $(12a + 5b)(3a - 8b)$

7. $(5\sqrt{2} - 2\sqrt{3})^2$

8. $(1.2a^3 - 6a) \div 0.2a$

9. $(-5rt^5)^3 \div (-10r^2t)^2$

10. $\sqrt{9.61} \cdot \sqrt{576}$

11. $3(\sqrt{1210} - 3\sqrt{40})$

12. $-6\sqrt{24} \div \sqrt{15}$

13. $\dfrac{10r^2 + 48r - 72}{20r^3 - 39r^2 + 18r}$

14. $\dfrac{15x^3 - 4x^2 + 1}{3x + 1}$

15. $\dfrac{6b}{25} - \dfrac{4b}{5} + \dfrac{3b}{50}$

16. $\dfrac{3n^4 - n^3}{n^5 - 3n^4} \div \dfrac{9n^2 - 1}{3n^2 + n}$

17. $\dfrac{3}{g - 2} + \dfrac{4}{4g + 1}$

18. $\dfrac{9 - c^2}{2c + 6} \cdot \dfrac{c^2 + 6c + 8}{c^2 + c - 12}$

19. If x and y are negative integers, graph the solution set of:

a. $3x + 2y = -17$

b. $y > -2x - 7$

c. $y - |x| = -5$

20. Find an equation of the line:

a. with slope 0 and containing $(-8, -2)$

b. passing through $(-7, 4)$ and $(2, -5)$

21. If $f: x \rightarrow x^2 + 3x - 4$, find $f(-5)$ and $f(\sqrt{2} + 1)$. Graph the function f.

22. Graph the solution set of the disjunction "$-2x < -8$ or $x + 1 > 7$."

23. Write $-1.4\overline{3}$ as a fraction in simplest form.

24. Solve graphically:

a. $\begin{aligned} x + y &= 7 \\ 2x - 3y &= 4 \end{aligned}$

b. $\begin{aligned} x - 2y &\le 6 \\ 3x + y &> 5 \end{aligned}$

Solve each equation, inequality, or system.

25. $1.4(m \cdot 3) = 3m + 2$

26. $-402 = |-3|t$

27. 42% of $x = 10.5$

28. $7k + 10 = 6k^2$

29. $7d^2 = 756$

30. $\sqrt{3 - 2x} = x$

31. $-9 \le 4y + 3 < 1$

32. $(z + 5)(z + 4) = 2$

33. $7(2w - 3) \ge 11w$

34. $\dfrac{3v}{2v - 1} + \dfrac{v - 1}{3} = 3$

35. $\dfrac{b - 5}{2} < \dfrac{b - 6}{3}$

36. $\dfrac{9s^2 - 16}{3s^2 - 4s} = 5$

37. $\begin{aligned} 4x + 7y &= 7 \\ -x &= 3y + 2 \end{aligned}$

38. $\begin{aligned} 9x - 2y &= 21 \\ 3x + 2y &= 39 \end{aligned}$

39. $\begin{aligned} 5x + 4y &= 1 \\ 4x + 6y &= 5 \end{aligned}$

40. Evaluate $-\sqrt{179}$ to the nearest hundredth.

41. Find the length of the diagonal of a rectangle whose dimensions are 14 m by 8 m. (Approximate the square root to the nearest hundredth.)

Maintaining Skills ━━━━━━━

Solve each system.

SAMPLE 1 (Substitution Method)

$$5x - y = 7 \longrightarrow y = 5x - 7$$
$$7x + 2y = 3$$

$$7x + 2(5x - 7) = 3$$
$$7x + 10x - 14 = 3$$
$$17x = 17$$
$$x = 1$$

$$y = 5(1) - 7 = -2$$

$\therefore$ the solution is $(1, -2)$. *Answer*

SAMPLE 2 (Multiplication with addition-or-subtraction method)

$$7x - 3y = -6 \longrightarrow \times 4$$
$$3x - 4y = 11 \longrightarrow \times 3$$

$$28x - 12y = -24$$
Subtract: $\quad \underline{9x - 12y = \quad 33}$
$$19x \qquad = -57; \; x = -3$$

Substitute -3 for x in the first equation:

$$7(-3) - 3y = -6; \; -21 - 3y = -6; \; -3y = 15; \; y = -5$$

$\therefore$ the solution is $(-3, -5)$. *Answer*

1. $-3x + 2y = 17$
$ -3x + 5y = 11$

2. $x = 4y$
$ 2x - 9y = 2$

3. $4a - b = -7$
$ 5a + 2b = 14$

4. $2r + 9s = 1$
$ 4r + 3s = 17$

5. $8m - 5n = -14$
$ 7m - 5n = -16$

6. $4 = 5x - 7y$
$ 21y = 15x - 12$

7. $18 = 12x - 11y$
$ -32 = 5x + 2y$

8. $3c + 2d = -6$
$ c + 3d = 5$

9. $2v - 5w = 0$
$ w = 2v$

10. $14x - 3y = 5$
$ -14x + 15y = 31$

11. $3 = 16c + 2d$
$ 2 = 14c + 3d$

12. $5j + 6k = 0$
$ 7j + 6k = -24$

13. $9x - 3y = 12$
$ 3x + 4 = y$

14. $10r + 7s = 87$
$ 9r + 5s = 90$

15. $-66 = 4c - 7d$
$ 12 = 13c + 15d$

16. $-7 = 4a - 2b$
$ 1 = 3a + b$

17. $5x + 3y = -36$
$ 5x - 12y = -31$

18. $4s - 20t = 0$
$ 3s - 15t = 0$

19. $\dfrac{1}{3}(5x - y) = 16$

$ 5x + 7y = 64$

20. $1 - \dfrac{2}{5}n = m$

$ \dfrac{m}{6} - \dfrac{n}{10} = 1$

21. $\dfrac{3x}{4} + \dfrac{5y}{6} = 12$

$ -\dfrac{7x}{8} + \dfrac{y}{2} = -14$

Each curved supporting cable of the Verrazano-Narrows Bridge is shaped like part of a parabola. When a cable carries no load, however, the curve it resembles is a catenary.

12

QUADRATIC FUNCTIONS

QUADRATIC EQUATIONS

12-1 *Solving Quadratic Equations with Perfect Squares*

OBJECTIVE   To solve quadratic equations using perfect squares.

In Chapter 5 you learned how to solve certain quadratic equations by factoring. In Chapter 11 you learned how to solve quadratic equations that are in the form $x^2 = k$. In this chapter you will learn how to determine whether a quadratic equation has no roots, one root, or two roots. You will also learn how to find all the equation's roots.

The property of square roots of equal numbers enables you to analyze equations of the form $x^2 = k$ as follows:

If $k > 0$, then $x^2 = k$ has two real-number roots: $\begin{array}{l} x = \sqrt{k} \\ x = -\sqrt{k} \end{array}$

If $k = 0$, then $x^2 = k$ has one real-number root: $x = 0$

If $k < 0$, then $x^2 = k$ has no real-number solution.

The property of square roots of equal numbers enables you to solve other equations as well.

EXAMPLE 1   Solve $(x - 1)^2 = 36$.

SOLUTION

$$(x - 1)^2 = 36$$
$$x - 1 = \pm 6$$
$$x = 1 \pm 6$$
$$x = -5 \text{ or } x = 7$$

Check: $(-5 - 1)^2 \overset{?}{=} 36$
$(-6)^2 \overset{?}{=} 36$
$36 = 36$ ✓

$(7 - 1)^2 \overset{?}{=} 36$
$6^2 \overset{?}{=} 36$
$36 = 36$ ✓

∴ the solution set is $\{-5, 7\}$.   **Answer**

An expression such as $(x - 1)^2$, x^2, or $(4x + 1)^2$ is called a **perfect square.** Whenever an equation can be expressed in the form

$$\text{perfect square} = k \ (k \geq 0)$$

you can solve it. (You may find it helpful to reread Section 5-6 about squaring binomials.)

EXAMPLE 2   Solve: **a.** $2(x - 1)^2 = 34$ **b.** $y^2 + 6y + 9 = 81$

SOLUTION

a. $2(x - 1)^2 = 34$
$$(x - 1)^2 = 17$$
$$x - 1 = \pm\sqrt{17}$$
$$x = 1 \pm \sqrt{17}$$

The check is left to you.

∴ the solution set is
$\{1 - \sqrt{17}, 1 + \sqrt{17}\}$.   **Answer**

b. $y^2 + 6y + 9 = 81$
$$(y + 3)^2 = 81$$
$$y + 3 = \pm\sqrt{81}$$
$$y = -3 \pm 9$$

The check is left to you.

∴ the solution set is
$\{-12, 6\}$.   **Answer**

The perfect squares occurring in Example 2 are $(x - 1)^2$ and $(y + 3)^2$. Note that Example 2(b) could have been solved by factoring.

An equation that has a negative number as one member and a perfect square as the other member has no real-number solutions. The reason is that the square of any real number is a nonnegative real number.

EXAMPLE 3   Solve $2(4x + 3)^2 + 9 = 1$

SOLUTION

$$2(4x + 3)^2 + 9 = 1$$
$$2(4x + 3)^2 = -8$$
$$(4x + 3)^2 = -4$$

∴ there is no real-number solution.   **Answer**

Oral Exercises

Rewrite each trinomial as the square of a binomial.

SAMPLE $x^2 + 8x + 16 = (x + 4)^2$

1. $x^2 + 10x + 25$

2. $x^2 + 6x + 9$

3. $x^2 - 14x + 49$

4. $x^2 + 22x + 121$

5. $x^2 - 4x + 4$

6. $x^2 - 18x + 81$

Solve.

7. $y^2 = \dfrac{1}{49}$ **8.** $4r^2 = 100$ **9.** $4m^2 - 25 = 0$

Written Exercises

Solve. Express irrational solutions in simplest radical form. If the equation has no solution, write "no solution."

A   **1.** $t^2 = 100$ **2.** $x^2 = \dfrac{25}{49}$ **3.** $y^2 = \dfrac{100}{121}$

    4. $b^2 = -1$ **5.** $2x^2 = 162$ **6.** $4r^2 = 60$

    7. $6x^2 = 54$ **8.** $x^2 - 28 = 0$ **9.** $x^2 + 28 = 0$

   10. $q^2 - 45 = 0$ **11.** $7x^2 - 14 = 0$ **12.** $6m^2 - 36 = 0$

   13. $3y^2 - 8 = 4$ **14.** $2t^2 - 5 = -3$ **15.** $2z^2 - 15 = -1$

   16. $5x^2 + 1 = 16$ **17.** $3y^2 + 7 = 1$ **18.** $(x + 2)^2 = 4$

   19. $(x - 1)^2 = 9$ **20.** $(x - 3)^2 = 7$ **21.** $(x + 4)^2 = 6$

   22. $(y - 2)^2 = 8$ **23.** $(m + 3)^2 = 27$ **24.** $2(m - 1)^2 = 6$

   25. $3(m - 5)^2 = 15$ **26.** $5(r + 4)^2 = 30$ **27.** $4(t + 2)^2 = 40$

   28. $(2z - 1)^2 = 49$ **29.** $3(5z + 1)^2 = 48$ **30.** $2(3z - 2)^2 = 18$

B   **31.** $y^2 - 2y + 1 = 4$ **32.** $r^2 + 10r + 25 = 81$ **33.** $t^2 + 12t + 36 = 49$

   34. $m^2 - 16m + 64 = 36$ **35.** $\dfrac{1}{2}x^2 - \dfrac{2}{9} = 0$ **36.** $\dfrac{1}{2}y^2 - \dfrac{8}{25} = 0$

   37. $\dfrac{1}{3}t^2 - 3 = \dfrac{2}{3}$ **38.** $\dfrac{1}{5}y^2 - 2 = \dfrac{3}{5}$ **39.** $1.21x^2 + 3 = 3.49$

   40. $0.36y^2 - 1 = 0.69$ **41.** $0.81m^2 - 0.3 = 0.19$ **42.** $7(y - 3)^2 = \dfrac{2}{7}$

   43. $3(x + 4)^2 = \dfrac{1}{27}$ **44.** $\left(y - \dfrac{1}{3}\right)^2 = \dfrac{1}{3}$ **45.** $\left(t - \dfrac{3}{5}\right)^2 = \dfrac{2}{5}$

Solve each equation by factoring.

   46. $6m^3 - 24m = 0$ **47.** $3z^3 - 27z = 0$ **48.** $\dfrac{1}{6}t^3 - 6t = 0$

   49. $5y - \dfrac{1}{5}y^3 = 0$ **50.** $5r^3 = 125r$ **51.** $7x^3 = 343x$

Solve.

C   **52.** $5(3x - 2)^2 = 20$ **53.** $3(2x + 5)^2 = 27$ **54.** $4(7x - 4)^2 + 1 = 9$

   55. $2(8x + 3)^2 + 7 = 1$ **56.** $x^2 + 2x\sqrt{5} + 5 = 0$ **57.** $y^2 + 2y\sqrt{7} + 7 = 2$

   58. How many real solutions are there to the equation $a(x - b)^2 = c$ if:
      a. $a > 0$ and $c > 0$?   **b.** $a > 0$ and $c < 0$?
      c. $a < 0$ and $c > 0$?   **d.** $a > 0$ and $c = 0$?

12-2 *Completing the Square*

OBJECTIVE To "complete the square" and to use the result to solve quadratic equations.

In the previous section you learned that it is always possible to solve a quadratic equation that has the form:

$$\text{perfect square} = k \quad (k \geq 0)$$

If a quadratic equation does not have this form, it may be possible to transform it into one which does by a method called **completing the square.**

Study the perfect squares shown at the right. The main idea behind completing the square is shown.

$$(x + 3)^2 = x^2 \underbrace{+ 6x} + 9$$
$$\left(\frac{6}{2}\right)^2 = 9$$

Notice that in each case the coefficient of x^2 is one, and the constant term is the square of half the coefficient of x. This observation leads to the method described below, which you may use to solve certain quadratic equations.

$$(x - 4)^2 = x^2 \underbrace{- 8x} + 16$$
$$\left(-\frac{8}{2}\right)^2 = 16$$

$$(x + a)^2 = x^2 \underbrace{+ 2ax} + a^2$$
$$\left(\frac{2a}{2}\right)^2 = a^2$$

METHOD OF COMPLETING THE SQUARE

For $x^2 + bx + \underline{}$:
1. Find half the coefficient of x.
2. Square the result of Step 1.
3. Add the result of Step 2 to $x^2 + bx$.

EXAMPLE 1 Complete the square.

a. $x^2 - 12x + \underline{}$ 　　　　**b.** $x^2 + 5x + \underline{}$

SOLUTION **a.** $x^2 \underbrace{- 12x} + 36 = (x - 6)^2$ 　**b.** $x^2 \underbrace{+ 5x} + \frac{25}{4} = \left(x + \frac{5}{2}\right)^2$

$\left(-\frac{12}{2}\right)^2 = 36$ 　　　　　　　　$\left(\frac{5}{2}\right)^2 = \frac{25}{4}$

EXAMPLE 2 Solve $x^2 + 14x + 24 = 0$ by completing the square.

SOLUTION

$$x^2 + 14x + 24 = 0$$
$$x^2 + 14x = -24$$
$$x^2 + 14x + \left(\frac{14}{2}\right)^2 = -24 + \left(\frac{14}{2}\right)^2 \quad \text{Complete the square.}$$
$$x^2 + 14x + 49 = -24 + 49$$
$$(x + 7)^2 = 25$$
$$x + 7 = \pm\sqrt{25}$$
$$x = -7 \pm 5$$
$$x = -2 \text{ or } x = -12$$

Solve using the method of Section 12-1.

The check is left to you.

∴ the solution set is $\{-2, -12\}$. *Answer*

EXAMPLE 3 Solve $3x^2 + 5x - 1 = 0$ by completing the square.

SOLUTION To use the method shown in Example 2, divide both sides by 3 so that the coefficient of x^2 will be 1.

$$x^2 + \frac{5}{3}x - \frac{1}{3} = 0$$
$$x^2 + \frac{5}{3}x = \frac{1}{3}$$
$$x^2 + \frac{5}{3}x + \left(\frac{5}{6}\right)^2 = \frac{1}{3} + \left(\frac{5}{6}\right)^2$$
$$x^2 + \frac{5}{3}x + \frac{25}{36} = \frac{1}{3} + \frac{25}{36}$$
$$\left(x + \frac{5}{6}\right)^2 = \frac{37}{36}$$
$$x + \frac{5}{6} = \pm\frac{\sqrt{37}}{6}$$
$$x = -\frac{5}{6} \pm \frac{\sqrt{37}}{6} = \frac{-5 \pm \sqrt{37}}{6}$$

∴ the solution set is $\left\{\dfrac{-5 - \sqrt{37}}{6}, \dfrac{-5 + \sqrt{37}}{6}\right\}$. *Answer*

You can use a table of square roots or a calculator to obtain decimal approximations to irrational roots. The roots obtained in Example 3 are approximated to the nearest tenth below by using approximations from the Table of Square Roots on page 526.

$$\frac{-5 + \sqrt{37}}{6} \approx \frac{-5 + 6.08}{6} = \frac{1.08}{6} = 0.18 \approx 0.2$$
$$\frac{-5 - \sqrt{37}}{6} \approx \frac{-5 - 6.08}{6} = -\frac{11.08}{6} \approx -1.8$$

Thus, the roots to the nearest tenth are 0.2 and -1.8.

Oral Exercises

Complete the square.

1. $x^2 + 4x + \underline{\ ?\ } = (x + \underline{\ ?\ })^2$

2. $x^2 + 10x + \underline{\ ?\ } = (x + \underline{\ ?\ })^2$

3. $y^2 - 6y + \underline{\ ?\ } = (y - \underline{\ ?\ })^2$

4. $y^2 - 12y + \underline{\ ?\ } = (y - \underline{\ ?\ })^2$

5. $z^2 - 5z + \underline{\ ?\ } = (z - \underline{\ ?\ })^2$

6. $m^2 + 7m + \underline{\ ?\ } = (m + \underline{\ ?\ })^2$

7. $t^2 + 1.8t + \underline{\ ?\ } = (t + \underline{\ ?\ })^2$

8. $r^2 - \dfrac{2}{3}r + \underline{\ ?\ } = (r - \underline{\ ?\ })^2$

Complete the step shown in the solution of the equation. Do not solve.

9. $x^2 + 2x - 1 = 0$

$x^2 + 2x \qquad = \underline{\ ?\ }$

10. $x^2 - 8x + 3 = 1$

$x^2 - 8x \qquad = \underline{\ ?\ }$

11. $2x^2 - 12x = -4$

$x^2 - \underline{\ ?\ }\, x = \underline{\ ?\ }$

Written Exercises

Solve by completing the square. Give irrational roots in simplest radical form and approximate them to the nearest tenth.

A

1. $x^2 - 4x = 22$

2. $x^2 + 6x = 30$

3. $x^2 + 8x = -4$

4. $z^2 - 10z = -3$

5. $q^2 - 6q + 3 = 0$

6. $x^2 - 8x + 7 = 0$

7. $m^2 - 2m - 5 = 0$

8. $r^2 + 12r - 288 = 0$

9. $y^2 - 16y - 476 = 8$

10. $t^2 - 6t - 135 = 25$

11. $3a^2 + 6a = 12$

12. $2z^2 - 8z = 3$

13. $b^2 + 3b = 4$

14. $c^2 - 5c = 1$

15. $d^2 + 11d - 5 = 2$

16. $k^2 - 2k - 399 = 0$

17. $y^2 + 6y - 1591 = 0$

18. $2y^2 + 20y - 278 = 0$

Solve the equations using two methods: **(a)** completing the square and **(b)** factoring.

19. $x^2 - 13x + 40 = 0$

20. $x^2 + 8x - 65 = 0$

21. $y^2 - 18y - 40 = 0$

22. $2m^2 + 5m = 12$

23. $4r^2 - 4r = 3$

24. $3r^2 - 13r - 10 = 0$

Solve. Write irrational roots in simplest radical form.

B

25. $\dfrac{s^2}{2} + s = 4$

26. $\dfrac{3x^2}{2} + x - 4 = 0$

27. $x^2 - 2 = \dfrac{2x}{3}$

28. $x^2 - \dfrac{x}{4} = 2$

29. $\dfrac{3m^2}{4} - 4 = \dfrac{5m}{2}$

30. $\dfrac{x^2}{2} - \dfrac{x}{4} = 2$

31. $x - 2 = \dfrac{4 + x}{5x}$

32. $x + 2 = \dfrac{15 + 11x}{6x}$

33. $6x = \dfrac{12 + x}{x + 1}$

34. $4x = \dfrac{x - 6}{x + 3}$

35. $4t + \dfrac{t - 6}{t + 1} = 2$

36. $3m + 5 = \dfrac{12}{m - 2}$

Solve for x in terms of a, b, and c. State the conditions for which the equation has real roots. Explain in terms of a, b, or c.

C

37. $x^2 + bx + 1 = 0$

38. $x^2 + bx + c = 0$

39. $ax^2 + bx + c = 0$

12-3 *The Quadratic Formula*

OBJECTIVE To learn the quadratic formula and use it to solve equations.

Recall from Chapter 5 (page 189) that the general form of the quadratic equation is

$$ax^2 + bx + c = 0$$

where $a \neq 0$. This equation is solved below by completing the square.

$$ax^2 + bx + c = 0$$

$$x^2 + \frac{b}{a}x + \frac{c}{a} = 0 \ (a \neq 0)$$

$$x^2 + \frac{b}{a}x = -\frac{c}{a}$$

$$x^2 + \frac{b}{a}x + \left(\frac{b}{2a}\right)^2 = -\frac{c}{a} + \left(\frac{b}{2a}\right)^2 \quad \text{Complete the square.}$$

$$\left(x + \frac{b}{2a}\right)^2 = -\frac{c}{a} + \frac{b^2}{4a^2}$$

$$\left(x + \frac{b}{2a}\right)^2 = \frac{b^2 - 4ac}{4a^2}$$

$$x + \frac{b}{2a} = \pm \sqrt{\frac{b^2 - 4ac}{4a^2}} \quad \text{(If } b^2 - 4ac \geq 0)$$

$$x = -\frac{b}{2a} \pm \sqrt{\frac{b^2 - 4ac}{4a^2}}$$

$$x = -\frac{b}{2a} \pm \frac{\sqrt{b^2 - 4ac}}{2a}$$

$$x = \frac{-b \pm \sqrt{b^2 - 4ac}}{2a}$$

The last equation in the preceding proof is called the **quadratic formula.** It gives the roots of $ax^2 + bx + c = 0$ in terms of the coefficients a, b, and c. In the proof, notice the assumptions that $a \neq 0$ and that $b^2 - 4ac \geq 0$.

THE QUADRATIC FORMULA

If $ax^2 + bx + c = 0$, $a \neq 0$,   and $b^2 - 4ac \geq 0$,

then $$x = \frac{-b \pm \sqrt{b^2 - 4ac}}{2a}$$

EXAMPLE Solve $7x^2 - 6x + 1 = 0$ using the quadratic formula.

SOLUTION $7x^2 - 6x + 1 = 0$

$$x = \frac{-b \pm \sqrt{b^2 - 4ac}}{2a} \quad \text{where } a = 7,\ b = -6,\ \text{and } c = 1$$

$$x = \frac{-(-6) \pm \sqrt{(-6)^2 - 4(7)(1)}}{2(7)} = \frac{6 \pm \sqrt{36 - 28}}{14}$$

$$= \frac{6 \pm \sqrt{8}}{14} = \frac{6 \pm 2\sqrt{2}}{14} = \frac{3 \pm \sqrt{2}}{7}$$

The check is left to you.

$\therefore$ the solution set is $\left\{ \dfrac{3 - \sqrt{2}}{7}, \dfrac{3 + \sqrt{2}}{7} \right\}$. **Answer**

Be sure to express a quadratic equation in the form $ax^2 + bx + c = 0$ before using the quadratic formula. To solve $2x^2 = 5x - 1$, first express the equation as $2x^2 - 5x + 1 = 0$ to see the values for a, b, and c.

Oral Exercises

State the values of a, b, and c for each equation.

1. $3x^2 + 8x + 2 = 0$
2. $2x^2 - 9x + 6 = 0$
3. $5x^2 + 3x - 1 = 0$
4. $6x^2 + 11x = 3$
5. $7y^2 - 9y = 2$
6. $3y^2 = 7 + 2y$
7. $4r^2 = 9 + 2r$
8. $7 - x^2 = 3x$
9. $x^2 = 6x$
10. $y = 7y^2$
11. $3x^2 = 4$
12. $9t^2 = 0$

Written Exercises

Use the quadratic formula to solve each equation. Give irrational roots in simplest radical form; also approximate them to the nearest tenth.

A
1. $x^2 + 2x - 1 = 0$
2. $x^2 + 5x + 2 = 0$
3. $x^2 + 6x + 4 = 0$
4. $2r^2 - 8r + 6 = 0$
5. $s^2 - 4s - 5 = 0$
6. $t^2 - 5t + 4 = 0$
7. $2m^2 + 5m + 2 = 0$
8. $4q^2 + 4q - 3 = 0$
9. $3a^2 - 10a - 8 = 0$
10. $3y^2 = 11y - 5$
11. $4x^2 + 5 = 9x$
12. $9x = 4 - 2x^2$

Solve.

B
13. $b^2 + 0.7b - 0.1 = 0$
14. $3z^2 - 1.2z + 0.02 = 0$
15. $4r^2 = 0.6r + 0.5$
16. $c^2 + \frac{2}{3}c - \frac{1}{2} = 0$
17. $\frac{3}{2}x^2 + \frac{1}{3}x + \frac{2}{3} = 0$
18. $\frac{1}{4}x^2 - \frac{2}{5}x = 4$

19. $\dfrac{3}{x} - \dfrac{1}{3x + 2} = \dfrac{1}{2}$
20. $\dfrac{3x}{x + 2} - \dfrac{x + 1}{x - 1} = 0$

21. $\dfrac{2.5}{x + 2} = 4x$　　　　　**22.** $\dfrac{4}{x - 2} - \dfrac{x - 3}{x + 4} = 2$

The roots of the quadratic equation $ax^2 + bx + c = 0$ are
$$\frac{-b \pm \sqrt{b^2 - 4ac}}{2a}.$$

C **23.** Find the sum of the roots.

24. Find the product of the roots.

25. Write a quadratic equation whose roots are $2 \pm \sqrt{3}$. (*Hint:* Find the sum and product of the roots. Then use the results of Exercises 23 and 24 to find values for a, b, and c.)

EXTRA

Imaginary Numbers

You know that there are no real-number solutions to the equation $x^2 = -9$. If you take another course in algebra, you will learn that equations like this have solutions that are *imaginary numbers*. Imaginary numbers involve the *imaginary unit, i,* defined to be the square root of -1. Thus:

$$x^2 = -9$$
$$x = \pm\sqrt{-9} = \pm 3\sqrt{-1} = \pm 3i$$

ﬁistorical Note Variables

The history of the use of symbols to denote unknown quantities is very closely tied to the history of exponents (see page 177). One method for representing unknown quantities was the use of words such as "root," "square," and "cube." The Hindus used the names of various colors.

Gradually the words used were abbreviated. In the sixteenth and seventeenth centuries, N, Q, C, QQ, QC, . . . were used to denote quantities you would represent by x, x^2, x^3, x^4, x^5, ... Some writers even used pictorial representations of squares and cubes.

At the close of the sixteenth century, François Vieta (or Viète), a French mathematician, published a mathematics book in which he used vowels to represent unknown quantities and consonants for known quantities, giving his algebra a nearly modern appearance.

12-4 *Graphs of Quadratic Equations: The Discriminant*

OBJECTIVE   To use the discriminant to determine the number of roots of the equation $ax^2 + bx + c = 0$ and the number of x-intercepts of the graph of the related equation $y = ax^2 + bx + c$.

You learned in Chapter 9 (page 338) that the graph of the function defined by the quadratic equation

$$y = x^2 - 2x - 3$$

is the parabola shown at the right. The x-coordinate of a point where the curve intersects the x-axis is called an **x-intercept** of the curve. This parabola has two x-intercepts, -1 and 3, because $y = 0$ for these values of x. You can also see that the equation

$$x^2 - 2x - 3 = 0$$

has -1 and 3 as roots.

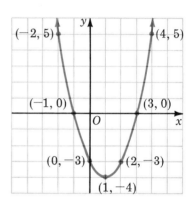

The roots of any quadratic equation of the form

$$ax^2 + bx + c = 0$$

are the x-intercepts of the graph of the related equation

$$y = ax^2 + bx + c.$$

The algebraic fact that a quadratic equation can have two, one, or no real number roots corresponds to the geometric fact that a parabola can have two, one, or no x-intercepts, as illustrated below and on the next page. In each example, the quadratic formula is used to solve the equation.

EXAMPLE 1

Equation: $x^2 - 4x + 1 = 0$

Solution: $x = \dfrac{-(-4) \pm \sqrt{(-4)^2 - 4(1)(1)}}{2(1)}$

$\qquad = \dfrac{4 \pm \sqrt{12}}{2}$

$\qquad = 2 \pm \sqrt{3}$

$\qquad \therefore$ the solution set is $\{2 + \sqrt{3}, 2 - \sqrt{3}\}$.

Number of roots: Two real-number roots

Related equation: $y = x^2 - 4x + 1$

Graph:

Number of x-intercepts: Two

EXAMPLE 2

Equation: $x^2 - 4x + 4 = 0$

Solution: $x = \dfrac{-(-4) \pm \sqrt{(-4)^2 - 4(1)(4)}}{2(1)}$

$\quad\quad = \dfrac{4 \pm \sqrt{0}}{2}$

$\quad\quad = 2$

∴ the solution set is {2}.

Related equation: $y = x^2 - 4x + 4$

Graph:

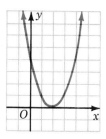

Number of roots: One real-number (double) root

Number of x-intercepts: One

EXAMPLE 3

Equation: $x^2 - 4x + 5 = 0$

Solution: $x = \dfrac{-(-4) \pm \sqrt{(-4)^2 - 4(1)(5)}}{2(1)}$

$\quad\quad = \dfrac{4 \pm \sqrt{-4}}{2}$

There is no real-number root since $\sqrt{-4}$ does not exist in the set of real numbers.

Related equation: $y = x^2 - 4x + 5$

Graph:

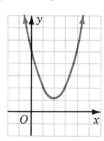

Number of roots: No real-number roots

Number of x-intercepts: None

In each of Examples 1–3, the value of $b^2 - 4ac$ in the quadratic formula is shown in color. This value is the key to the number of real roots, as shown in the following chart.

	Value of $b^2 - 4ac$	Number of different real roots of $ax^2 + bx + c = 0$	Number of x-intercepts of the graph of $y = ax^2 + bx + c$
Case 1	positive	2	2
Case 2	zero	1 (a double root)	1
Case 3	negative	0	0

Note that when $b^2 - 4ac$ is negative, no real-number root of the equation exists because square roots of negative numbers do not exist in the set of real numbers.

Because the value of $b^2 - 4ac$ discriminates, or distinguishes, the three cases, it is called the **discriminant** of the quadratic equation.

Oral Exercises

Classify each statement as true or false.

1. The x-coordinates of the points where the parabola $y = x^2 + 5x + 6$ crosses the x-axis are the roots of the equation $x^2 + 5x + 6 = 0$.

2. Since the discriminant of the equation $x^2 + 5x + 6 = 0$ is 1, the equation has exactly one real-number root.

3. The value of the discriminant of the equation $x^2 - 2x - 3 = 0$ indicates whether the roots are positive, negative, or zero.

4. The value of $b^2 - 4ac$ in the quadratic formula is a root of the equation $ax^2 + bx + c = 0$.

5. When the discriminant of a quadratic equation is known, the number of real roots is known.

6. Since the discriminant of $x^2 + x + 1 = 0$ is -3, the equation has no real-number root.

Written Exercises

Write the value of the discriminant of each equation. Then use it to decide how many different real-number roots the equation has. (Do not solve the equations.)

A 1. $x^2 + 3x - 5 = 0$ 2. $x^2 - x + 3 = 0$ 3. $3x^2 - 5x - 1 = 0$

4. $2x^2 - 8x + 8 = 0$ 5. $x^2 - 5x + 2 = 0$ 6. $x^2 + 4x + 9 = 0$

7. $2x^2 - 3x - 2 = 0$ 8. $\frac{1}{2}x^2 - 2x + 2 = 0$ 9. $3y^2 - y + 1 = 0$

10. $-4y^2 - 5y + 4 = 0$ 11. $2t^2 - 12t + 18 = 0$ 12. $\frac{1}{3}t^2 + 2t + 3 = 0$

Without drawing the graph of the given equation, determine (a) how many points the parabola has in common with the x-axis, and (b) whether its vertex lies above, below, or on the x-axis.

SAMPLE $y = 2x - 3 - x^2$

SOLUTION   a. The x-intercepts of the graph are solutions of the equation
$$2x - 3 - x^2 = 0, \quad \text{or} \quad -x^2 + 2x - 3 = 0.$$
Its discriminant is $(2)^2 - 4(-1)(-3) = -8$ and therefore it has no real-number roots. The parabola has *no* points in common with the x-axis.

b. Since the parabola opens downward (see page 339), its vertex must be *below* the x-axis (otherwise the parabola would intersect the x-axis).

B 13. $y = x^2 + 4x + 1$ 14. $y = x^2 - 4x + 1$

15. $y = 3 - 2x - x^2$ 16. $y = 2x - 4 - x^2$

17. $y = 6 + x - 2x^2$ 18. $y = 4x - 4 - x^2$

C **19.** Find k so that the equation $kx^2 + 4x + 1 = 0$ has one real-number (double) root.

20. Find k so that the equation $x^2 - kx + 9 = 0$ has one real-number (double) root.

Self-Test 1

VOCABULARY perfect square (p. 444) x-intercept (p. 452)
completing the square (p. 446)   discriminant (p. 453)
quadratic formula (p. 449)

Solve by using perfect squares.

1. $4x^2 = 64$ **2.** $(y - 5)^2 = 4$ Obj. 12-1, p. 443

Solve by completing the square.

3. $a^2 + 4a - 12 = 0$ **4.** $2x^2 - 12x + 10 = 0$ Obj. 12-2, p. 446

Solve by the quadratic formula.

5. $b^2 - 3b - 2 = 0$ **6.** $3c^2 + 7c + 1 = 0$ Obj. 12-3, p. 449

Give the number of real roots.

7. $x^2 - 10x + 24 = 0$ **8.** $2x^2 - 4x + 1 = 0$ Obj. 12-4, p. 452

Check your answers with those at the back of the book.

Just for Fun

According to the legend, the inventor of the game of chess asked to be rewarded by having one grain of wheat put on the first square of a chessboard, two grains on the second, four grains on the third, eight grains on the fourth, and so on. The total number of grains would be $2^{64} - 1$, which is several thousand times the world's annual wheat yield.

1. To find out how large 2^{64} is approximately, you could enter the number 2 on the calculator and press the squaring button a number of times. How many times?

2. Factor $2^{64} - 1$ as a difference of squares to show that it is divisible by 3, 5, and 17.

USING QUADRATIC EQUATIONS

12-5 *Methods of Solution*

OBJECTIVE   To choose the best method for solving a quadratic equation.

You have learned the following four methods for solving quadratic
equations.

METHODS FOR SOLVING A QUADRATIC EQUATION

1. Factoring
2. Using the property of square roots of equal numbers (p. 419)
3. Completing the square
4. Using the quadratic formula

Although the quadratic formula can be used to solve any quadratic
equation in the form

$$ax^2 + bx + c = 0$$

one of the other methods may be easier. Here are some guidelines that
suggest when one of the other methods may be easier:

1. If the equation is in the form $ax^2 + bx = 0$ or if the factors are easily
   seen, use factoring;
2. If the equation is in the form $ax^2 + c = 0$, use the property of square
   roots of equal numbers;
3. If the equation is in the form $x^2 + bx + c = 0$ and b is an even number, use the method of completing the square.

EXAMPLE   Solve each quadratic equation using the most convenient
method.

    a. $3x^2 - 75 = 0$ **b.** $2y^2 + 7y + 4 = 0$

    c. $5z^2 - 15z = 0$ **d.** $k^2 + 10k - 5 = 0$

SOLUTION   **a.** $3x^2 - 75 = 0$ Use the property of square
                          $3x^2 = 75$ roots of equal numbers.

$$x^2 = 25$$

$$x = \pm 5$$

∴ the solution set is $\{-5, 5\}$.   *Answer*

b. $2y^2 + 7y + 4 = 0$

Since no other method suggests itself, use the quadratic formula.

$$x = \frac{-7 \pm \sqrt{(7)^2 - 4(2)(4)}}{2(2)} = \frac{-7 \pm \sqrt{17}}{4}$$

$\therefore$ the solution set is $\left\{ \dfrac{-7 - \sqrt{17}}{4}, \dfrac{-7 + \sqrt{17}}{4} \right\}$. ***Answer***

c. $5z^2 - 15z = 0$ Factor.

$$5z(z - 3) = 0$$
$$5z = 0 \quad \text{or} \quad z - 3 = 0$$

$\therefore$ the solution set is $\{0, 3\}$. ***Answer***

d. $k^2 + 10k - 5 = 0$ Complete the square.

$$k^2 + 10k = 5$$
$$k^2 + 10k + 25 = 30$$
$$(k + 5)^2 = 30$$
$$k + 5 = \pm\sqrt{30}$$
$$k = -5 \pm \sqrt{30}$$

$\therefore$ the solution set is $\left\{ -5 - \sqrt{30}, -5 + \sqrt{30} \right\}$. ***Answer***

Oral Exercises

For each of the following equations, state which method you would use to solve.

1. $x^2 + 3x + 2 = 0$ **2.** $5x^2 = 30$ **3.** $x^2 - 12x = 85$

4. $2x^2 + 7x - 8 = 0$ **5.** $6x^2 + 18x = 0$ **6.** $2x^2 + 6x + 3 = 0$

7. $10x^2 = 90$ **8.** $x^2 + 8x + 5 = 0$ **9.** $3x^2 - 10x = 4$

10. $9x^2 + 8x = 0$ **11.** $(x + 3)^2 = 5$ **12.** $x^2 - 6x = 60$

Written Exercises

A   **1–12.** Solve the quadratic equations given in Oral Exercises 1–12. Write the answers in simplest radical form.

Solve by the most efficient method. Write irrational answers in simplest radical form.

13. $3(x + 2)^2 = 12$ **14.** $x^2 - 10x = 20$ **15.** $3x^2 + 2x - 1 = 0$

16. $4x^2 + 7x - 11 = 0$ **17.** $\dfrac{1}{3}x^2 + \dfrac{2}{5}x - 2 = 0$ **18.** $\dfrac{-1}{2x} = \dfrac{4x - 5}{3}$

19. $\dfrac{x + 9}{2x - 3} = \dfrac{x + 7}{3x + 2}$ **20.** $0.3x^2 - 0.2x = 0.25$ **21.** $1.2x^2 - 4x - 0.6 = 0$

Solve by the most efficient method. Write irrational answers in simplest radical form.

B 22. $4x(x + 3) + 7(x - 2) = 1 - 6x^2$

23. $3x(x + 2) + 4(x^2 - 2) = 11 - 7x$

24. $(x + 3)^2 - 2(x + 4) = 10$

25. $(2x + 5)^2 - 3x(x - 3) = -5$

26. $(2x - 3)(x + 1) - 32 = x(3 - x)$

27. $(5x - 2)^2 = (2x + 3)^2$

Solve. Be sure that you have found all the real roots of each equation. Write irrational answers in simplest radical form. (*Hint:* Substitute y for x^2.)

C 28. $6x^4 - 19x^2 + 10 = 0$

29. $4x^4 - 25x^2 - 21 = 0$

30. $7x^4 + 5x^2 + 3 = 0$

31. $3x^4 - 2x^2 = 0$

Career Note Architect

Very tall skyscrapers sway slightly. They need some flexibility to withstand strong winds. Architects who design skyscrapers, office buildings, houses, schools, and shopping malls must consider more than just style. A building must be functional, structurally sound, and in compliance with local building codes and zoning laws.

Once an architect has discussed function, style, and cost of a proposed structure with a client, floor plans, elevations, and models are made. When the plans are approved by the client, the architect may work with a contractor on the construction site to make sure the plans are carried out correctly.

Architects must pass a licensing examination. The requirements for taking this test are a bachelor's degree in architecture and three years of experience in an architect's office, or a master's degree and two years of experience.

12-6 *Using Quadratic Equations to Solve Problems*

OBJECTIVE To use quadratic equations to solve problems.

EXAMPLE

A theater director needs to determine the dimensions of an area that is to be in the shape of a right triangle on the stage floor. The longest side of the triangle, which is to face the audience, is to be 8 m long. One of the shorter sides is to be 2 m longer than the other. To the nearest tenth of a meter, what are the lengths of the two shorter sides?

SOLUTION

Step 1 The problem asks for the lengths of the two shorter sides.

Step 2 Let x = the length of the shortest side. Then $(x + 2)$ = the length of the other unknown side.

Step 3 Use the Pythagorean theorem to write an equation.
$$x^2 + (x + 2)^2 = 8^2$$

Step 4
$$x^2 + x^2 + 4x + 4 = 64$$
$$2x^2 + 4x + 4 = 64$$
$$2x^2 + 4x - 60 = 0$$
$$x^2 + 2x - 30 = 0$$

Use the quadratic formula
$$x = \frac{-2 \pm \sqrt{(2)^2 - 4(1)(-30)}}{2} = \frac{-2 \pm \sqrt{124}}{2} = \frac{-2 \pm 2\sqrt{31}}{2}$$
$$x = -1 \pm \sqrt{31}$$

From the Table of Square Roots on page 526:
$$-1 + \sqrt{31} \approx -1 + 5.57 = 4.57 \approx 4.6$$
$$-1 - \sqrt{31} \approx -1 - 5.57 = -6.57 \approx -6.6$$

Step 5 Discard the negative root because a negative length has no meaning. Check 4.6.
$$(4.6)^2 + (4.6 + 2)^2 \overset{?}{=} 8^2$$
$$21.16 + 43.56 \overset{?}{=} 64$$
$$64.7 \approx 64 \quad \checkmark$$

The numbers are approximately equal so the approximate solution is correct.

$\therefore$ the shorter sides of the triangle will be 4.6 m and 6.6 m long. *Answer*

Problems

Solve. Give irrational roots to the nearest tenth. Use the Table of Square Roots on page 526 as necessary.

A **1.** The length of a rectangle is 3 m longer than the width. If the area of the rectangle is 40 m², find the length and width.

    2. The length of a rectangle is twice the width. The area of the rectangle is 200 cm². Find the length and width.

    3. The width of a rectangular playing area is 50 m shorter than its length. If the area is 8400 m², find the playing area's length and width.

    4. A rectangular bolt of cloth, purchased to make drapes, has an area of 12 m². If the piece of material is three times as long as it is wide, find its dimensions.

    5. The base of a triangle is 3 cm longer than its altitude. Find the altitude if the area of the triangle is 44 cm². (*Hint:* The area of a triangle $= \frac{1}{2} \cdot$ base $\cdot$ altitude.)

    6. The altitude of a triangle is 4 cm shorter than its base. Find the altitude if the area of the triangle is 90 cm².

    7. The dimensions of a framed picture are 50 cm by 30 cm. The area of the picture itself is 444 cm². Find the distance from the edge of the picture to the edge of the frame if this distance is uniform around the picture.

    8. Martha's garden is 5 m wide and 8 m long. Next year she plans to double the garden's area by increasing the width and length by the same number of meters. What will the new dimensions of the garden be?

B **9.** A box without a top is to be made by cutting squares measuring 5 cm on a side from each corner of a square piece of cardboard and folding up the sides. If the box is to have a volume of 3125 cm³, what should the length of a side of the original piece of cardboard be?

  10. A mathematics class bought a $45 calculator for class use. Each student donated the same amount of money. If there had been 5 more students in the class, each would have had to pay 30¢ less. How many students were in the class?

  11. Working together, Dan and Leah can mow a lawn in one hour and twelve minutes. Working alone, Leah can mow the lawn in one hour less time than it would take Dan. Find the time it takes each of them to mow the lawn working alone.

12. A class planned a field trip at a cost of $36 to be shared equally by the students. The day before the trip 6 students found they could not go. Consequently, the other students had to pay an additional 50¢ each. How many students went on the trip?

13. One train travels at a rate 10 km/h faster than another train. If the faster train takes one hour less time than the other to travel 720 km, what is the rate of the faster train?

C 14. A boat can travel to a city 24 km downriver and back in five hours. If the rate of the current is 2 km/h, find the rate of the boat in still water.

Self-Test 2

Solve the following quadratic equations using the most convenient method.

1. $2x^2 + 3x - 7 = 0$ **2.** $5x^2 = 100$ Obj. 12-5, p. 456

3. $3x^2 - 9x = 0$ **4.** $x^2 + 4x + 2 = 0$

Solve. Give irrational roots to the nearest tenth. Use the Table of Square Roots on page 526 as necessary.

5. The areas of a square and a rectangle have a sum of 42 cm². If the rectangle is as wide as the square, but is 3 cm longer, find the length of a side of the square.   Obj. 12-6, p. 459

6. A soccer field is approximately 110 m by 60 m. A section of uniform width for spectators is to be placed around the field. The area of the field and the spectator section is to be 9375 m². Find the width of the spectator section.

Check your answers with those at the back of the book.

Computer Key-In

Write a program to find the solution set of any quadratic equation by using the quadratic formula. Be sure to include a special print-out if $b^2 - 4ac < 0$. Recall (page 421) that the BASIC language has a built-in square root function.

Quadratic Inequalities

The graph of $y = x^2 - 2x - 3$ can be used to illustrate the solutions of the following:

(1) $x^2 - 2x - 3 < 0$

(2) $x^2 - 2x - 3 = 0$

(3) $x^2 - 2x - 3 > 0$

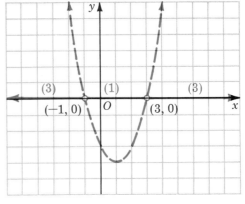

The solution set of the quadratic equation (2) is $\{-1, 3\}$. These two values of x are called the *zeros* of the quadratic function.

To solve inequality (3), reason as follows:

a. If (x, y) is on the graph, then $y = x^2 - 2x - 3$.

b. If (x, y) is *above* the x-axis, then $y > 0$.

c. Therefore, if (x, y) is on the graph *and* above the x-axis, then $y = x^2 - 2x - 3 > 0$.

d. $\therefore$ the solution set for (3) is {all real numbers less than -1 or greater than 3} because these values of x give points that are on the graph above the x-axis.

Similar reasoning shows that the solution set for (1) is {all real numbers between -1 and 3} because these values of x give points on the graph *below* the x-axis.

EXAMPLE   Solve the inequalities.

(1) $x^2 + 4x + 4 > 0$ (2) $x^2 + 4x + 4 < 0$

SOLUTION   Use the graph of $y = x^2 + 4x + 4$.

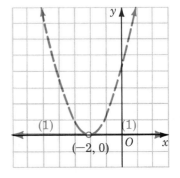

(1) Since the graph lies above the x-axis for all x except -2, $x^2 + 4x + 4 > 0$ for all $x \neq -2$.
(2) There are no values of x for which $x^2 + 4x + 4 < 0$, since the graph does not go below the x-axis.

Graph each equation and mark the sections of the x-axis which correspond to $y = 0$, $y > 0$, and $y < 0$.

1. $y = x^2 - 4$ **2.** $y = 4 - x^2$ **3.** $y = x^2 + 3x$

4. $y = x^2 - 6x + 8$ **5.** $y = x^2 - 3x - 10$ **6.** $y = 2x^2 + x - 3$

Find the values of x for which each expression represents a real number.

7. $\sqrt{x^2 + 6x}$ **8.** $\sqrt{x^2 - 5x + 6}$

Application Newton's Law of Motion

Newton's Law of Motion relates the force acting on an object to the object's mass and acceleration. The acceleration of an object is the rate at which the speed of the object is changing. For example, an object with a constant acceleration of 2 m/s^2 (meters per second squared) will increase its speed by 10 m/s in 5 s. The force acting on the object is expressed in newtons (N). A *newton* is the amount of force required to give a 1 kg object an acceleration of 1 m/s^2.

Before you use Newton's Law, you must know the units involved. The mass (*m*) of the object is expressed in kilograms, the object's acceleration (*a*) is expressed in meters per second squared, and the force (*F*) acting on the object is expressed in newtons. Newton's Law can then be written as follows:

$$F = ma$$

1. What force is needed to give a 9000 kg truck an acceleration of 15 m/s^2?

2. A baseball that has been hit with a force of 5.4 N accelerates at 36 m/s^2. What is the mass of the baseball in grams?

3. A 7.2 kg bowling ball has a force of 43.2 N applied to it. What is the bowling ball's acceleration?

Biography Santiago Ramón y Cajal

Santiago Ramón y Cajal (1852–1934), born in Petilla de Aragon, Spain, received a degree in medicine from the University of Zaragoza in 1873. From 1892 to 1922 Cajal was a professor of histology, the study of the microscopic structure of human tissues. He made major contributions to this branch of medicine. Using stains, he was able to display nerve cells and fibers. This technique enabled him to investigate in detail the structure of the nervous system. He demonstrated that each nerve cell has its own network of fibers that do not touch the fibers of any other cell. For his work in this field he shared the Nobel prize for medicine in 1906.

Chapter Summary

1. Any quadratic equation can be solved using the quadratic formula (see item 2 below). Some quadratic equations, however, may be more easily solved by factoring, applying the property of square roots of equal numbers, or by completing the square.

2. When $ax^2 + bx + c = 0$ and $a \neq 0$, the quadratic formula is expressed as follows:

$$x = \frac{-b \pm \sqrt{b^2 - 4ac}}{2a}$$

3. The graph of a quadratic equation of the form $y = ax^2 + bx + c$ is a parabola. The x-intercepts of the parabola correspond to the roots of the related quadratic equation $ax^2 + bx + c = 0$.

4. The discriminant, $b^2 - 4ac$, is used to determine the number of roots of a quadratic equation.

   If $b^2 - 4ac > 0$, there are two real-number roots.
   If $b^2 - 4ac = 0$, there is one (double) real-number root.
   If $b^2 - 4ac < 0$, there are no real-number roots.

Chapter Review

Solve.

1. $4x^2 = 144$ 12-1
   a. $\{6\}$ **b.** $\{6, -6\}$ **c.** $\{36\}$ **d.** $\{36, -36\}$

2. $(r - 7)^2 = 9$
   a. $\{10, -10\}$ **b.** $\{2, -2\}$ **c.** $\{4, 10\}$ **d.** $\{16, -2\}$

Solve by completing the square.

3. $x^2 + 14x + 24 = 0$ 12-2
   a. $\{-12, -2\}$ **b.** $\{12, 2\}$ **c.** $\{12, -2\}$ **d.** $\{-12, 2\}$

4. $3x^2 + 18x - 12 = 0$
   a. $\left\{ \dfrac{\sqrt{13}}{3}, \dfrac{-\sqrt{13}}{3} \right\}$ **b.** $\left\{ -3 + \sqrt{13}, -3 - \sqrt{13} \right\}$
   c. $\left\{ \sqrt{13} - 3, \sqrt{13} + 3 \right\}$ **d.** $\left\{ 3 + \sqrt{13}, 3 - \sqrt{13} \right\}$

Solve by the quadratic formula.

5. $x^2 + 5x - 84 = 0$ 12-3
   a. $\{-12, 7\}$ **b.** $\{7, 12\}$ **c.** $\{-7, 12\}$ **d.** $\{-12, -7\}$

6. $2x^2 + 7x + 5 = 0$
   a. $\left\{ \dfrac{5}{2}, 1 \right\}$ **b.** $\{5, 2\}$ **c.** $\{-5, -2\}$ **d.** $\left\{ -\dfrac{5}{2}, -1 \right\}$

7. Give the discriminant of $x^2 + 16x + 48 = 0$. 12-4

    a. 8   **b.** 12   **c.** 4   **d.** 64

8. How many real roots does $x^2 - 6x + 5 = 0$ have?

    a. 0   **b.** 1   **c.** 2   **d.** 3

9. Give the best method for solving $6x^2 - 42 = 0$. 12-5

    a. Factoring   **b.** Property of square roots of equal numbers

    c. Completing the square   **d.** Quadratic formula

Solve.

10. The length of a rectangle is 6 cm less than twice its width. If the 12-6
area is 108 cm² find the length and width.

    a. $l = 9$ cm   **b.** $l = 18$ cm   **c.** $l = 6$ cm   **d.** $l = 12$ cm
         $w = 12$ cm $w = 6$ cm $w = 18$ cm $w = 9$ cm

Chapter Test ━━━━━━━━━━━━━━━━━━━━━━━

Solve.

    1. $25x^2 = 100$ **2.** $9x^2 = 121$ 12-1

Solve by completing the square.

    3. $x^2 - 8x + 4 = 0$ **4.** $3x^2 + 12x - 9 = 0$ 12-2

Solve by the quadratic formula.

    5. $a^2 + 5a - 2 = 0$ **6.** $4c^2 - 9c + 9 = 0$ 12-3

State the number of real roots.

    7. $x^2 + 6x + 9 = 0$ **8.** $5x^2 + 10x - 3 = 0$ 12-4

Solve by the easiest method.

    9. $5x^2 - 20x = 0$ **10.** $3x^2 - 9x + 5 = 0$ 12-5

Solve. Approximate irrational roots to the nearest tenth.

11. A rectangle is 5 cm longer than it is wide. If the area is 84 cm², find 12-6
the length and width.

12. The side of one square is 3 times as long as the side of a second
square. If the combined area is 160 m², find the lengths of the sides
of both squares.

Cumulative Review (Chapters 1-12)

Evaluate if $a = -8$, $b = -5$, $c = 3$, $d = 4$, and $e = \dfrac{9}{2}$.

1. $a(2b + d)$ **2.** $ae \div cd + b$ **3.** $ed^2 - b^3$ **4.** $(3a - c) \div e$

Factor completely, if possible. If not, write "prime."

5. $-21z^4 + 12z^3 - 15z^8$ **6.** $35g^2 - 2gh - 6h^2$ **7.** $100b^2 - 144y^2$

8. $6df + 7e + 2ef + 21d$ **9.** $20s^3 - 33s^2t + 10st^2$ **10.** $6r^4 + 10r^2 - 16$

Simplify. Each variable represents a positive real number.

11. $(-58 + 47) - (-58)$ **12.** $8e - 18e^2 \div 2e$ **13.** $(-4 - 9)(-2 + 5)$

14. $6a - (0.8a + 1.2b)$ **15.** $3(7c - 8) + 5 - 4c$ **16.** $(-4x^3y^2z^2)(-8xy^3z^5)$

17. $-\dfrac{2}{3}t^3v^2(-9t^2 + 3tv)$ **18.** $\dfrac{-252e^3f^2g}{-98ef^2g^3}$ **19.** $\dfrac{(6m^2n^4)^3}{(-3m^4n^3)^4}$

20. $(r^3 - r + 3)(4r - 5)$ **21.** $(9m - 2)(3m + 5)$ **22.** $(2a^2 - 7b)^2$

23. $\dfrac{49c^2 - 14cd + d^2}{49c^2 + 7cd - 2d^2}$ **24.** $\dfrac{64k^5 + 2}{2k + 1}$ **25.** $\dfrac{m^4 - 16}{2m^3 + 8m} \div \dfrac{m^3 - 2m^2}{4m^3}$

26. $\dfrac{45e^5 - 25e^3 - 27e^2}{-15e^2}$ **27.** $\dfrac{-5x^3y^2z}{-65xz^2} \cdot \dfrac{13yz^4}{x^2y^3}$ **28.** $\dfrac{s}{18} - \dfrac{s}{8} + 2$

29. $\dfrac{3n - 1}{6 - 2n} + \dfrac{4}{n - 3}$ **30.** $\dfrac{4}{w + 3} - \dfrac{3}{w - 3}$ **31.** $\dfrac{t + 1}{t + 3} - \dfrac{t}{t - 2}$

32. $-\sqrt{2.56y^8z^3}$ **33.** $3\sqrt{2}(\sqrt{45} - \sqrt{125})$ **34.** $(2\sqrt{3} - 1)^2$

35. $\sqrt{\dfrac{27a^3}{5}} \cdot \sqrt{\dfrac{160}{3a}}$ **36.** $(6 + \sqrt{6})(6 - \sqrt{10})$ **37.** $\dfrac{7 + \sqrt{5}}{1 + \sqrt{5}}$

38. Find the prime factorizations of 135 and 180, and their GCF.

39. Write $0.7\overline{81}$ as a fraction in lowest terms.

40. If x and y are whole numbers, graph the solution set of:
     a. $5x + 3y = 28$ **b.** $2x + 3y \leq 9$ **c.** $xy = 4$

41. Find an equation in standard form of the line:
     a. with slope -5 and containing $(-2, -7)$
     b. containing $(8, -1)$ and $(4, 5)$

42. Graph each solution set on a number line:
     a. $5(7 - 2x) + 4 = -3(8x + 1)$ **b.** $-9 \leq 1 - 2x < 3$

43. If $f(x) = 2x^2 - 3x - 2$, find $f(-4)$ and $f(2\sqrt{3})$. Graph $f(x)$.

44. If a varies directly as b^2 and inversely as c, and $a = 75$ when $b = 5$ and $c = 2$, find a when $b = 4$ and $c = 3$.

Solve each equation, inequality, or system.

45. $-3(2x - 1) = 4x + 8$

46. $7w + 1 = -|-125|$

47. $18 = 6.4h + 0.72$

48. 5.4% of $y = 43.2$

49. $32 = 5b^2 + 36b$

50. $(6q + 5)(3q - 1) = 4$

51. $\dfrac{5}{2}t + \dfrac{1}{3} > 7$

52. $-\dfrac{44}{7} \le -\dfrac{3p}{5} - \dfrac{2}{7}$

53. $\dfrac{4}{3s + 2} + \dfrac{1}{s} = 1$

54. $2 = 14 + 3r^2$

55. $\sqrt{1 - 5x} - 2 = 2$

56. $(m + 3)^2 = 56$

57. $\dfrac{3j + 1}{5j - 2} = \dfrac{j + 1}{j + 5}$

58. $3\sqrt{2x} = 12$

59. $\dfrac{1}{(x - 3)^2} - \dfrac{1}{3 - x} \ge 0$

60. $n^2 - 30n = -225$

61. $d^2 = 6d + 15$

62. $8c^2 - 4c = 1$

63. $a - 12b = -25$
$6a + 5b = 4$

64. $7r + 4s = 23$
$5r - 4s = 13$

65. $5x - 8y = 7$
$4x - 7y = 11$

66. If y varies directly as x and $y = 3$ when $x = 54$, find y when $x = 63$.

67. Two numbers differ by 6. The sum of their squares is 218. Find the numbers.

68. Find three consecutive odd integers whose sum is -225.

69. If x and $x + 7$ represent the lengths of the two shorter sides of a right triangle, and $2x + 1$ represents the length of the longest side, find the value of x.

70. Ed Jones invests $2800, part at $9\frac{1}{2}$% and the rest at 9%. If his annual interest is $258.50, how much is invested at each rate?

71. The length and the width of a rectangle are in the ratio $8:5$. If the perimeter of the rectangle is 104 cm, find the area.

72. How many liters of water must be evaporated from 18 L of a 24% ammonia solution to produce a 30% solution?

73. Marcy needs 40 min to wash and wax the family car, and Sue needs 1 h. Marcy was working for 25 min when Sue joined her. How long did it take them to finish the job?

74. A two-digit number is 7 times the sum of its digits. If the product of the digits is 18, find the number.

75. A plane flew 1600 km with a 20 km/h tail wind. The return trip took 10 min more. Find the speed of the plane in still air.

76. Two cars traveling in opposite directions left a tollbooth at 7 P.M. One car was traveling at 76 km/h and the other at 84 km/h. At what time were the cars at least 120 km apart?

LOOKING AHEAD

GEOMETRY

Lines and Angles

OBJECTIVE   To represent points, lines, planes, and angles and to measure angles.

You have been using the ideas of a *line* and a *plane* to help you visualize number relationships on a number line and in a coordinate plane. The concepts of a line and a plane as certain kinds of sets of points come from a branch of mathematics called *geometry.*

To represent a *geometric point,* you draw a dot, but a geometric point is an abstract idea, not a concrete object. The lines you draw represent the idea of a *geometric line,* which has no thickness.

A line determined by points A and B is denoted by $\overleftrightarrow{AB}$, or $\overleftrightarrow{BA}$. The arrowheads indicate that the line extends in both directions without ending.

line AB: $\overleftrightarrow{AB}$

The part of $\overleftrightarrow{AB}$ that consists of points A and B and all points of $\overleftrightarrow{AB}$ between A and B is a **line segment,** or a **segment,** denoted by $\overline{AB}$, or $\overline{BA}$. The length of $\overline{AB}$ is denoted by AB.

segment AB: $\overline{AB}$

The part of $\overleftrightarrow{AB}$ that starts at point A and extends without ending through point B is a **ray** denoted by $\overrightarrow{AB}$. A is the **endpoint** of $\overrightarrow{AB}$.

An **angle** is a figure formed by two different rays that have the same endpoint. The rays are called the **sides** of the angle and the common endpoint is the **vertex** of the angle. The angle shown above is formed by $\overrightarrow{AB}$ and $\overrightarrow{AC}$. It is denoted by $\angle A$, $\angle BAC$, or $\angle CAB$.

468

To find the **degree measure** of an angle, you use a *protractor*, as shown below. Using the outer scale, you can see that the measure of $\angle POQ$ is 35° (35 *degrees*). You may write this fact as $\angle POQ = 35°$. Also, $\angle POR = 90°$ and $\angle POS = 125°$.

Angles are classified according to their measures.

> An **acute angle** measures between 0° and 90°.
> A **right angle** measures 90°.
> An **obtuse angle** measures between 90° and 180°.
> A **straight angle** measures 180°.

You can find $\angle QOR$ in the diagram above by subtracting 35 from 90: $\angle QOR = 55°$. Do you see that $\angle QOS$ is a right angle? that $\angle ROS = 35°$? To state that $\angle ROS$ and $\angle POQ$ have equal measures, you write $\angle ROS = \angle POQ$.

Oral Exercises

Exercises 1–8 refer to the diagram below.

Name each angle whose measure is given.

1. 110°   **2.** 60°   **3.** 25°   **4.** 90°

State the measure of each angle.

5. $\angle EOF$ **6.** $\angle BOE$ **7.** $\angle COF$ **8.** $\angle DOF$

Written Exercises

In Exercises 1–4, name 5 different line segments in each diagram.

A   1.

2.

3.

4.

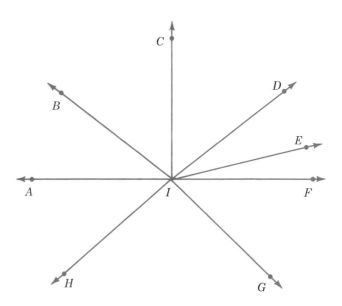

Classify each angle as acute, obtuse, or right.

5. ∠FIE   **6.** ∠CIF

7. ∠BIF   **8.** ∠HIG

9. ∠HIA   **10.** ∠CIG

11. ∠BID   **12.** ∠CID

Graph the solution set of each sentence on a number line. Identify the graph as a point, a line, a segment, or a ray.

B   13. $x = 3$ **14.** $x \leq 2$ **15.** $1 \leq x \leq 3$

16. $x + 5 = 1$ **17.** $x + 2 = 5 + x - 3$ **18.** $-4 \leq x - 2 \leq 4$

C   19. $x + 5 \geq 3$ and $x - 1 \leq 3$ **20.** $x + 2 \leq 7$ or $x + 3 \leq 6$

21. $2x \geq 6$ or $3x < 15$ **22.** $5x - 8 \leq 2$ and $3x + 5 \geq 11$

Pairs of Angles

OBJECTIVE To learn the names and properties of some special pairs of angles.

Some pairs of angles whose measures are related are given special names.

The diagram shows two lines intersecting at O and forming $\angle AOB$, $\angle BOC$, $\angle COD$, and $\angle DOA$. Two angles, such as $\angle AOB$ and $\angle COD$, whose sides are rays in the same lines but in opposite directions are called **vertical angles.** $\angle BOC$ and $\angle DOA$ are also a pair of vertical angles.

Vertical angles are equal. Use a protractor to check that $\angle AOB = \angle COD$ and $\angle BOC = \angle DOA$.

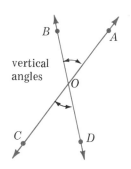

vertical angles

Two angles are **complementary angles** if the sum of their measures is 90°. Each angle is a **complement** of the other. The diagram at the left below shows a pair of complementary angles.

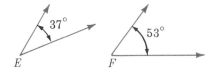

$\angle E$ and $\angle F$ are complementary.
$\angle E$ is a complement of $\angle F$.

$\angle Q$ and $\angle R$ are supplementary.
$\angle Q$ is a supplement of $\angle R$.

Two angles are **supplementary angles** if the sum of their measures is 180°. Each angle is a **supplement** of the other. The diagram at the right above shows a pair of supplementary angles.

EXAMPLE Find the measure of an angle such that the sum of the measures of its complement and its supplement is 150°.

SOLUTION Let $n =$ the measure of the angle in degrees.
Then $90 - n =$ the measure of its complement,
and $180 - n =$ the measure of its supplement.

$$90 - n + 180 - n = 150$$
$$270 - 2n = 150$$
$$-2n = -120$$
$$n = 60$$

The measure of the complement is $(90 - 60)°$, or 30°.
The measure of the supplement is $(180 - 60)°$, or 120°.

Is the sum of these measures 150°? Yes, $30 + 120 = 150$.

∴ the measure of the angle is 60°. **Answer**

Oral Exercises

State the measure of the complement of an angle with the given measure.

1. 70°   **2.** 8°   **3.** 35°   **4.** 13°   **5.** y degrees   **6.** $3y$ degrees

State the measure of the supplement of the angle with the given measure.

7. 130°   **8.** 20°   **9.** 90°   **10.** 46°   **11.** x degrees   **12.** $5x$ degrees

Classify each statement as true or false.

13. If two angles have equal measures, then their supplements have equal measures.

14. The measures of two complementary angles are never equal.

15. If an angle is obtuse, its supplement is acute.

16. If an angle is a right angle, its supplement is a right angle.

17. If an angle is acute, its complement is obtuse.

Written Exercises

In Exercises 1–4 use the diagram. Assume that the measures of $\angle ACB$ and $\angle EGF$ are equal.

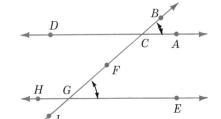

A **1.** List all the angles with measures equal to the measure of $\angle ACB$.

    2. List all the angles that are supplementary to $\angle ACB$.

    3. If $\angle ACB = 40°$, then $\angle BCD =$ __?°__.

    4. If $\angle FGH = 140°$, then $\angle FGE =$ __?°__.

    5. What are the measures of two supplementary angles, the larger of which measures 4 times the smaller?

    6. What are the measures of two supplementary angles, the smaller of which measures 32° less than the larger?

    7. Find the measure of the angle which measures 20° more than its complement.

    8. Find the measures of two complementary angles if the measure of the larger is twice the measure of the smaller.

B **9.** An acute angle has a measure of $(x + 2y)°$. What is the difference between the measures of the supplement and complement of this angle?

10. The sum of the measures of two vertical angles is 10 times the measure of the supplement of one of the angles. Find the measure of one of the vertical angles.

11. The sum of the measures of a complement and a supplement of an angle is 140.° Find the measure of the angle.

C 12. The ratio of the measures of the complements of two angles is 3:4, while the ratio of the measures of their supplements is 9:10. Find the measure of each angle.

Just for Fun

Find the value of x such that the sum of the expressions is the same in each row, column, or diagonal.

x	5	$x - 2$
$x - 5$	9	11
8	$x + 1$	$x - 6$

Historical Note Multiplication Sign

The arrows in the diagram below show the pattern for finding the product 25 × 43 as calculated at the right below.

$$5 \times 3 = 15$$
$$5 \times 40 = 200$$
$$20 \times 3 = 60$$
$$20 \times 40 = \underline{800}$$
$$1075$$

This method for multiplication was used in the sixteenth century by some mathematicians.

William Oughtred, an English clergyman, used a small raised cross to indicate multiplication in a mathematics book published in 1631. This symbol was not widely used until the latter half of the nineteenth century, however.

In 1698, the dot for multiplication was introduced by Gottfried W. von Leibniz, a German mathematician. He thought the sign × could be mistaken too easily for the letter x. In the United States, the multiplication dot is raised and the decimal point is on the line of writing. In some other countries, the usage is reversed.

Triangles

OBJECTIVE To learn some properties of triangles.

A **triangle** is the figure formed by three segments joining three points not on a line, as shown below. Each segment is a **side** of the triangle. Each of the three points is a **vertex** of the triangle.

"Triangle ABC" can be written $\triangle ABC$.

Sides of $\triangle ABC$: $\overline{AB}$, $\overline{BC}$, $\overline{CA}$

Vertices of $\triangle ABC$: A, B, C

Angles of $\triangle ABC$: $\angle A$, $\angle B$, $\angle C$

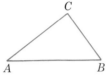

In any triangle, the sum of the measures of the angles is $180°$. You can check this statement for a particular triangle by measuring its angles with a protractor and finding the sum of the measures. Also, if you tear off the corners of a paper triangle and fit them together, you will find that they form a straight angle, as shown below.

 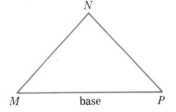

Here are some special triangles:

  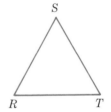

Right triangle	**Isosceles triangle**	**Equilateral triangle**
$\angle C = 90°$	$MN = NP$; $\angle M = \angle P$	$RS = ST = TR$
$AC^2 + BC^2 = AB^2$	**Base:** MP	$\angle R = \angle S = \angle T = 60°$
(Pythagorean theorem,	**Base angles:** $\angle M$ and $\angle P$	
p. 422; converse, p. 423)		

The small square in the right triangle above indicates the right angle.

Oral Exercises

Identify $\triangle ABC$ as right, isosceles, or equilateral given the information below.

1. $AC = BC$

2. $\angle C = 90°$

3. $AB = BC = CA$

4. $\angle A = 30°$, $\angle C = 120°$

5. $\angle A = 21°$, $\angle B = 69°$

6. $AC = 11$, $BC = 11$

7. $AC = 3$, $AB = 5$, $BC = 4$

8. $\angle A = 60°$, $\angle C = 60°$

Written Exercises

The measures of two angles of a triangle are given. Find the measure of the third angle.

A
1. $42°$, $69°$

2. $73°$, $22°$

3. $12°$, $43°$

4. $63°$, $100°$

5. $90°$, $41°$

6. $53°$, $67°$

In Exercises 7-12, use the converse of the Pythagorean theorem to determine whether the triangle is a right triangle.

7. $\triangle ABC$: $AB = 4$, $BC = 3$, $AC = 5$

8. $\triangle DEF$: $DE = 4$, $EF = 6$, $FD = 7$

9. $\triangle GHI$: $GH = 12$, $HI = 5$, $IG = 13$

10. $\triangle JKL$: $JK = 6$, $KL = 8$, $LJ = 10$

11. $\triangle MNO$: $MN = 9$, $NO = 8$, $OM = 17$

12. $\triangle PQR$: $PQ = 24$, $QR = 7$, $RP = 25$

13. If $\triangle STU$ is a right triangle with $\angle T = 90°$, $ST = 9$, and $TU = 12$, find US.

14. If $\triangle XYZ$ is a right triangle with $\angle Y = 90°$, $XY = 15$, and $XZ = 17$, find YZ.

15. If $\triangle MNR$ is isosceles, $\angle M = 50°$, and $MN = MR$, find the measure of $\angle R$.

16. If $\triangle ABC$ is a right isosceles triangle and $\angle A = 90°$ find the measures of $\angle B$ and $\angle C$.

In Exercises 17-22, $\angle C = 90°$ in $\triangle ABC$. Find the length of the third side in simplest radical form given the lengths of the other two sides.

B
17. $AC = 6$, $BC = 10$

18. $AC = 9$, $BC = 6$

19. $AC = 4$, $AB = 6$

20. $AB = 15$, $AC = 6$

C
21. $AC = BC = x$

22. $AC = y$, $AB = 2y$

Problems

Solve.

A 1. In a right triangle the measure of one of the acute angles is 4 times the measure of the other. Find the measure of each angle.

2. Find the measure of each angle of an isosceles triangle if the measure of the third angle is 7 times the measure of either of the two base angles.

3. Find the measure of each angle of a triangle if the measure of the second angle is 3 times that of the first, and the measure of the third angle is 6 times that of the first.

4. The measures of the angles of a triangle are in the ratio 2 to 3 to 4. Find the measure of each angle.

5. The measure of the second angle of a triangle is $\frac{1}{2}$ that of the first, and the measure of the third angle is 5° more than twice that of the second. Find the measure of each angle.

6. The measures of two angles of a triangle are equal. The measure of the third is $\frac{2}{7}$ of the sum of the first two. Find the measures of the angles.

B 7. The measure of the second angle of a triangle is 2° more than twice the first, and the measure of the third angle is 26° less than 3 times the second. Find the measure of each angle.

8. The sum of four angles about a point is 360°. The measure of the second angle is 6° more than 3 times the first, the measure of the third is 3° more than twice the first, and the measure of the fourth is 20° less than the third. What is the measure of each angle?

C 9. The measure of the second angle of a triangle is 20° more than the complement of the first angle, and the third angle is 4° less than half the supplement of the first. Find the measure of each angle.

Just for Fun ⎯⎯⎯⎯⎯⎯⎯⎯⎯⎯

Arrange sixteen toothpicks to form the pattern shown, which has eight small equilateral triangles. Remove four toothpicks so that only four of the triangles are left.

Similar Triangles

OBJECTIVE To use similar triangles.

An object viewed under a magnifying lens appears larger than it is, but its shape is not changed. Two figures that have the same shape are called *similar*.

Two triangles are **similar triangles** when the measures of two angles of one triangle equal the measures of two angles of the other triangle. (Since the sum of the measures of the angles of a triangle is 180°, it follows that the remaining angles also have equal measures.) The triangles shown below are similar.

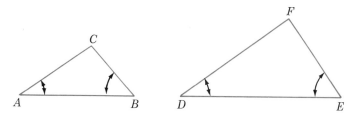

$$\angle A = \angle D, \ \angle B = \angle E, \ \angle C = \angle F$$

You can denote that triangles ABC and DEF are similar by writing

$$\triangle ABC \sim \triangle DEF.$$

Here angles with equal measures are listed in corresponding positions. They are called **corresponding angles.** The sides opposite corresponding angles are called **corresponding sides.** $\overline{AB}$ corresponds to $\overline{DE}$, and so on. *It is a geometric fact that the lengths of corresponding sides of similar triangles are proportional.* Thus,

$$\frac{AB}{DE} = \frac{BC}{EF} = \frac{CA}{FD}.$$

EXAMPLE 1 In the diagram, $\triangle ABC \sim \triangle DEF$. Find AC and BC.

SOLUTION Corresponding sides are proportional:

$$\frac{AC}{25} = \frac{18}{30} \quad \text{and} \quad \frac{BC}{20} = \frac{18}{30}$$

Solving each proportion, you will find that

$$AC = 15 \text{ and } BC = 12.$$

$\qquad\qquad\qquad\qquad\quad$ ***Answer***

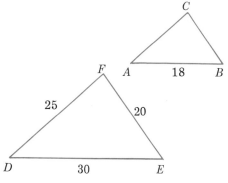

EXAMPLE 2 In the diagram, $\triangle ABC \sim \triangle AEF$.
Find EF and AF.

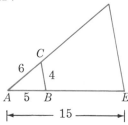

SOLUTION Corresponding sides
are proportional:

$$\frac{5}{15} = \frac{4}{EF} \quad \text{and} \quad \frac{5}{15} = \frac{6}{AF}$$

Completing the solution
is left to you.

Oral Exercises

In the diagram for Exercises 1–3, $\triangle RST \sim \triangle RWQ$.

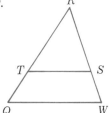

1. Name the corresponding angles.
2. Name the corresponding sides.
3. State three equal ratios.

Written Exercises

A 1. In $\triangle DEF$, $\angle D = 50°$ and $\angle E = 70°$. In $\triangle JKL$, $\angle K = 50°$ and
$\angle L = 70°$. Write the corresponding angles and corresponding
sides.

2. In $\triangle MNP$ and $\triangle RST$, $\angle M = \angle T$ and $\angle P = \angle S$. Write three
equal ratios.

Classify each statement as true or false.

3. All isosceles triangles are similar.
4. All equilateral triangles are similar.
5. All right triangles are similar.
6. All isosceles right triangles are similar.

In Exercises 7–11, $\triangle ABC \sim \triangle DEF$. Find the lengths of the sides not
given.

7. $AB = 5$, $BC = 3$, $AC = 4$, $ED = 10$
8. $ED = 8$, $EF = 6$, $DF = 4$, $AC = 6$
9. $AB = 6$, $BC = 9$, $AC = 12$, $EF = 3$
10. $ED = 6$, $EF = DF = 9$, $AB = 8$
11. $AB = 8$, $BC = 10$, $AC = 12$, $DF = 8$

Problems

Solve.

A **1.** A triangle has sides with lengths 9 cm, 15 cm, and 18 cm. If the longest side of a similar triangle is 24 cm, find its shortest side.

2. A vertical stick 2 m long casts a shadow 1 m long at the same time a building casts a shadow 15 m long. How tall is the building?

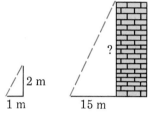

3. A person 2 m tall casts a shadow 3 m long at the same time a tree casts a shadow 15 m long. Find the height of the tree.

4. To find the length of a pond, two similar triangles were paced off. The measurements are shown on the diagram. How long is the pond?

B **5.** Jose rides his bike 3 m up a ramp and is 1 m above the ground. If he were to ride 6 m farther, how far above the ground would he be?

6. From a point on the ground 4 m from the base of a 5 m tree, it is possible to see the top of a 200 m building just over the top of the tree. How far is the point from the base of the building?

Just for Fun _____

A parallelogram is a figure in geometry. Geometry is a branch of mathematics. Therefore, a parallelogram is a figure in mathematics.

No canaries are in my house. My house is in the Canary Islands. Therefore, no canaries are in the Canary Islands.

Is this reasoning logical?

TRIGONOMETRY

Trigonometric Ratios

OBJECTIVE To find the sine, cosine, and tangent of an acute angle.

In the branch of mathematics called *trigonometry* you learn more about the measurement of triangles.

Any acute angle, such as $\angle A$ in the diagram, can be made an angle of a right triangle ABC. The legs opposite and adjacent to this angle are labeled. Ratios of the lengths of the sides of $\triangle ABC$ are called **trigonometric ratios** associated with $\angle A$. These ratios have special names and symbols.

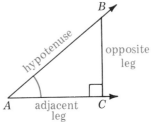

sine of $\angle A$ (symbol, $\sin A$) $= \dfrac{\text{length of leg opposite } \angle A}{\text{length of hypotenuse}} = \dfrac{BC}{AB}$

cosine of $\angle A$ (symbol, $\cos A$) $= \dfrac{\text{length of leg adjacent to } \angle A}{\text{length of hypotenuse}} = \dfrac{AC}{AB}$

tangent of $\angle A$ (symbol, $\tan A$) $= \dfrac{\text{length of leg opposite } \angle A}{\text{length of leg adjacent to } \angle A} = \dfrac{BC}{AC}$

EXAMPLE 1 Find the sine, cosine, and tangent of $\angle A$ and $\angle B$.

SOLUTION

$\sin A = \dfrac{3}{5}$ $\qquad$ $\sin B = \dfrac{4}{5}$

$\cos A = \dfrac{4}{5}$ $\qquad$ $\cos B = \dfrac{3}{5}$

$\tan A = \dfrac{3}{4}$ $\qquad$ $\tan B = \dfrac{4}{3}$

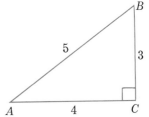

EXAMPLE 2 Find the sine, cosine, and tangent of $\angle K$.

SOLUTION First use the Pythagorean theorem to find the length of the hypotenuse.

$c^2 = 6^2 + 4^2 = 36 + 16 = 52$
$\therefore c = \sqrt{52} = 2\sqrt{13}$

$\sin K = \dfrac{4}{2\sqrt{13}} = \dfrac{2\sqrt{13}}{13}$ $\qquad$ $\cos K = \dfrac{6}{2\sqrt{13}} = \dfrac{3\sqrt{13}}{13}$ $\qquad$ $\tan K = \dfrac{4}{6} = \dfrac{2}{3}$

The values of the trigonometric ratios of an angle depend only on the measure of the angle and not on the particular right triangle which contains the angle. For example, in the two right triangles below, $\angle A$ and $\angle D$ have equal measures. It can be shown that the trigonometric ratios of $\angle A$ and $\angle D$ are also equal.

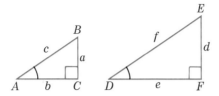

Since $\angle A = \angle D$ and $\angle C = \angle F = 90°$, the triangles are similar and their corresponding sides are proportional:

$$\frac{a}{d} = \frac{c}{f}$$

Multiplying both ratios by $\frac{d}{c}$, you obtain the equivalent proportion

$$\frac{a}{c} = \frac{d}{f}, \text{ or } \sin A = \sin D.$$

You can show similarly that $\cos A = \cos D$ and $\tan A = \tan D$.

Because the values of $\sin A$, $\cos A$, and $\tan A$ depend only on the measure of $\angle A$ and not on the triangle containing $\angle A$, you can think of these trigonometric ratios as the values of three functions each having the set of acute angles as its domain. These functions are called **trigonometric functions.**

Oral Exercises

State the value of each trigonometric ratio for the triangle shown.

1. $\sin A$
2. $\cos A$
3. $\tan A$
4. $\sin B$
5. $\cos B$
6. $\tan B$

7. $\sin X$
8. $\cos X$
9. $\tan X$
10. $\sin Y$
11. $\cos Y$
12. $\tan Y$

Written Exercises

For each right triangle shown, find cos A, sin A, tan A, cos B, sin B, and tan B. Write your answers in simplest radical form.

A 1.

2.

3.

4.

5.

6.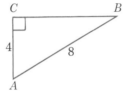

Show that for all right triangles ABC, where $\angle C$ is a right angle and $\angle A$ is an acute angle, the following statements are true.

B 7. $\cos A = \sin B$ **8.** $\sin A = \cos B$

    9. $(\sin A)^2 + (\cos A)^2 = 1$ **10.** $\tan A = \dfrac{\sin A}{\cos A}$

C 11. If $\cos A = \dfrac{6}{10}$, find $\sin A$.

   12. If $\sin B = \dfrac{3}{8}$, find the sine of the complement of $\angle B$.

   13. If $\tan D = \dfrac{20}{21}$, find $\sin D$ and $\cos D$.

Using Trigonometric Tables

OBJECTIVE To find values of trigonometric ratios for given angles, and measures of angles for given trigonometric ratios.

Values of the trigonometric ratios for degree measures of angles are needed to solve practical problems involving right triangles. A few values can be easily computed using the properties of special triangles and the Pythagorean theorem. For an isosceles right triangle:

$$\sin 45° = \frac{1}{\sqrt{2}} = \frac{\sqrt{2}}{2} \approx 0.707$$

$$\cos 45° = \frac{1}{\sqrt{2}} = \frac{\sqrt{2}}{2} \approx 0.707$$

$$\tan 45° = \frac{1}{1} = 1$$

Most values of trigonometric ratios have to be computed by advanced methods. Approximate values are listed in the table of trigonometric ratios at the back of the book. You can use the table to find $\sin A$, $\cos A$, and $\tan A$ for any angle with whole-number measure from 1° to 89°.

To find the value of $\sin 63°$, locate 63° in the left-hand column of the table and then read across the row to find:

$\sin 63° \approx 0.8910$

$\cos 63° \approx 0.4540$

$\tan 63° \approx 1.9626$

For ordinary computation you may write = instead of $\approx$ in equations such as these.

Angle	Sine	Cosine	Tangent
1°	.0175	.9998	.0175
61°	.8746	.4848	1.8040
62°	.8829	.4695	1.8807
63°	.8910	.4540	1.9626
64°	.8988	.4384	2.0503
65°	.9063	.4226	2.1445

The trigonometric table can also be used to approximate the measure of an angle if one of its trigonometric ratios is given. For example, the table indicates that an angle whose sine is approximately 0.8746 has a measure of 61°.

Suppose that $\cos A = 0.4273$, a number not listed in the table. To find the approximate measure of $\angle A$, locate in the cosine column the entries between which 0.4273 lies:

$$\cos 64° = 0.4384 \text{ and } \cos 65° = 0.4226.$$

Thus, $$64° < \angle A < 65°.$$

Since 0.4273 is closer to 0.4226 than it is to 0.4384,

$$\angle A = 65°, \text{ to the nearest degree.}$$

Oral Exercises

For Exercises 1-12, use the portion of the table of trigonometric ratios shown on the preceding page.

State the value of each trigonometric ratio.

1. $\sin 1°$	**2.** $\tan 1°$	**3.** $\cos 61°$
4. $\tan 62°$	**5.** $\sin 65°$	**6.** $\cos 64°$

Find the measure of $\angle A$ to the nearest degree.

7. $\cos A = 0.9998$	**8.** $\tan A = 2.0503$	**9.** $\sin A = 0.8746$
10. $\sin A = 0.9000$	**11.** $\cos A = 0.4700$	**12.** $\tan A = 2.1337$

Written Exercises

Use the table at the back of the book to find $\sin A$, $\cos A$, and $\tan A$ for the given measure of $\angle A$.

A
1. $20°$	**2.** $80°$	**3.** $35°$	**4.** $51°$	**5.** $17°$	**6.** $39°$
7. $43°$	**8.** $26°$	**9.** $62°$	**10.** $18°$	**11.** $73°$	**12.** $84°$

Find the measure of $\angle A$ to the nearest degree.

13. $\sin A = 0.4695$	**14.** $\cos A = 0.9511$	**15.** $\cos A = 0.3762$
16. $\sin A = 0.9751$	**17.** $\tan A = 0.4245$	**18.** $\cos A = 0.8835$
19. $\sin A = 0.6939$	**20.** $\tan A = 4.0940$	**21.** $\tan A = 0.3788$
22. $\sin A = 0.8384$	**23.** $\cos A = 0.0710$	**24.** $\tan A = 1.2511$

Biography Shibasaburo Kitasato

Shibasaburo Kitasato (1852–1931) was the eldest son of the mayor of a small mountain village in Japan. He studied medicine at the University of Tokyo and graduated in 1883. After working for the Public Health Bureau, he spent six years in Germany studying under the famous bacteriologist, Robert Koch. During this time he isolated the bacterium that causes the infectious diseases symptomatic anthrax and tetanus. A paper he coauthored in 1890 marked the beginning of the science of serology, the use of immune serums or antitoxins to cure infectious diseases and prevent epidemics.

Kitasato was elected the first president of the Japanese Medical Association in 1923 and was given the title of baron in 1924 by the emperor of Japan.

Numerical Trigonometry

OBJECTIVE To use trigonometric ratios to solve problems.

Using trigonometric ratios, you can solve many practical problems involving right triangles.

EXAMPLE 1 A van is moving along a straight road which makes a 7° angle with the level ground. The van passes two signposts 1500 m apart. How much higher, to the nearest meter, is the base of the second signpost above the base of the first signpost?

SOLUTION Draw a triangle showing the known values.

You wish to find x, the height of the base of the second signpost above the base of the first signpost. Since $\triangle ABC$ is a right triangle,

$$\sin 7° = \frac{x}{1500}, \quad \text{or} \quad x = 1500(\sin 7°).$$

From the table, $\sin 7° = 0.1219$.
Then $x = 1500(0.1219) = 182.85$

∴ to the nearest meter, the second signpost is 183 m above the first signpost. *Answer*

In surveying and navigation problems involving right triangles, the terms *angle of elevation* and *angle of depression* are used.

In the diagram below, $\angle CBA$ is an angle of elevation, since the point A is elevated with respect to the observer at B. $\angle DAB$ is an angle of depression, since the point B is depressed with respect to the observer at A.

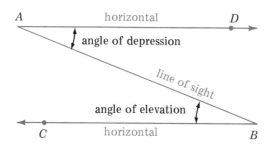

EXAMPLE 2 On the top of a vertical cliff 320 m above sea level, the angle of depression of a boat out at sea is 42°. To the nearest meter, what is the distance of the boat from the base of the cliff?

SOLUTION Draw a triangle. You wish to find x, the distance of the boat from the base of the cliff. In right $\triangle ABC$ $\angle CAB = (90 - 42)° = 48°$.

$$\tan 48° = \frac{x}{320}$$

$$x = 320 \tan 48°$$

From the table, $\tan 48° = 1.1106$.
Then, $x = 320(1.1106) = 355.392$.

∴ to the nearest meter, the boat is 355 m from the base of the cliff.
Answer

Oral Exercises

State whether you would use the cosine, sine, or tangent ratio to find x for each figure.

1.

2.

3.

4.

5.

6.

Written Exercises

Use the table at the back of the book as needed.

A **1–6.** In the Oral Exercises, find x for each figure. Give each length to the nearest whole number.

In right triangle ABC, with $\angle C = 90°$, find the other sides of the triangle to the nearest whole number from the following facts.

7. $\angle A = 39°$, $AB = 64$
9. $\angle A = 16°$, $AC = 60$

8. $\angle A = 35°$, $AB = 61$
10. $\angle B = 68°$, $BC = 85$

In right $\triangle MNR$, $\angle N = 90°$. Find the measures of $\angle M$ and $\angle R$ to the nearest degree from the following facts.

B **11.** $MN = 25$, $NR = 45$
13. $RM = 40$, $MN = 38$

12. $MR = 32$, $NR = 28$
14. $MR = 45$, $NR = 27$

In right $\triangle XYZ$, $\angle Z = 90°$. Find the measures of the other sides of the triangle to the nearest whole number from the following facts.

15. $\angle Y = 38°$, $XY = 50$
17. $\angle X = 24°$, $XY = 47$

16. $\angle X = 72°$, $XY = 38$
18. $\angle Y = 42°$, $XY = 80$

Problems

Solve each problem, drawing a sketch for each. Express distances to the nearest unit. Use the table in the back of the book as needed.

A **1.** To the nearest meter, how far is it across the swamp?

2. To the nearest centimeter, how high is the flagpole?

220 m

65°

200 cm

3. A 28 m long cable connects a point on the ground to the top of a pole. The cable makes a 32° angle with the ground. Find the height of the pole.

28 m

32°

x

4. A 400 cm ladder resting against a building makes a 58° angle with the ground. How far is the bottom of the ladder from the base of the building?

5. A train increases its altitude by 11 m when traveling along 200 m of track. Find the angle of elevation of the track.

Ex. 5

Ex. 6

6. A ramp 400 cm long is dropped from the rear of a van to the ground. If the ramp makes a 10° angle with the ground, find how high the floor of the van is from the ground.

7. If a rocket flies 1° off course for 5000 km, how far away from the correct path will the rocket be?

8. A surveyor is determining the direction in which tunnel AB is to be dug through a mountain. She locates point C so that $\angle C = 90°$, $AC = 1.5$ km, and $BC = 3.5$ km. Find $\angle A$ to the nearest degree.

B 9. Jon is standing 150 m from the base of a cliff. He determines that the angle of elevation to the top of the cliff is 48°. Find the height of the cliff.

10. From a helicopter the angle of depression of a stranded car is 22°. The altimeter shows that the helicopter is 1300 m above the ground. Assuming that the ground is flat in that location, determine how far the car is from a point directly below the helicopter.

11. From the bow of a ship 50 m long heading directly north, a lighthouse is sighted directly west. At the same time the lighthouse is sighted at an 80° angle from the stern of the ship. Find the distance from the bow to the lighthouse.

12. A diving submarine travels through water at a steady rate of 320 m/min on a diving path that forms a 4° angle of depression with the surface of the water. After 5 min, how far is the submarine below the surface?

C 13. A trail bike driven in a straight path for 200 m makes an angle turn and travels 200 m again. At this point, the driver returns directly 240 m to the starting point. Through what angle did the driver turn?

14. From a 1400 m high observation tower the angles of depression of two cars in the same direction are found to be 18° and 28°. Find the distance between the two cars.

15. From a point in the street between two buildings, the angles of elevation of the tops of the buildings are 45° each. When the observer moves 6 m toward one of the buildings, the angles of elevation are 30° and 60°. How high is each building?

Summary

1. Geometry deals with the properties of sets of points such as lines, rays, angles, and triangles.

2. Two angles whose sides are rays in the same lines but in opposite directions are vertical angles. Any pair of angles the sum of whose measures is 90° are complementary angles. Two angles are supplementary if the sum of their measures is 180°.

3. The sum of the measures of the angles of a triangle is 180°. Some special triangles are right triangles, isosceles triangles, and equilateral triangles.

4. Similar triangles have the same shape. Their corresponding angles have the same measure and corresponding sides are proportional.

5. Trigonometric ratios: $\cos A = \frac{b}{c}$, $\sin A = \frac{a}{c}$, $\tan A = \frac{a}{b}$

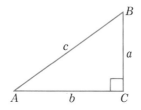

Review

Give the letter of the best answer.

1. Which symbol denotes the measure of a line segment joining points A and B?

    a. AB **b.** $\overline{AB}$ **c.** $\overrightarrow{AB}$ **d.** $\overleftrightarrow{AB}$

2. Which angle is an acute angle?

    a. $\angle A = 99°$ **b.** $\angle B = 89°$ **c.** $\angle C = 90°$ **d.** $\angle D = 100°$

3. Find the measure of the complement of an angle of $36°$.

    a. $154°$ **b.** $144°$ **c.** $64°$ **d.** $54°$

4. Find the supplement of an angle with measure $x°$.

    a. $(90 - x)°$ **b.** $(90 + x)°$ **c.** $(180 - x)°$ **d.** $(180 + x)°$

5. Find the sum of the measures of the angles of an isosceles triangle.

    a. $45°$ **b.** $90°$ **c.** $180°$ **d.** $360°$

6. If $\triangle ABC \sim \triangle DEF$, $\dfrac{AB}{DE} = \dfrac{7}{2}$, and $CA = 10$, find FD.

    a. 35 **b.** $\dfrac{20}{7}$ **c.** $\dfrac{7}{20}$ **d.** 5

7. Use the diagram to find $\sin A$.

    a. $\dfrac{6}{8}$ **b.** $\dfrac{4}{5}$

    c. $\dfrac{3}{5}$ **d.** $\dfrac{4}{3}$

8. Use the table at the back of the book to find $\tan 72°$.

    a. 0.1228 **b.** 2.3090 **c.** 0.0777 **d.** 3.0777

9. The top of a stairway is 2 m higher than the bottom. The angle of elevation from the bottom of the stairs to the top is $25°$. Find the approximate horizontal length of the stairway.

    a. 4.3 m   **b.** 1.8 m   **c.** 4.7 m   **d.** 0.9 m

EXTRA PRACTICE

CHAPTER 1

Simplify.

1. $4 + (3 \times 6)$ **2.** $(4 + 3) \times 6$ **3.** $(20 + 2) \times (7 + 3)$

4. $(20 \div 2) - (7 - 3)$ **5.** $(20 - 2) \div (7 + 2)$ **6.** $(20 \times 2) + (7 \times 3)$

Evaluate each expression if $a = 1$, $b = 2$, $c = 3$, and $d = 4$.

7. $ab + cd$ **8.** $(b + c)(c + d)$ **9.** $a(b + c - d)$

10. $\dfrac{c + d}{a + 3b}$ **11.** $5a - 2a$ **12.** $5c - 2c$

13. $\dfrac{ab + 2c}{a + c}$ **14.** $2(a + bc)$ **15.** $2a + 2bc$

16. $d[a + b(c + d)]$ **17.** $\dfrac{2c + b}{2a} - \dfrac{(a + b)(c + d)}{3b + a}$

Solve each equation if $x \in \{2, 4, 6, 8, 10\}$. If there is no solution over the given domain, write "no solution."

18. $2 + x = 8$ **19.** $8 + x = 2$ **20.** $2x + 4 = x + 8$

21. $5(x - 2) = 10$ **22.** $x \div (4 - x) = 1$ **23.** $(x + 4) - (x \div 4) = 7$

24. $x(x + 1) = 27$ **25.** $(x - 1)(x + 1) = (x)(x) - 1$

26. $x(x + 1)(x - 1) = 6$ **27.** $(2x)(3x)(4x) = 24x$

Represent each phrase by a variable expression. Use n to represent the number referred to.

28. Three times a number

29. Three more than a number

30. Three less than a number

31. Three divided by a number

32. Twice a number, decreased by five

33. Twice a number that has been decreased by five

34. One less than half a number

Complete each statement with an expression involving the given variable.

35. Charles is x years old now. Two years from now he will be __?__ years old.

36. Charles is x years old now. Two years ago he was __?__ years old.

37. Susan can run r km/h. Francis can run twice as fast. Francis can run __?__ km/h.

Complete each statement with an expression involving the given variable.

38. Mary can do m pushups. Julia can do 3 fewer. Julia can do __?__ pushups.

39. A box has 22 pieces of chocolate. There are d pieces of dark chocolate and __?__ pieces of light chocolate.

40. Four years ago David was d years old. Now David is __?__ years old.

41. A record and a poster together cost m dollars. If the poster costs p dollars, then the record costs __?__ dollars.

For each exercise, write an equation that represents the given facts in terms of the given variable.

42. The perimeter of a square is x cm and each side is 12 cm long.

43. The side of a square is x cm long, and the perimeter is 32 cm.

44. Pam can run at m km/h. In 2.5 h (hours) she can run 30 km.

45. Scott can run at 12 km/h. In t hours he can run 8 km.

46. Sarah received t on her first test and 87 on her next test. The average of her grades is 82.

47. The smallest of three consecutive numbers is m. The sum of the three numbers is 4224.

48. The smallest of three consecutive numbers is m. The product of the three numbers is 716.

49. One number is x, and a second number is 3 times the first. The sum of the two numbers equals their product.

50. The length of a rectangle is x cm, and the width is 6 cm less than the length. The perimeter is 24 cm.

51. Brad pays x cents for one ride on the subway. He pays \$1.75 (175 cents) for 7 rides.

52. Harold is h years old now. Nine years ago he was 27 years old.

53. A record costs r dollars. The cost of a cassette is \$3 more than twice the cost of the record. Together, the record and tape cost \$11.40.

CHAPTER 2

Add.

1. $\begin{array}{r} -7 \\ 2 \\ \hline \end{array}$

2. $\begin{array}{r} 6 \\ -7 \\ \hline \end{array}$

3. $\begin{array}{r} -4 \\ 6 \\ \hline \end{array}$

4. $\begin{array}{r} -4 \\ -3 \\ \hline \end{array}$

5. $\begin{array}{r} -3 \\ -2 \\ \hline \end{array}$

6. $\begin{array}{r} -2 \\ 1 \\ \hline \end{array}$

7. $\begin{array}{r} 1 \\ -1 \\ \hline \end{array}$

8. $\begin{array}{r} -7 \\ 8 \\ \hline \end{array}$

9. $\begin{array}{r} 8 \\ -2 \\ \hline \end{array}$

10. $\begin{array}{r} -2 \\ -5 \\ \hline \end{array}$

11. $\begin{array}{r} -5 \\ -10 \\ \hline \end{array}$

12. $\begin{array}{r} -10 \\ 5 \\ \hline \end{array}$

Simplify.

13. $(-4 + 5) + (-3)$

14. $(4 + 5) + (-3)$

15. $(6 + 8) + (-10)$

16. $[6 + (-10)] + 12$

17. $[-4 + (-5)] + 3$

18. $[4 + (-5)] + (-3)$

19. $[-4 + (-7)] + (-8)$

20. $[12 + (-5)] + 5$

21. $(6 + 7) + (-1 + 5)$

22. $(-6 + 7) + (-1 + 5)$

23. $[6 + (-7)] + [4 + (-6)]$

24. $[8 + (-2)] + 8 + (-12)$

25. $[-6 + (-7)] + (-8)$

26. $(2 + 8 + 10) + (-20)$

27. $-[35 + (-7)] + [-(-3 + 8)]$

28. $-[8 + (-2)] + [3 + (-10)]$

29. $-[35 + 5] + [-(-2 + (-8))]$

30. $[-(10 + (-1)) + (-3)] + [-6 + (-4)]$

Replace each __?__ with a numeral to make a true statement.

31. $8 + \underline{\ ?\ } = 10$

32. $-5 + \underline{\ ?\ } = 2$

33. $5 + \underline{\ ?\ } = -2$

34. $-8 + \underline{\ ?\ } = -10$

35. $8 + \underline{\ ?\ } = -10$

36. $5 + \underline{\ ?\ } = 2$

37. $-7 + \underline{\ ?\ } = -7$

38. $-2 + 3 + (-5) + \underline{\ ?\ } = 3$

Solve each sentence if the domain of m is $\{-4, -2, 0, 2, 4\}$. If there is no solution over the given domain, write "no solution."

39. $|m + 5| = 9$

40. $m + 5 < 2$

41. $|m + (-3)| = 1$

42. $|m + (-6)| < 3$

43. $|m| + 5 = 9$

44. $|m + (-6)| < -2$

45. $|m| + (-5) = -3$

46. $m + |m| + |m + 2| = 2$

Solve.

47. $x + 12 = -2$

48. $x + 12 = 2$

49. $x + 2 = 12$

50. $x + (-8) = -5$

51. $x + (-5) = -8$

52. $x + (-12) = 2$

53. $x + 8 = -88$

54. $x + 51 = 50$

In Exercise 55:

a. Name a positive or a negative number to represent each measurement given in the problem.

b. Compute the sum of the numbers. **c.** Answer the question.

55. In a game, a playing piece is moved 3 spaces forward, 2 spaces back, 7 spaces forward, and then 2 more spaces forward. How many spaces forward from its original position is the piece now?

In each of Exercises 56–58:

   a. Name a positive or a negative number to represent each measurement given in the problem.

   b. Compute the sum of the numbers.

   c. Answer the question.

56. A bus starts with 12 people. It stops and discharges 5, and picks up 21. On the next stop it discharges 8, and picks up 12. On the next stop it discharges 20 and picks up 2. On the next stop it discharges 2. How many people are left on the bus?

57. The temperature of a liquid is 20°C at the beginning of an experiment. During the experiment, the temperature of the liquid drops 8°C, then rises 2°C, and then drops 1.5°C. What is the final temperature of the liquid?

58. A balloon rises 1.2 km from the ground. It then rises 0.2 km, falls 0.8 km, rises 1.1 km, rises another 0.5 km, and falls 0.8 km. How high is the balloon above the ground after these changes in its position?

Simplify.

59. $10\left(\dfrac{1}{2} + \dfrac{1}{5}\right)$ **60.** $13\left(1 + \dfrac{1}{13}\right)$ **61.** $\dfrac{2}{3}(4) + \dfrac{2}{3}(2)$

62. $3\left(\dfrac{1}{3}\right) + 8\left(\dfrac{1}{8}\right)$ **63.** $21(98) + 21(2)$ **64.** $2p + 8p$

65. $6x + (-2)x$ **66.** $28w + 2w$ **67.** $-23a + 3a$

68. $-22x + 21x$ **69.** $22x + (-21)x$ **70.** $-22x + (-21)x$

71. $12 + 8y + 6y$ **72.** $-12 + 3d + (-9)d$

73. $-3h + (-3)h + (-2)h$ **74.** $6(x + 2y) + 3(x + 2y)$

75. $98(x + 2) + 2(x + 2)$ **76.** $3(x + 1) + 2(x + 2) + (x + 3)$

77. $0.2(x + 6) + 2.2(x + 2)$ **78.** $12(x + 4 + y) + 8(x + y + 4)$

79. $5\left(k + \dfrac{1}{5}\right) + 3(2k + m) + 2m$

Multiply.

80. $\begin{array}{r} -6 \\ \underline{-1} \end{array}$ **81.** $\begin{array}{r} -4 \\ \underline{-2} \end{array}$ **82.** $\begin{array}{r} -3 \\ \underline{2} \end{array}$ **83.** $\begin{array}{r} -2 \\ \underline{-3} \end{array}$

84. $\begin{array}{r} -1 \\ \underline{3} \end{array}$ **85.** $\begin{array}{r} 0 \\ \underline{-4} \end{array}$ **86.** $\begin{array}{r} 2 \\ \underline{-5} \end{array}$ **87.** $\begin{array}{r} 4 \\ \underline{-6} \end{array}$

Simplify.

88. $(-1)(-2)(-3)$ **89.** $(-12)(0)(12)$

90. $(-2)(2) + (-1)(5)$ **91.** $(-3)(98) + (-3)(2)$

92. $(21)(2) + (-2)(-21)$

93. $(1.2)(-2) + (2)(0.3)$

94. $6[5 + (-2)]$

95. $(6)(5) + (6)(-2)$

96. $(-2)[-3 + (-4)]$

97. $(-2)(-3) + (-2)(-4)$

98. $3[(-1) + (-2) + (-3) + (-4)]$

99. $(-3)(1) + (-3)(2) + (-3)(4)$

100. $-2[x + y]$

101. $2(x + 3) + (-4)(x + 3)$

102. $2(x + y + z) + (-2)(x + y + z)$

103. $\left(-\frac{1}{2}\right)[32x + (-12)y]$

104. $-10 + (-3)[2 + (-8)]$

105. $5[5 + (-5 + 2)5] + (-5)$

106. $\frac{1}{-2} \cdot \frac{1}{5}$

107. $\frac{1}{-3} \cdot \frac{1}{-21}$

108. $\frac{1}{r} \cdot \frac{1}{-5}, \; r \neq 0$

109. $\frac{1}{5}(-25)$

110. $(-35)\left(-\frac{1}{7}\right)\left(-\frac{1}{5}\right)$

111. $(-111)\left(\frac{1}{3}\right)(-10)$

112. $(2ab)\left(\frac{1}{a}\right), \; a \neq 0$

113. $\frac{1}{2}[22x + 44y]$

114. $-\frac{1}{2}[44x + (-6)]$

115. $-8\left[\frac{1}{4}(-x) + \frac{1}{2}(-y)\right]$

116. $(-6)\left[\frac{1}{3}p + (-2) + \left(-\frac{1}{2}\right)r + \left(-\frac{1}{6}\right)s\right]$

CHAPTER 3

Solve each equation by transformation by addition.

1. $r + (-12) = 2$

2. $y + 3 = 12$

3. $m + (-12) = -3$

4. $8 + t = 0$

5. $8 + t = -4$

6. $8 + (-t) = -4$

7. $9 = 21 + (m + 2)$

8. $-x + (-2) = 6$

9. $612 + x = 0$

10. $x + (-5) = |2 - 8|$

11. $x + (-1) + 2 + (-3) = 10$

Simplify.

12. $4 - 21$

13. $12 - 6$

14. $6 - 12$

15. $27 - (-3)$

16. $4 - (-5)$

17. $321 - (320 + 1)$

18. $(42 - 52) - 61$

19. $(42 - 52) - (51 - 2)$

20. $-10 - 3 - [-8 + 2]$

21. $-(10 + 3) - [2 - 8]$

22. $12 - 21 + 22$

23. $1.23 - 2.23$

24. $-3.5 - 2.5$

25. $-3.5 - (-2.5)$

26. $21 - [-12 - 8 - 10]$

27. $12 - (-3) - [3 - (-12)]$

28. $x + [x - z]$

29. $x - [x - z]$

30. $-x - [-x - z]$

31. $3x + [8x - 2x]$

32. $(3x - 5x) - (5x - 3x)$

33. $3m + 7 - (-7 + m)$

34. $(2t + 8) - (8t + 2) - (8 - 2t)$

Write each phrase using symbols of algebra. Then simplify.

35. -3 decreased by 8

36. -7 decreased by -3

37. $(x - 5)$ less than x

38. $(7 + y)$ less than y

39. Subtract $3\pi + 2$ from $3\pi - 2$.

40. From $5 - 6\pi$ subtract $8 - 6\pi$.

41. Decrease the sum of -8 and 17 by -6.

42. Decrease -18 by the sum of -34 and 12.

Evaluate each expression if $x = 2$ and $y = -5$.

43. $x + y$

44. $x - y$

45. $y - x$

46. $x(x - y)$

47. $(x)(x) - (x)(y)$

48. $2x + 3y - 3y - 2y$

49. $-2(x - y)$

50. $xy - 2x - 2y$

51. $2xy - x - y$

Solve.

52. $x + 8 = 42$

53. $x + 42 = 8$

54. $x - 8 = 42$

55. $x - 42 = 8$

56. $x - (-4) = 3$

57. $x - 1 = 10$

58. $2 + x = -8$

59. $-2 + x = -8$

60. $6 - x = -7$

61. $-6 - x = -7$

62. $12 = x + 10$

63. $12 = x - 10$

64. $8t = -24$

65. $(-8)t = 32$

66. $\frac{1}{2}x = -7$

67. $\frac{1}{5}x = -8$

68. $6m = -312$

69. $\frac{2}{3}m = 10$

70. $-6f = -66$

71. $-5y = 210$

72. $-27x = -675$

Evaluate each expression if $r = -3$ and $s = -21$.

73. rs

74. $\dfrac{s}{r}$

75. $\dfrac{-s}{r}$

76. $\dfrac{s}{-r}$

77. $-\dfrac{s}{r}$

78. $r(r + s)$

79. $\dfrac{rs}{-s}$

80. $\dfrac{r}{s} + \dfrac{r + s}{s}$

81. $\dfrac{2r + s}{9r}$

82. $\dfrac{2s}{21r - s}$

83. $\dfrac{s}{r}(2r - 8r)$

Solve.

84. $2x + 8 = 12$

85. $\dfrac{x}{3} + 5 = -2$

86. $18 = 6 - 4m$

87. $-12 = -3 - t$

88. $5m - 2m = 0$

89. $x - 4x - 8x = 22$

90. $0 = 2x - 2 + 8x - 8$

91. $2(x - 8) = -11$

92. $-3(x - 5) = 30$

93. $2(x - 2) + 4 = 0$

94. $8 - 8(x - 8) = 88$

95. $2r + 3(r + 4) = 0$

96. $12x = 4x + 16$ **97.** $11m + 4 = 12m$ **98.** $3x - 4x = x + 2$

99. $2t = 8t - 12$ **100.** $8t = 2t - 12$ **101.** $12t = 12 - 8t$

102. $6x + 5 = 8x - 1$ **103.** $8r - 3 = 3r - 8$ **104.** $3r + 8 = 8r + 3$

105. $2(x + 4) = 12x - 42$ **106.** $8(x - 3) = 3(x - 8)$ **107.** $4(2x - 1) = 2(1 - 4x)$

108. $3m - 3(2 - m) = -18$ **109.** $2r = 6(3 - r) - r$

110. $3(a + 7) - 7(a - 3) = 2(a - 2) - 4(a - 8)$

CHAPTER 4

Simplify.

1. 5^2 **2.** $5^2 \cdot 5^2$ **3.** 5^4

4. 4^3 **5.** $\left(\dfrac{1}{2}\right)^2$ **6.** $\left(\dfrac{3}{4}\right)^3$

7. $(5^2 - 2^5) \div (6^2 - 2^6)$ **8.** $6(3^2 - 2^3) + (-3)^2$ **9.** -5^2

10. $(-5)^2$ **11.** $(-5)^3 \cdot (2)^5$ **12.** $(-5)^3 + (2)^5$

Evaluate each expression if $a = 3$ and $x = -3$.

13. $a^2 - ax$ **14.** $a - ax^2$ **15.** $a - (ax)^2$

16. $(a - ax)^2$ **17.** $\dfrac{a + x^2}{a - x^2}$ **18.** $\dfrac{x^2 + a^2}{x^2} - \dfrac{x^2 + a^2}{a^2}$

Simplify.

19. $(2x^2 - 5x + 2) + (x^2 - 2x + 5)$ **20.** $(2x^2 - 5x + 2) - (x^2 - 2x + 5)$

21. $(-6x + 2y - 3) + (2x - 4y - 7)$ **22.** $(-6x + 2y - 3) - (2x - 4y - 7)$

23. $(a + 2b + 3c + 4d) + (4a + 3b + 2c + d)$

24. $(a + 2b + 3c + 4d) - (4a + 3b + 2c + d)$

Solve.

25. $3x - (x + 2) = 8$ **26.** $(x + 2) - 3x = 8$

27. $(x + 1) - (2x + 3) = 7$ **28.** $(2x + 1) + (7x + 2) = 21$

Simplify.

29. $a^3 \cdot a^4 \cdot a^5$ **30.** $2 \cdot x^5 \cdot x^3 \cdot x$

31. $3x^5 \cdot 4x^6 \cdot 5x^7$ **32.** $(a^5x)(ax^5)$

33. $(-4n^2m)(2n^5m^2)$ **34.** $(-2c^2d^2)(-3c^3d^3)$

35. $\left(\dfrac{1}{3}a^3b\right)(3ab)$ **36.** $(2^x)(2^y)$

37. $(2x)(3y^2)$ **38.** $x^n \cdot x^{n+2} \cdot x^{n+3}$

39. $(-1)^3(-1)^4(-1)^5$ **40.** $(-a)^2(-a)^3(-a)^4(-a)^5$

Simplify.

41. $(3x^2)(4x) + (-2x)(5x^2) + (2x^3)(3)$ **42.** $(2x^2yt^5)(xyt) - (3x^3yt^3)(2yt^3)$

43. $(x^3)^4$ **44.** $(x^4)^3$ **45.** $(2xy^2)^2$

46. $(-2x^2y)^3$ **47.** $(-3x^2)(-3x)^2$ **48.** $(3t)^2(3t^2)^2$

49. $(2a^2b^2)^2 + 6a^4b^4$ **50.** $(x^2y)^4 - (x^4y^2)^2$ **51.** $(-uv)^2(2v^2)^3(u^2v)^2$

Evaluate each expression if $x = -2$ and $y = 2$.

52. $(2x)^3$ **53.** $8x^3$ **54.** $(xy)^3$

55. $x^3 + y^3$ **56.** $x^2 + y^2$ **57.** $(2x + y)^2$

Multiply.

58. $3(x^2 + 5x + 6)$ **59.** $-3x(x^2 + 5x + 6)$

60. $(-3x)^2(x^2 + 5x + 6)$ **61.** $-3x^2(x^2 + 5x + 6)$

Simplify.

62. $2x(3x + 4) + 4x(3x + 2)$ **63.** $2x(3x + 4) - 4x(3x + 2)$

64. $7t(t^2 + 4) + 8t(t^2 - 4)$ **65.** $7t(t^2 + 4) - 8t(t^2 - 4)$

66. $\frac{1}{5}(10n + 20) - \frac{3}{5}(5n - 25)$ **67.** $\frac{1}{2}(x + 2) + \frac{1}{2}(x - 2)$

Solve.

68. $2(x - 2) - x = 6$ **69.** $6(x - 2) + 3(x - 2) = 18$

70. $2x(x - 7) - 2x^2 = 14$ **71.** $\frac{1}{2}x(x + 2) + 2 = \frac{1}{2}(x^2 - 2)$

72. $3(x + 4) - 4(x + 3) = 4(x + 4) + 3x$

73. $7x^2 - x[2x + 5(x + 1)] = 100$

Multiply.

74. $(m + 3)(m - 2)$ **75.** $(m - 3)(m + 2)$ **76.** $(m + 3)(m + 2)$

77. $(m - 3)(m - 2)$ **78.** $(2x + 3)(x + 4)$ **79.** $(2x - 3)(x + 4)$

80. $(2x + 3)(x - 4)$ **81.** $(2x - 3)(x - 4)$ **82.** $(5t + 1)(5t + 1)$

83. $(3x + 2)^2$ **84.** $(x + 1)(x^2 - x + 1)$ **85.** $(2x - 1)(4x^2 + 2x + 1)$

CHAPTER 5

For each number give all the factors between 1 and 12, inclusive.

1. 132   **2.** 231   **3.** 858   **4.** 885

5. 102   **6.** 201   **7.** 120   **8.** 210

Give the prime factorization of each number.

9. 280   **10.** 600   **11.** 252   **12.** 455

Simplify each expression, assuming that no variable equals 0.

13. $\dfrac{(2x^3)(3x^2)}{(6x)^2}$ **14.** $\dfrac{(2x)^3(3x^2)}{6x^2}$

15. $\dfrac{(2x)^3(3x)^2}{(6x)^2}$ **16.** $\dfrac{(2x)^3(3x)^2}{6x^2}$

Divide. Assume that no denominator equals 0.

17. $\dfrac{8r^3 - 4r}{4}$ **18.** $\dfrac{8r^3 - 4r}{4r}$ **19.** $\dfrac{8r^3 - (4r)^2}{4r}$

20. $\dfrac{8x^2y - 12xy^2 + 2xy}{2xy}$ **21.** $\dfrac{8x^2y - 12xy^2 + 2xy}{(2xy)^2}$

Evaluate by factoring first.

22. $12 \times 48 + 12 \times 52$ **23.** $1980 \times 111 - 1980 \times 11$

24. $\dfrac{121 \times 12 + 121 \times 3}{15 \times 9 + 15 \times 2}$ **25.** $28 \times 3 - 16 \times 9 + 28 \times 9 - 16 \times 3$

Factor each polynomial as a product of its greatest monomial factor and another polynomial.

26. $2x^3y^2 - 4xy$ **27.** $8x^2y - 8xy$ **28.** $2u^2 - 100u$

29. $2\pi r^2 - 2\pi r$ **30.** $lw^2 + 3lw$ **31.** $\frac{1}{3}\pi r^2 h + \pi r h$

32. $2x^3 + 8x$ **33.** $-3x^2 + 6x$ **34.** $16x^2y^2 - 8xy^2$

35. $10x^2y - 5xy^2$ **36.** $12a^2b + 6ab^2$ **37.** $10m^3r - 20mr^2 + 15mr$

Express each product as a trinomial or as a binomial.

38. $(2m + 3)(m + 1)$ **39.** $(2m - 3)(m + 1)$ **40.** $(2m - 3)(m - 1)$

41. $(2m + 3)(m - 1)$ **42.** $(4x + 5)(4x - 5)$ **43.** $(4x + 5)(4x + 5)$

44. $(2w - 1)(5w + 3)$ **45.** $(2w - 1)(5w - 3)$ **46.** $(2w + 1)(5w + 3)$

Factor. Check by multiplying the factors.

47. $4x^2 - 1$ **48.** $25 - u^6$ **49.** $b^4 - 1600c^2$

50. $4x^2 + 4x + 1$ **51.** $16a^2 + 8ab + b^2$ **52.** $144 - 24m + m^2$

53. $k^2 + 12k + 35$ **54.** $m^2 + 7m + 6$ **55.** $m^2 - 7m + 6$

56. $m^2 + 11m + 10$ **57.** $p^2 + 8p + 12$ **58.** $p^2 + 7p + 12$

59. $k^2 + 12k + 20$ **60.** $n^2 - 9n + 20$ **61.** $y^2 - 21y + 20$

62. $x^2 + 5x + 6$ **63.** $x^2 - 5x + 6$ **64.** $y^2 - 12y + 35$

65. $x^2 + 7x - 8$ **66.** $x^2 - 7x - 8$ **67.** $x^2 + 2x - 8$

Factor. Check by multiplying the factors.

68. $x^2 - 2x - 8$

69. $y^2 + 8y - 20$

70. $r^2 - 6r - 7$

71. $a^2 + a - 12$

72. $a^2 - a - 12$

73. $r^2 + 8r - 33$

74. $z^2 - 4z - 12$

75. $m^2 + 19m - 20$

76. $x^2 - 9x - 22$

77. $8p^2 + p - 7$

78. $8k^2 - 55k - 7$

79. $8x^2 - x - 7$

80. $8m^2 + 55m - 7$

81. $8r^2 - 10r - 7$

82. $8x^2 - 26x - 7$

83. $8y^2 + 10y - 7$

84. $8y^2 + 26y - 7$

85. $6x^2 - 11x - 2$

86. $x^2 - 4x + 3$

87. $2x^2 - 5x - 3$

88. $6a^2 + 7a - 3$

89. $12d^2 - 5d - 2$

90. $18a^2 + 27a - 5$

91. $6x^2 - 17x + 12$

92. $2h^2 + h - 6$

93. $3x^2 + 14x - 24$

94. $6x^2 - 5x - 4$

Factor by grouping. Check by multiplying the factors.

95. $a(a + 3) + 3(a + 3)$

96. $x(x - 2y) - (2y - x)$

97. $x^2 + 2x + xy + 2y$

98. $7ax + 3a - 7bx - 3b$

99. $x(x + 1)(x - 2) - 3x - 3$

100. $x^3 + x^2 - 6x - 6$

101. $64 - 64a^2 + a^4 - a^6$

102. $12y^2 - 8y - 3yx^2 + 2x^2$

Solve and check.

103. $(x + 1)(x + 2) = x(x + 2) + 1$

104. $(2x + 1)(x + 2) = 2x^2 + 3x + 10$

105. $x(x - 5) + (x - 2)(x - 3) = (2x - 7)(x - 3)$

106. $(x + 4)(x - 2) = 0$

107. $(2x + 1)(x + 7) = 0$

108. $(3x - 1)(7x + 2) = 0$

109. $x(x + 1)(x + 2) = 0$

110. $(x + 200)(x - 300) = 0$

111. $2(x + 2)(x - 12) = 0$

112. $3x^2 - 2x - 1 = 0$

113. $2x^2 - 5x = 3$

114. $x^2 = 9x - 8$

115. $9x^2 - 39x - 30 = 0$

116. $3x^2 = 12x$

117. $2z^2 - 1 = z$

118. $(3x - 4)(2x + 1) = 2(2x + 1)(2x - 1)$

Find an equation in standard form having the given solution set. Let the variable be x.

119. $\{-1, 2\}$

120. $\{3, \frac{1}{3}\}$

121. $\{-7, 7\}$

CHAPTER 6

Express in simplest form, noting any restrictions on the variables.

1. $\dfrac{64}{16}$

2. $\dfrac{abc}{a^2b}$

3. $\dfrac{2(x + y)}{3(x + y)}$

4. $\dfrac{2x - 4y}{x - 2y}$

5. $\dfrac{a + ab}{2a}$

6. $\dfrac{p}{2p^2 - p}$

7. $\dfrac{xy + ax}{x^2y + xy}$

8. $\dfrac{r^2 + 2r + 1}{2r + 2}$

9. $\dfrac{16r^2 + 8r + 1}{16r^2 - 1}$

10. $\dfrac{4a^2 - 1}{4a^2 - 4a + 1}$

11. $\dfrac{k^2 - 8k + 16}{k^2 - 9k + 20}$

12. $\dfrac{x^2 - 7x + 12}{x^2 - x - 12}$

13. $\dfrac{1 - 2x}{2x - 1}$

14. $\dfrac{2(x - 2y)}{4(2y - x)}$

15. $\dfrac{(2x - 5)(3x - 1)}{(5 - 2x)(3 - x)}$

16. $\dfrac{x^2 - 4x - 1}{x^2 - 2x - 1}$

17. $\dfrac{-4a^2}{2a^2 - 4a^3}$

18. $\dfrac{r^2 + rh - 12h^2}{r^2 - 9h^2}$

Simplify.

19. $\dfrac{2}{7} \cdot 7$

20. $\dfrac{2}{7} \div 7$

21. $2m \div \dfrac{2}{3}$

22. $2m \cdot \dfrac{2}{3}$

23. $36r^2 \div \dfrac{18r}{5}$

24. $25a \div \dfrac{25}{a^2}$

25. $\dfrac{c - 1}{c} \cdot \dfrac{c^2}{c^2 - 1}$

26. $\dfrac{2x - 2y}{3x + 3y} \cdot \dfrac{6x + 6y}{x^2 - y^2}$

27. $\dfrac{x^2 - 9}{x^2 + 5x + 6} \div (x + 3)$

28. $2x^2 \div (2x)^2$

29. $(3ab^2)^3 \div 9(ab)^3$

30. $\dfrac{x}{x + 1} \cdot \dfrac{x^2 - 1}{x^2}$

31. $\dfrac{3}{a + b} + \dfrac{4}{a + b}$

32. $\dfrac{a + b}{3} + \dfrac{a + b}{4}$

33. $\dfrac{2}{3x + y} - \dfrac{1}{3x + y}$

34. $\dfrac{x + y}{12} - \dfrac{2x + y}{20}$

35. $\dfrac{3x}{a + b} - \dfrac{x}{a + b}$

36. $\dfrac{3a}{a + b} + \dfrac{3b}{a + b}$

37. $\dfrac{2}{3x + 5} - \dfrac{1}{6x + 10}$

38. $\dfrac{4}{m^2 - 4} + \dfrac{2}{m + 2}$

39. $\dfrac{3}{a - 1} + \dfrac{2}{1 - a}$

40. $2 + \dfrac{1}{a + b}$

41. $m - \dfrac{mr}{m + r}$

42. $3x^2 + \dfrac{3x}{3 + x}$

43. $\dfrac{2}{2x + 1} + \dfrac{3}{3x + 1}$

44. $\dfrac{1}{2x} + \dfrac{3}{x^2 + 2x}$

45. $\dfrac{r^2}{(r + 2)^2} - \dfrac{r}{r + 2}$

46. $\dfrac{2}{x^2 - 2x} + \dfrac{1}{2 - x}$

47. $\dfrac{4}{4m + 4} - \dfrac{2}{2m + 2}$

48. $\dfrac{m}{n} + 3 + \dfrac{n}{m}$

49. $\dfrac{1}{x^2 - 5x + 6} - \dfrac{1}{x^2 - 3x + 2}$

50. $\dfrac{1}{10x - 21} + \dfrac{x^2 + x - 6}{10x^2 + 9x - 63}$

51. $\dfrac{2}{a^2 + 4a + 4} - \dfrac{1}{a - 2} + \dfrac{6}{a + 2}$

52. $\dfrac{2}{1 + x} + \dfrac{3}{1 - x} + \dfrac{2x}{x^2 - 1}$

53. $1 + \dfrac{2x}{2x - 1} + \dfrac{8x^2 - 2}{1 - 4x^2}$

54. $\dfrac{3x + 1}{2} - \dfrac{5}{x - 4} + \dfrac{x^2}{3}$

Divide. Write your answer as a polynomial or mixed expression. Check.

55. $\dfrac{10x^2 - 7x - 12}{2x - 3}$

56. $\dfrac{6x^2 - 23x + 7}{2x - 7}$

57. $\dfrac{18a^2 + 27a + 10}{3a + 2}$

58. $\dfrac{6x^2 - 39x + 60}{2x - 5}$

59. $\dfrac{x^3 + x^2 + 2x - 4}{x - 1}$

60. $\dfrac{x^3 + 2x^2 - 16}{x - 2}$

Divide. Write your answer as a polynomial or mixed expression. Check.

61. $\dfrac{x^3 - 2x + 4}{x + 2}$

62. $\dfrac{2r^2 + 5r + 3}{2r + 3}$

63. $\dfrac{7k^2 - 9k + 2}{7k - 2}$

64. $\dfrac{r^3 + r^2 + r + 1}{r - 2}$

65. $\dfrac{p^4 + p^3 + 4p^2 + 3}{p^2 + p + 1}$

66. $\dfrac{6x^3 + 5x^2 + 9}{3 + 2x}$

67. $\dfrac{6m^4 + 11m^3 + m^2 - 7m - 6}{-2m - 3}$

68. $\dfrac{6r^3 - 5r^2k + 7rk^2 - 8k^3}{r - k}$

CHAPTER 7

State each ratio in simplest form.

1. $25 : 40$

2. $14 \text{ kg to } 140 \text{ g}$

3. $28 \text{ min to } 2 \text{ h } 8 \text{ min}$

4. $\dfrac{13(ab)^2}{169abc}$

5. $90¢ \text{ to } \$60$

6. $12x^2y : 4xy^2$

Solve.

7. $\dfrac{18}{81} = \dfrac{2x}{3}$

8. $\dfrac{m + 3}{7} = 8$

9. $\dfrac{4y}{2 - y} = \dfrac{5}{3}$

10. $\dfrac{x - 1}{2} = \dfrac{x}{4}$

11. $\dfrac{3}{4} = \dfrac{c - 1}{c + 5}$

12. $\dfrac{12}{u + 1} = \dfrac{3}{u}$

13. $\dfrac{x + 1}{x + 2} = \dfrac{x + 5}{x + 4}$

14. $\dfrac{x}{x - 1} = \dfrac{x + 1}{x + 2}$

15. $\dfrac{4x}{5} + \dfrac{x}{10} = \dfrac{27}{2}$

16. $\dfrac{1}{3}k + \dfrac{1}{16} = \dfrac{1}{12} + \dfrac{1}{4}k$

17. $\dfrac{4}{9}b - \dfrac{1}{5}b = 11$

18. $\dfrac{3x}{7} + \dfrac{1}{2} + \dfrac{x + 4}{2} = 0$

19. $\dfrac{3d + 1}{2} + \dfrac{2d + 1}{3} = 3d + 5$

20. $\dfrac{1}{2} + \dfrac{1}{y} = \dfrac{1}{3} - \dfrac{1}{y}$

21. $\dfrac{18}{x} = \dfrac{3}{x} + 3$

22. $\dfrac{1}{n} + \dfrac{5}{3n} = \dfrac{3}{4}$

23. $\dfrac{a}{a + 3} - \dfrac{2}{5} = 0$

24. $\dfrac{4}{5b} + \dfrac{b - 2}{b} = -\dfrac{1}{5}$

25. $\dfrac{1}{a^2 - a} = \dfrac{3}{a} - 1$

26. $1 + \dfrac{2}{y - 1} = \dfrac{2}{y^2 - y}$

27. $\dfrac{x}{x - 2} - \dfrac{4}{x + 3} = 1$

28. $\dfrac{x + 5}{6} - \dfrac{2x + 1}{12} + \dfrac{x - 10}{x - 3} = 0$

29. $\dfrac{1}{x + 1} + \dfrac{x^2}{x^2 - 1} = 1 + \dfrac{1}{1 - x}$

Replace each __?__ by a number that makes the statement true.

30. 12% of 21 is __?__.

31. $13\frac{1}{2}$% of 22 is __?__.

32. 12.6% of 2.4 is __?__.

33. 10% of 3.14 is __?__.

34. 2% of __?__ is 122.

35. 30% of __?__ is 24.

36. 250% of __?__ is 35.

37. 18% of __?__ is 39.96.

38. __?__% of 12 is 8.

39. __?__% of 42 is 24.

40. __?__% of 45 is 72.

41. __?__% of 158 is 52.14.

CHAPTER 8

Solve each equation for y in terms of x.

1. $2x + y = 8$
2. $2x - y = 8$
3. $3x + 2y = 12$
4. $x + 2y = 6$
5. $x - 2y = 4$
6. $4x - 3y = 7$
7. $8x = 4y + 20$
8. $3y - 2x = 150$
9. $2x = 10 - 3y$

Complete each ordered pair to form a solution of the given equation. Assume that x and y represent real numbers.

10. $y = 3x + 3;\ (15, ?)$
11. $y = -2x - 5;\ (-3, ?)$
12. $y = 7x + 5;\ (6, ?)$
13. $2x + y = 7;\ (3, ?)$
14. $3x + 2y = 8;\ (2, ?)$
15. $4x - 5y = 12;\ (-10, ?)$

Find the coordinates of the points where the graph of each equation crosses (a) the x-axis and (b) the y-axis.

16. $3x = 11y$
17. $x - 4y = 20$
18. $3x + y = 12$
19. $2x - 10y = 20$
20. $4x - y = 120$
21. $3x + 10y = 300$

Graph each equation in a coordinate plane.

22. $x + y = 8$
23. $2x + y = 8$
24. $x + 2y = 8$
25. $x + 2y = 10$
26. $x + 2y = 1$
27. $5x + y = 10$
28. $x - y = 1$
29. $y = 3x - 1$
30. $3y = x + 1$

Solve each system by the graphic method.

31. $x + y = 3$
    $2x - y = 3$
32. $3x - 2y = 4$
    $2x + y = 5$
33. $x + y = 1$
    $3x - y = -9$

Solve each system by the substitution method.

34. $y = 6$
    $7x + y = 34$
35. $x + 2y = 3$
    $2x + 3y = 9$
36. $2x + y = 2$
    $x - 2y = 1$

Let $s =$ the number of students at a school association meeting. Let $a =$ the number of adults at the meeting. Write each sentence as an equation in s and a.

37. The total number of people at the meeting is 640.

38. The number of students is one third the number of adults.

39. The number of adults is 160 more than twice the number of students.

40. Half the number of adults is 80 less than twice the number of students.

Solve each system by the addition-or-subtraction method.

41. $c + 2n = -20$
$\quad c - 2n = 30$

42. $25x + 16y = 91$
$\quad 16x + 16y = 64$

43. $3x + 2y = 13$
$\quad 3x - 4y = 19$

Solve each system by using multiplication with the addition-or-subtraction method.

44. $7m - 5n = 11$
$\quad 3m + n = -11$

45. $3a + 4b = -25$
$\quad 2a - 3b = 6$

46. $\dfrac{x}{3} + \dfrac{y}{4} = \dfrac{1}{12}$
$\quad 2x + 5y = 1$

Let n = Nadya's age now and d = Darrell's age now. Write the following in terms of n and d.

47. Nadya's age in 6 years

48. Darrell's age 2 years ago

49. Twice the sum of their ages

50. The sum of their ages in 1 year

A two-digit number is represented by $10t + u$, where t is the tens digit and u is the units digit. Write the following in terms of t and u.

51. The new number obtained when each digit is doubled.

52. The new number obtained when the units digit is halved.

53. A fraction is represented by $\dfrac{n}{d}$. Write in terms of n and d the new

fraction obtained by tripling the numerator and decreasing the denominator by 7.

Let s = the rate of a swimmer in still water and r = the rate of the Raft River. Write the following in terms of s and r.

54. The rate of the swimmer swimming downstream

55. The rate of the swimmer swimming upstream

56. The rate of the swimmer swimming upstream in a river which flows at one quarter of the rate of the Raft River

CHAPTER 9

In each exercise, the coordinates of two points of a line are given. Find the slope of the line.

1. $(1, 1)$ $(8, 15)$

2. $(2, 8)$ $(\frac{1}{3}, 3)$

3. $(0, 3)$ $(-2, 11)$

4. $(-1, 0)$ $(8, -45)$

5. $(2, 4)$ $(8, 7)$

6. $(2, 5)$ $(-1, -3)$

Find the slope of each line whose equation is given.

7. $y = -2x + 6$

8. $y = \frac{1}{3}x - 4$

9. $y = 2 - x$

10. $3x + 2y = 48$

11. $5x - 2y = 8$

12. $y = 14$

In each exercise, determine whether the points lie on the same line. If they do, find the slope of the line.

13. $(2, 8)$
$(5, 12)$
$(8, 16)$

14. $(-3, 6)$
$(2, 7)$
$(12, 8)$

15. $(-2, -6)$
$(-4, -3)$
$(-8, 3)$

16. $(0, 7)$
$(5, 9)$
$(10, 11)$

Draw the line that passes through $(6, 4)$ and has the given slope.

17. 5
18. $\frac{1}{5}$
19. -5
20. $-\frac{1}{5}$

Write in standard form an equation of the line that has the given slope and y-intercept.

21. $m = 5;\ b = 10$
22. $m = \frac{1}{3};\ b = -3$
23. $m = -3;\ b = \frac{1}{2}$
24. $m = -\frac{2}{3};\ b = -\frac{2}{3}$

25. The same slope as the graph of $2x - y = 2;\ b = 4$

26. The same slope as the graph of $y = 4x - 4$; the same y-intercept as the graph of $x + y = 2$

Change each equation to the slope-intercept form and draw the graph using only the y-intercept and the slope.

27. $5x = -3y$
28. $2x - y = 5$
29. $5x + 5y + 4 = 0$
30. $x - y = 5$
31. $4x + 4y = 8$
32. $-3x + y = 0$

Write in standard form an equation of the line that has the given slope and passes through the given point.

33. $m = 2;\ (2, 2)$
34. $m = -\frac{2}{3};\ (-1, 3)$
35. $m = 4;\ (0, 0)$

Write in standard form an equation of the line passing through the given points.

36. $(0, 4)\quad (2, -5)$
37. $(2, 4)\quad (5, 4)$
38. $(4, 8)\ (6, -10)$

39. If $f\colon x \to x + 5$, find: **a.** $f(2)$ **b.** $f(\frac{1}{2})$.

40. If $g(v) = 2 - v^2$, find: **a.** $g(-2)$ **b.** $g(-3)$.

41. If $h\colon u \to 2u + u^2$, find: **a.** $h(-4)$ **b.** $h(\frac{1}{4})$.

42. If $k(m) = m - \dfrac{1}{m}$, find: **a.** $k(3)$ **b.** $k(-3)$.

43. Find all the values of $F\colon x \to x^2 + 2$ if the domain $D = \{-1, 0, 1\}$.

44. Find the range of the function G if $G(x) = \dfrac{1}{x} + x$ and $D = \{1, 2, 3\}$.

Find the coordinates of the vertex of the graph of each equation.

45. $y = x^2 - 4x$
46. $y = 2x^2 - 10x + 1$
47. $y = x^2 + 2x + 4$
48. $y = -x^2 + 4x - 8$
49. $y = -\frac{2}{3}x^2 + 6x - 12$
50. $y = -4x^2 - 4x - 8$

Find the greatest value of each function.

51. $f: x \rightarrow -x^2 - 10x$　　　　　　　　　　　　**52.** $g: x \rightarrow -x^2 - 10x + 4$

53. $h: x \rightarrow -x^2 - 10x - 12$　　　　　　　　　**54.** $k: x \rightarrow -2x^2 + 8$

55. $F: x \rightarrow -2x^2 + 12$　　　　　　　　　　　**56.** $G: x \rightarrow -2x^2 - 100$

Find the least value of each function.

57. $f: x \rightarrow 2x^2 + 4x + 4$　　　　　　　　　　**58.** $g: x \rightarrow 2x^2 + 8$

59. $h: x \rightarrow 2x^2 + 4x + 3$　　　　　　　　　　**60.** $k: x \rightarrow 3x^2 + 9x + 6$

In each exercise, (a) find the constant of variation and (b) find y when $x = 4$.

61. y varies directly as x, and $y = 30$ when $x = 10$.

62. y varies directly as x, and $y = 24$ when $x = 3$.

63. y is directly proportional to x, and $y = 11$ when $x = 22$.

Translate each statement into *two* formulas expressing direct variation. Use k as the constant of variation.

64. The elongation, e, of a coil spring varies directly as the mass, m, suspended from it.

65. The circumference, C, of a circle is directly proportional to the diameter, d, of the circle.

66. The length, l, of a shadow of a vertical object at a given time and location varies with the height, h, of the object.

State whether each equation defines a direct variation or an inverse variation. Then state the constant of variation, if it can be determined.

67. $xy = 3$　　　　　　　**68.** $b = \dfrac{4}{c}$　　　　　　　**69.** $m = \dfrac{n}{3}$

70. $\dfrac{x}{y} = \dfrac{1}{3}$　　　　　　　**71.** $q = 7.5p$　　　　　　　**72.** $5ab = 6$

73. $x_1 y_2 = x_2 y_1$　　　　　　　**74.** $\dfrac{x_1}{x_2} = \dfrac{y_2}{y_1}$　　　　　　　**75.** $\dfrac{1}{8} = uv$

Find the missing value in each exercise if (x_1, y_1) and (x_2, y_2) are ordered pairs of the same inverse variation.

76. $x_1 = 2, y_1 = 3$　　　　**77.** $x_1 = 2, y_1 = 6$　　　　**78.** $x_1 = 1, y_1 = 6$
　　　$x_2 = 6, y_2 = \underline{\ ?\ }$　　　　　　$x_2 = 6, y_2 = \underline{\ ?\ }$　　　　　　$x_2 = \underline{\ ?\ }, y_2 = 16$

Translate each statement into *two* formulas expressing inverse variation. Use k as the constant of variation.

79. The height, h, of a triangle of constant area varies inversely as the base length, b.

80. The monthly rent, r, for each roommate in an apartment is inversely proportional to the number, n, of roommates sharing the apartment.

Translate each statement into a formula. Use k as a constant where needed.

81. Wind pressure, p, on a flat surface varies directly as the square of the wind velocity, v.

82. The height, h, of a right circular cylinder of given volume is inversely proportional to the square of the radius, r.

83. The volume, V, of a rectangular container varies jointly as the length, l, the width, w, and the depth, d.

84. The volume, V, of a regular square pyramid varies jointly as the height, h, and the square of the length, b, of a side of the base.

85. Centrifugal force, F, varies directly as the square of the velocity, v, of a moving body and inversely as the radius, r, of its circular path.

86. The rate of speed, r, of a moving body varies directly as the distance traveled, d, and inversely as the time traveled, t.

CHAPTER 10

Draw the graph of each inequality on a number line.

1. $5x < 15$ **2.** $-2x > 8$ **3.** $8 \leq x < 10$

Solve each inequality.

4. $8x + 3 < 15$ **5.** $3x - 8 < 15$ **6.** $3 - x > 2$
7. $-2r + 3 < r + 1$ **8.** $0 < 6r + 4$ **9.** $0 < 4 - 6r$

Classify each statement as true or false.

10. $|2 + 8| = |2| + |8|$ **11.** $|2 - 8| = |2| - |8|$
12. $|(4)(-2)| = |4| \cdot |-2|$ **13.** $|2| + |-3| = |-2| + |3|$

Solve each open sentence.

14. $|x| = 2$ **15.** $|x| = \frac{1}{2}$ **16.** $|x + 1| = 3$
17. $|x - 8| = 1$ **18.** $|2x + 3| = 15$ **19.** $|2 - 3x| = 7$
20. $|x| < 2$ **21.** $|x| > 2$ **22.** $|x| < 20$
23. $|x + 4| < 1$ **24.** $|x - 3| > 1$ **25.** $|2x - 4| < 5$

Write an inequality based on the information given in each exercise.

26. The sum of two numbers is less than 28.

27. The product of two consecutive integers is more than 152.

Write an inequality based on the information given in each exercise.

28. The difference between two even integers is more than 22.

29. The distance between two cities is at least 42 km.

30. The number of boxes of lunch packed is at least 28.

31. The number of peaches eaten is at most 3.

32. The number of dimes Jason has is at most $\frac{1}{2}$ as many as Dick has.

33. The number of cards Julia has is no more than 28.

34. A number is no more than $\frac{1}{2}$ and no less than $-\frac{2}{7}$.

35. Six times Clare's age is at least 4 more than Beth's age.

36. The sum of two consecutive integers is no more than twice their product.

Solve each open sentence.

37. $x \leq 2$ and $x > 0$

38. $-3 < y \leq 2$

39. $4 \leq m$ and $m \leq 4$

40. $2 < n$ or $n \geq 4$

41. $-2 < x + 2 < 2$

42. $-1 \leq x - 4 \leq 8$

43. $x + 7 < 8$ or $x + 8 > 7$

44. $-3 \leq 2x - 3 < 4$

45. $2r + 3 < 1$ or $2r + 3 > 4$

46. $-2 < 3 - x < 3$

47. $4 < 2 + 3x \leq 5$

48. $4 - x > 5$ or $x - 4 > 5$

Determine whether or not $(0, 0)$ belongs to the graph of each inequality.

49. $2x - y < -4$

50. $x + 47 \geq 0$

51. $2x - 3y < 4$

Graph each inequality in a coordinate plane.

52. $x < 2$

53. $y \geq 2x + 4$

54. $y < 4x - 1$

Graph each pair of inequalities in a coordinate plane and indicate the solution set of the system with crosshatching or shading.

55. $y \geq 3$
    $x \geq 2$

56. $y \leq 4$
    $x > 3$

57. $y > 4$
    $x \leq -5$

CHAPTER 11

Write each number as a quotient of integers.

1. 1.3

2. $2\frac{1}{7}$

3. 12%

4. $8\frac{1}{2}\%$

5. $-2\frac{5}{8}$

6. 21.3

Replace the __?__ with $<$, $=$, or $>$ to make a true statement.

7. -3 __?__ $-4\frac{1}{2}$

8. $8\frac{1}{2}$ __?__ $\frac{15}{2}$

9. $\frac{9}{5}$ __?__ $\frac{7}{3}$

10. $\frac{3}{4}$ __?__ $\frac{8}{10}$

11. $\frac{2}{5}$ __?__ $\frac{21}{50}$

12. 1.24 __?__ 1.204

13. $14\frac{1}{3}$ __?__ $\frac{44}{4}$

14. $\frac{111}{4}$ __?__ $\frac{249}{9}$

15. $-\frac{5}{7}$ __?__ $-\frac{12}{15}$

Find the number halfway between the given numbers.

16. 2 and 24

17. 32 and -12

18. $\frac{1}{2}$ and $\frac{5}{6}$

19. $\frac{4}{5}$ and $\frac{2}{15}$

20. $\frac{1}{4}$ and $\frac{7}{12}$

21. $-\frac{2}{3}$ and $-\frac{12}{13}$

22. Find the number one third of the way from $-\frac{2}{3}$ to $\frac{1}{12}$.

23. Find the number one fifth of the way from $1\frac{1}{2}$ to $1\frac{6}{7}$.

Express each rational number as a terminating or repeating decimal.

24. $\frac{3}{6}$

25. $\frac{2}{3}$

26. $\frac{10}{9}$

27. $\frac{281}{10}$

28. $\frac{2}{5}$

29. $\frac{7}{4}$

30. $\frac{1}{16}$

31. $\frac{11}{81}$

32. $\frac{2}{7}$

33. $\frac{9}{5}$

34. $\frac{5}{9}$

35. $\frac{81}{11}$

Express each rational number as a fraction in simplest form.

36. 0.22

37. 0.14

38. 0.444...

39. 2.8

40. 0.625

41. $0.\overline{62}$

42. $1.\overline{23}$

43. $1.2\overline{3}$

44. 28.82

Find the difference of the given numbers. Then find the number halfway between them.

45. $\frac{1}{2}$ and 1.25

46. $\frac{2}{3}$ and $0.\overline{8}$

47. 0.22 and 0.11

48. 0.22 and $0.1\overline{5}$

49. -2.12 and $-2\frac{1}{2}$

50. 0.17 and $0.\overline{17}$

Find the indicated square roots.

51. $\sqrt{961}$ **52.** $\sqrt{196}$ **53.** $\sqrt{1764}$

54. $\sqrt{(36)(81)}$ **55.** $\sqrt{(144)(441)}$ **56.** $\sqrt{(2116)(900)}$

57. $\sqrt{\dfrac{16}{625}}$ **58.** $\sqrt{\dfrac{128}{162}}$ **59.** $\sqrt{\dfrac{450}{1250}}$

60. $\sqrt{0.16}$ **61.** $\sqrt{0.81}$ **62.** $\sqrt{0.1024}$

Use the Table of Square Roots to approximate each square root to the nearest hundredth.

63. $\sqrt{40}$ **64.** $\sqrt{83}$ **65.** $\sqrt{8300}$

66. $\sqrt{0.12}$ **67.** $\sqrt{0.02}$ **68.** $\sqrt{0.0062}$

Approximate each square root to the nearest hundredth using the divide-and-average method.

69. $\sqrt{38}$ **70.** $\sqrt{50}$ **71.** $\sqrt{25.8}$

Simplify.

72. $\sqrt{4t^2}$ **73.** $\sqrt{81m^4}$ **74.** $\sqrt{0.04y^2}$

75. $\sqrt{a^2 + 2a + 1}$ **76.** $\sqrt{576a^2b^4}$ **77.** $\sqrt{m^{100}n^{200}}$

78. $\sqrt{\dfrac{27}{3}}$ **79.** $\sqrt{16a^2 - 8a + 1}$ **80.** $\sqrt{2^{10} \cdot 3^6}$

Solve. Find both roots of each equation to the nearest tenth if the roots are irrational.

81. $m^2 = 1444$ **82.** $x^2 - 82 = 0$ **83.** $36t^2 - 1 = 0$

84. $3x^2 = 243$ **85.** $5x^2 - 4205 = 0$ **86.** $2t^2 = 100$

87. $8r^2 - 88 = 0$ **88.** $3a^2 - 12 = 0$ **89.** $b^2 - 7.5 = 0$

Refer to a right triangle with hypotenuse of length c and shorter sides of lengths a and b. Find the missing length correct to the nearest hundredth.

90. $a = 4$, $b = 5$, $c = \underline{\ ?\ }$ **91.** $a = 8$, $b = 6$, $c = \underline{\ ?\ }$

92. $a = 20$, $b = \underline{\ ?\ }$, $c = 21$ **93.** $a = \sqrt{2}$, $b = \underline{\ ?\ }$, $c = \sqrt{12}$

94. $a = \underline{\ ?\ }$, $b = 17$, $c = 19$ **95.** $a = 7$, $b = 24$, $c = \underline{\ ?\ }$

96. $a = \underline{\ ?\ }$, $b = 1.2$, $c = 5.8$ **97.** $a = 2\dfrac{1}{2}$, $b = 3\dfrac{1}{3}$, $c = \underline{\ ?\ }$

Express in simplest form. Assume the radicands are nonnegative real numbers.

98. $\sqrt{5} \cdot \sqrt{5}$ **99.** $2\sqrt{3} \cdot 3\sqrt{7}$ **100.** $\sqrt{24}$

101. $\sqrt{200}$ **102.** $\dfrac{3}{\sqrt{7}}$ **103.** $\sqrt{\dfrac{2}{13}}$

104. $\sqrt{2} \cdot \sqrt{6} \cdot \sqrt{8}$ 105. $\sqrt{\dfrac{2}{9}}$ 106. $\sqrt{125}$

107. $\sqrt{180}$ 108. $2\sqrt{60} \cdot 6\sqrt{15}$ 109. $8\sqrt{x} \cdot 4\sqrt{x}$

110. $\sqrt{m}(\sqrt{m} + m)$ 111. $\sqrt{3x} \cdot \sqrt{27x}$ 112. $\sqrt{111x} \cdot \sqrt{3x} \cdot \sqrt{37}$

113. $\sqrt{\dfrac{1}{2}} \cdot \sqrt{\dfrac{2}{9}}$ 114. $\sqrt{\dfrac{10}{3}} \cdot \sqrt{\dfrac{15}{2}}$ 115. $\sqrt{\dfrac{3}{2}} \cdot \sqrt{\dfrac{2}{5}} \cdot \sqrt{\dfrac{5}{7}} \cdot \sqrt{21}$

116. $\dfrac{3}{\sqrt{3}}$ 117. $\dfrac{8}{\sqrt{8}}$ 118. $\sqrt{1\dfrac{1}{2}} \cdot \sqrt{1\dfrac{1}{3}} \cdot \sqrt{1\dfrac{1}{4}}$

Simplify.

119. $5\sqrt{7} + 8\sqrt{7}$ 120. $6\sqrt{2} - 4\sqrt{2}$ 121. $\sqrt{32} + \sqrt{\dfrac{1}{2}}$

122. $\sqrt{27} - \sqrt{3}$ 123. $2\sqrt{\dfrac{5}{3}} - \sqrt{60}$ 124. $\sqrt{\dfrac{5}{6}} + \sqrt{\dfrac{6}{5}}$

125. $\dfrac{2}{\sqrt{2}} - 2\sqrt{\dfrac{1}{2}}$ 126. $\sqrt{2} + 2\sqrt{3} + 3\sqrt{4}$ 127. $\sqrt{162} + 16\sqrt{2}$

128. $20\sqrt{4\dfrac{1}{2}} - 16\sqrt{2}$ 129. $10\sqrt{\dfrac{3}{5}} - 30\sqrt{\dfrac{5}{3}}$ 130. $3\sqrt{18} - 5\sqrt{\dfrac{1}{2}} - 4\sqrt{\dfrac{1}{4}}$

Express in simplest form.

131. $(5 - \sqrt{2})(5 + \sqrt{2})$ 132. $(\sqrt{6} + 3)(\sqrt{6} - 3)$

133. $(7 + \sqrt{12})(7 - \sqrt{12})$ 134. $(2\sqrt{6} + 1)(2\sqrt{6} - 1)$

135. $(\sqrt{12} - \sqrt{5})(\sqrt{12} + \sqrt{5})$ 136. $(2 + \sqrt{5})^2$

137. $(5 - \sqrt{7})^2$ 138. $(2 + \sqrt{8})^2$

139. $(\sqrt{7} + \sqrt{2})^2$ 140. $(\sqrt{10} + \sqrt{5})^2$

141. $\sqrt{3}(2 + \sqrt{3})$ 142. $2\sqrt{7}(\sqrt{7} + \sqrt{2})$

143. $\left(-\dfrac{5}{2} - \dfrac{5}{2}\sqrt{3}\right)^2$ 144. $\sqrt{3}(\sqrt{3} - 3)$

145. $(7\sqrt{7} + \sqrt{3})(2\sqrt{7} - \sqrt{3})$ 146. $(2\sqrt{3} + 3\sqrt{2})^2$

147. $(\sqrt{3} - \sqrt{2})^3$ 148. $\sqrt{6}(\sqrt{2} - \sqrt{3})$

Rationalize the denominator.

149. $\dfrac{2}{2\sqrt{7} - 5}$ 150. $\dfrac{3}{3 - \sqrt{6}}$ 151. $\dfrac{2 + 2\sqrt{3}}{1 + \sqrt{3}}$

152. $\dfrac{6}{\sqrt{3} + \sqrt{2}}$ 153. $\dfrac{4\sqrt{7}}{\sqrt{7} - \sqrt{5}}$ 154. $\dfrac{\sqrt{5} + \sqrt{2}}{\sqrt{5} - \sqrt{2}}$

Solve and check.

155. $\sqrt{x + 5} = 1$ 156. $\sqrt{4x - 11} = 1$

157. $\sqrt{x - 5} = 5$ 158. $\sqrt{3r - 2} - 8 = -6$

Solve and check.

159. $\sqrt{\dfrac{2x + 1}{2}} = 3$

160. $2\sqrt{3x} - 5 = 0$

161. $\sqrt{2m - 1} = m - 2$

162. $\sqrt{x + 8} = \sqrt{x}$

CHAPTER 12

Rewrite each trinomial as the square of a binomial.

1. $x^2 + 6x + 9$

2. $4x^2 + 4x + 1$

3. $x^2 - 22x + 121$

4. $36x^2 + 12x + 1$

Solve. Express irrational solutions in simplest radical form. If the equation has no real-number solution, write "no solution."

5. $m^2 = \dfrac{1}{25}$

6. $2x^2 = 200$

7. $(x + 8)^2 = 81$

8. $(x - 4)^2 = 4$

9. $6m^2 + 1 = 8$

10. $7r^2 + 4 = 2$

11. $2(m - 3)^2 = 14$

12. $r^2 - 10r + 25 = 144$

13. $\left(x - \dfrac{2}{3}\right)^2 = \dfrac{1}{9}$

14. $\left(t + \dfrac{8}{5}\right)^2 = \dfrac{2}{5}$

Complete the square.

15. $x^2 + 12x + \underline{\ ?\ } = (x + \underline{\ ?\ })^2$

16. $x^2 - 8x + \underline{\ ?\ } = (x - \underline{\ ?\ })^2$

17. $x^2 - 7x + \underline{\ ?\ } = (x - \underline{\ ?\ })^2$

18. $x^2 + 14x + \underline{\ ?\ } = (x + \underline{\ ?\ })^2$

Solve by completing the square. Express irrational roots in simplest radical form.

19. $x^2 + 6x = 16$

20. $x^2 - 20x = 21$

21. $2m^2 - 24m = 20$

22. $d^2 - 22d = 1$

23. $y^2 - 8y = 1361$

24. $m^2 - 8m - 3410 = 0$

25. $t^2 - 18t - 1600 = 0$

26. $p^2 = 4p + 4$

27. $x(x + 1) = 1$

28. $3x(x + 5) = 3x + 4$

29. $\dfrac{4x - 2}{x + 4} = 4x - 2$

30. $\dfrac{x + 1}{x + 2} = x$

Use the quadratic formula to solve each equation. Write irrational answers in simplest radical form.

31. $x^2 + 2x - 2 = 0$

32. $x^2 + 3x + 2 = 0$

33. $x^2 - 8x + 1 = 0$

34. $x^2 - 7x + 8 = 0$

35. $x^2 - 10x + 10 = 0$

36. $x^2 = x + 12$

37. $2x^2 - 7x + 6 = 0$

38. $5x^2 = 5x + 1$

39. $\frac{1}{2}c^2 = \frac{1}{3}c + \frac{1}{4}$

40. $\frac{x+2}{x-2} = \frac{x-5}{6}$

Write the value of the discriminant of each equation. Then use it to decide how many different real roots the equation has. (Do not solve the equations.)

41. $x^2 + x - 3 = 0$

42. $3x^2 + x - 1 = 0$

43. $x^2 + 2x + 10 = 0$

44. $10x^2 + 2x + 1 = 0$

45. $x^2 - 4x + 3 = 0$

46. $2x^2 + 5x - 1 = 0$

47. $2x^2 + 8x + 21 = 0$

48. $\frac{1}{3}k^2 + 2k + 3 = 0$

Solve by the most efficient method. Write irrational answers in simplest radical form.

49. $3x^2 - 4x - 5 = 0$

50. $x^2 - 8x = 60$

51. $5x^2 + 10x = 0$

52. $8t^2 - 9 = 0$

53. $x(x - 5) = x + 10$

54. $13x - x^2 = 0$

55. $x^2 + (x + 1)^2 = (x + 3)^2$

56. $(2x + 1)^2 = x^2 + x + 7$

The problems on the following pages provide extra practice in problem solving for Chapters 3-12.

PROBLEMS

Chapter 3

Solve each problem by using an equation.

3-1

1. Twelve more than a number is -122. Find the number.

2. The sum of a number and -21 is 2. Find the number.

3. A number increased by 21 is -2. Find the number.

4. A town's population increased by 2000. If the new population is 19,500, what was the previous population?

5. A bird is 320 cm above the surface of a pond. How many centimeters does the bird have to dive down to catch a fish that is 25 cm below the surface of the pond?

6. Liz sold 12 dozen eggs on a day she collected 9 dozen from her hens. If she had 20 dozen eggs at the end of the day, how many eggs did she have at the beginning of the day?

Express the answer to each question as the difference between two real numbers. Compute the difference. Answer the question.

3-2

7. One evening the temperature in Portland, Maine, was $-6°C$ and the temperature in Portland, Oregon, was $12°C$. How much warmer was it in Portland, Oregon, than in Portland, Maine?

8. Over a summer a bird loses 1.35 g and a mouse loses 0.12 g. How much more does the bird lose?

9. In a certain game David's score went from 1230 to -22. How many points did he lose?

10. A typical daytime temperature on the surface of Mars is about $-30°C$. On Earth it is about $20°C$. About how much warmer is Earth than Mars?

11. Mercury freezes at $-38.87°C$, and carbon dioxide freezes at $-78°C$. What is the difference between their freezing points?

12. The warmest shade temperature on Earth was recorded by the National Geographic Society at El Azizia, Libya (September 13, 1922). It was $58°C$. The coldest reading was obtained at Vostok, Antarctica (August 24, 1960). It was $-88.3°C$. What is the difference between the record temperatures?

Solve each problem by using an equation.

3-3

13. A number is 3 less than 21. Find the number.

14. A number decreased by 12 is 32. Find the number.

15. Eight less than a number is 10. Find the number.

16. Six less than a number is -13. Find the number.

17. Ilona received a grade of 82 on her chemistry exam. This grade was 12 points less than her previous grade. What was her previous grade?

18. Jim ran the 1000 m race and cut 2.5 s off his time for last week's run. His run this week was timed at 2 min 28 s. What was his time for last week's run?

19. Sean must trim down from 72 kg to 68 kg in order to be on the wrestling team. How much does he have to lose?

20. Today Soomi did 40 sit-ups in one minute, which is 6 more sit-ups in one minute than she did yesterday. How many sit-ups in one minute did she do yesterday?

21. One sixth of a fruit pie is sold for 75¢. How much will be received when all the pieces of the pie have been sold at this price?

3-4

22. A car traveled for 3 h at the rate of 50 km/h. How far did it travel?

23. The area of a rectangular piece of property bought by a city for a park is 24 km². Its length is 6 km. What is its width?

24. Twelve-year-old Angela is one fourth as old as her father. How old is her father?

25. Eight times a number is −256. Find the number.

3-6

26. A package of 6 pencils costs 96¢. How much does each pencil cost?

27. A 12-ride commuter ticket costs $25.92. How much is that for each ride?

28. A box of 15 note cards costs $2.50. About how much does one card cost?

29. Three times a number, increased by 7, is 40. Find the number.

3-7

30. Forty, decreased by twice a number, is 6. Find the number.

31. Together, a salad and a cup of soup cost $2.55. Find the price of each if the salad costs twice as much as the soup.

32. Together, shipping and handling a package cost $2.30. The cost of shipping is 20¢ more than the cost of handling. Find the shipping cost.

33. Rene's bicycle costs $50 more than Pat's. Together, the value of the bicycles is $334. Find the cost of Rene's bicycle.

34. Find a number that is 12 less than twice itself.

3-8

35. The sum of a number and twice its opposite is the same as 8 more than the number. Find the number.

36. Twice a number, decreased by 12, is the same as the number increased by 12. Find the number.

37. Twelve, decreased by twice a number, is the same as the number increased by 6. Find the number.

38. Alice Ames is twice as old as Guy Gifford. Ten years from now, Alice will be 22 years older than Guy. How old is Alice Ames now?

Solve.

1. Find three consecutive integers whose sum is 96.

4-2

2. Find four consecutive integers whose sum is 94.

3. Find three consecutive integers whose sum is -57.

4. Find two consecutive integers whose sum is 89.

5. Find two consecutive odd integers whose sum is 88.

6. Find two consecutive even integers whose sum is 86.

7. Find three consecutive integers such that the sum of the greatest and the least is the same as the sum of the middle integer and 5.

8. Anne is 2 years older than Mary. Last year Anne was 3 times as old as Mary. How old is Anne now?

4-7

9. Twelve-year-old Joe's grandfather is 66. How many years ago was his grandfather 10 times older than Joe?

10. Melissa's cat is 5 years younger than she is. In 2 years, Melissa will be twice as old as her cat. How old is each now?

11. Student tickets to a play cost $2.00 each and adult tickets cost $3.00 each. On Monday 26 tickets were sold and $64.00 was collected. How many student tickets were sold on Monday?

4-8

12. A collection of 23 coins is worth $4.35 and contains only nickels and quarters. How many of each kind of coin are in the collection?

13. Lee Clayton makes $8 per hour doing tutoring in mathematics and $15 per hour giving music lessons. Over the weekend he worked a total of 10 hours and made $108. How many hours did he work in each subject?

14. Marcia rode out of town on her bicycle at a rate of 24 km/h. When her bicycle broke down, she walked it back to town at a rate of 6 km/h. If she was gone a total of 5 hours, how far from town did her bicycle break down and how long did it take her to walk back?

4-9

15. Kate and Terry started hiking up a hill at 8:00 A.M. at a rate of 4 km/h. At 11:00 A.M. their mother discovered that they had forgotten their lunches and started after them in her car at 64 km/h. When did she overtake them?

16. Two bicyclists started at the same time from towns 84 km apart and rode toward each other. One rode twice as fast as the other. If they met after two hours, find the speed of each bicyclist.

17. A rectangular swimming pool is 7 m longer than it is wide. It is surrounded by a concrete walk 1.5 m wide that has an area of 120 m². Find the dimensions of the pool.

4-10

18. A rectangular picture is 3 times as long as it is wide. When it is in a frame 10 cm wide, the total area is 3600 cm² more than that of the picture alone. Find the dimensions of the picture alone.

19. A square corner lot lost 94 m² of area when the two adjacent streets were widened, one by 2 m and the other by 3 m. Find the original dimensions of the lot.

Chapter 5

Solve.

1. A rectangle is twice as long as it is wide. If the length is increased by 3 cm and the width by 5 cm, the new area will be 28 cm² more than the old area. Find the dimensions of the original rectangle.

5-6

2. Find two consecutive positive integers whose product is 72.

5-14

3. The sum of the squares of two consecutive negative odd integers is 202. Find the integers.

4. The sum of the squares of three consecutive positive even integers is 2360. Find the integers.

5. The length of a rectangle is 5 m greater than twice its width, and its area is 33 m². Find its dimensions.

6. The perimeter of a rectangular wildlife preserve is 8 km, and its area is 3 km². Find its dimensions.

7. A corner lot had dimensions 20 m by 40 m before it lost two strips of equal width when the adjacent streets were widened. Find the new dimensions of the lot if its area is now 525 m².

8. A room can be covered with 1440 square tiles. If each tile were 2 cm longer and wider, then the room could be covered with 1210 tiles. Find the original dimensions of a tile.

Chapter 7

Solve.

1. The lengths of the sides of a triangle are in the ratio 5 : 12 : 13. The perimeter of the triangle is 90 cm. Find the length of each side.

7-1

2. Two numbers are in the ratio 4 : 5 and their sum is 45. Find the numbers.

3. A mutual fund invests $30,000 in bonds and stocks in the ratio 3 : 5. How much is invested in bonds?

Solve.

4. If the Dorsey Corporation paid an annual dividend of $25 on 350 shares of stock, how much of an annual dividend did it pay on 1050 shares?

7-2

5. A certain car consumes 60 L of gasoline in 3 hours. Assuming that the rate of gasoline consumption remains constant, how much gasoline will the car use on a 35-hour trip?

6. An automatic doughnut machine can produce 1000 doughnuts in 6 hours. How long would it take the machine to produce 300 doughnuts?

7. In a survey of 40 of the 300 residences in a certain neighborhood, it was found that 16 residences were occupied by families with children. Assuming that the residences surveyed are a representative sample, estimate the number of families with children in the neighborhood.

8. One ninth of a number is 2 less than one third of the number. Find the number.

7-3

9. Two sides of a triangle are *each* 3 cm longer than the third side. The length of the third side is one sixth of the perimeter. Find the length of each side of the triangle.

10. The sum of two numbers is 80. If the greater number is divided by the smaller, the quotient is 3 and the remainder is 8. Find the numbers.

7-4

11. What number must be subtracted from the numerator and denominator of $\frac{7}{9}$ to make the resulting fraction equal to $\frac{2}{3}$?

12. Find two consecutive integers such that the sum of their reciprocals is $\frac{5}{6}$.

13. The sum of two integers is 7. The difference of their reciprocals is $\frac{3}{10}$. Find the integers.

14. The population of sheep in a farming community is 2500. What percent of the community's sheep is owned by the Skethley family if that family owns 800 sheep?

7-5

15. Out of 1360 persons surveyed, 35% felt that the most serious problem facing the world today is environmental pollution. How many people gave this reply?

16. Pat invested a total of $14,000 in a term savings account at 12% simple interest and in a regular savings account at $5\frac{1}{2}$% simple interest. The total interest for the first year came to $1127.50. How much money did she invest at each rate?

17. One year Alfredo put a sum of money into a savings account that yielded 5% simple interest and $754.00 into bonds that yielded 8% simple interest. The money he invested earned a total of $86.92 in interest that year. How much did he invest in the savings account?

7-6

18. The price of one share of Alcron Trucking Company stock rose from $55.20 to $57.96. Find the percent of increase.

19. The list price of a typewriter is $140. If a discount of $10.50 is given for cash payment, what is the percent of discount?

20. Six years ago the KwiKalc calculator sold for $58.00. This year it is selling for $20.30. Find the percent of decrease.

21. An article with a list price of $36.00 is on sale at a 15% discount. If sales tax is 5%, how much would it cost to purchase the article on sale?

7-7

22. How many kilograms of water must be added to 160 kg of a 5% salt solution in order to produce a 4% solution?

23. How many kilograms of pure acid must be added to 60 kg of a 70% acid solution in order to produce an 80% acid solution?

24. A building supplies company has two kinds of sand, a white sand that sells for 12¢ per kilogram and a red-and-gray sand mix that sells for 7¢ per kilogram. How much of each type of sand should go into making 800 kg of a multicolored sand mix that sells for 9¢ per kilogram?

25. The owner of a delicatessen has pickled hot peppers that sell for $4.60 per kilogram and pickled pearl onions that sell for $5.80 per kilogram. How much of each should the deli owner mix in order to get 15 kg of a mixture that sells for $5.00 per kilogram?

7-8

26. One bulldozer can complete a job in 3 days and a second, smaller bulldozer can complete the job in 5 days. How many days are required for the job if both bulldozers are used?

27. Pearson College owns a tabulator that can process registration data in 6 hours. Wanting to speed up the processing, the school authorized the purchase of a second tabulator that can do the job in 8 hours. How many hours will it take the two tabulators working together to process all the data?

28. With drain pipes A and B open, a swimming pool can be emptied in 1.5 h. If drain pipe A can empty the pool in 3 h, how long would it take drain pipe B to empty the pool?

29. John and Mary can spade a garden in 4 days, but John can do it alone in 6 days. How long will it take Mary alone to finish the job after John works on it for 4 days by himself?

Solve by using a system of equations in two variables and the substitution method.

1. In a school ecology project, the ninth-grade class collected 25 more bags of aluminum cans than the tenth-grade class. The two classes collected a total of 65 bags. How many bags did each class collect?

8-6

2. The perimeter of a rectangle is 54 cm. Two times the width is 3 cm more than the length. Find the dimensions of the rectangle.

3. In one week, an engineer worked for 6 days and an assistant worked for 7 days investigating the effects of manufacturing processes which lead to air pollution. Together, they received a salary of $900. The following week, the engineer worked 5 days and the assistant worked 3 days for a combined salary of $580. Find the daily wages of each.

4. The *average* of two numbers is one half the sum of the numbers. Find two numbers whose average is 44 and whose difference is 44.

5. Ten more than the first of two numbers is 3 times the second of the two numbers. Ten less than the second number is -3 times the first number. Find the two numbers.

Solve by using a system of equations in two variables and whatever method you prefer.

6. The sum of two numbers is 56. The larger exceeds twice the smaller by 2. Find the numbers.

8-7

7. A store received $823 one month from the sale of 5 tape players and 7 radios. The receipts from the tape players exceeded the receipts from the radios by $137. Find the price of each.

8. A rectangular rug is 1 m longer than it is wide. It is in a room with a perimeter of 18 m, and the perimeter of the rug is 4 m less than the perimeter of the room. Find the dimensions of the rug.

8-8

9. Two boxes of apples and 3 boxes of apricots cost $24.00. Four boxes of apples and 5 boxes of apricots cost $44.00. Find the prices of a box of apples and a box of apricots.

10. In 4 years Marcie will be as old as Lynn is now. Eight years ago the sum of their ages was 16. Find their ages.

8-9

11. A father, being asked his age and that of his son, said, "If you add 4 to my age and divide the sum by 4, you will have my son's age. But 6 years ago I was $7\frac{1}{2}$ times as old as my son." Find their ages.

Solve, assuming that each number is a two-digit number.

12. The sum of the digits of a number is 9. If the digits are reversed, the number is increased by 45. Find the original number.

13. The sum of the digits of a number is 13. If the digits are reversed, the new number is 27 less than the original number. Find the original number.

Using two variables, find the original fraction.

14. The denominator exceeds the numerator by 3. If 1 is added to the denominator, a fraction is obtained whose value is $\frac{2}{3}$.

15. When simplified, a fraction has the value $\frac{4}{5}$. When its numerator is increased by 9, the resulting fraction is equal to the reciprocal of the value of the original fraction.

Solve by using a system of equations in two variables.

16. A boat can go 72 km downstream in 2 h. In the same time it can go 48 km upstream. Find the rate of the boat in still water and the rate of the current.

8-10

17. An airplane flew 1800 km in 5 hours with the wind. The return trip against the wind took twice as long. Find the rate of the plane in still air and the rate of the wind.

Chapter 9

Solve.

1. A certain brand of salad dressing contains 7 parts oil to 3 parts vinegar. How much oil must be blended with 51 L of vinegar to make the dressing?

9-7

2. Twelve grams of calcium chloride can absorb 5 cm^3 of water. How much calcium chloride is needed to absorb 138 cm^3 of water?

3. What is the mass of a 500 m reel of cable if a 1 m section has a mass of 0.87 kg?

4. What sum at 4% simple interest yields the same yearly income as $800 at 5% simple interest?

9-8

5. A gear with 28 teeth makes 45 revolutions per minute (r.p.m.) and meshes with a gear having 20 teeth. What is the rate of the second gear if the number of r.p.m. varies inversely as the number of teeth?

6. The length of a rectangle of a given area varies inversely as the width. If a certain rectangle has a length of 42 cm and a width of 12 cm, find the length of another rectangle of equal area whose width is 14 cm.

Solve.

7. A diamond's price varies directly as the square of its number of carats. If a diamond that is $\frac{3}{8}$ of a carat is worth \$900, find the cost of a similar diamond that is $\frac{7}{8}$ of a carat.

8. The distance which a freely falling body falls varies directly as the square of the time it falls. If it falls 44.1 m in 3 s, how far will it fall in 8 s?

9. The height of a cone of a given volume varies inversely as the square of the radius of the base. If a cone with a radius of 6 cm has a height of 15 cm, what is the height of a cone of equal volume with a radius of 4 cm?

Chapter 10

Solve.

1. Four times the smaller of two consecutive even integers is less than 3 times the larger. What are the largest possible values for the integers?

2. Bill has at least \$12.45 in dimes and quarters. He has 12 more quar-ters than dimes. At least how many of each coin does Bill have?

3. Two ships are no more than 240 km apart and are sailing toward one another. The rate of one ship is 4 km/h greater than the rate of the other ship. If they meet in 3 h, find the greatest possible rate of each ship.

10-3

Chapter 11

Solve. Find each answer to the nearest tenth. Use the approximation $\pi \approx 3.14$ when needed. Use the Table of Square Roots on page 526 as necessary.

1. The length of a rectangle is 3 times the width. Find the dimensions of the rectangle if its area is 123 cm².

2. Find the diameter of a circular plot that has the same area as a rectangular one that is 22 m wide and 35 m long.

3. The length of the base of a triangle is 8 times the length of the altitude. Find the length of the base if the area of the triangle is 300 cm².

11-5

EXTRA PRACTICE

Solve. Make a sketch for each problem. Approximate each square root to the nearest hundredth.

4. Find the length of a diagonal of a rectangle whose dimensions are 30 cm by 50 cm. 11-6

5. The bottom of a 6 m ramp is 5 m from a loading platform. How high is the platform?

6. The lengths of the two shorter sides of a right triangle are two consecutive positive integers. The length of the hypotenuse is 29 cm. Find the lengths of the two shorter sides.

Solve.

7. One fifth of the square root of a number is 2. Find the number. 11-10

8. When 7 is added to 3 times a number, the square root of the result is 5. Find the number.

9. The formula for finding the altitude length h of an equilateral triangle with side length s is $h = \dfrac{\sqrt{3}}{2} s$. Find the length of a side of an equilateral triangle with altitude of length $5\sqrt{3}$.

Chapter 12

Solve. Give irrational roots to the nearest tenth. Use the Table of Square Roots on page 526 as necessary.

1. The dimensions of a cube are such that the number of cubic centimeters in the volume is 3 times the number of centimeters in the sum of the lengths of the 12 edges. Find the length of an edge of the cube. 12-6

2. The length of a rectangular framework is 3 times the width. If the length were shortened by 30 cm and the width were lengthened by 40 cm, the new area would be one half of the original area. Find the original width of the framework.

3. One number is 2 less than another number. The sum of their squares is 3700. Find the two numbers.

4. A mat is to be made for a picture whose dimensions are 10 cm by 12.5 cm. The width of the mat is to be 0.8 times the length of the mat, so that the mat will have the same proportions as the picture. The area of the mat is to be twice the area of the picture. Find the dimensions of the mat.

Solve. Give irrational roots to the nearest tenth. Use the Table of Square Roots on page 526 as necessary.

5. The length of an edge of one cube is 2 cm longer than the length of an edge of a smaller cube. If the volumes differ by 488 cm³, find the edge length of each cube.

6. A rug is 6 m long and 3 m wide. It has a rectangular design in the middle that takes up one half of its area. The border surrounding the design is of uniform width. Find the width of the border.

7. A rectangular box without a top has a total surface area of 700 cm². The length of the box is $\frac{3}{2}$ times the width. The height of the box is 1 cm greater than the width. Draw a sketch and find the dimensions of the box.

Table of Squares of Integers from 1 to 100

Number	Square	Number	Square	Number	Square	Number	Square
1	1	26	676	51	2601	76	5776
2	4	27	729	52	2704	77	5929
3	9	28	784	53	2809	78	6084
4	16	29	841	54	2916	79	6241
5	25	30	900	55	3025	80	6400
6	36	31	961	56	3136	81	6561
7	49	32	1024	57	3249	82	6724
8	64	33	1089	58	3364	83	6889
9	81	34	1156	59	3481	84	7056
10	100	35	1225	60	3600	85	7225
11	121	36	1296	61	3721	86	7396
12	144	37	1369	62	3844	87	7569
13	169	38	1444	63	3969	88	7744
14	196	39	1521	64	4096	89	7921
15	225	40	1600	65	4225	90	8100
16	256	41	1681	66	4356	91	8281
17	289	42	1764	67	4489	92	8464
18	324	43	1849	68	4624	93	8649
19	361	44	1936	69	4761	94	8836
20	400	45	2025	70	4900	95	9025
21	441	46	2116	71	5041	96	9216
22	484	47	2209	72	5184	97	9409
23	529	48	2304	73	5329	98	9604
24	576	49	2401	74	5476	99	9801
25	625	50	2500	75	5625	100	10,000

Table of Square Roots of Integers from 1 to 100

Exact square roots are shown in red. For the others, rational approximations are given correct to three decimal places.

Number	Positive Square Root	Number	Positive Square Root	Number	Positive Square Root	Number	Positive Square Root
N	$\sqrt{N}$	N	$\sqrt{N}$	N	$\sqrt{N}$	N	$\sqrt{N}$
1	1	26	5.099	51	7.141	76	8.718
2	1.414	27	5.196	52	7.211	77	8.775
3	1.732	28	5.292	53	7.280	78	8.832
4	2	29	5.385	54	7.348	79	8.888
5	2.236	30	5.477	55	7.416	80	8.944
6	2.449	31	5.568	56	7.483	81	9
7	2.646	32	5.657	57	7.550	82	9.055
8	2.828	33	5.745	58	7.616	83	9.110
9	3	34	5.831	59	7.681	84	9.165
10	3.162	35	5.916	60	7.746	85	9.220
11	3.317	36	6	61	7.810	86	9.274
12	3.464	37	6.083	62	7.874	87	9.327
13	3.606	38	6.164	63	7.937	88	9.381
14	3.742	39	6.245	64	8	89	9.434
15	3.873	40	6.325	65	8.062	90	9.487
16	4	41	6.403	66	8.124	91	9.539
17	4.123	42	6.481	67	8.185	92	9.592
18	4.243	43	6.557	68	8.246	93	9.644
19	4.359	44	6.633	69	8.307	94	9.695
20	4.472	45	6.708	70	8.367	95	9.747
21	4.583	46	6.782	71	8.426	96	9.798
22	4.690	47	6.856	72	8.485	97	9.849
23	4.796	48	6.928	73	8.544	98	9.899
24	4.899	49	7	74	8.602	99	9.950
25	5	50	7.071	75	8.660	100	10

TABLE OF TRIGONOMETRIC RATIOS

Angle	Sine	Cosine	Tangent	Angle	Sine	Cosine	Tangent
1°	.0175	.9998	.0175	46°	.7193	.6947	1.0355
2°	.0349	.9994	.0349	47°	.7314	.6820	1.0724
3°	.0523	.9986	.0524	48°	.7431	.6691	1.1106
4°	.0698	.9976	.0699	49°	.7547	.6561	1.1504
5°	.0872	.9962	.0875	50°	.7660	.6428	1.1918
6°	.1045	.9945	.1051	51°	.7771	.6293	1.2349
7°	.1219	.9925	.1228	52°	.7880	.6157	1.2799
8°	.1392	.9903	.1405	53°	.7986	.6018	1.3270
9°	.1564	.9877	.1584	54°	.8090	.5878	1.3764
10°	.1736	.9848	.1763	55°	.8192	.5736	1.4281
11°	.1908	.9816	.1944	56°	.8290	.5592	1.4826
12°	.2079	.9781	.2126	57°	.8387	.5446	1.5399
13°	.2250	.9744	.2309	58°	.8480	.5299	1.6003
14°	.2419	.9703	.2493	59°	.8572	.5150	1.6643
15°	.2588	.9659	.2679	60°	.8660	.5000	1.7321
16°	.2756	.9613	.2867	61°	.8746	.4848	1.8040
17°	.2924	.9563	.3057	62°	.8829	.4695	1.8807
18°	.3090	.9511	.3249	63°	.8910	.4540	1.9626
19°	.3256	.9455	.3443	64°	.8988	.4384	2.0503
20°	.3420	.9397	.3640	65°	.9063	.4226	2.1445
21°	.3584	.9336	.3839	66°	.9135	.4067	2.2460
22°	.3746	.9272	.4040	67°	.9205	.3907	2.3559
23°	.3907	.9205	.4245	68°	.9272	.3746	2.4751
24°	.4067	.9135	.4452	69°	.9336	.3584	2.6051
25°	.4226	.9063	.4663	70°	.9397	.3420	2.7475
26°	.4384	.8988	.4877	71°	.9455	.3256	2.9042
27°	.4540	.8910	.5095	72°	.9511	.3090	3.0777
28°	.4695	.8829	.5317	73°	.9563	.2924	3.2709
29°	.4848	.8746	.5543	74°	.9613	.2756	3.4874
30°	.5000	.8660	.5774	75°	.9659	.2588	3.7321
31°	.5150	.8572	.6009	76°	.9703	.2419	4.0108
32°	.5299	.8480	.6249	77°	.9744	.2250	4.3315
33°	.5446	.8387	.6494	78°	.9781	.2079	4.7046
34°	.5592	.8290	.6745	79°	.9816	.1908	5.1446
35°	.5736	.8192	.7002	80°	.9848	.1736	5.6713
36°	.5878	.8090	.7265	81°	.9877	.1564	6.3138
37°	.6018	.7986	.7536	82°	.9903	.1392	7.1154
38°	.6157	.7880	.7813	83°	.9925	.1219	8.1443
39°	.6293	.7771	.8098	84°	.9945	.1045	9.5144
40°	.6428	.7660	.8391	85°	.9962	.0872	11.4301
41°	.6561	.7547	.8693	86°	.9976	.0698	14.3007
42°	.6691	.7431	.9004	87°	.9986	.0523	19.0811
43°	.6820	.7314	.9325	88°	.9994	.0349	28.6363
44°	.6947	.7193	.9657	89°	.9998	.0175	57.2900
45°	.7071	.7071	1.0000				

ANSWERS TO SELF-TESTS

Chapter 1, Self-Test 1, page 11
1. 17 **2.** 10 **3.** 2 **4.** 3 **5.** 2 **6.** 4

Chapter 1, Self-Test 2, page 25
1. $n + 3 = 5$ **2.** $2t - 1 = 11$ **3. a.** $a - 5$
b. $a - 5 = 9$ **4.** 5

Chapter 2, Self-Test 1, page 39

1.

2. $^-3$ is less than 2 **3.** $^-6, ^-1, 0, 5$ **4.** 8900
5. $2x + 11$

Chapter 2, Self-Test 2, page 52
1. $^-5$ **2.** 6 **3.** 13 **4.** -4 **5.** -12
6. -20

Chapter 2, Self-Test 3, page 64
1. $5x + 5$ **2.** $3y - 5$ **3.** -42 **4.** $-a + 6$
5. x **6.** $-6a + b$

Chapter 3, Self-Test 1, page 83
1. 8 **2.** 22 **3.** -11 **4.** -21 **5.** 20
6. -6 **7.** 41 **8.** 26 **9.** 7

Chapter 3, Self-Test 2, page 94
1. 64 **2.** -20 **3.** -6 **4.** -6 **5.** 2
6. $-4x$ **7.** -9 **8.** 7 **9.** 24

Chapter 3, Self-Test 3, page 107
1. 6 **2.** 2 **3.** 6 **4.** 5 **5.** 6 years old
6. (1) Associative axiom for addition;
(2) Axiom of opposites; (3) Identity axiom
for addition

Chapter 4, Self-Test 1, page 121
1. $2a^3bc^2$ **2.** -6 **3.** 16 **4.** $6x^2 - 4$
5. $2a^2 + 4ab + 6b^2$

Chapter 4, Self-Test 2, page 133
1. x^8 **2.** $12y^7$ **3.** a^{15} **4.** $9x^4y^6$
5. $5x^2 + 20x$ **6.** $2a^4 - 2a^3b + 2a^2b^2$
7. $n^2 - 9$ **8.** $x^3 + x^2 - 12x + 12$

Chapter 4, Self-Test 3, page 148

1.

	Age now	Age in 5 years
Dan	x	$x + 5$
Ruth	$x - 3$	$x + 2$

2. $w = \dfrac{V}{lh}$ **3.** 2 **4.** $2h$ **5.** 41 cm by 51 cm

Chapter 5, Self-Test 1, page 165
1. $3 \cdot 5^2$ **2.** $(1)(45), (3)(15), (5)(9),$
$(-1)(-45), (-3)(-15), (-5)(-9)$ **3.** 15
4. $-\dfrac{3x}{y}$ **5.** $\dfrac{m^4}{4k}$ **6.** 12 **7.** $-5ab^4$
8. $7t^2 + 5t - 3$ **9.** $2xy^2(2x^3y - 4x + 3)$

Chapter 5, Self-Test 2, page 174
1. $6y^2 - 8y - 30$ **2.** $6x^3 - 28x^2 + 16x$
3. $x^2 - 49$ **4.** $4a^2 - 49b^2$
5. $(2x + 7)(2x - 7)$ **6.** $9(2x^2 + 3)(2x^2 - 3)$
7. $4y^2 + 20y + 25$ **8.** $9z^2 - 30zk + 25k^2$
9. $(3a + 2)^2$ **10.** $(4m - 3n)^2$

Chapter 5, Self-Test 3, page 182
1. $(y + 3)(y + 5)$ **2.** $(x - 8)(x - 2)$
3. $(n - 7)(n + 4)$ **4.** $(v + 12)(v - 3)$
5. $(3x - 5)(2x - 3)$ **6.** $(3x - 2)(x + 4)$

Chapter 5, Self-Test 4, page 186
1. $(y - 2)(x + 6)$
2. $(n + 4 - 3m)(n + 4 + 3m)$
3. $4a(x - 2)^2$ **4.** $4x(y - 3)^2$

Chapter 5, Self-Test 5, page 195
1. $\{5, 9\}$ **2.** $\{0, 2, -5\}$ **3.** $\{2, 5\}$
4. $\{5, -4\}$ **5.** $\{-4\}$ **6.** $\{0, 4, -7\}$ **7.** 8, 9

Chapter 6, Self-Test 1, page 210
1. $\dfrac{k + 4}{k - 5}$ **2.** $\dfrac{n + 5}{n - 5}$ **3.** $\dfrac{36a}{25b^5}$ **4.** $\dfrac{4z}{3(z + 1)}$
5. $\dfrac{x^2y^2}{16}$ **6.** $\dfrac{2m}{3n^3}$

Chapter 6, Self-Test 2, page 219

1. $\dfrac{5}{16kz^2}, \dfrac{12k^2z^2}{16kz^2}$

2. $\dfrac{x+1}{3(x-1)(x+1)}, \dfrac{6}{3(x-1)(x+1)}$ 3. $\dfrac{5}{3c}$

4. $\dfrac{n^2-5}{3}$ 5. $\dfrac{k+1}{(k+2)(k-2)}$

6. $\dfrac{14b-a+2}{4ab}$

Chapter 6, Self-Test 3, page 225

1. $\dfrac{-4x-1}{x+2}$ 2. $\dfrac{4a-b}{a+b}$ 3. $3x-5$

4. $2x+5+\dfrac{3}{4x-1}$

Chapter 7, Self-Test 1, page 243
1. 4:5 2. 12:1 3. 93, 217 4. 12 5. \$492

Chapter 7, Self-Test 2, page 250
1. 48 2. $\frac{8}{3}$ 3. 4 4. 1

Chapter 7, Self-Test 3, page 258
1. 30% 2. 200 3. 11 4. 9% 5. \$75

Chapter 7, Self-Test 4, page 268
1. 8 kg 2. 25 kg 3. 24 min 4. 1.8 h

Chapter 8, Self-Test 1, page 286
1, 2.

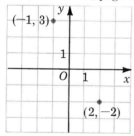

3. no 4. {(3, 0), (2, 1), (1, 2), (0, 3)} 5. a, b
6.

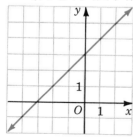

Chapter 8, Self-Test 2, page 303
1.

2. (1, 6) 3. width = 10 m; length = 20 m
4. (1, 1) 5. (2, 2)

Chapter 8, Self-Test 3, page 312
1. Eve is 24 years old; Uncle Bill is 48.
2. 64 3. $\frac{11}{20}$ 4. rate of boat = 16.5 km/h,
rate of current = 8.5 km/h

Chapter 9, Self-Test 1, page 330
1. $\frac{3}{2}$ 2. 0 3. Slope is $\frac{2}{3}$; y-intercept is $-\frac{1}{3}$.
4. $2x-y=-4$ 5. $x-y=-3$

Chapter 9, Self-Test 2, page 342
1. 5 2. {0, −3, −4}
3. a. D = {N7621, N6523, V2231, V2232},
R = {\$12.88, \$9.85, \$3.39}
b. {(N7621, \$12.88), (N6523, \$9.85),
(V2231, \$3.39), (V2232, \$3.39)} 4. (−1, −3)
5. 0

Chapter 9, Self-Test 3, page 359
1. 3 h 2. 20 min 3. 20 4. 9π cm^2
5. 30 cm^2

Chapter 10, Self-Test 1, page 378
1. $-6 < -3 < 0$, or $0 > -3 > -6$
2. {−4, −3, −2, −1, 0, 1, 2}
3. {the real numbers less than 4}

4. {the real numbers greater than or equal to $-\frac{1}{2}$}

5. 44, 46

Chapter 10, Self-Test 2, page 388
1. {the real numbers less than 1 or greater than 3}

2. {7, and the real numbers between 0 and 7}

3. {1, 5}

4. {−1, 5, and the real numbers less than −1 or greater than 5}

Chapter 10, Self-Test 3, page 396
1.

2.

3.

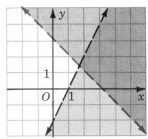

Chapter 11, Self-Test 1, page 415
1. $\frac{17}{24}$ **2.** $1\frac{4}{15}$ **3.** $\frac{4}{5}$ **4.** $\frac{3}{4}$ **5.** 0.74 **6.** $0.15\overline{90}$

7. $\frac{211}{99}$ **8.** 27 **9.** $\frac{21}{32}$ **10.** 1.2

Chapter 11, Self-Test 2, page 426
1. 80.62 **2.** −0.91 **3.** $7|mn^3|$
4. $13x^2y^2\sqrt{x}$ **5.** $\{2, -2\}$ **6.** $\{\frac{7}{2}, -\frac{7}{2}\}$
7. 10.30 **8.** no

Chapter 11, Self-Test 3, page 437
1. $20\sqrt{5}$ **2.** $4|x|y^2\sqrt{2}$ **3.** $5\sqrt{5} - \sqrt{3}$
4. $2\sqrt{2}$ **5.** $9 + 4\sqrt{5}$ **6.** 9 **7.** $6 + 3\sqrt{3}$
8. $\dfrac{4\sqrt{5} - 5}{11}$ **9.** 25 **10.** 49

Chapter 12, Self-Test 1, page 455
1. $\{4, -4\}$ **2.** $\{3, 7\}$ **3.** $\{-6, 2\}$ **4.** $\{1, 5\}$
5. $\left\{\dfrac{3 + \sqrt{17}}{2}, \dfrac{3 - \sqrt{17}}{2}\right\}$
6. $\left\{\dfrac{-7 + \sqrt{37}}{6}, \dfrac{-7 - \sqrt{37}}{6}\right\}$ **7.** two **8.** two

Chapter 12, Self-Test 2, page 461
1. $\left\{\dfrac{-3 + \sqrt{65}}{4}, \dfrac{-3 - \sqrt{65}}{4}\right\}$
2. $\{2\sqrt{5}, -2\sqrt{5}\}$ **3.** $\{0, 3\}$
4. $\{-2 + \sqrt{2}, -2 - \sqrt{2}\}$
5. 3.9 cm **6.** 7.5 m

GLOSSARY

abscissa (p. 276). The first coordinate in an ordered pair of numbers that is associated with a point in the coordinate plane.

absolute value (p. 44). The positive number of any pair of opposite real numbers is called the absolute value of each of the numbers. The absolute value of 0 is 0.

acute angle (p. 469). An angle measuring between 0° and 90°.

addition axiom of order (p. 370). For all real numbers a, b, and c:

1. If $a < b$, then $a + c < b + c$;
2. If $a > b$, then $a + c > b + c$.

addition property of equality (p. 71). For all real numbers a, b, and c, if $a = b$ then $a + c = b + c$ and $c + a = c + b$.

additive inverse (p. 43). The additive inverse of the real number a is the real number $-a$ such that $a + (-a) = 0$ and $-a + a = 0$. Also called *opposite of a*.

angle (p. 468). A figure formed by two rays starting from the same point. The point is called the *vertex* of the angle, and the rays are called the *sides*.

angles of a triangle (p. 474). *See under* triangle.

area. The area of a region is the number of unit squares it contains.

associative axioms (p. 37). For all real numbers a, b, c:

Addition: $(a + b) + c = a + (b + c)$

Multiplication: $(ab)c = a(bc)$.

average (p. 90). The average of n numbers is the sum of the numbers divided by n.

axes (p. 276). *See under* coordinate axes.

axiom (p. 36). A statement that is assumed to be true.

axiom of comparison (p. 369). For all real numbers a and b, one and only one of the following statements is true: $a < b$, $a = b$, $b < a$.

axiom of opposites (p. 43). For every real number a, there is a real number $-a$ such that $a + (-a) = 0$ and $(-a) + a = 0$.

axiom of reciprocals (p. 61). For every nonzero real number a, there is a real number $\frac{1}{a}$ such that

$$a \cdot \frac{1}{a} = 1 \text{ and } \frac{1}{a} \cdot a = 1.$$

axioms of closure (p. 36). For all real numbers a and b:

Addition: $a + b$ is a real number.

Multiplication: ab is a real number.

base (in a power) (p. 113). One of the equal factors.

base angles of an isosceles triangle (p. 474). *See under* isosceles triangle.

base of an isosceles triangle (p. 474). *See under* isosceles triangle.

between (p. 365). b is between a and c if $a < b < c$ or $c > b > a$.

binomial (p. 117). A polynomial of two terms.

boundary line (p. 389). A line which separates the plane into two half-planes.

circumference. The perimeter of a circle.

closed half-plane (p. 389). The union of an open half-plane and its boundary.

combined variation (p. 356). A function defined by an equation of the form $z = \dfrac{kx}{y}$, k a nonzero constant.

commutative axioms (p. 36). For all real numbers a and b:

Addition: $a + b = b + a$

Multiplication: $ab = ba$

complementary angles (p. 471). A pair of angles the sum of whose measures is $90°$.

completing the square (p. 446). Adding a term to an expression in the form "$x^2 + bx$" to produce a trinomial square.

complex fraction (p. 225). A fraction whose numerator or denominator contains one or more fractions.

conjugates (p. 432). Two binomials of the form $x + \sqrt{y}$ and $x - \sqrt{y}$.

conjunction (p. 382). A sentence formed by joining two sentences by the word *and*.

consecutive even numbers (p. 13). Obtained by counting by twos from any even integer.

consecutive numbers (p. 12). Obtained by counting by ones from any given integer.

consecutive odd numbers (p. 13). Obtained by counting by twos from any odd integer.

constant monomial (p. 117). A numerical term with no variable expression.

constant of variation (p. 343). In a direct variation expressed by $y = kx$, k is the constant of variation. Also called *constant of proportionality*.

converse (p. 187). The converse of a theorem is obtained by interchanging the "if" and "then" portions.

coordinate (p. 30). The number assigned to a point on the number line.

coordinate axes (p. 276). The axes (horizontal and vertical) of a coordinate system set up in a plane.

coordinate plane (p. 276). A plane in which a coordinate system has been set up.

coordinate system (pp. 275–277). A system of graphing ordered pairs of numbers in relation to two *axes* (*horizontal* and *vertical*) which intersect at right angles at their zero point (the *origin*).

coordinates of a point (p. 276). The abscissa and ordinate of the point, written as an ordered pair of numbers.

correspondence (p. 334). A matching between the members of two sets.

corresponding angles (p. 477). *See under* similar triangles.

corresponding sides (p. 477). *See under* similar triangles.

cosine (p. 480). The cosine of $\angle A$ of a right triangle =
$$\frac{\text{length of leg adjacent to } \angle A}{\text{length of hypotenuse}}.$$

cubic equation (p. 189). A polynomial equation of degree three.

degree (measure of an angle) (p. 469). $\frac{1}{180}$ of the rotation of a ray from one direction to its opposite.

degree of a monomial (p. 117). The number of times that a variable occurs as a factor in a monomial is the degree of the monomial in that variable. The sum of the degrees in each of the variables is the degree of the monomial. A nonzero constant has degree 0. 0 has no degree.

degree of a polynomial (p. 118). The greatest of the degrees of its terms after it has been simplified.

denominator (p. 158). In the fraction $\dfrac{a}{b}$, b is the denominator.

difference (p. 76). For any two real numbers a and b, the difference $a - b$ is the number whose sum with b is a.

directly proportional (p. 344). y is directly proportional to x if (x_1, y_1) and (x_2, y_2) are ordered pairs of a function, neither of which is $(0, 0)$, and this statement is true: $\frac{y_1}{x_1} = \frac{y_2}{x_2}$.

direct variation (p. 343). A function defined by an equation of the form $y = kx$, where k is a nonzero constant.

discriminant (p. 453). The value of $b^2 - 4ac$ is called the discriminant of the quadratic equation $ax^2 + bx + c = 0$.

disjoint sets (p. 380). Sets that have no members in common.

disjunction (p. 382). A sentence formed by joining two sentences by the word *or*.

distance formula (p. 426). For any points $P_1(x_1, y_1)$ and $P_2(x_2, y_2)$:
$$P_1P_2 = \sqrt{(x_2 - x_1)^2 + (y_2 - y_1)^2}.$$

distributive axiom of multiplication with respect to addition (p. 53). For all real numbers a, b, and c:
$$a(b + c) = ab + ac$$
$$(b + c)a = ba + ca.$$

divide-and-average method (p. 417). A way to find closer and closer approximations to the square root of a number that is not a perfect square by continuing to average pairs of factors.

domain of a function (p. 331). *See under* function.

domain of a variable (p. 9). The set of numbers that the variable may represent. Also called *replacement set.*

empty set (p. 100). The set with no members.

equal expressions (p. 2). Expressions that name the same number.

equation (p. 9). A statement formed by placing an equality symbol between two numerical or variable expressions.

equilateral triangle (p. 474). A triangle with all sides of equal length.

equivalent equations (inequalities) (pp. 72, 370). Equations (inequalities) having the same solution set over a given domain.

equivalent expressions (p. 54). Expressions which represent the same number for all values of the variables that they contain.

equivalent systems (p. 291). Systems of equations having the same solution set.

evaluate an expression (p. 2). Replace each variable in the expression by a given value of the variable, and simplify the result.

exponent (p. 113). In a power, the number of times the base occurs as a factor.

exponential form (p. 114). The expression "x^3" is the exponential form of the third power of x.

expressing in simplest form (p. 201). Dividing the numerator and the denominator of a fraction by their greatest common factor.

extremes (p. 240). In the proportion $\frac{a}{b} = \frac{c}{d}$, a and d are the extremes.

factor (p. 37). When two or more numbers are multiplied, each of the numbers is a factor of the product.

factored form (p. 114). The expression "$x \cdot x \cdot x$" is the factored form of the third power of x, that is, x^3.

factoring (pp. 155, 162). Finding the factors of a number or an expression over a specified factor set.

factor set (p. 155). The set from which factors of a number may be selected.

formula (p. 17). An expression of numerical relationships between quantities such as physical or other measurements.

fraction (p. 201). An expression in the form $\frac{a}{b}$, $b \neq 0$.

fractional equation (p. 247). An equation which has a variable in the denominator of one or more terms.

function (p. 331). A function consists of two sets, the domain and the range, together with a rule which assigns to each member of the domain exactly one member of the range. Each member of the range must be assigned to at least one member of the domain.

graph of an equation (p. 283). All points, and only those points, whose coordinates satisfy the equation.

graph of a function (p. 338). The graphs in the coordinate plane of all the ordered pairs that form the function.

graph of a number (p. 30). The point on the number line paired with the number.

graph of an ordered pair of numbers (p. 276). The point in the plane paired with an ordered pair of real numbers.

greatest common factor (p. 156). The greatest integer which is a factor of each of two or more integers.

greatest monomial factor (p. 159). The common monomial factor of two or more monomials that has the greatest coefficient and the greatest degree in each variable.

greatest monomial factor of a polynomial (p. 162). The greatest monomial factor of the terms of the polynomial.

grouping symbol (p. 5). A device used to enclose a numerical expression. Examples include parentheses, brackets, and fraction bars.

half-plane (p. 389). *See under* closed half-plane *and* open half-plane.

histogram (p. 336). A bar graph used to summarize a large set of data.

horizontal axis (p. 275). Horizontal number line in a plane.

hyperbola (p. 348). The graph of an equation of the form
$$xy = k,\ k \neq 0\ (x \neq 0, y \neq 0).$$

hypotenuse (p. 422). The side of a right triangle opposite the right angle.

identity (p. 101). An equation which is true for every value of the variable(s).

identity axioms (pp. 41, 57). For any real number a:

Addition: $\quad\quad\quad a + 0 = 0 + a = a$

Multiplication: $\quad a \cdot 1 = 1 \cdot a = a$.

identity elements (pp. 41, 57). 0 is the identity element for addition. 1 is the identity element for multiplication.

inequality (p. 33). A statement formed by placing an inequality symbol between two numerical or variable expressions.

integers (p. 30). The numbers in the set
$$\{\ldots, -3, -2, -1, 0, 1, 2, 3, \ldots\}.$$

integral factors (p. 155). Factors taken from the set of integers.

intersection of sets (p. 380). For any two sets A and B, the set consisting of all members belonging to both A and B is the intersection of A and B.

inverse operations (p. 96). Operations that "undo" each other; for example, addition and subtraction.

inverse variation (p. 348). A function defined by an equation of the form $xy = k$, where k is a nonzero constant.

inverse variation as the square (p. 353). A function defined by an equation of the form $x^2y = k$, where k is a nonzero constant.

irrational number (p. 416). A real number which cannot be expressed in the form $\frac{r}{s}$, where r and s are integers, $s \neq 0$.

irreducible polynomial (p. 176). A polynomial which is not the product of polynomials of lower positive degree belonging to a specified set.

isosceles triangle (p. 474). A triangle with two sides of equal length. If $MN = NP$ in $\triangle MNP$, MP is the *base* of the triangle and $\angle M$ and $\angle P$ are the *base angles*.

joint variation (p. 356). A function defined by the equation $z = kxy$, where k is a nonzero constant.

least common denominator (L.C.D.) (p. 212). The least positive common multiple of the denominators of two or more fractions.

leg of a right triangle (p. 474). One of the two sides which form the right angle.

linear direct variation (p. 343). *See under* direct variation.

linear equation in one variable (p. 189). A polynomial equation of degree one.

linear equation in two variables (p. 283). Any equation equivalent to one of the form $Ax + By = C$, where A, B, and C are real numbers with A and B not both zero.

linear function (p. 338). A function whose ordered pairs satisfy a linear equation.

linear term (p. 166). A term of degree one in the variable.

line segment (p. 468). A subset of a line consisting of two points and the part of the line between them.

maximum point of a quadratic function (p. 339). The point whose y-coordinate is the greatest value the function can have.

means (p. 240). In the proportion $\frac{a}{b} = \frac{c}{d}$, b and c are the means.

member of a set (p. 10). Any object in the set.

minimum point of a quadratic function (p. 338). A point whose y-coordinate is the least value the function can have.

mixed expression (p. 220). The sum or difference of a polynomial and a fraction.

mixed numeral (p. 220). A numeral, like $3\frac{2}{5}$, which denotes the sum of an integer and a fraction.

monomial (p. 117). A term which is either a numeral, a variable, or a product of a numeral and one or more variables.

monomial factor (p. 159). A monomial which is a factor of each of the terms of a polynomial.

multiple (p. 121). The product of any real number and an integer is a multiple of the real number.

multiplication axiom of order (p. 370). For all real numbers a, b, and c:

1. If $a < b$ and $c > 0$, then $ac < bc$; if $a > b$ and $c > 0$, then $ac > bc$.
2. If $a < b$ and $c < 0$, then $ac > bc$; if $a > b$ and $c < 0$, then $ac < bc$.

multiplication property of equality (p. 84). If $a = b$, then $ac = bc$ and $ca = cb$.

multiplicative inverse (p. 61). For a nonzero real number b, the real number $\frac{1}{b}$, for which $b \cdot \frac{1}{b} = 1$ and $\frac{1}{b} \cdot b = 1$. Also called *reciprocal*.

multiplicative property of −1 (p. 57). For all real numbers a, $a(-1) = -a$ and $(-1)a = -a$.

multiplicative property of zero (p. 57). $a \cdot 0 = 0$ and $0 \cdot a = 0$.

negative number (p. 30). A number paired with a point on the negative side of a number line.

nonterminating decimal (p. 408). A decimal for which the division process is unending.

numeral (p. 2). A name for a number. Also called *numerical expression*.

numerator (p. 158). In the fraction $\frac{a}{b}$, a is the numerator.

numerical coefficient (p. 117). In a term, the factor which is not a variable; for example, 5 in $5xy$.

obtuse angle (p. 469). An angle measuring between 90° and 180°.

open expression (p. 2). *See under* variable expression.

open half-plane (p. 389). One of the two regions into which a line separates the plane. The boundary line is not a member of either open half-plane.

open sentence (p. 9). An equation or inequality which contains a variable.

open sentence in two variables (p. 280). An equation or inequality which contains two variables.

opposite of a number (p. 43). *See under* additive inverse.

ordered pair (p. 275). A pair of elements in which the order is specified.

ordinate (p. 276). The second coordinate in an ordered pair of numbers that is associated with a point in a coordinate plane.

origin (pp. 29, 275). The starting point, labeled "0", on a number line; the zero point of both of two number lines that intersect at right angles.

parabola (p. 338). The graph of a quadratic function.

parallel lines (p. 287). Lines that lie in the same plane but have no point in common.

percent (p. 251). A notation for a ratio with the denominator 100; $\frac{3}{100} = 3\%$.

perimeter. The perimeter of a geometric figure is the distance around it.

plotting a point (p. 276). Locating the graph of an ordered pair of real numbers on the coordinate plane.

polynomial (p. 117). A sum of monomials.

polynomial equation (p. 189). An equation in which both members are polynomials in one variable.

positive number (p. 30). A number paired with a point on the positive side of a number line.

power (p. 113). A product in which all the factors, except 1, are the same. For example, the fourth power of 5 is defined by $5^4 = 5 \cdot 5 \cdot 5 \cdot 5$.

prime factorization (p. 156). The expression of a positive integer as a product of prime factors is the prime factorization of the integer.

prime factors (p. 156). Factors which are prime numbers or prime polynomials.

prime number (p. 155). An integer, greater than one, which has no positive integral factor other than itself and one.

prime polynomial (p. 176). An irreducible polynomial whose greatest monomial factor is 1.

principal square root (p. 412). The positive square root, denoted by $\sqrt{}$.

proof (p. 104). Logical reasoning from known facts and axioms to a theorem.

property of betweenness (p. 404). Between every pair of different rational numbers there is another rational number.

property of completeness (p. 417). Every decimal represents a real number, and every real number has a decimal representation.

property of the opposite of a sum (p. 47). $-(a + b) = (-a) + (-b)$.

property of square roots of equal numbers (p. 419). If r and s are any real numbers, then $r^2 = s^2$ if and only if $r = s$ or $r = -s$.

proportion (p. 240). An equation made up of two equal ratios.

protractor (p. 469). An instrument used to find the degree measure of an angle.

Pythagorean theorem (p. 422). In any right triangle, the square of the length of the hypotenuse equals the sum of the squares of the lengths of the other two sides.

quadrant (p. 275). One of the four regions into which the coordinate axes separate the plane.

quadratic direct variation (p. 353). A function defined by an equation of the form $y = kx^2$, where k is a nonzero constant.

quadratic equation (p. 189). A polynomial equation of degree two.

quadratic formula (p. 449). If $ax^2 + bx + c = 0$, $a \neq 0$, and $b^2 - 4ac \geq 0$, then

$$x = \frac{-b \pm \sqrt{b^2 - 4ac}}{2a}.$$

quadratic function (p. 338). A function defined by an equation of the form $y = ax^2 + bx + c$, $a \neq 0$.

quadratic polynomial (p. 166). A polynomial of degree two that contains a single variable.

quadratic term (p. 166). A term of degree two in the variable.

quotient (p. 88). The quotient $a \div b$, $b \neq 0$, is the number whose product with b is a.

radical (p. 412). An expression of the form $\sqrt{a}$.

radical equation (p. 434). An equation having a variable in a radicand.

radical sign (p. 412). The symbol $\sqrt{}$.

radicand (p. 412). An expression beneath a radical sign.

range of a function (p. 331). *See under* function.

ratio (p. 235). The ratio of one number to another (not zero) is the quotient of the first number divided by the second.

rational expression (pp. 201, 403). A fraction; an expression for a rational number.

rational number (p. 403). A real number that can be expressed as a ratio of two integers (the second integer not zero).

rationalizing a denominator (p. 428). The process of changing the form of a fraction with an irrational denominator to an equal fraction with a rational denominator.

ray (p. 468). A part of a line that consists of a point A and all points on the line on one side of A.

real number (p. 30). Any number paired with a point on the number line.

reciprocal (p. 61). *See under* multiplicative inverse.

reflexive property of equality (p. 38). $a = a$.

repeating decimal (p. 408). A nonterminating decimal in which the same digit or block of digits repeats unendingly. Also called *periodic decimal*.

replacement set (p. 9). *See under* domain of a variable.

right angle (p. 469). An angle measuring $90°$.

right triangle (p. 474). A triangle with a right angle.

root of an open sentence (p. 9). A solution of the sentence.

rounding a decimal (p. 410). Breaking off a decimal to achieve an approximation, by adding 1 to the value of the last digit kept if the first digit dropped is 5 or more, or, otherwise, by leaving unchanged the digits that are kept.

satisfy (p. 9). Each member of the solution set of an open sentence satisfies that sentence.

set (p. 9). Collection of objects.

sides of an angle (p. 468). *See under* angle.

sides of an equation (p. 9). The expressions joined by the symbol of equality.

sides of an inequality (p. 366). The expressions joined by an inequality symbol.

sides of a triangle (p. 474). *See under* triangle.

significant digits (p. 128). The following numbers are expressed with 6 significant digits: 123,475; 2.00027; 235.650; 0.0123456; 243,724,000 or 2.43724×10^8.

similar terms (p. 117). Terms that are exactly alike or that differ only in their numerical coefficients.

similar triangles (p. 477). $\triangle ABC$ and $\triangle DEF$ are similar triangles if $\angle A = \angle D$, $\angle B = \angle E$, and $\angle C = \angle F$. $\angle A$ and $\angle D$ are corresponding angles (as are $\angle B$ and $\angle E$, $\angle C$ and $\angle F$). The sides opposite corresponding angles are corresponding sides.

simple form of a polynomial (p. 117). A polynomial is in simple form if no two of its terms are similar.

simple interest (p. 4). Simple interest I on an investment of P dollars at the interest rate R for T years is given by the formula $I = PRT$.

simplest form of a fraction (p. 201). The fraction $\frac{a}{b}$ is in simplest form when a and b have no common factor other than 1 and -1.

simplest form of a radical (p. 428). A radical expression in which no integral radicand has a square factor other than 1, no fractions are under a radical sign, and no radicals are in a denominator.

simplify (p. 2). Replace a numerical expression by the simplest, or most common, name of its value.

simultaneous equations (p. 287). *See under* system of simultaneous equations.

sine (p. 480). The sine of $\angle A$ of a right triangle =

$$\frac{\text{length of leg opposite } \angle A}{\text{length of hypotenuse}}.$$

slope of a line (p. 320). The steepness of a nonvertical line as defined by the quotient

$$\frac{\text{difference of } y\text{-coordinates}}{\text{difference of } x\text{-coordinates}}.$$

A horizontal line has slope 0; a vertical line has no slope.

slope-intercept form of a linear equation (p. 325). $y = mx + b$, where m is the slope of the line represented by the equation and b is its y-intercept.

solution (p. 9). A value of a variable that converts an open sentence into a true statement.

solution of an open sentence in two variables (p. 280). An ordered pair of values for which the sentence becomes a true sentence.

solution of a system of two equations in two variables (p. 287). An ordered pair of numbers that satisfies both equations.

solution set of an open sentence (p. 9). The set that consists of the members of the domain of the variable for which the sentence is true is called the solution set of the sentence over that domain.

solve (p. 9). Find the solution set of an open sentence over a given domain.

square root (p. 412). The number a is a square root of the number b if $a^2 = b$.

straight angle (p. 469). An angle measuring 180°.

substitution method (p. 291). A method for finding the solution of a pair of linear equations in two variables by: (1) solving one equation for one of the variables, (2) substituting the resulting expression in the other equation, (3) solving this derived equation, (4) finding the corresponding value of the other variable.

substitution principle (p. 2). Changing the numeral by which a number is named in an expression does not change the value of the expression.

supplementary angles (p. 471). Two angles the sum of whose measures is 180°.

symmetric property of equality (p. 38). If $a = b$, then $b = a$.

system of simultaneous equations (p. 287). A set of equations in the same variables.

tangent (p. 480). The tangent of $\angle A$ of a right triangle $=$

$$\frac{\text{length of leg opposite } \angle A}{\text{length of leg adjacent to } \angle A}.$$

term (p. 37). A mathematical expression using numerals or variables or both to indicate a product or a quotient.

terminating decimal (p. 408). A decimal for which the division process stops because a remainder of 0 is reached.

theorem (p. 104). A statement that is shown to be true using axioms, definitions, and other theorems in a logical development.

transformation. Each of the following always produces an equation equivalent to the original equation:

by addition (p. 72). Adding the same number to each member.

by division (p. 92). Dividing each member by the same nonzero number.

by multiplication (p. 84). Multiplying each member by the same nonzero number.

by substitution (p. 72). Replacing either member by an expression equivalent to it.

by subtraction (p. 81). Subtracting the same number from each member.

transitive axiom of order (p. 369). For all real numbers a, b, and c:

1. If $a < b$ and $b < c$, then $a < c$.
2. If $c > b$ and $b > a$, then $c > a$.

transitive property of equality (p. 38). If $a = b$ and $b = c$, then $a = c$.

triangle (p. 474). A figure formed by connecting three points not on a line by segments. In $\triangle ABC$: $\overline{AB}$, $\overline{BC}$, and $\overline{CA}$ are the *sides* of the triangle; A, B, and C are the *vertices* of the triangle; and $\angle BAC$, $\angle ACB$, and $\angle CBA$ are the *angles* of the triangle.

trigonometric functions (p. 481). Functions having the values $\cos A$, $\sin A$, and $\tan A$, where A is a member of the set of acute angles.

trigonometric ratios (p. 480). In a right triangle, the ratios (sine, cosine, tangent) of the sides associated with an acute angle of the triangle.

trinomial (p. 117). A polynomial of three terms.

trinomial square (p. 171). A trinomial obtained by squaring a binomial. The pattern of the terms is

$$a^2 + 2ab + b^2 \text{ or } a^2 - 2ab + b^2.$$

uniform motion (p. 142). An object which moves without changing its speed, or rate, is said to be in uniform motion.

union of sets (p. 380). For any two sets A and B, the set consisting of all members belonging to at least one of the sets A and B is the union of A and B.

unit distance (p. 29). The distance between 0 and 1 on a number line.

values of a function (p. 332). Members of the range of the function.

values of a variable (p. 1). Numbers in the domain of the variable.

variable (p. 1). A symbol used to represent one or more numbers.

variable expression (p. 2). An expression containing a variable. Also called *open expression*.

vertex of an angle (p. 468). *See under* angle.

vertex of a parabola (p. 339). The maximum or minimum point of the graph of

$$y = ax^2 + bx + c, a \neq 0.$$

vertical angles (p. 471). Two angles whose sides are rays in the same line but in opposite directions.

vertical axis (p. 275). A vertical number line at right angles to a horizontal number line such that both lines have the same zero point.

vertices of a triangle (p. 474). *See under* triangle.

volume. The volume of a solid is the number of unit cubes it contains.

whole numbers (p. 12). The numbers in the set $\{0, 1, 2, 3, \ldots\}$.

x-coordinate (p. 283). *See under* abscissa.

x-intercept (p. 452). The x-coordinate of a point where a graph intersects the x-axis.

y-coordinate (p. 283). *See under* ordinate.

y-intercept (p. 324). The y-coordinate of a point where a graph intersects the y-axis.

zero of a function (p. 462). A zero of a function f is a solution of the equation $f(x) = 0$.

zero-product property (p. 187). For all real numbers a and b, $ab = 0$ if and only if $a = 0$ or $b = 0$.

INDEX

Abscissa, 276
Absolute value, 44
  in open sentences, 386
Acute angle, 469
Addition
  axioms for, *see under* Axioms
  of fractions, 216–217
  identity element for, 41
  and the number line, 40
  of polynomials, 117–118
  of radical expressions, 430
  of real numbers, 40–41, 43–44, 47–48
  rules for, 48
Addition-or-subtraction method, 296–297, 299–300
Addition property of equality, 71
Additive inverse, 43
algebra, 11
Angle(s), 468–469
  of depression, 485
  of elevation, 485
  of a triangle, 474
Application
  balancing a checkbook, 65
  computation shortcut, 298
  electrical power and energy, 94
  gear ratios, 268
  histograms, 336
  line of best fit, 327
  Newton's law of motion, 463
  nutrition labeling, 397
  optics, 249
  unit pricing, 207
  See also Problems
Area, 4, 7, 17
Arrow notation, 331
Associative axiom(s), 37
Associative operations, 77, 89
Average, 90
Axes, coordinate, 276
Axiom(s), 36, 104
  addition, of order, 370
  additive, of zero; *see* identity axiom for addition
  associative, 37
  of closure, 36

commutative, 36
of comparison, 369
distributive, 53
identity, for addition, 41
identity, for multiplication, 57
multiplication, of order, 370
multiplicative, of one; *see* identity axiom for multiplication
of opposites, 43
of reciprocals, 61
transitive, of order, 369
See also Property
Axis
  horizontal, 275
  vertical, 275

Bar graph, 334
Base of an isosceles triangle, 474
Base of a power, 113
between, 365
Betweenness, property of, 404
Binomial(s), 117
  containing square-root radicals, 432
  factoring products of, 168
  multiplying, mentally, 166
  product of, 131, 166, 168
  squaring, 171
Biography
  Boyd, Louise Arner, 203
  Braun, Wernher von, 312
  Cannon, Annie Jump, 16
  del Rio, Andres Manuel, 80
  Fermat, Pierre de, 407
  Franklin, Rosalind Elsie, 174
  Gilbreth, Lillian Moller, 255
  Julian, Percy Lavon, 330
  Kitasato, Shibasaburo, 484
  Lovelace, Ada Byron, 378
  McCoy, Elijah, 145
  McLennan, John Cunningham, 56
  Ramon y Cajal, Santiago, 463
Boundary line of a half-plane, 389

Linear equations, 189, 283
  graphs of, 283
  slope-intercept form of, 325
  standard form of, 283
  in two variables, 283
Linear function, 338
  graphs of, 338
Linear term, 166

Maintaining Skills, 27, 69, 111, 153, 199, 233, 273, 317, 363, 401, 441
Maximum point, 339
Mean, *see* Average
Means of a proportion, 240
Member of a set, 10
Metric units of measure, xii
Minimum point, 338
Mixed expression, 220
Monomial(s), 117
  degree of, 117
  dividing, 158
  multiplying, 122, 129
  powers of, 126
Monomial factor, 159
Multiple, 121, 212
Multiplication
  axioms for, *see under* Axioms
  of binomials, 166
  of binomials containing square-root radicals, 432
  of fractions, 204
  identity element for, 57
  of monomials, 122
  of a polynomial by a monomial, 129
  of polynomials, 131
  of radical expressions, 428
  of real numbers, 53-54, 57-59, 61-62
  rules for, 58
  of the sum and difference of two numbers, 168
Multiplication property of equality, 84
Multiplication rule for fractions, 204
Multiplicative inverse, 61
Multiplicative property of -1, 57
Multiplicative property of zero, 57

Negative integers, 29
Negative numbers, 30
Negative side, 29
Nonterminating decimal, 408
Null set, 100

Number(s), 2
  comparing, 33, 369
  consecutive, 12
  directed, 30
  graphing, 29-30
  integers, 30
  irrational, 416
  negative, 30
  opposite, 43
  positive, 30
  prime, 155
  rational, 403
  real, 30
  square, 116
  triangular, 15
  whole, 12
Number line, 29
  addition on, 40
  coordinate of a point on, 30
  displacements on, 40-41
  origin of, 29
Numeral, 2
Numerator, 158
Numerical coefficient, 117
Numerical expression, 2
Numerical trigonometry, 469

Obtuse angle, 469
Odd integers, 30
One as identity element for multiplication, 57
Open half-plane, 389
Open sentence(s), 9
  solution set of, 9
  in two variables, 280
  See also Equation(s), Inequalities, Graphs
Opposite(s)
  addition property of, 43
  of a number, 43
Order of operations, 5-6, 114
Order of real numbers, 33
Ordered pairs, 275, 334
Ordinate, 276
Origin, 29, 275

Parabola, 338
Parallel lines, 287
Parallelogram, 7
Percent, 111, 251
Perfect square, 444
Perimeter, 4

ACKNOWLEDGMENTS

Illustrations by ANCO/Boston and Dan Collins

Photographs provided by the following sources: opposite p. 1, United States Parachute Association; p. 11, Historical Pictures Service, Inc.; p. 16, Harvard College Observatory; p. 20, Photo Researchers/Jan Lukas; p. 21, The Foxboro Company; p. 28, Woods Hole Oceanographic Institution/Dr. John Edmond; p. 35 (left), Leo DeWys, Inc./Arthur Lavine, (right), Black Star/Gil Kerry; p. 56, University of Toronto Archives; p. 70, Leo DeWys, Inc./Rocky Weldon; p. 80, From *Discovery of the Elements*, p. 370, published by the Journal of Chemical Education; p. 112, Editorial Photocolor Archives/Beckerman; p. 139, Daniel Bernstein for New England Medical Center Hospital; p. 145, Burton Historical Collection of the Detroit Public Library; p. 154, Photo Researchers (Rapho)/Paolo Koch; p. 174, Birkbeck College of the University of London; p. 182, Photo Researchers/Harmit Singh; p. 200, Stock, Boston/Milton Feinberg; p. 203, The American Geographical Society; p. 211, Radio Shack, a Division of Tandy Corporation; p. 231, Eric A. Roth; p. 234, NFB Phototheque/George Hunter; p. 249, Bausch & Lomb; p. 255, Historical Pictures Service, Inc.; p. 267, City of Boston Public Schools; p. 274, Stock, Boston/Barbara Alper; p. 279, North American Rockwell Microelectronics Company; p. 282, The Bettmann Archive, Inc.; p. 312, NASA; p. 318, Stock, Boston/George Bellerose; p. 323, USDA/Soil Conservation Service; p. 330, Diamond Shamrock Corporation; p. 352, The Bettmann Archive, Inc.; p. 364, Sara Lee; p. 378, British Crown copyright, reproduced with permission of the Controller of Her Britannic Majesty's Stationery Office; p. 379, Digital Equipment Corporation; p. 385, Photo Researchers/Alice Kandell; p. 402, Photo Researchers/Joe Munroe; p. 407, The Bettmann Archive, Inc.; p. 415, The Bettmann Archive, Inc.; p. 442, Monkmeyer Press Photo Service/White; p. 451, The Bettmann Archive, Inc.; p. 458, Photo Researchers (Rapho)/Ray Ellis; p. 463, Historical Pictures Service, Inc.; p. 484, National Library of Medicine

ANSWERS TO ODD-NUMBERED EXERCISES

CHAPTER 1   INTRODUCTION TO ALGEBRA

Written Exercises, pages 3–4 1. 10 **3.** 60
5. 9 **7.** 6 **9.** 180 **11.** 2 **13.** 10 **15.** 6
17. 21 **19.** 31 **21.** 36 **23.** 2 **25.** 0
27. 1 **29.** equal **31.** not equal **33.** 336
35. 40 **37.** $720

Written Exercises, pages 6–8 1. 1 **3.** 3
5. 39 **7.** 26 **9.** 7 **11.** 2 **13.** 5 **15.** 9
17. 12 **19.** 61.4 **21.** 937.5 **23.** 11.14
25. not equal **27.** equal **29.** not equal
31. equal **33.** equal **35.** not equal

Calculator Key-In, page 8 1. 0 **3.** 0.1
5. 333,333

Written Exercises, page 10 1. $\{5\}$ **3.** $\{5\}$
5. $\{1\}$ **7.** $\{5\}$ **9.** $\{3\}$ **11.** $\{2\}$ **13.** $\{6\}$
15. $\{0, 1, 2, 3, 4, 5, 6\}$ **17.** $\{4\}$ **19.** $\{2\}$
21. $\{6\}$ **23.** $\{4\}$ **25.** $\{0, 3\}$ **27.** $\{0, 9\}$
Answers may vary for Exs. 29 and 31.
29. $x + 3 = 5$ **31.** $2x = x + x$

Written Exercises, pages 14–15 1. g **3.** f
5. a **7.** $8t$ **9.** $\frac{1}{2}n$ **11.** $a + 7$ **13.** $b - 2$
15. $2q + 1$ **17.** $t - 1; t - 2$ **19.** $15 - y$
21. $x - 6$ **23.** odd; $2n + 6; 2n + 7$
25. $\frac{1}{2}r = 34$ **27.** $15 = 2z + 3$
29. $\frac{1}{3}x + 5 = 9$ **31.** $3(4 + t) = 42$
33. $2x = x + 8$
35. $x + (x + 1) + (x + 2) = 153$
37. $d + (d + 2) = (d + 4) + 9$

Just for Fun, page 15

1.

21   28   36

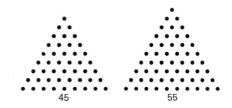

45   55

Calculator Key-In, page 16 1. a. 1 **b.** 2
c. 3 **d.** 4

Written Exercises, pages 18–20 1. $y + 3$
3. $6x$ **5.** $7x$ **7.** $15t$ **9.** $2w - 18; 6w - 36$
11. $4s = 28$ **13.** $4x = 120$ **15.** $x - 4 = 11$
17. $x - 1 = 1.50$
19. $2w + 2(w + 37) = 348$
21. $w + (w + 5) = 23$ **23.** $c + 7c = 1200$
25. $80\left(\frac{1}{2}t\right) + 100\left(\frac{1}{2}t\right) = 600$

Problems, pages 23–24 1. 5 touchdowns
3. $400 **5.** $3.50 **7.** 1650 students
9. a. 36 **b.** 9 **11.** 3 m **13.** $40 **15.** $200

Chapter Review, page 26 1. b **3.** b **5.** a
7. d

Maintaining Skills, page 27 1. 10,518
3. 6999 **5.** 13,268 **7.** 8392 **9.** 18,606
11. 71,288 **13.** 2,840,376 **15.** 36,279,972
17. 85 R9 **19.** 96 **21. a.** 70,570 **b.** 71,000
23. a. 87,920 **b.** 88,000 **25.** 1500
27. 1600 **29.** 15,300

CHAPTER 2   WORKING WITH REAL NUMBERS

Written Exercises, pages 31–32 1. 2; $^-2$;
two floors down **3.** 250; $^-250$; 250 m below
sea level **5.** 6; $^-6$; a loss of 6 points **7.** 8;
$^-8$; 8 km west **9.** 1; $^-1$; one second before
liftoff **11.** 28.09; $^-28.09$; payments of
$28.09 **13.** $^-1, 0, 1$ **15.** $^-1, 2, 5$ **17.** $^-5, ^-3,$
$^-1, 0$ **19.** $^-\frac{1}{2}, \frac{1}{2}$ **21.** E, N **23.** I, A

25. *B, Q* 27. *F, H*

29.

31.

33.

35.

37. 5 39. $^-1$ 41. 0 43. 4

Written Exercises, pages 34–35 1. $5 > {}^-2$
3. $^-10 > {}^-15$ **5.** $4 < 4.5$ **7.** $^-12 < 0$
9. $<$ **11.** $<$ **13.** $>$ **15.** $>$ **17.** $<$
19. $>$ **21.** $^-6, {}^-4, 0, 7$ **23.** $^-5, {}^-1, 2, 3$
25. $^-\frac{1}{2}, {}^-\frac{1}{3}, {}^-\frac{1}{4}, {}^-\frac{1}{5}$ **27.** $^-1.4, {}^-0.6, 0.8, 1.5$
29. 3.14, 3.1416, 3.142 **31.** $^-2\frac{1}{2}, {}^-2\frac{1}{4}, {}^-2\frac{1}{6}$
33. false **35.** true **37.** false **39.** true

Written Exercises, page 39 1. 450 **3.** 990
5. 5700 **7.** 15 **9.** 10.0
11. $x + y + z + 15$ **13.** $30kpq$
15. $4500abc$ **17. a.** 6 **b.** yes **c.** yes
19. a. 10 **b.** yes **c.** no

Written Exercises, page 42 1. 0 **3.** $^-1$
5. $^-64$ **7.** $^-68$ **9.** $^-18$ **11.** $^-0.4$ **13.** $^-3\frac{2}{3}$
15. 2.25 **17.** $y = {}^-1$ **19.** $z = {}^-12$
21. $k = 4$ **23.** $d = {}^-24$ **25.** $n = {}^-0.5$
27. $q = 0$ **29.** $r = 4$ **31.** $a = 0$ **33.** $y = 5$

Written Exercises, pages 45–46 1. 18
3. -4 **5.** -17 **7.** 20 **9.** -5 **11.** 6
13. 15 **15.** 17 **17.** 7 **19.** -8 **21.** 7
23. -18 **25.** $\{-2\}$ **27.** $\{2\}$ **29.** $\{2\}$
31. $\{-1, 1\}$ **33.** $\{-2, 2\}$ **35.** $\{-2\}$
37. always **39.** sometimes

Just for Fun, page 46

3	-4	1	0
-2	0	2	0
-1	4	-3	0
0	0	0	0

Written Exercises, pages 49–50 1. 15
3. 62 **5.** 41 **7.** 18 **9.** -12 **11.** -33
13. 158 **15.** -40 **17.** 10 **19.** -11
21. -1.4

Problems, pages 50–51 1. 7 yards
3. $272 **5.** 7650 m **7.** 5 m below sea level
9. a net gain of $31,770 **11.** 126 km/h
13. 9 over par **15.** 68 beats per minute

Calculator Key-In, page 52 1. $26.67
3. 0.0909

Written Exercises, pages 55–56 1. 36
3. 4 **5.** 370 **7.** $15x$ **9.** $30z$ **11.** $15t$
13. $5x + 8$ **15.** $2a + 7$ **17.** $3c + 16$
19. $13a + 4$ **21.** $7x + 2$ **23.** $11x$ **25.** $2b$
27. $2m + 17k$ **29.** $8x + 10y + 3$
31. $20n + 20r$ **33.** $18x + 60$
35. $11z + 10x + 44$ **37.** $12x + 10y$
39. $6x + 6y + 3$ **41.** $182x + 172$
43. $622p + 258q + 340$

Written Exercises, pages 59–60 1. 120
3. 480 **5.** -105 **7.** 0 **9.** -400 **11.** 240
13. 18 **15.** -90 **17.** -60 **19.** $-6r + 42t$
21. $3a + 15b$ **23.** $2m - 1$ **25.** $8q + (-12p)$
27. $0.6a + (-2.0b)$ **29.** $-\frac{1}{4}x + 3y$
31. $-7a + 3b$ **33.** $t + (-9s)$ **35.** $d + 7e$
37. $-7m + (-26n)$ **39.** -4
41. (1) Identity axiom for multiplication
(2) Distributive axiom (3) Axiom of
opposites (4) Multiplicative property of
zero

Calculator Key-In, page 60 1. -1156
3. 11,115,556 **5.** -888 **7.** 9876 **9.** 987,654

Just for Fun, page 60

Written Exercises, page 63 1. -4
3. -10 **5.** 1 **7.** -4 **9.** $-xy$ **11.** $7y$
13. $-5x + 3$ **15.** $3c + (-2d)$
17. $-2a + 3b$ **19.** $2x + 7y$

21. $11a + (-3b)$ **23.** $-24r$ **25.** w
27. -3 **29.** π **31.** 3

Calculator Key-In, page 64 **1.** 8 **3.** -16
5. the original number

Application, page 65 To make the
checkbook register balance with the bank
statement, correct the error in subtracting
Check 320 from the balance in the
checkbook register.

Chapter Review, pages 67–68 **1.** c **3.** c
5. d **7.** b **9.** a **11.** a **13.** b **15.** a

Maintaining Skills, page 69 **1.** 47.106
3. 255.101 **5.** 22.56 **7.** 133.068 **9.** 62.909
11. 35.062 **13.** 21.827 **15.** 64.008
17. 4.3505 **19.** 0.245 **21.** 10,240
23. 0.1078 **25.** 45.756 **27.** 35.75 **29.** 6.788

CHAPTER 3 SOLVING EQUATIONS

Written Exercises, pages 73–74 **1.** 25
3. 19 **5.** 30 **7.** -16 **9.** -36 **11.** -28
13. -27 **15.** -27 **17.** 48 **19.** -4 **21.** 8
23. 0 **25.** 2 **27.** -6 **29.** 3 **31.** -4
33. -9 **35.** 9 **37.** 6, -6 **39.** 5, -5

Problems, pages 74–75 **1.** 29 **3.** -7
5. 9 touchdowns **7.** 97°C **9.** 7:30 A.M.
11. 418 employees

Written Exercises, pages 78–79 **1.** -170
3. 51 **5.** -14 **7.** -68 **9.** 176 **11.** 285
13. 117 **15.** 355 **17.** 0 **19.** -8
21. -2202 **23.** 9 **25.** 22 **27.** $-33x$
29. $x + 3$ **31.** y **33.** $h + 16$ **35.** -18
37. 4 **39.** -7 **41.** -12
43. (1) Rule for subtraction
(2) Distributive axiom of multiplication
with respect to addition (3) Property of
opposites in products (4) Rule for
subtraction

Problems, pages 79–80 **1.** 5°C **3.** 75
5. 73° **7.** 5730 m **9.** 146.3°C

Calculator Key-In, page 80 **1.** 963
3. -693 **5.** -2695 **7.** 0

Written Exercises, page 82 **1.** 26 **3.** -52
5. 0 **7.** 17 **9.** 21 **11.** 19 **13.** 24
15. -7 **17.** 9 **19.** 16 **21.** -13 **23.** 7
25. 6, -6

Problems, pages 82–83 **1.** 34 **3.** 44
5. 29 students **7.** 94 **9.** \$10.99
11. 18.5 km

Written Exercises, page 86 **1.** 168
3. -144 **5.** 7 **7.** -170 **9.** 512 **11.** -7
13. 5 **15.** -3 **17.** 6 **19.** $-\dfrac{2}{5}$ **21.** $\dfrac{4}{11}$
23. $-\dfrac{1}{34}$ **25.** 2 **27.** -50

Problems, pages 86–87 **1.** \$0.09 **3.** \$5.20
5. 35 m **7.** 13 **9.** \$54.75

Written Exercises, pages 90–91 **1.** -8
3. -108 **5.** 125 **7.** -60 **9.** $-11x$
11. -142 **13.** z **15.** $3x$ **17.** -5 **19.** -2
21. -3 **23.** 9 **25.** 15 **27.** 0 **29.** $-\dfrac{5}{7}$
31. (1) Rule for division (2) Distributive
axiom of multiplication with respect to
addition (3) Rule for division

Calculator Key-In, page 91 **1.** 0.25
3. -0.0625 **5.** 0.025 **7.** -0.12 **9.** 0.96875
11. 0.25 **13.** -0.0625 **15.** 0.025
17. -0.12 **19.** 0.96875

Just for Fun, page 91 (Answers may vary)
11, 23, 35

Written Exercises, page 93 **1.** 30 **3.** -16
5. -19 **7.** 26 **9.** 24 **11.** -43 **13.** 35
15. -11 **17.** 370 **19.** 680 **21.** -25
23. 26

Problems, page 93 **1.** -29 **3.** \$21.50
5. \$.59 **7.** \$.24 **9.** \$7840.40

Application, pages 94–95 **1.** 16.1 W
3. 120.05 V **5.** \$5.12

Written Exercises, page 97 **1.** 3 **3.** -6
5. 24 **7.** -175 **9.** -2 **11.** -7 **13.** -4
15. 0 **17.** -21 **19.** -5 **21.** -1 **23.** -7
25. 4 **27.** -5 **29.** -1 **31.** -4 **33.** -5
35. -5 **37.** 3 **39.** 1 **41.** 4 **43.** -17
45. $-\dfrac{10}{3}$ **47.** 5 **49.** 6, -6

Problems, pages 98–99 1. 64 **3.** 8 **5.** 34
7. 11 **9.** 6 **11.** soft drink, $.55; sandwich,
$1.65 **13.** 9 years **15.** 123 and 140
17. side of triangle, 12 cm; side of square,
24 cm **19.** Juan, 9 subscriptions; Ingrid, 14
subscriptions **21.** $-85.2°$C **23.** 13 years
25. $9.50

Just for Fun, page 99 $8.75

Written Exercises, pages 101–102 1. 7
3. 17 **5.** 13 **7.** -9 **9.** 14 **11.** -5
13. -22 **15.** -6 **17.** no root **19.** -6
21. 3 **23.** 17 **25.** -12 **27.** 3 **29.** 13
31. 0 **33.** identity **35.** identity **37.** -2
39. 1

Problems, pages 102–103 1. 12 **3.** 5
5. 19 and 57 **7.** 35 and 51 **9.** 10 g
11. $15 on a three-speed; $45 on a ten-
speed **13.** Steve, 8 baskets; Mike, 24
baskets **15.** 807 m; 57 m **17.** Harry, 16
years; Tom, 24 years; Dick, 12 years
19. 10%; 25%; 62%

Written Exercises, pages 105–107
1. (1) Associative axiom for multiplication
(2) Axiom of reciprocals (3) Identity axiom
for multiplication (4) Commutative axiom
for multiplication (5) Commutative axiom
for multiplication
3. (2) Addition property of equality
(3) Theorem proved on page 104
5. (1) Rule for subtraction (2) Property of
the opposite of a sum (3) Definition of the
opposite of a number (4) Commutative
axiom for addition (5) Rule for subtraction

Chapter Review, pages 108–109 1. c **3.** b
5. b **7.** a **9.** b **11.** c **13.** b **15.** b

Cumulative Review, page 110 1. 57
3. -23 **5.** 8 **7.** $r + 10$ **9.** $-9 - t$
11. -8 **13.** $-600z$ **15.** $-5m - n$ **17.** 3
19. -1 **21.** $-3.5, -2, 0, 1$ **23.** $\{0, 3\}$
25. $\{6, -6\}$ **27.** 9 **29.** 7 **31.** -8 **33.** 14
35. -53 **37.** -6 **39.** $\dfrac{6}{5}$ **41.** 11 **43.** $2.49

Maintaining Skills, page 111 1. 0.74
3. 1.75 **5.** 0.83 **7.** $\dfrac{7}{25}$ **9.** $\dfrac{93}{100}$ **11.** $\dfrac{2}{125}$
13. 37% **15.** 30% **17.** 7.5% **19.** 5.4
21. 2.25 **23.** 48.96 **25.** 60 **27.** 450
29. 5.8 **31.** 25% **33.** 64% **35.** 93.8%

CHAPTER 4 POLYNOMIALS AND PROBLEM SOLVING

Written Exercises, pages 115–116 1. x^3
3. z^3 **5.** $7b^2$ **7.** $-5r^2s$ **9.** $6y^3t^2$
11. $(a + b)^3$ **13.** $(c - 2)^2$ **15.** $17(m + p)^3$
17. $(d + e)^6$ **19.** 8 **21.** 5 **23.** 39 **25.** 18
27. 9 **29.** -13 **31.** 49 **33.** 1 **35.** -1
37. 0 **39.** 5

Calculator Key-In, page 116 1. 0.01
3. 0.16 **5.** 0.0144 **7.** 0.0009 **9.** 0.008
11. 0.125

Just for Fun, page 116 1. $4 = 1 + 3$;
$9 = 3 + 6$; $16 = 6 + 10$; $25 = 10 + 15$;
$36 = 15 + 21$; $49 = 21 + 28$;
$64 = 28 + 36$; $81 = 36 + 45$;
$100 = 45 + 55$

Written Exercises, pages 119–120
1. $3rt - 6$ **3.** $-x^2 + x$
5. $-4abc + 2bc - 3ac$
7. $2m^2n - 2mn^2 - 2mn$ **9.** $6x + 1$
11. $-2r + 5s$ **13.** $8s + 8t - 3$
15. $4x^2 + 3x + 1$ **17.** $n^2 + 4n - 7$
19. $8x^2 + 2x - 2$ **21.** $2x - 7$ **23.** $8r - 9s$
25. $-2s + 6t + 1$ **27.** $2x^2 + 7x + 3$
29. $3n^2 - 4n - 3$ **31.** $7a + 2b + 3$
33. $6a^2 - 2ab$ **35.** $x^3 + 2x^2 + 3x - 16$
37. $5b - 9$ **39.** $-4a + 4b - 3$
41. $-x^2 - 8x + 8$ **43.** $a^2 + ab - 2b^2$
45. 2 **47.** 6 **49.** 2 **51.** 2 **53.** -2
55. $-6a^4 + 4a^3 + 3$

Integer Problems, pages 120–121 1. 16, 17
3. 26, 28, 30, 32 **5.** 25 **7.** $-9, -8$
9. 7, 9, 11 **11.** 17, 18, 19, 20 **13.** 23 m by
25 m **15.** 12, 16, 20

Written Exercises, pages 123-124 **1.** a^{10}
3. $15c^6$ **5.** $30c^{10}$ **7.** x^4y^3 **9.** $90n^3m^7$
11. $3x^6y^{12}$ **13.** n^4p^4 **15.** $6n^5m^5$ **17.** b^{6n}
19. 2^{2k+3} **21.** x^{3n+7} **23.** $(-x)^{10}$ **25.** $11a^5$
27. $44x^6$ **29.** $12a^6b^5$ **31.** $11a^3b^5$
33. $17a^2b^3c^4$ **35.** $12a^2b^2$ **37.** $19a^2$
39. $46x^2$ **41.** $6a^3$ **43.** $18a^3$

Extra, pages 124-125 **1.** 2×10^5
3. 4.08×10^{10} **5.** 1.9×10^{-7} **7.** 6×10^{14}
9. 3.6×10^{-9} **11.** 1.24×10^2
13. 2.4596×10^9 **15. a.** 10^2 **b.** 10^3 **c.** 10^5
d. 10^{-3} **e.** 10^3 **f.** 10^{-6}

Written Exercises, pages 127-128 **1.** x^8
3. $8b^3$ **5.** $16a^{12}$ **7.** $\frac{1}{32}x^{10}$ **9.** $-8b^6y^{15}$
11. $81t^8s^{16}$ **13.** $36a^3$ **15.** $125a^4$
17. $576n^5$ **19.** $r^{18}s^8$ **21.** 45 **23.** -28
25. -8 **27.** 1 **29.** $72c^9$ **31.** $16u^{10}v^{14}$
33. $16a^{7n}$ **35.** $x^{4n}y^{4n}$ **37.** $7a^8b^{12}$
39. $2x^5y^4$ **41. a.** $8x^3, 64x^3$ **b.** 8 times

Written Exercises, pages 129-130
1. $6x^2 + 15y + 12$ **3.** $-14x^3 + 7x^2 - 35x$
5. $3x^4 - 6x^3y + 3x^2y^2$ **7.** $a^3 + 2a^2b - 4ab^2$
9. $16n^3m - 6n^2m^2 + 2m^3$ **11.** $-6a^3b^3 +$
$14a^2b^4$ **13.** $8n^3 + 6n^2 + 14n$ **15.** $-8a^3b +$
$6a^2b^2 - 2ab^3$ **17.** $10x^2 - 2x$ **19.** $a^3 - 8a$
21. -9 **23.** $-a^4 - 3a^3 + 5a^2 + 4a$ **25.** 10
27. 14 **29.** -4 **31.** 1 **33.** $a - 1$
35. $-4pq - 5pqr - 6p^2q$
37. $6a^3 - 10a^2 - 3a$ **39.** 2 **41.** 7 **43.** -1
45. $2x^{2n} - 3x^{n+1} + 4x^n$ **47.** $2b^{2n+2} + 3b^{n+3}$

Written Exercises, pages 132-133
1. $n^2 + 7n + 12$ **3.** $y^2 - 4y - 21$
5. $2a^2 + 18a + 28$ **7.** $2c^2 - 7c - 4$
9. $3p^2 - 19p + 20$ **11.** $x^3 - x^2 - 5x + 2$
13. $6b^3 + 11b^2 + 8b + 2$ **15.** $3n^4 - 17n^3 +$
$27n^2 - 8n$ **17.** $6a^2 - 7a + 2$ **19.** $6x^3 +$
$17x^2 + x - 10$ **21.** $6r^2 + 7rs - 3s^2$
23. $2c^3 - 3c^2d + 2cd^2 - d^3$ **25.** $2n^3 -$
$11n^2 + n + 35$ **27.** $x^3 - 1$ **29.** $2p^4 -$
$11p^3q + p^2q^2 + 35pq^3$ **31.** $5x^3 - 6x^2y -$
$4xy^2 + y^3$ **33.** $12a^3 + a^2b - 5ab^2 + b^3$
35. $8x^3 + 22x^2 + 5x$ **37.** $3a^4 - a^3b -$
$4a^2b^2 - 3ab^3 - b^4$ **39.** 0 **41.** 2 **43.** 4
45. $4x^3 + 4x^2 - 13x + 5$ **47.** $a^{2n} - 1$
49. $b^{2m} - a^{2n}$

Just for Fun, page 133 **1.** $4^4 + 4$

Written Exercises, pages 136-138
1.

length	width	Area
$2x + 5$	x	$2x^2 + 5x$
$x + 4$	$x - 3$	$x^2 + x - 12$
$a + 1$	$\dfrac{24}{a + 1}$	24
$3n + 2$	$\dfrac{15}{3n + 2}$	15

3.

	number $\times$	value per coin $=$	Total value
nickels	x	5	$5x$
dimes	$x + 5$	10	$10x + 50$
quarters	$x + 8$	25	$25x + 200$

5.

	length $\times$	width $=$	Area
first rect.	$x + 12$	x	$x^2 + 12x$
second rect.	$x + 10$	$x + 5$	$x^2 + 15x + 50$

7. a.

	Age now	Age in 2 years
Woofie	x	$x + 2$
Janet	$7x$	$7x + 2$

b. $7x + 2 = 4(x + 2)$

9. a.

	number	× price	=	Cost
Apples bought	n	10		$10n$
Apples sold	$n-2$	15		$(n-2)15$

b. $(n-2)15 - 10n = 20$

11. $x = a - c$ **13.** $z = a$ **15.** $y = \dfrac{a}{4}$

17. $t = \dfrac{I}{Pr}$ **19.** $a = \dfrac{2s}{t^2}$ **21.** $t = \dfrac{A-P}{Pr}$

23. $r = \dfrac{C}{2\pi}$ **25.** $h = \dfrac{T - 2\pi r^2}{2\pi r}$ **27. a.** 70

b. $R = \dfrac{4P - 100}{3}$ **c.** 76

Age Problems, pages 138–139 1. Juan, 21; Ben, 25 **3.** Bill, 20; father, 40 **5.** 15 years **7.** Ann, 19; Jill, 35 **9.** Jefferson, 7; Washington, 18 **11.** 1851

Problems, pages 140–141
1.

	number × price		=	Cost
hot dogs	x	80		$80x$
lemonade	$\dfrac{1}{2}x$	50		$25x$

16 hot dogs
3. 27 covers **5.** 30 sets **7.** 5 nickels, 10 dimes, 3 quarters **9.** $3.80

Problems, pages 144–145 1. 3 h **3.** noon **5.** 2 h **7.** 4.5 km **9.** 50 m **11.** 1.2 km **13.** 45 km

Problems, pages 147–148 1. 6 cm by 12 cm **3.** 20 m by 28 m **5.** 10 cm by 16 cm **7.** 13 m **9.** 20 cm by 20 cm; 30 cm by 30 cm

Chapter Review, pages 149–150 1. d **3.** c **5.** d **7.** a **9.** a **11.** c **13.** d **15.** d **17.** c

Cumulative Review, page 152 1. 9 **3.** $\dfrac{1}{2}$
5. -23 **7.** 11 **9.** $-4m + 6n$
11. $-6b^2 + 19b - 8$ **13.** -0.5 **15.** -27

17. -1 **19.** -2 **21.** 3 **23.** -0.2 **25.** 0 **27.** no root **29.** identity **31.** identity **33.** 2 **35.** $-12, -10, -8$ **37.** Florence, 6.0 km; Trudy, 7.5 km

Maintaining Skills, page 153 1. $\dfrac{2}{3}$ **3.** $\dfrac{18}{49}$
5. $\dfrac{3}{4}$ **7.** $\dfrac{1}{3}$ **9.** $\dfrac{13}{15}$ **11.** $\dfrac{1}{2}$ **13.** $\dfrac{5}{9}$ **15.** $\dfrac{5}{6}$
17. $\dfrac{47}{40}$ **19.** $\dfrac{59}{189}$ **21.** $\dfrac{5}{8}$ **23.** $\dfrac{3}{11}$ **25.** $\dfrac{21}{170}$
27. $\dfrac{9}{20}$ **29.** $\dfrac{5}{7}$ **31.** $\dfrac{39}{44}$ **33.** 63 **35.** $\dfrac{3}{5}$
37. $\dfrac{25}{36}$

CHAPTER 5   FACTORING POLYNOMIALS

Written Exercises, page 157 1. 1, 2, 3, 6, 9, 18 **3.** 1, 37 **5.** 1, 2, 4, 8, 16, 32, 64 **7.** 1, 101 **9.** 1, 23 **11.** (1)(18), (2)(9), (3)(6), $(-1)(-18), (-2)(-9), (-3)(-6)$
13. (1)(37), $(-1)(-37)$ **15.** (1)(64), (2)(32), (4)(16), (8)(8), $(-1)(-64), (-2)(-32),$ $(-4)(-16), (-8)(-8)$ **17.** (1)(101), $(-1)(-101)$ **19.** (1)(23), $(-1)(-23)$
21. $(1)(-18), (2)(-9), (3)(-6), (6)(-3),$ $(9)(-2), (18)(-1)$ **23.** $(1)(-37), (37)(-1)$
25. $(1)(-64), (2)(-32), (4)(-16), (8)(-8),$ $(-1)(64), (-2)(32), (-4)(16)$ **27.** $(1)(-101),$ $(101)(-1)$ **29.** $(-1)(23), (1)(-23)$
31. $2 \cdot 17$ **33.** $3^2 \cdot 7$ **35.** 2^7 **37.** $2^2 \cdot 7 \cdot 17$
39. $2^3 \cdot 3 \cdot 17$ **41.** 6 **43.** 6 **45.** 1

Calculator Key-In, page 157 1. 14 **3.** 12 **5.** 1240 **7.** 1011 **9.** 10

Written Exercises, pages 160–161 1. a^5
3. $-c^4$ **5.** $3a^3$ **7.** $\dfrac{1}{3y^2}$ **9.** $\dfrac{3x^2y^2}{4}$ **11.** $\dfrac{2}{3b^4}$
13. $\dfrac{1}{x}$ **15.** $\dfrac{1}{3y}$ **17.** 8 **19.** $\dfrac{-8}{y^3}$ **21.** $\dfrac{4b^2}{a^5}$
23. $\dfrac{c^5}{13d^4}$ **25.** $3a^4$ **27.** $-2c^2d$
29. $-8x^4y^2$ **31.** $7b^3$ **33.** $(a^2b)^2$ **35.** x^4y
37. $2a^3b^2$ **39.** $5x$ **41.** rs^2t^2 **43.** ab^2
45. (1) Rule for division (2) Property of the reciprocal of a product
(3) Commutative axiom for multiplication; Associative axiom for multiplication
(4) Rule for division

Written Exercises, pages 163–164
1. $a + 2$ **3.** $6x - 3$ **5.** $x - 2y + 3$
7. $2y - 3x$ **9.** $2 - 3y - y^2$ **11.** $-4d^3 + 3cd + 2$ **13.** $6s^3t^2 - 5$ **15.** $3d^2k^2 - 5dk + 2d^2$ **17.** 780 **19.** 380 **21.** 8100 **23.** 850
25. 770 **27.** $2(7a - 6b)$ **29.** $4(x - 2y + 4)$
31. $6x(x + 2)$ **33.** $6x(2x^2 - x + 4)$
35. $6a^2x(4a^2 - 3a + 2x)$ **37.** $7y(s^2 - 3xy)$
39. $5cd(5c^2 - 3cd + d^2)$
41. $7k(3e^2 - 7e^2k + 12k^2)$ **43.** $\frac{h}{2}(b - a)$
45. 3 **47.** $6a + 3b$ **49.** $b^2 - b$

Problems, pages 164–165 **1.** $r^2(4 - \pi)$
3. $r^2(4 + \pi)$ **5.** $r^2(4 - \pi)$ **7.** $r^2(3\pi + 4)$

Written Exercises, page 167
1. $x^2 + 9x + 14$ **3.** $a^2 - 9a + 20$
5. $c^2 + 10c + 21$ **7.** $a^2 - 14a + 45$
9. $2a^2 + 11a + 5$ **11.** $2a^2 + 3a - 27$
13. $x^2 - 2x - 63$ **15.** $b^2 + 5b - 24$
17. $6k^2 + 17k + 5$ **19.** $35a^3 - 74a^2 + 35a$
21. $12x^3 - 26x^2 - 10x$
23. $14k^3 - 27k^2 - 20k$ **25.** $6x^2 + 16xy + 8y^2$ **27.** $27a^2 - 51ab + 10b^2$
29. $2a^4 + a^2 - 21$ **31.** $x^6 + 4x^4 - 21x^2$
33. $3a^8 - 11a^4b^2 + 10b^4$ **35.** 26 **37.** 3
39. 1

Written Exercises, pages 169–170
1. $a^2 - 9$ **3.** $9b^2 - 25$ **5.** $81a^2 - 49$
7. $64a^2 - 25b^2$ **9.** $9u^4 - v^2$ **11.** $r^2s^2 - t^4$
13. 391 **15.** 3596 **17.** 2499 **19.** 39,984
21. $(5y + 3)(5y - 3)$ **23.** $(12 + x)(12 - x)$
25. $(3a + bc)(3a - bc)$
27. $(x^3 + y^3)(x^3 - y^3)$
29. $(4x^2 + 3)(4x^2 - 3)$
31. $(15 - ab^2)(15 + ab^2)$
33. $(a^2b^2 + c^4)(ab + c^2)(ab - c^2)$
35. $(a^8 + 1)(a^4 + 1)(a^2 + 1)(a + 1)(a - 1)$
37. $3(2x + 3)$ **39.** $4a$ **41.** $2(x + 5)(x - 5)$
43. $5(3 + a)(3 - a)$ **45.** $x(x + 3)(x - 3)$
47. $4(9 + k^2)(3 + k)(3 - k)$
49. $(x^n + y^n)(x^n - y^n)$
51. $(b^n + c^{2n})(b^n - c^{2n})$
53. $(a^{2n} + b^{3n})(a^{2n} - b^{3n})$
55. $y^3(y^n + 1)(y^n - 1)$

Extra, page 170 **3.** $(n + 3)(n^2 - 3n + 9)$
5. $(x + 4)(x^2 - 4x + 16)$

Written Exercises, pages 172–174
1. $x^2 + 4x + 4$ **3.** $a^2 - 8a + 16$
5. $4x^2 + 12x + 9$ **7.** $16k^2 - 40k + 25$

9. $16p^2 + 24pq + 9q^2$ **11.** $9x^2 + 42xy + 49y^2$ **13.** $a^2b^2 - 10ab + 25$
15. $y^4 - 14y^2 + 49$ **17.** $25a^2 - 30a + 9$
19. $64x^4 - 16x^2 + 1$ **21.** $(n - 1)^2$
23. $(r - 2)^2$ **25.** $(b - 9)^2$ **27.** $(2x + 1)^2$
29. $(6 - 5a)^2$ **31.** $(8x - y)^2$ **33.** $(x^2 + 1)^2$
35. $(ab - 6)^2$ **37.** $(a^2 - 12)^2$
39. a. $25x^2 - 20x + 4$ **b.** $25x^2 - 20x + 4$
41. $x^4 - 18x^2 + 81 = (x^2 - 9)(x^2 - 9) = (x - 3)(x + 3)(x - 3)(x + 3) = (x - 3)^2(x + 3)^2$
43. 10 **45.** 0 **47.** $3(a + 3)^2$
49. $2(3x - 1)^2$ **51.** $5(2x^2 + 3)^2$
53. $4k(2k - 3)^2$ **55.** 2 **57.** 3 **59.** 4 cm by 16 cm **61. a.** 1225, 3025, 7225
b. $(10t + 5)^2 = 100t^2 + 100t + 25 = 100t(t + 1) + 25 = t(t + 1) \times 100 + 25$

Written Exercises, pages 176–177
1. $(x + 5)(x + 1)$ **3.** $(a - 3)(a - 1)$
5. $(r + 6)(r + 3)$ **7.** $(k - 7)(k - 4)$
9. $(z - 7)(z - 6)$ **11.** prime
13. $(y + 11)(y + 5)$ **15.** $(p - 9)(p - 8)$
17. $(10 - c)(2 - c)$ **19.** $(x - 5y)(x - 7y)$
21. $(s - 6t)(s - 5t)$ **23.** $(b + 8c)(b + 5c)$
25. $(s - 7t)(s - 6t)$ **27.** prime
29. $(d + 3e)(d + 9e)$ **31.** $(a - 8)(a - 15)$
33. $(12 - a)(9 - a)$ **35.** $(14n - x)(7n - x)$
37. 7, 11, -7, -11 **39.** 8, 16, -8, -16
41. 7, 8, 13, -7, -8, -13
43. $(x + 3)(x + 6)$
45. $(a + b - 4)(a + b - 2)$
47. $(a + 3)(a - 3)(a + 1)(a - 1)$
49. $(x^2 + 3)(x + 3)(x - 3)$

Written Exercises, page 179
1. $(a + 5)(a - 1)$ **3.** $(y - 6)(y + 1)$
5. prime **7.** prime **9.** $(a + 7)(a - 5)$
11. $(z + 9)(z - 4)$ **13.** $(p - 7)(p + 3)$
15. prime **17.** $(a - 5b)(a + 4b)$
19. $(p - 10q)(p + 5q)$
21. $(k - 15d)(k + 4d)$
23. $(x - 11y)(x + 2y)$
25. $(1 - 10ab)(1 + 2ab)$
27. $(1 - 8ab)(1 + 7ab)$ **29.** $(r - 24)(r + 6)$
31. $(40 + b)(20 - b)$ **33.** $(40 + x)(8 - x)$
35. 1, 8, 19, -1, -8, -19
(Answers may vary for Exs. 37–41.)
37. -4, -10 **39.** -12, -5
41. -12, -26 **43.** $(x + 4)(x - 4)$
45. $(2x - y + 10)(2x - y + 6)$
47. $(x + 3)(x - 3)(x^2 + 1)$
49. $3(a - 5)(a + 5)(a^2 + 4)$

Written Exercises, pages 181–182

1. $(2x + 3)(x + 1)$ **3.** $(5a + 1)(a + 1)$
5. $(7n - 1)(n - 1)$ **7.** $(5y - 1)(y - 3)$
9. prime **11.** $(2t + 3)(t - 2)$
13. $(4y + 3)(y - 1)$ **15.** $(7k - 2)(k + 3)$
17. $(1 - 2b)(1 + 3b)$ **19.** $(5 - 2y)(2 + y)$
21. $(a - b)(a + 2b)$ **23.** $(9r + 2s)(r - 3s)$
25. $(5a - b)(5a + 3b)$
27. $(4x + 9y)(3x - 2y)$
29. $(6x + 7)(2x - 3)$
31. $(15 - 16c)(1 + 3c)$
33. $(3x + 1)(36x - 7)$
35. $(14y + 9)(3y + 1)$ **37.** $(2y + 5)(y + 5)$
39. $x^2(x + 4)(x - 4)$
41. $((3x + 1)(2x - 5)(5x - 7))^2$

Written Exercises, page 184

1. $(a + b)(x - 5)$ **3.** $(x^2 + 1)(5 - r)$
5. $(2a - b)(4 - y)$ **7.** $(x + y)(a + b)$
9. $(x^2 + 1)(2d - e + f)$
11. $(3a - 7)(2 - y)$ **13.** $(6c + 1)(z - 3)$
15. $(1 - x)(2a - b + 3c)$
17. $(p + q)(2 + a)$ **19.** $(2r + p)(q + r)$
21. $(b + c)(a - 2)$ **23.** $(x^2 + 4)(2x + 1)$
25. $(4x - 3)(x - 2y)$ **27.** $(4y - 1)(y + 2a)$
29. $(2x + 7z)(2x - y)$
31. $(a + 2b + 3c)(a - 2b - 3c)$
33. $(6k + 2a - c)(6k - 2a + c)$
35. $(x - 4y - 3)(x - 4y + 3)$
37. $(x + 3 - y)(x + 3 + y)$
39. $(h - 6 + k)(h - 6 - k)$
41. $(5 + a + 2b)(5 - a - 2b)$
43. $(4y + 1 + 4z)(4y + 1 - 4z)$
45. $(a + 2b - 2)(a - 2b + 2)$
47. $(a + b + 5c)(a - b - 5c)$
49. $9(a - b + c)(a - b - c)$
51. $(a - b)(a - b - 3)$
53. $(2x^2 - 2x + 1)(2x^2 + 2x + 1)$

Written Exercises, page 186

1. $3a(b + 3a)(b - 3a)$ **3.** $2(4x^2 - 4x - 1)$
5. $4(a - 4)(a + 2)$
7. $(x^2 + y^2)(x + y)(x - y)$
9. $2(x^2 + 9)(x + 3)(x - 3)$
11. $(a + 2b + 1)(a - 2b - 1)$
13. $(y + 2)(y - 2)(y + 1)(y - 1)$
15. $((b + 3)(b - 3))^2$
17. $5k(2k - 5)(k + 1)$
19. $2(x - 2y + 2)(x + 2y - 2)$
21. $4(a - 4)(a - 2)$

23. $(x - 1)(x + 2)(x - 2)$
25. $(m - k)(m + k + 1)$
27. $c(a - 2b - 3c)(a - 2b + 3c)$
29. $(x - a)(a^2 + ax - x)$
31. $(b - 3c)(a + 3b)(a - 3b)$
33. $2(1 + 2x + y)(1 - 2x - y)$
35. $(x + 1)^2(x - 2)$
37. $(x + 2y)(a - 3x + 6y)$
39. $2(p + 1)(p - 4)(p - 2)$
41. $(p - 2q + r - 2s)(p - 2q - r + 2s)$
43. $3(15x + y)(x - 4y)$
45. $(b + c + a)(b + c - a) \times$
$(a + b - c)(a - b + c)$
47. $(a + 3b)^2(1 + a - 3b)(1 - a + 3b)$
49. $(x + y + x^2 - 2y^2)(x + y - x^2 + 2y^2)$
51. $(x - 1)(x - 2)(x + 2)$

Written Exercises, page 188 1. $\{0, 7\}$

3. $\{7, 8\}$ **5.** $\{15, 100\}$ **7.** $\left\{\dfrac{1}{3}, -\dfrac{5}{2}\right\}$

9. $\left\{0, -\dfrac{5}{4}\right\}$ **11.** $\left\{0, \dfrac{5}{2}, -\dfrac{2}{5}\right\}$

13. (2) Axiom of reciprocals
(3) Multiplication property of equality
(4) Multiplicative property of zero
(5) Associative axiom for multiplication
(6) Axiom of reciprocals (7) Identity axiom
for multiplication

Written Exercises, page 190 1. $\{4, 9\}$

3. $\{2, -4\}$ **5.** $\{3, -2\}$ **7.** $\{8, -3\}$

9. $\{0, 16\}$ **11.** $\left\{\dfrac{3}{2}, -\dfrac{3}{2}\right\}$ **13.** $\left\{\dfrac{1}{3}, -1\right\}$

15. $\{2, 0, -2\}$ **17.** $\left\{3, -\dfrac{1}{2}\right\}$ **19.** $\{6, -6\}$

21. $\left\{\dfrac{1}{3}, -1\right\}$ **23.** $\{0, 2\}$ **25.** $\left\{\dfrac{7}{2}, -\dfrac{11}{3}\right\}$

27. $\left\{-\dfrac{3}{2}, -\dfrac{4}{3}\right\}$ **29.** $\left\{5, -\dfrac{4}{3}\right\}$

31. $\{0, 4, 8\}$ **33.** $\{2, 3, -2, -3\}$
35. $\{1, -1\}$ **37.** $\{1, -1\}$ **39.** $\{0, 5, -5\}$
41. $\{9, -2\}$ **43.** $\{6, 0, -2\}$ **45.** $\{3, -2\}$
47. $\{1, 3\}$ **49.** $x^2 - 4x + 3 = 0$
51. $9x^2 - 3x - 2 = 0$ **53.** $25x^2 - 16 = 0$
55. Since $a = b$, $a - b = 0$. Thus, division
by $a - b$ in Step 4 is not allowed.

Problems, pages 192–194 1. 8 or -9
3. -6 **5.** $-11, -10$ **7.** 7 cm by 16 cm
9. 8 m by 13 m **11.** 11 m by 11 m
13. 15, -2 **15.** 2 s, 3 s **17.** 30 s

8 *ANSWERS TO ODD-NUMBERED EXERCISES*

19. a. 3 s **b.** 44.1 m is the maximum height because this height is attained only at 3 s. If 44.1 m were less than the maximum height, it would be reached twice, once going up and once coming down. **21.** 6 cm **23.** 2 m **25.** 5 m **27.** 40 cm by 60 cm

Chapter Review, pages 195–197 1. b **3.** b **5.** a **7.** c **9.** c **11.** b **13.** d **15.** d **17.** c **19.** b

Cumulative Review, page 198 1. -0.6 **3.** $2y - 28$ **5.** 0 **7.** $6b^3 - 18b^2 + 3b$ **9.** $2a^3 - a - 3$ **11.** $r^2s^2 - 49t^4$ **13.** 3 **15.** 19 **17.** $6s(2r^2s - 3rs^2 - 8)$ **19.** prime **21.** $(9 - 7x)(1 + 2x)$ **23.** 0 **25.** 1 **27.** 4 **29.** -2 **31.** no root **33.** -2.5 **35.** $\frac{5}{3}, -\frac{4}{3}$ **37.** $0, \frac{1}{2}$ **39.** 15¢; 18¢ **41.** 8 m by 15 m

Maintaining Skills, page 199 1. $9\frac{5}{6}$ **3.** $8\frac{2}{9}$ **5.** $13\frac{7}{12}$ **7.** $\frac{21}{8}$ **9.** $\frac{123}{14}$ **11.** $\frac{41}{24}$ **13.** $12\frac{5}{12}$ **15.** $4\frac{11}{40}$ **17.** $\frac{11}{14}$ **19.** $\frac{10}{3}$ **21.** 90 **23.** $\frac{25}{12}$ **25.** 10 **27.** $\frac{1}{4}$ **29.** 9

CHAPTER 6 FRACTIONS

Written Exercises, pages 202–203

1. $2 \ (x \neq 2)$ **3.** $\frac{x - y}{x + y} \ (x \neq -y)$

5. $\frac{x - y}{x + y} \ (x \neq 0, x \neq -y)$

7. $\frac{2}{a - b} \ (a \neq 0, b \neq 0, a \neq b)$

9. $\frac{x + 6}{2} \ (x \neq 6)$

11. $\frac{4}{x - 5} \ (x \neq 5, x \neq -5)$

13. $\frac{b + 3}{b + 4} \ (b \neq -2, b \neq -4)$

15. $\frac{r}{r + 1} \ (r \neq 3, r \neq -1)$

17. $\frac{-1}{x + 3} \ (x \neq 3, x \neq -3)$

19. $\frac{1}{a - b} \ (a \neq b)$

21. $\frac{4c + 1}{1 - 4c} \left(c \neq \frac{1}{4}, c \neq -\frac{1}{4}\right)$

23. $\frac{-x}{x - 1} \ (x \neq 5, x \neq 1)$

25. $(6x - 4)$ cm $(x \neq 3)$

27. $\frac{2(x + 2)}{x + 6} \ (x \neq 2, x \neq -6)$

29. $\frac{4a + 7b}{4a - 7b} \left(a \neq \frac{7b}{4}\right)$

31. $\frac{s - 5}{s + 7} \ (s \neq -7, s \neq -3)$

33. $\frac{2(a + 2b)}{a + 3b} \ (a \neq b, a \neq -3b)$

35. $\frac{2x + 3y}{x - 2y} \left(x \neq 2y, x \neq -\frac{5y}{2}\right)$

37. $1 \ (x \neq y, x \neq -y)$

39. $2x + y$; cannot be evaluated

41. $\frac{c + 2d}{d(c - 2d)}; -\frac{8}{3}$

43. $\frac{5 - x}{x + 5} \left(x \neq 0, x \neq \frac{3}{2}, x \neq -5\right)$

45. $\frac{a - 3b}{a + 3b + 2} \ (a \neq 2 - 3b, a \neq -3b - 2)$

47. $\frac{a - 3b + 3}{3} \ (a \neq 3b + 3)$

Written Exercises, pages 205–207 1. $\frac{5}{3}$

3. $\frac{1}{15}$ **5.** $\frac{1}{2}$ **7.** 6 **9.** $\frac{a}{c}$ **11.** $\frac{3}{2c}$ **13.** $3pq$

15. $\frac{2y^3}{x^2}$ **17.** -2 **19.** $\frac{x}{x - 2}$

21. $\frac{1}{2xy(4 + y)}$ **23.** $2(1 - x)$ **25.** $\frac{3xy}{2}$ km

27. $\frac{nc}{3}$ cents **29.** $\frac{1}{b^3}$ **31.** $\frac{64d^3}{125}$ **33.** $\frac{d^4}{k^2}$

35. $\frac{x^{10}}{y^{15}}$ **37.** $\frac{8a^3n^3}{v^6}$ **39.** $\frac{x^2 + y^2}{2(x + y)}$ **41.** $\frac{y}{x}$

43. $\frac{2(x - 1)}{x + 2}$ **45.** $\frac{-2}{5y - 2x}$

47. $\frac{-2(2x + 1)(x - 3)}{x(x^2 - 3)}$ **49.** $8(2 - x^2)$

51. $\frac{-(z - 1)^2(z^2 - 1)^2}{z(1 + z^2)}$ **53.** $\frac{x^2 + 3}{6x}$

Application, page 207 1. $4.60 per kilogram **3.** The 1 L bottle

Written Exercises, pages 209–210 1. $\frac{3}{2}$

3. $\frac{6}{y}$ **5.** $\frac{a^3}{8}$ **7.** $2pq$ **9.** 1 **11.** $\frac{3a}{8b^2}$ **13.** 2

15. $\frac{y - 2}{2y}$ **17.** $(x - y)(x + y)$ **19.** $\frac{6}{a(a - b)}$

21. $\dfrac{x-y}{x+y}$ **23.** $\dfrac{x^2}{6}$ **25.** $\dfrac{9}{4z^6x^4y^5}$ **27.** $\dfrac{q^3}{p^3r^{10}}$

29. c **31.** $\dfrac{b-2a}{b^2}$ **33.** $\dfrac{2a-3}{a}$

35. $\dfrac{8(5-2x)}{3}$ **37.** $\dfrac{5(s-2)}{s-4}$ **39.** $\dfrac{2(a+3)}{a-2}$

Written Exercises, pages 214–215 **1.** 6
3. $24x$ **5.** $3(2a+3)$ **7.** $6(1-7x)$ **9.** x^3
11. $6a$ **13.** $2(x+2)$ **15.** -3 **17.** $x+1$
19. 10 **21.** $2x$ **23.** $-5a$ **25.** 18
27. $10xy$ **29.** $9cd^2$ **31.** $2(x+1)(x-1)$
33. $\dfrac{20}{72}, \dfrac{27}{72}$ **35.** $\dfrac{4(2x-1)}{60}, \dfrac{3(1+x)}{60}$
37. $\dfrac{24(2x-3)}{144}, \dfrac{16(7+3y)}{144}, \dfrac{9x}{144}$
39. $\dfrac{2y}{8x^2y^2}, \dfrac{3x^3}{8x^2y^2}$
41. $\dfrac{4}{(3-x)(3+x)}, \dfrac{3(3-x)}{(3-x)(3+x)}$
43. $\dfrac{x+2}{x(x-3)(x+2)}, \dfrac{x-3}{x(x-3)(x+2)}$
45. $\dfrac{x}{4(x-5)(x+5)}, \dfrac{8(x-5)}{4(x-5)(x+5)},$
$\dfrac{12(x+5)}{4(x-5)(x+5)}$ **47.** $\dfrac{4}{6(x+3)(x-3)},$
$\dfrac{3x(x-3)}{6(x+3)(x-3)}, \dfrac{-6(x+3)^2}{6(x+3)(x-3)}$

Written Exercises, pages 217–218 **1.** $\dfrac{11}{a}$
3. $\dfrac{1}{c}$ **5.** 1 **7.** $y-2$ **9.** $\dfrac{(x-3)^2}{(x+3)^2}$ **11.** $\dfrac{a}{3}$
13. $\dfrac{3x+2}{x^2}$ **15.** $\dfrac{5a-6}{2a^2}$ **17.** $\dfrac{4-7y}{50}$
19. $\dfrac{8n+9}{15}$ **21.** $\dfrac{2(7y-x)}{45}$
23. $\dfrac{3y+2}{(y+2)(y-2)}$ **25.** $\dfrac{2}{3a-b}$
27. $\dfrac{3}{a(2a-3)}$ **29.** $\dfrac{8(2x+1)}{15}$ m; $\dfrac{x^2-4}{15}$ m^2
31. $\dfrac{2x+1}{x(x+1)}$ **33.** $\dfrac{1}{4(x+1)}$
35. $\dfrac{x^2+y^2}{(x-y)(x+y)}$ **37.** $\dfrac{-a-b}{ab}$
39. $\dfrac{-2}{(a-3)(a+3)}$
41. $\dfrac{3c+5}{(c+1)(c-2)(c+2)}$

43. $\dfrac{2a}{(a+1)^2(a-1)}$ **45.** $\dfrac{3(3x+2)}{(x+1)(x+2)^2}$
47. $\dfrac{2x-1}{2x+1}$ **49.** $\dfrac{-2x^2-15x-9}{3(x+3)(x-3)}$ **51.** 0

Just for Fun, page 219 **1. a.** $\dfrac{2}{3}; \dfrac{3}{4}; \dfrac{4}{5}$
b. $\dfrac{100}{101}$ **c.** $\dfrac{n}{n+1}$

Written Exercises, page 221 **1.** $\dfrac{22}{7}$
3. $\dfrac{5x+2}{x}$ **5.** $\dfrac{4b+a}{b}$ **7.** $\dfrac{3+2n^2}{2n}$
9. $\dfrac{2x+7y}{3}$ **11.** $\dfrac{3(5x-8)}{2x-3}$ **13.** $\dfrac{x^2+4}{(x-2)^2}$
15. $\dfrac{4b+a-2ab}{ab}$ **17.** $\dfrac{18}{(x+3)(x-3)}$
19. $\dfrac{(x^2-3)(x^2+2)}{x^2}$ **21.** $\dfrac{x+y}{x}$
23. $x-1$ **25.** $\dfrac{a(a+b-c)}{c(c-a+b)}$ **27.** $A=-1,$
$B=1$

Just for Fun, page 221 Diophantus was 84 years old.

Written Exercises, pages 223–224
1. $x+4$ **3.** $x+4$ **5.** $a+1+\dfrac{5}{a+3}$
7. $z-2-\dfrac{7}{z-4}$ **9.** $x+12+\dfrac{29}{x-3}$
11. $x-1+\dfrac{5}{x+1}$ **13.** $x-2+\dfrac{1}{2x-1}$
15. $y-1+\dfrac{6}{5y-1}$ **17.** $2n+2+\dfrac{5}{3n-1}$
19. $3x-y-\dfrac{y^2}{2x+y}$ **21.** x^2-x+1
23. x^2-2x-3 **25.** $x^2+3x+15$
27. $a^2+5ab-7b^2$ **29.** $3a+2$
31. $(3n+2)(n-2)(n-1)$
33. $(2x+1)(2x+3)(x-5)$ **37.** -6 **39.** 1

Just for Fun, page 224 In 20 s; in 60 s

Extra, pages 225–227 **1.** $\dfrac{1}{3}$ **3.** ab **5.** $\dfrac{1}{3}$
7. 9 **9.** $\dfrac{1}{y}$ **11.** $\dfrac{a}{a-1}$ **13.** $\dfrac{a+3}{a-3}$
15. $x+1$ **17.** 1 **19.** $\dfrac{1-2y}{2(1-y)}$ **21.** $\dfrac{t}{2-t}$
25. $\dfrac{8n}{8+n}$ **27.** $\dfrac{-2-x}{x-6}$ **29.** a^2+1 **31.** 1

Calculator Key-In, page 227 1. $0.\overline{5}$ 3. 1.125 5. $24.\overline{3}$ 7. 0.375

Chapter Review, pages 228–230 1. d 3. a 5. b 7. d 9. c 11. b 13. c 15. a 17. c

Just for Fun, page 231

[1] 6	3	▨	▨	[2] 3	[3] 6
2	▨	[4] 2	1	▨	4
[5] 5	[6] 2	8	▨	[7] 1	6
▨	[8] 4	0	[9] 3	2	▨
[10] 9	▨	[11] 8	1	▨	[12] 8
[13] 9	0	▨	▨	[14] 4	2

Cumulative Review, page 232 1. $2b - 3$
3. $21j^5k^4$ 5. $24z^3 + 11z^2 - 18z$ 7. $\frac{3s}{r^4}$
9. $49x^2 - 112xy + 64y^2$ 11. 3
13. $4(5a - b^2)(5a + b^2)$
15. $(x - 18y)(x - 3y)$
17. $k(3k + 2m)(2k + m)$ 19. 26 21. 5
23. 2 25. -7 27. $\frac{2}{5}$, -8 29. $\frac{-1}{2y^3}$ 31. $\frac{r}{5}$
33. $\frac{4x^2 + 9x - 12}{(x + 4)(x + 3)}$ 35. $m^2 - 5m + 10$
37. 23, 25, 27 39. 11 cm by 12 cm
41. 40 km

Maintaining Skills, page 233 1. 14 dimes and 9 quarters 3. 12 cm by 14 cm

CHAPTER 7 APPLYING FRACTIONS

Written Exercises, page 237 1. 12:1
3. 1:10 5. 20:1 7. 26:1 9. 3:1 11. 3:5
13. 9:8 15. 20:1 17. 9:4 19. 2:5
21. 3:4 23. 2:1 25. 1:1

Problems, pages 238–239 1. 24, 40
3. 450 5. $960, $360, $480 7. $2,400,000
9. Marvin 11. 40 m, $4800; 50 m, $6000;
70 m, $8400 13. 56 quarters 15. 30, 80, 32

Written Exercises, pages 241–242 1. 21
3. $\frac{4}{15}$ 5. $\frac{28}{15}$ 7. $\frac{27}{2}$ 9. 0 11. $\frac{6}{7}$ 13. 34
15. 1 17. 5 19. 2.5 21. identity 23. no
root 25. $\frac{ac}{b}$ 27. $na - b$ 29. $-\frac{3}{8}$ 31. $\frac{1}{18}$

Problems, pages 242–243 1. 3840 L
3. $560 5. 128 g 7. 960 shares 9. 40 ha
11. the cube of gold; 4.5384 g

Written Exercises, pages 244–245 1. 6
3. 1 5. 36 7. 15 9. $\frac{3}{2}$ 11. $-\frac{3}{4}$ 13. 2
15. -8 17. 7 19. -3 21. -1 23. 12
25. 4 27. 3 29. $-\frac{11}{4}$ 31. $\frac{4a}{3}$ 33. $-\frac{13c}{3}$

Problems, pages 245–246 1. 60 3. 12 cm
by 18 cm 5. Sam, 2; Kathy, 4 7. Beverly,
$20; Ann, $30 9. 3 km 11. 27 dimes

Written Exercises, page 248 1. 1 3. 6
5. 5 7. 2 9. 8 11. -6 13. 22
15. 20 km/h 17. 1 19. $\frac{16}{5}$ 21. $\frac{1}{4}$, 2
23. 2 25. -4, 1 27. 9 29. 8 31. 4, 1
33. 4, -2

Application, pages 249–250 1. a. 180 mm
b. 2 3. a. 24.5 cm b. 49

Written Exercises, pages 253–254 1. 88
3. 55 5. 4.4 7. 91 9. 11 11. 75%
13. 64% 15. 125% 17. 25% 19. 10%
21. 150% 23. 30 25. 42 27. 400 29. 18
31. 40 33. 9 35. 30 37. 4 39. $-64,000$
41. -13

Problems, pages 254–255 1. 4 mg
3. $425 5. 10.8 min 7. $1200
9. $8000 at 7% and $4000 at 9% 11. $9000

Problems, pages 257–258 1. 13%
3. $30.50 5. 5% 7. 125,000 subscribers
9. $75,000 11. 8% 13. 40%

Calculator Key-In, page 258 1. 1440.55
3. 682.5 5. 1275 7. $5382.73

Problems, pages 261–262 1. 25 kg of the $4.80 coffee and 15 kg of the $4.00 coffee
3. $\frac{1}{3}$, or 0.33, kg **5.** 150 kg of the $2.90 cheese and 50 kg of the $3.10 cheese
7. 60 g **9.** 150 g **11.** 3 kg **13.** 20 kg of oatmeal and 10 kg of bran flakes **15.** 300 discount tickets **17.** 11 pennies, 55 nickels, 20 dimes, 14 quarters **19.** 75 kg **21.** 4:7

Problems, pages 265–267 1. $1\frac{5}{7}$, or 1.71, h **3.** $\frac{4}{7}$, or 0.57, day **5.** $1\frac{5}{7}$, or 1.71, h **7.** $30\frac{10}{13}$, or 30.77, s **9.** 30 min **11.** 22.5 min **13.** $12\frac{36}{47}$, or 12.766, min **15.** $8\frac{4}{7}$, or 8.57, min **17.** 5 h **19.** 4.2 h

Application, page 268 1. 1.6:1

Chapter Review, pages 269–271 1. d **3.** c **5.** b **7.** a **9.** d **11.** a **13.** d **15.** b **17.** c

Cumulative Review, page 272 1. $2x + 4y$ **3.** $-7cd^4 + 14c^2d^3 + 21c^2d$ **5.** $\frac{b^6}{4}$ **7.** $16w^4 + 22w^2z - 3z^2$ **9.** $9g^2 - 41g + gh + 20 - 4h$ **11.** 92 **13.** $3(c + 14)(c - 5)$ **15.** $(2 - cd)(d - 1)$ **17.** prime **19.** 500 **21.** $-5r + 9s$ **23.** $\dfrac{-(m + 2)(m - 1)}{(m + 1)^2}$ **25.** $k + 1$ **27.** $\dfrac{(3a - b)(2a + b)}{(a - b)(a + b)}$ **29.** no root **31.** $\frac{7}{2}$, 1 **33.** $-\frac{2}{3}$ **35.** -6 **37.** 30.8 min **39.** $6000

Maintaining Skills, page 273 1. $-4m - 6$ **3.** $-2x + 9y$ **5.** $-w$ **7.** $-3h^2 - h + 2$ **9.** $14x^5y^3z^5$ **11.** $24t^{2n+2}$ **13.** $54c^{10}$ **15.** $-4m^7n^8$ **17.** $63c^7d^{12}$ **19.** $24b^5 - 8b^4 + 48b^3$ **21.** $-14p^3q^4 + 7p^2q^5 - 35pq^6$ **23.** $y^2 + 4y - 45$ **25.** $6k^2 + 17k - 28$ **27.** $4g^2 - 12g + 9$ **29.** $2r^3 - 11r^2 - 4r + 45$

CHAPTER 8 LINEAR EQUATIONS AND SYSTEMS

Written Exercises, pages 278–279

1–15.

17. isosceles triangle

19. rectangle

21. O **23.** A **25.** O, W **27.** W, A, Q **29.** G, H **31.** $(-9, -5)$ **33.** $(5, -2)$, $(3, -8)$ **35.** The points all lie on a line.

Written Exercises, pages 281–282 1. 5, 2, 0 **3.** 0, -1, -2 **5.** 1, $\frac{1}{2}$, -1 **7.** 4, 6, 11 **9.** -5, -4, -1 **11.** 0, 4, 2 **13.** $y = 6 - x$ **15.** $y = x - 6$ **17.** $y = -\frac{2}{3}x + 4$ **19.** $\{(-1, 2), (0, 1), (1, 0), (2, -1)\}$ **21.** $\{(-1, 0), (1, -1)\}$ **23.** $\{(1, 2), (2, -1)\}$ **25.** $\{(0, 8), (1, 7), (2, 6), (3, 5), (4, 4),$ $(5, 3), (6, 2), (7, 1), (8, 0)\}$ **27.** $\{(0, 5), (2, 4), (4, 3), (6, 2), (8, 1), (10, 0)\}$ **29.** $\{(0, 0), (1, 1), (2, 4)\}$ **31.** $\{(1, 0), (2, 3)\}$ **33.** $\{(3, 4), (4, 3)\}$ **35.** $\{(4, 0)\}$ **37.** $(1, 4)$ **39.** $(2, 6)$

Written Exercises, pages 285–286   1. 4, 8, 3
3. $-7, 7, 8$ **5. a.** $(4, 0)$ **b.** $(0, 3)$

7. a. $(0, 0)$ **b.** $(0, 0)$

9.

11.

13.

15.

17.

19.

21. $x - y = 2$

23. $x - y = -1$

25. $5x - 2y = -3$

27.

29.

31. The lines are parallel.

33. The lines are parallel.

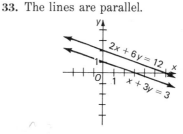

35. The lines are perpendicular.

Written Exercises, page 289   1. $(3, -5)$ is a
solution.   **3.** $(0, 0)$ is not a solution.

5.

7.

9.

11.

13.

15. no solution **17.** (0, 0)

19. (4, 0)

21. $A = 3$, $B = -2$ **23.** $A = 6$, $B = 6$
25. (5, 5) **27.** 27

Written Exercises, page 292 1. (6, 2)
3. (5, 1) **5.** (−3, −1) **7.** (4, 4) **9.** (3, 0)
11. (−1, 3) **13.** (−1, 2) **15.** $\left(\frac{5}{3}, \frac{1}{3}\right)$
17. $\left(-1, \frac{2}{3}\right)$ **19.** (−4, −3) **21.** (−10, 5)
23. (8, −2) **25.** $A = 3$, $B = -1$
27. (3, 5, −8) **29.** (3, 2, 4) **31.** (4, 0, −5)

Problems, pages 294–295 1. 86 and 92
3. 4000 trout; 8000 perch **5.** 213 adult; 426
student **7.** 432 people Friday; 658 people
Saturday **9.** 828 blue jays; 388 chickadees

11. a. 11 m by 14 m **b.** $280 **13.** engine
A, 280 L; engine B, 206 L

Written Exercises, page 297 1. (5, 2)
3. (0, −4) **5.** (6, 3) **7.** (3, 4) **9.** (0, 4)
11. (8, 6) **13.** (4, −3) **15.** (2, 0)
17. (1, −1) **19.** (1, −3) **21.** (−3, −1)
23. (−5, 0)

Problems, page 298 1. 72 and 98 **3.** first
car, 58 L; second car, 42 L **5.** 3 trout; 10
bass **7.** $10 for membership; $3 for each
session

Application, page 298 1. 14.8 **3.** 17.82
5. 41.51

Written Exercises, page 301 1. (3, 4)
3. (−3, −2) **5.** (2, 0) **7.** (0, −2)
9. (1, −1) **11.** (−2, 1) **13.** (0, −3)
15. (1, −1) **17.** (−3, −4) **19.** (2, −1)
21. (−4, −6) **23.** (3, 4) **25.** (5, 4)
27. (2, −3) **29.** $\left(\frac{1}{2}, -1\right)$ **31.** $\left(\frac{1}{3}, -\frac{1}{2}\right)$

Problems, page 302 1. 15 and 16 **3.** 22
and 38 **5.** membership fee, $25; monthly
dues, $2 **7.** father, 24; mother, 20 **9.** 50
cows

Calculator Key-In, page 303 1. (2, 3)

Problems, pages 306–308 1. Dixie, 16;
sister, 10 **3.** Joe, 23; Della, 20 **5.** Mary,
37; son, 7 **7.** 71 **9.** 28 **11.** 13 **13.** $\frac{2}{9}$
15. $\frac{7}{8}$ **17.** $\frac{3}{4}$ **19.** Grandmother, 21;
Grandfather, 24 **21.** 397 **23.** $\frac{458}{854}$
27. father, 39; son, 16

Problems, pages 310–312 1. 23 km/h;
7 km/h **3.** wind's speed, 40 km/h; plane's
speed, 280 km/h **5.** wind's rate,
120 m/min; robin's rate, 180 m/min
7. $128\frac{1}{3}$, or 128.33, km **9.** 175 km/h;
75 km/h **11.** 125 km/h; 50 km/h
13. glider's rate, 75 km/h; wind's rate,
5 km/h **15.** $s = 3w$, or $w = \frac{1}{3}s$ **17.** $s = 5c$,
or $c = \frac{1}{5}s$

Chapter Review, pages 313–315 **1.** d **3.** c
5. a **7.** c **9.** c **11.** d **13.** a **15.** c

Cumulative Review, page 316
1. $-2y^3 + 14y^2 + 18y$ **3.** $64r^4 - 9s^2$
5. $7d - 12$ **7.** $(1 - 9v)^2$
9. $(5 - m)(m - 3n)$ **11.** prime
13. $\dfrac{2x + 5y}{2x + 3y}$ **15.** $\dfrac{1}{4}$ **17.** $n^2 + 2n - 1$
19. 3 **21.** 15 **23.** 2250 **25.** 1, 3 **27.** $\dfrac{5}{2}, -2$
29. $(-1, -11)$ **31.** $(-2, 4)$ **33.** 84

Maintaining Skills, page 317
1. $2c^2(c + 2d)$ **3.** prime
5. $8a(8a^2 - 5a + 9)$ **7.** $a(8 - a)(8 + a)$
9. $(3p - 1)^2$ **11.** prime **13.** $(m^2 + 2n)^2$
15. $3(z - 6t)^2$ **17.** $(g - 10)(g + 4)$
19. $5(z - 6)(z - 4)$ **21.** $s(s + 9)(s - 8)$
23. $(c - 3d)(c - 11d)$ **25.** $(a - 6)(r - 5)$
27. prime **29.** $(4z + 3)(m - 2n)$
31. $(3a - 5)(4a - 1)$ **33.** $(5r + 9s)(r + 2s)$
35. $z(9z + 5)(3z - 2)$ **37.** prime
39. $(4x + v)(10x + 9v)$

CHAPTER 9 INTRODUCTION TO FUNCTIONS

Written Exercises, pages 322–323 **1.** $-\dfrac{1}{2}$

3. 1 **5.** $-\dfrac{1}{9}$ **7.** 1 **9.** no slope **11.** 0

13. 4 **15.** 2 **17.** 1 **19.** $\dfrac{2}{3}$ **21.** $\dfrac{4}{5}$ **23.** 0
25. same line, -2 **27.** not the same line

29.

31.

33.
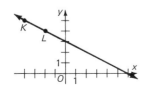

35. $\overline{AC}$, no slope; $\overline{AB}$, slope 0; $\overline{BC}$, slope $\dfrac{8}{9}$

37. Yes; if the slopes from $(-2, -4)$ to $(2, 8)$ and from $(2, 8)$ to $(0, 2)$ are the same, then all 3 points are on the same line.
39. $y = -2$ **41.** The slopes of $\overline{AC}$ and $\overline{AM}$ are both $-\dfrac{5}{3}$; so M is on $\overline{AC}$. The slopes of $\overline{BM}$ and $\overline{BD}$ are both $\dfrac{3}{5}$, so M is on $\overline{BD}$.

Written Exercises, page 326
1. $6x - 2y = -1$ **3.** $x - 4y = -12$
5. $15x - 3y = 2$ **7.** $x - 3y = -2$
9. $8x + 10y = 25$ **11.** $y = -3$

13. $y = -x + 8$

15. $y = x - 6$

17. $y = \dfrac{1}{2}x - 4$

19. $y = -\dfrac{2}{3}x$

21. $y = \dfrac{5}{3}x + \dfrac{20}{3}$

23. $y = \dfrac{2}{3}x - 4$

25. $y = 3x - 3$ **27.** $-3; 3$
29. slope $= -\dfrac{A}{B}$; y-intercept $= \dfrac{C}{B}$

Application, page 327 **1. a–d.** Answers may vary.

Written Exercises, page 329 **1.** 2 **3.** $-\dfrac{1}{3}$

5. $2x - y = 5$ **7.** $4x + y = -22$
9. $2x - 3y = 6$ **11.** $5x - 4y = 15$
13. $x + 2y = -7$ **15.** $y = -2$
17. $7x - 4y = 8$ **19.** $y = 0$
21. $2x + y = 7$ **23.** $8x - 3y = 22$
25. $5x - y = -3$ **27.** $3x + 4y = -13$
29. $2x - y = -6$ **31.** $3x - y = -4$
33. $x - 2y = -6$

Written Exercises, page 333 **1.** 4 **3.** 1

5. -5 **7.** 3 **9.** 0 **11.** 8 **13.** 0 **15.** $\dfrac{5}{4}$

17. $\{-1, 2, 5\}$ **19.** $\{3, -1, -13\}$

21. $\left\{-\dfrac{3}{2}, -6, 3\right\}$ **23.** $\{7, 3, -1\}$

25. $\{6, 3, 2\}$ **27.** $\{-2, 3, 1\}$ **29.** $\{8, -1\}$
31. $\{0, 2\}$ **33.** $\{-27, 0, 1\}$
35. $\{-8, -5, 4\}$ **37.** 24 **39.** 1 **41. a.** 3
b. 2 **c.** 6 **d.** 18 **43. a.** No **b.** 0

Written Exercises, page 336

1.

3.

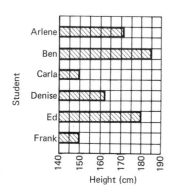

5. $\{(1967, 49{,}700{,}000), (1969, 53{,}200{,}000),$
$(1971, 59{,}800{,}000), (1973, 63{,}200{,}000),$
$(1975, 54{,}300{,}000), (1977, 63{,}700{,}000)\}$

Application, page 337
1.

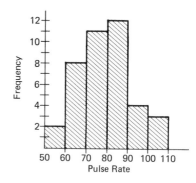

3. 8 **5.** 33

Written Exercises, page 341

1. $(0, 0)$

3. $(0, 0)$

5. $(0, 0)$

7. $(-2, -4)$

9. $(-1, 2)$

11. $(0, -2)$

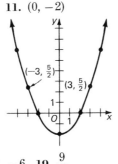

13. $-\dfrac{9}{4}$ **15.** $-\dfrac{25}{4}$ **17.** -6 **19.** $\dfrac{9}{4}$

21. -1 **23.** $\dfrac{1}{8}$

25. a.

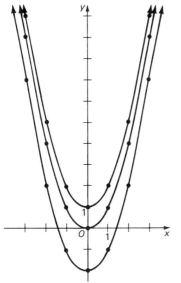

b. As c increases, the graph moves up; as c decreases, the graph moves down.

Written Exercises, page 345 **1.** $\dfrac{1}{6}$ **3.** 5

5. 25 **7.** 1000 **9.** 600 **11.** 21 **13.** 2.4

15. $\dfrac{1}{2}$ **17.** $M = kE$ or $\dfrac{M_1}{E_1} = \dfrac{M_2}{E_2}$

19. $m = kh$ or $\dfrac{m_1}{h_1} = \dfrac{m_2}{h_2}$ **21.** $P = kT$ or

$\dfrac{P_1}{T_1} = \dfrac{P_2}{T_2}$ **23.** $i = kn$ or $\dfrac{i_1}{n_1} = \dfrac{i_2}{n_2}$

Problems, pages 346–347 **1.** \$130 **3.** 15 min **5.** 4.5 cups **7.** 7.5 units **9.** 20 km

Calculator Key-In, page 347 9.4542×10^{15} m

Written Exercises, pages 350–351

1.

3.

5. 125 **7.** 2.1 **9.** $ih = k$, or $i_1 h_1 = i_2 h_2$
11. $fl = k$, or $f_1 l_1 = f_2 l_2$ **13.** $fl = k$, or
$f_1 l_1 = f_2 l_2$

Problems, pages 351–352 **1.** 2 m **3.** 7 people **5.** 800 km/h **7.** 8 m **9.** 0.75 h, or

45 min **11.** $\dfrac{1}{2}$ **13.** 0.4 m

Problems, pages 354–355 **1.** 25 cm² **3.** 1.6 min **5.** 144 km **7.** 5 cm **9.** The force is multiplied 256 times. **11. a.** 1 cm **b.** 27:8

Problems, pages 357–358 **1.** 57 cm²
3. 36 cm **5.** 10 students **7.** 21 ohms
9. a. It is doubled. **b.** It is quadrupled.
c. It is multiplied by 18.

Chapter Review, pages 360–361 **1.** b
3. d **5.** a **7.** b **9.** c **11.** c **13.** d

Cumulative Review, page 362
1. $-16 + 5x$ **3.** $3p^2 + 5pq - p - 2q^2 - 2q$
5. $-3x + y$ **7.** $5a(5a + 6)(a - 2)$
9. $(4t^2 - 3v)(4t^2 + 3v)$ **11.** $\dfrac{2b - 1}{b - 1}$

13. $\dfrac{2c^2 + 6cd - 2d^2}{(c - 2d)(c + d)(c)}$ **15.** $r(7r + 4)$

17. $\{-3, 2, 3, 0, -7\}$

19. a.   **b.**

21. $\{28, -28\}$ **23.** -27.9 **25.** $\left(2, -\dfrac{1}{3}\right)$

27. $\dfrac{1}{2}$ **29.** $(2, -2)$ **31.** $\left(\dfrac{1}{3}, \dfrac{1}{2}\right)$

33. $36\pi \text{ cm}^3$

Maintaining Skills, page 363 **1.** $-\dfrac{1}{3y}$

3. $\dfrac{5a}{b}$ **5.** $\dfrac{28}{3(t-1)}$ **7.** $-\dfrac{4z^2}{5}$ **9.** $\dfrac{d+2}{d-7}$

11. $\dfrac{m-1}{m+1}$ **13.** $\dfrac{x^3(x-2y)}{(x+4y)^2}$ **15.** $4-g$

17. $\dfrac{-6r^2 - 2r + 8}{3r + 1}$ **19.** $\dfrac{10x - 2x^3 + 3}{2x}$

21. $\dfrac{3a+8}{18a^2}$ **23.** $-\dfrac{x+3}{x+4}$

25. $\dfrac{-2p+1}{(p-3)(p-4)}$

CHAPTER 10 INEQUALITIES

Written Exercises, pages 367–368

1. $5 > -2$ **3.** $-15 \le -10$ **5.** $2 < 4 < 4.5$
7. $-20 < -12 < -10$ **9.** $8 > 1 > -2$
11. F **13.** T **15.** T
17. $\{-4, -3, -2, -1, 0, 1, 2\}$
19. $\{-4, -3\}$
21. $\{-4, -3, -2, -1, 0, 1, 2, 3, 4\}$
23. $\{-4, -3, -2, -1, 0, 1\}$

25. {the real numbers greater than 4}

27. $\{-4, -3, -2, -1, 0, 1\}$

29. {the real numbers greater than or equal to 0 and less than 5}

31. $\{-6, -5, -4, -3, -2, -1\}$

33. Answers may vary. **a.** $x = 6, y = -3$
b. $x = 6, y = -7$ **35.** Answers may vary.
a. $x = 4, y = 1$ **b.** $x = -2, y = -5$

Calculator Key-In, page 368 **1.** T **3.** F

Written Exercises, pages 372–373 **1.** d
3. c **5.** b **7.** e
9. {the real numbers greater than 15}

11. {the real numbers less than -24}

13. {the real numbers less than -48}

15. {the real numbers less than or equal to -1}

17. {the real numbers greater than -4}

19. {the real numbers less than or equal to -20}

21. {the real numbers less than 6}

23. {the real numbers greater than -15}

25. {the real numbers less than 6}

27. {the real numbers less than 8}
29. {the real numbers greater than -4}
31. {the real numbers less than or equal to 3} **33.** {the negative real numbers}
35. {the real numbers less than or equal to -1}

37. $\left\{\text{the real numbers less than } \dfrac{5}{2}\right\}$

39. {the real numbers greater than or equal to 6}

41. {the real numbers greater than or equal to 2}

43. {the real numbers less than -9}

45. {the real numbers less than or equal to 11}

47. {the real numbers greater than 13}

49. the negative real numbers **51.** the positive real numbers **53.** all real numbers except 0 **55.** 0 **57.** F **59.** T **61.** T **63.** T

Written Exercises, pages 375–376
1. $c - 12 < 75$ **3.** $k + 10k > 2800$

5. $\frac{1}{2}a + 12 < 100$

7. $9 < n + (n + 2) < 25$
9. $x - 2 \le 2x + 4$
11. $4(x + 2) - 2(x + 1) \ge 3x + 1$

Problems, pages 376–377 **1.** 15 **3.** 11 and 12 **5.** 38 and 39 **7.** 4.2 h, or 4 h 12 min **9.** 42 **11.** 9 quarters, 13 dimes **13.** 6, 8 **15.** 3, 5, 7, 9 **17.** 34 **19.** 19 km^2 **21.** 0, 1, 2

Extra, pages 380–381
1. $\{0, 1, 2, 3, 5, 6, 7, 8, 9\}$ **3.** $\{6, 8\}$ **5.** $\{6\}$
7. $\{5, 6, 8\}$ **9.** $\{5, 6, 7, 9\}$ **11.** union: $\{0, 1, 2, 3, 4\}$; intersection: $\{2, 3\}$ **13.** union: $\{1, 2, 3, 4, 5, 6\}$; intersection: $\emptyset$; disjoint **15.** union: $\{1, 2, 3, 5, 7, 9, 11\}$; intersection: $\{3, 5, 7\}$ **17.** {the real numbers} **19.** {the real numbers between -2 and 3} **21.** {the real numbers less than 3} **23.** {the real numbers between -2 and 1}
25.

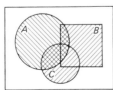

27. $A \cap (B \cup C) = (A \cap B) \cup (A \cap C)$

29.

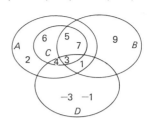

Written Exercises, pages 384–385
1.

3.

5. {the real numbers between -3 and 2}

7. {5, and the real numbers between 0 and 5}

9. $\{-1$, and the real numbers between -1 and 2}

11. $\{-2$, and the real numbers between -2 and 1}

13. {3, and the real numbers less than -1 or greater than 3}

15. $\{-2, 2$, and the real numbers less than -2 or greater than 2}

17. $\{-1, 2$, and the real numbers less than -1 or greater than 2}

19. $\{-5$, and the real numbers between -5 and 3}

21. $\{-2, 3$, and the real numbers between -2 and 3}

23. {the real numbers less than -2 or greater than 2}

25. ∅

27. {5, and the real numbers between -2 and 5}

number line from -3 to 7, open circle at -2, closed dot at 5

29. {the real numbers less than -1 or greater than 7}

number line from -2 to 8, open circles at -1 and 7

31. {the real numbers less than -1 or greater than 5}

number line from -3 to 7, open circles at -1 and 5

33. {-2, 2, and the real numbers between -2 and 2}

number line from -5 to 5, closed dots at -2 and 2

35. {4, and the real numbers between 1 and 4}

number line from -5 to 5, open circle at 1, closed dot at 4

37. {the real numbers less than or equal to 6}

number line from 0 to 10, closed dot at 6

39. 5

Written Exercises, pages 387–388

1. $|x| = 4$ **3.** $|x| < 3$ **5.** $|x| \geq 2$

7. {3, -1}

number line from -5 to 5, closed dots at -1 and 3

9. {0, 2}

number line from -5 to 5, closed dots at 0 and 2

11. {the real numbers between -2 and 2}

number line from -5 to 5, open circles at -2 and 2

13. {-4, 4, and the real numbers between -4 and 4}

number line from -5 to 5, closed dots at -4 and 4

15. {2, -2}

number line from -5 to 5, closed dots at -2 and 2

17. {-2, 2, and the real numbers between -2 and 2}

number line from -5 to 5, closed dots at -2 and 2

19. {the real numbers between -3 and 1}

number line from -5 to 5, open circles at -3 and 1

21. {-1, 7, and the real numbers between -1 and 7}

number line from -3 to 7, closed dots at -1 and 7

23. {3, -2}

number line from -5 to 5, closed dots at -2 and 3

25. {2}

number line from -5 to 5, closed dot at 2

27. {the real numbers between -7 and 7}

number line from -9 to 11, open circles at -7 and 7

29. {the real numbers less than -3 or greater than 4}

number line from -5 to 5, open circles at -3 and 4

31. $\left\{ -\dfrac{3}{2}, \dfrac{3}{2},$ and the real numbers less than $-\dfrac{3}{2}$ or greater than $\dfrac{3}{2} \right\}$

number line from -2 to 2, closed dots at $-\frac{3}{2}$ and $\frac{3}{2}$

33. {15, -3}

number line from -3 to 17, closed dots at -3 and 15

35. {5, -1}

number line from -5 to 5, closed dots at -1 and 5

37. {the real numbers less than 2}

number line from -5 to 5, open circle at 2

39. ∅

number line from -5 to 5

Written Exercises, pages 391–392

1.

3.

5.

7.

9.

11.

13. $y < 3 - x$

15. $y \geq \frac{1}{2}x + \frac{5}{2}$

17. $y < 3x - 6$

19. $y \leq \frac{3}{2}x - 4$
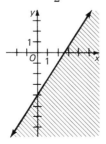

21. $\frac{1}{3}x + \frac{2}{3} \leq y$
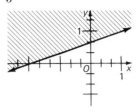

23. $y \leq -\frac{1}{2}x - \frac{5}{2}$

25. $y > -1$ **27.** $y \leq 0$ **29.** $y > \frac{1}{2}x - 3$

31. $y \leq 3x + 6$ **33.** $y > \frac{1}{2}x + 2$

35.

Written Exercises, pages 394–396

1.

3.

5.

7.

9.

11.

13.

15.

17.

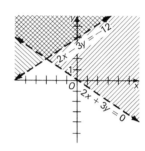

19. $x \geq -4$ **21.** $y \leq x - 3$
$y > x + 4$ $4y \geq -3x - 12$

23. $y \geq -3$
$y < -x + 1$
$y < 8x + 37$

25. $(0, 0); (-1, -1); (1, -1)$

27. $(0, 3); (6, 0); \left(-\dfrac{3}{2}, 0\right)$

Just for Fun, page 396

1.

Application, page 397   1. 105%   **3.** 12%

Chapter Review, pages 398–399   1. c
3. a   **5.** d   **7.** b   **9.** a

Cumulative Review, page 400
1. $(5u - 3v)(3u - 7v)$ **3.** $(2 - 3h)(g - 1)$
5. $-16y$ **7.** $-4m^3 + 6$
9. $c^2 + 2cd + d^2 - 2c - 2d + 1$
11. $\dfrac{7x^2 - 112}{24x}$ **13.** $-\dfrac{c - 6}{c - 4}$, or $\dfrac{6 - c}{c - 4}$
15. $\dfrac{(z^2 + 9)(z + 3)}{2}$
17. 3, 33

19. a.

b.

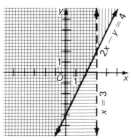

21. $\{9, -9\}$ **23.** $\{2.7\}$ **25.** $\{8, -3\}$
27. {the real numbers greater than or equal to 14}   **29.** $\{6, -3\}$ **31.** {the real numbers less than or equal to 8}   **33.** $\left(2, \dfrac{2}{3}\right)$
35. $2\,\text{km/h}$

Maintaining Skills, page 401
1. $n + 2 + \dfrac{-9}{n + 4}$ **3.** $r + 3 + \dfrac{3}{r + 5}$
5. $6s - 9 + \dfrac{7}{2s + 3}$
7. $c^2 - 2c + 2 - \dfrac{1}{c + 1}$ **9.** $\{-4\}$
11. $\{-5\}$ **13.** $\{21\}$ **15.** $\{10\}$ **17.** $\left\{-\dfrac{2}{3}\right\}$
19. $\left\{-\dfrac{8}{3}\right\}$ **21.** $\{0\}$ **23.** $\left\{\dfrac{35}{11}, -4\right\}$
25. $\{-1\}$

CHAPTER 11   RATIONAL AND IRRATIONAL NUMBERS

Written Exercises, pages 406–407   1. $<$
3. $<$ **5.** $>$ **7.** $>$ **9.** $>$ **11.** $-\dfrac{5}{7}, -\dfrac{3}{5}, \dfrac{2}{9}$
13. $\dfrac{91}{40}, \dfrac{57}{25}, 2.3$ **15.** $\dfrac{3}{7}, \dfrac{3}{5}, \dfrac{7}{9}, \dfrac{5}{6}$ **17.** $\dfrac{13}{24}$
19. $-\dfrac{27}{140}$ **21.** $\dfrac{28}{45}$ **23.** decreases
25. decreases   **27.** $\dfrac{27}{32}$ **29.** $-\dfrac{41}{72}$ **31.** $\dfrac{5}{12}$,
for example   **33.** $\dfrac{29a}{84}$
35. (2) Cancellation rule for fractions
(3) Multiplication axiom of order
(5) Multiplication axiom of order
(6) Cancellation rule for fractions

Written Exercises, pages 410–411   1. $0.\overline{4}$
3. 0.625   **5.** $0.\overline{6}$ **7.** $1.\overline{38}$ **9.** 0.5625
11. $-0.\overline{55}$ **13.** $-0.\overline{45}$ **15.** -3.875
17. $\dfrac{33}{100}$ **19.** $\dfrac{2}{9}$ **21.** $\dfrac{7}{11}$ **23.** $-\dfrac{5}{12}$ **25.** $\dfrac{22}{15}$
27. $-\dfrac{139}{45}$ **29.** $\dfrac{1}{4}, \dfrac{1}{2}, \dfrac{1}{8}$ **31.** $\dfrac{4}{9}, \dfrac{3}{4}, \dfrac{1}{3}$
33. $\dfrac{9}{11}, \dfrac{22}{27}, \dfrac{2}{3}$ **35.** 0.008; 0.754, for example   **37.** $0.00\overline{6}$; 0.663, for example
39. $0.00\overline{02}$; 0.1137, for example

41. a. $\frac{1}{7} = 0.\overline{142857}$, $\frac{3}{7} = 0.\overline{428571}$ **b.** Each block contains the same digits, which would all be in the same order if arranged around a circle. **c.** $\frac{2}{7} = 0.\overline{285714}$, $\frac{4}{7} = 0.\overline{571428}$, $\frac{6}{7} = 0.\overline{857142}$ **43. a.** $\frac{7}{99} = 0.\overline{07}$, $\frac{15}{99} = 0.\overline{15}$, $\frac{86}{99} = 0.\overline{86}$ **b.** $1 = \frac{99}{99} = 0.\overline{99} = 0.\overline{9}$

Written Exercises, page 414 1. 16 **3.** 15 **5.** 19 **7.** -52 **9.** 72 **11.** $\frac{7}{60}$ **13.** $\frac{13}{8}$ **15.** $\frac{11}{25}$ **17.** $\frac{1}{5}$ **19.** $-\frac{22}{17}$ **21.** $\frac{1}{5}$ **23.** $-\frac{6}{5}$ **25.** $\frac{23}{10}$ **27.** $\pm\frac{27}{100}$ **29.** $\pm\frac{7}{100}$ **31.** -2 **33.** -8 **35.** $\frac{2}{5}$ **37.** $-\frac{1}{2}$ **39.** $\frac{9}{10}$ **41.** $\frac{3}{13}$ **43.** $\pm\frac{13}{20}$

Calculator Key-In, page 414 1. 2.236 **3.** 1.775 **5.** 0.673 **7.** 59.4390 **9.** 61.2372

Written Exercises, page 418 1. -22.4 **3.** 28.3 **5.** 99.5 **7.** 9.43 **9.** 0.76 **11.** 854 **13.** 510 **15.** 970 **17.** 3.61 **19.** -18.71

Written Exercises, page 420 1. $-0.6|t^3|$ **3.** $1.5a^2|b|$ **5.** $1.9|k^3 n|$ **7.** $\frac{|n^3|}{13}$ **9.** $\frac{90}{|k^5|}$ **11.** $|x + 5|$ **13.** $|k + 9|$ **15.** $\{9, -9\}$ **17.** $\left\{\frac{3}{5}, -\frac{3}{5}\right\}$ **19.** $\{2, -2\}$ **21.** $\left\{\frac{1}{3}, -\frac{1}{3}\right\}$ **23.** $\{27.3, -27.3\}$ **25.** $\{2.6, -2.6\}$ **27.** $\{11.4, -11.4\}$ **29.** $\{11.1, -11.1\}$ **31.** $\{0.5, -0.5\}$ **33.** $\{2.7, -2.7\}$ **35.** $\{6.2, -6.2\}$

Problems, pages 420–421 1. 17.3 cm **3.** 7.1 cm by 28.4 cm **5.** 4.6 cm **7.** 42.4 cm **9.** 11.2 s **11.** 35.5 cm^2

Computer Key-In, page 421 1. 3.87298

Written Exercises, pages 424–425 1. 10.00 **3.** 10.30 **5.** 18.38 **7.** 12.00 **9.** 2.24 **11.** no **13.** no **15.** no **17.** 15.56 **19.** 12.37 **21.** 21.63 **23.** 8.49 **25.** 8.94, 17.89

Problems, page 425 1. 9.43 cm **3.** 5 m **5.** 6, 8, 10 **7.** 34.64 cm **9.** 1.6 m

Just for Fun, page 425 13 peanuts

Extra, pages 426–427 1. 9.0 **3.** 10.0 **5.** 7.8 **7.** 8.5 **9.** 9.0 **11.** 14.2 **13.** For $A(0, 3)$, $B(3, 9)$, $C(6, 0)$, $D(9, 6)$: $AB = BD = DC = CA = 3\sqrt{5}$

Written Exercises, page 429 1. 6 **3.** 6 **5.** $3\sqrt{42}$ **7.** $12\sqrt{2}$ **9.** $36\sqrt{3}$ **11.** $\sqrt{2}$ **13.** 1 **15.** $\frac{1}{3}$ **17.** $\frac{\sqrt{2}}{12}$ **19.** $24\sqrt{3}$ **21.** $\frac{28\sqrt{2}}{3}$ **23.** $\frac{\sqrt{2}}{2}$ **25.** $-6|a|b$ **27.** $5\sqrt{m} + m$ **29.** -108 **31.** $4x^2\sqrt{22x}$ **33.** $45x$ **35.** $-2\sqrt{22}$ **37.** $2m\sqrt{3} - 12m\sqrt{3m}$ **39.** $24y^4\sqrt{3y}$

Written Exercises, pages 430–431 1. $3\sqrt{3}$ **3.** $-11\sqrt{21}$ **5.** $9\sqrt{3}$ **7.** $6\sqrt{3} - 5\sqrt{2}$ **9.** $12\sqrt{2}$ **11.** $14\sqrt{5}$ **13.** $4\sqrt{17} + 7\sqrt{6}$ **15.** $21\sqrt{5} + 6\sqrt{3}$ **17.** $\frac{2\sqrt{3}}{3}$ **19.** $\frac{47\sqrt{2}}{3}$ **21.** $\frac{\sqrt{6}}{12}$ **23.** $-\frac{23\sqrt{10}}{5}$ **25.** $\frac{55\sqrt{6} - 24\sqrt{3}}{30}$ **27.** $8\sqrt{3} + 48$ **29.** $\frac{5x}{24}$ **31.** $\frac{x\sqrt{a^2 + b^2}}{ab}$ **33.** $7\sqrt{5}$

Just for Fun, page 431 The ant will reach the top on the eighth day.

Written Exercises, pages 432–433 1. 13 **3.** 42 **5.** 6 **7.** $19 + 8\sqrt{3}$ **9.** $67 + 16\sqrt{3}$ **11.** $169 + 24\sqrt{10}$ **13.** $21\sqrt{3} + 21$ **15.** $90\sqrt{2} - 18\sqrt{30}$ **17.** $50 + 8\sqrt{7}$ **19.** $163 - 26\sqrt{55}$ **21.** $742 + 79\sqrt{77}$ **23.** $\frac{-3 + 3\sqrt{3}}{2}$ **25.** $\frac{15 - 5\sqrt{5}}{4}$ **27.** $-4 - 2\sqrt{3} - \sqrt{15} - 2\sqrt{5}$ **29.** $\frac{18\sqrt{5} + 12}{41}$ **31.** $4 - 2\sqrt{2}$ **33.** 8 **39.** $x^2 - y$ **41.** $12m^2 n - 19mp\sqrt{n} + 5p^2$

Written Exercises, page 435 1. 400 **3.** 27 **5.** $\frac{1}{48}$ **7.** 9 **9.** $\frac{16}{9}$ **11.** 100 **13.** 71 **15.** $\frac{32}{25}$ **17.** 45 **19.** $\frac{14}{3}$ **21.** $\frac{12}{5}$ **23.** $\frac{343}{9}$ **25.** 33 **27.** 61 **29.** 20 **31.** $\left\{\frac{5\sqrt{15}}{3}, -\frac{5\sqrt{15}}{3}\right\}$ **33.** $\{\sqrt{17}, -\sqrt{17}\}$ **35.** 4 **37.** $\{1, -4\}$ **39.** 1

Problems, pages 435–436 **1.** 81 **3.** 80
5. 23 **7.** 100π cm^2 **9.** 54 and 56

Calculator Key-In, page 436 **1.** 0.618
3. 0.429 **5.** 1.754 **7.** 4.614

Chapter Review, pages 438–439 **1.** b **3.** c
5. a **7.** d **9.** d **11.** a **13.** b **15.** a

Cumulative Review, page 440
1. $(h - 3r^2)(h + 3r^2)(h^2 + 9r^4)$
3. $(3z - 5)(4z - 9)$ **5.** $x^5y^3 - x^3y^3 + 9x^3y$
7. $62 - 20\sqrt{6}$ **9.** $\dfrac{-5t^{13}}{4r}$ **11.** $15\sqrt{10}$
13. $\dfrac{2(r + 6)}{r(4r - 3)}$ **15.** $-\dfrac{b}{2}$
17. $\dfrac{16g - 5}{(g - 2)(4g + 1)}$
19. a. **b.**

c.

21. $f(-5) = 6, f(\sqrt{2} + 1) = 2 + 5\sqrt{2}$

$\left(-\frac{3}{2}, -\frac{25}{4}\right)$

23. $-\dfrac{43}{30}$ **25.** $\dfrac{5}{3}$ **27.** 25
29. $\{6\sqrt{3}, -6\sqrt{3}\}$ **31.** {the real numbers greater than or equal to -3 and less than $-\frac{1}{2}$} **33.** {the real numbers greater than or equal to 7} **35.** {the real numbers less than 3} **37.** $(7, -3)$ **39.** $\left(-1, \dfrac{3}{2}\right)$
41. 16.12 m

Maintaining Skills, page 441 **1.** $(-7, -2)$
3. $(0, 7)$ **5.** $(2, 6)$ **7.** $(-4, -6)$ **9.** $(0, 0)$
11. $\left(\dfrac{1}{4}, -\dfrac{1}{2}\right)$ **13.** no solution **15.** $(-6, 6)$
17. $\left(-7, -\dfrac{1}{3}\right)$ **19.** $(10, 2)$ **21.** $(16, 0)$

CHAPTER 12 QUADRATIC FUNCTIONS

Written Exercises, page 445 **1.** $\{10, -10\}$
3. $\left\{\dfrac{10}{11}, -\dfrac{10}{11}\right\}$ **5.** $\{9, -9\}$ **7.** $\{3, -3\}$
9. no solution **11.** $\{\sqrt{2}, -\sqrt{2}\}$
13. $\{2, -2\}$ **15.** $\{\sqrt{7}, -\sqrt{7}\}$ **17.** no
solution **19.** $\{4, -2\}$
21. $\{-4 + \sqrt{6}, -4 - \sqrt{6}\}$
23. $\{-3 + 3\sqrt{3}, -3 - 3\sqrt{3}\}$
25. $\{5 + \sqrt{5}, 5 - \sqrt{5}\}$
27. $\{-2 + \sqrt{10}, -2 - \sqrt{10}\}$ **29.** $\left\{\dfrac{3}{5}, -1\right\}$
31. $\{3, -1\}$ **33.** $\{1, -13\}$ **35.** $\left\{\dfrac{2}{3}, -\dfrac{2}{3}\right\}$
37. $\{\sqrt{11}, -\sqrt{11}\}$ **39.** $\left\{\dfrac{7}{11}, -\dfrac{7}{11}\right\}$
41. $\left\{\dfrac{7}{9}, -\dfrac{7}{9}\right\}$ **43.** $\left\{-\dfrac{37}{9}, -\dfrac{35}{9}\right\}$
45. $\left\{\dfrac{3 + \sqrt{10}}{5}, \dfrac{3 - \sqrt{10}}{5}\right\}$ **47.** $\{0, 3, -3\}$
49. $\{0, 5, -5\}$ **51.** $\{0, 7, -7\}$
53. $\{-1, -4\}$ **55.** no solution
57. $\{\sqrt{2} - \sqrt{7}, -\sqrt{2} - \sqrt{7}\}$

Written Exercises, page 448
1. $\{2 + \sqrt{26}, 2 - \sqrt{26}\}$ or $\{7.1, -3.1\}$
3. $\{-4 + 2\sqrt{3}, -4 - 2\sqrt{3}\}$ or
$\{-0.5, -7.5\}$ **5.** $\{3 + \sqrt{6}, 3 - \sqrt{6}\}$ or
$\{5.4, 0.6\}$ **7.** $\{1 + \sqrt{6}, 1 - \sqrt{6}\}$ or
$\{3.4, -1.4\}$ **9.** $\{8 + 2\sqrt{137}, 8 - 2\sqrt{137}\}$ or
$\{31.4, -15.4\}$ **11.** $\{-1 + \sqrt{5}, -1 - \sqrt{5}\}$
or $\{1.2, -3.2\}$ **13.** $\{1, -4\}$
15. $\left\{\dfrac{-11 + \sqrt{149}}{2}, \dfrac{-11 - \sqrt{149}}{2}\right\}$ or
$\{0.6, -11.6\}$ **17.** $\{37, -43\}$ **19.** $\{8, 5\}$
21. $\{-2, 20\}$ **23.** $\left\{\dfrac{3}{2}, -\dfrac{1}{2}\right\}$ **25.** $\{2, -4\}$
27. $\left\{\dfrac{1 + \sqrt{19}}{3}, \dfrac{1 - \sqrt{19}}{3}\right\}$
29. $\left\{\dfrac{5 + \sqrt{73}}{3}, \dfrac{5 - \sqrt{73}}{3}\right\}$
31. $\left\{\dfrac{11 + \sqrt{201}}{10}, \dfrac{11 - \sqrt{201}}{10}\right\}$

33. $\left\{\dfrac{-5 + \sqrt{313}}{12}, \dfrac{-5 - \sqrt{313}}{12}\right\}$

35. $\left\{\dfrac{-3 + \sqrt{137}}{8}, \dfrac{-3 - \sqrt{137}}{8}\right\}$

37. $\left\{\dfrac{-b + \sqrt{b^2 - 4}}{2}, \dfrac{-b - \sqrt{b^2 - 4}}{2}\right\}$;
$b \geq 2$ or $b \leq -2$

39. $\left\{\dfrac{-b + \sqrt{b^2 - 4ac}}{2a}, \dfrac{-b - \sqrt{b^2 - 4ac}}{2a}\right\}$;
$a \neq 0$ and $b^2 - 4ac \geq 0$

Written Exercises, pages 450–451
1. $\{-1 + \sqrt{2}, -1 - \sqrt{2}\}$ or $\{0.4, -2.4\}$
3. $\{-3 + \sqrt{5}, -3 - \sqrt{5}\}$ or $\{-0.8, -5.2\}$
5. $\{5, -1\}$ **7.** $\left\{-\dfrac{1}{2}, -2\right\}$ **9.** $\left\{4, -\dfrac{2}{3}\right\}$

11. $\left\{\dfrac{5}{4}, 1\right\}$ **13.** $\left\{\dfrac{-7 + \sqrt{89}}{20}, \dfrac{-7 - \sqrt{89}}{20}\right\}$

15. $\left\{\dfrac{3 + \sqrt{209}}{40}, \dfrac{3 - \sqrt{209}}{40}\right\}$ **17.** no

solution **19.** $\left\{\dfrac{7 + \sqrt{85}}{3}, \dfrac{7 - \sqrt{85}}{3}\right\}$

21. $\left\{\dfrac{-4 + \sqrt{26}}{4}, \dfrac{-4 - \sqrt{26}}{4}\right\}$ **23.** $-\dfrac{b}{a}$
25. $x^2 - 4x + 1 = 0$

Written Exercises, pages 454–455 **1.** 29;
two **3.** 37; two **5.** 17; two **7.** 25; two
9. -11; none **11.** 0; one **13.** two; below
15. two; above **17.** two; above **19.** 4

Just for Fun, page 455 **1.** 6

Written Exercises, pages 457–458
1. $\{-1, -2\}$ **3.** $\{17, -5\}$ **5.** $\{0, -3\}$
7. $\{3, -3\}$ **9.** $\left\{\dfrac{5 + \sqrt{37}}{3}, \dfrac{5 - \sqrt{37}}{3}\right\}$
11. $\{-3 + \sqrt{5}, -3 - \sqrt{5}\}$ **13.** $\{0, -4\}$
15. $\left\{\dfrac{1}{3}, -1\right\}$
17. $\left\{\dfrac{-3 + \sqrt{159}}{5}, \dfrac{-3 - \sqrt{159}}{5}\right\}$
19. $\{-9 + \sqrt{42}, -9 - \sqrt{42}\}$
21. $\left\{\dfrac{10 + \sqrt{118}}{6}, \dfrac{10 - \sqrt{118}}{6}\right\}$
23. $\left\{\dfrac{-13 + \sqrt{701}}{14}, \dfrac{-13 - \sqrt{701}}{14}\right\}$
25. $\left\{\dfrac{-29 + \sqrt{721}}{2}, \dfrac{-29 - \sqrt{721}}{2}\right\}$
27. $\left\{\dfrac{5}{3}, -\dfrac{1}{7}\right\}$ **29.** $\{\sqrt{7}, -\sqrt{7}\}$

31. $\left\{0, \dfrac{\sqrt{6}}{3}, -\dfrac{\sqrt{6}}{3}\right\}$

Problems, pages 460–461 **1.** 8 m by 5 m
3. 70 m by 120 m **5.** 8 cm **7.** 8.3 cm
9. 35 cm **11.** Dan, 3 h; Leah, 2 h
13. 90 km/h

Extra, page 462
1.

3.

5.

7. {all real numbers that are greater than
or equal to 6 or less than or equal to 0}

Application, page 463 **1.** 135,000 N
3. 6 m/s^2

Chapter Review, pages 464–465 **1.** b
3. a **5.** a **7.** d **9.** b

Cumulative Review, pages 466–467 **1.** 48
3. 197 **5.** $3z^3(-7z + 4 - 5z^5)$
7. $4(5b - 6y)(5b + 6y)$
9. $s(5s - 2t)(4s - 5t)$ **11.** 47 **13.** -39
15. $17c - 19$ **17.** $6t^5v^2 - 2t^4v^3$ **19.** $\dfrac{8}{3m^{10}}$

21. $27m^2 + 39m - 10$ **23.** $\dfrac{7c - d}{7c + 2d}$

25. $2m + 4$ **27.** z^3 **29.** $-\dfrac{3}{2}$

31. $\dfrac{-4t - 2}{(t + 3)(t - 2)}$ **33.** $-6\sqrt{10}$

35. $12a\sqrt{2}$ **37.** $\dfrac{1 - 3\sqrt{5}}{-2}$ **39.** $\dfrac{43}{55}$

41. a. $5x - y = -17$ **b.** $3x + 2y = 22$
43. $f(-4) = 42;\ f(2\sqrt{3}) = 22 - 6\sqrt{3}$

45. $-\dfrac{1}{2}$ **47.** 2.7 **49.** $\left\{\dfrac{4}{5}, -8\right\}$ **51.** {all

real numbers that are greater than $\dfrac{8}{3}$}

53. $\left\{-\dfrac{1}{3}, 2\right\}$ **55.** -3 **57.** $\left\{-\dfrac{1}{2}, 7\right\}$

59. {all real numbers that are greater than
or equal to 2, except for 3}
61. $\{3 + 2\sqrt{6}, 3 - 2\sqrt{6}\}$ **63.** $(-1, 2)$
65. $(-13, -9)$ **67.** 7 and 13 or -13 and
-7 **69.** 8 **71.** 640 cm² **73.** 9 min
75. 620 km/h

LOOKING AHEAD

Written Exercises, page 470 Answers may
vary for Exercises 1 and 3. **1.** any five of
$\overline{PQ}$, $\overline{QR}$, $\overline{RS}$, $\overline{PR}$, $\overline{QS}$, $\overline{PS}$ **3.** $\overline{XY}$, $\overline{YZ}$, $\overline{XZ}$,
$\overline{WY}$, $\overline{WZ}$ **5.** acute **7.** obtuse **9.** acute
11. obtuse

13. point

15. segment

17. line

19. segment

21. line

Written Exercises, pages 472–473
1. (Answers may vary.) $\angle EGF$, $\angle DCF$,
$\angle HGJ$ **3.** 140° **5.** 36° and 144° **7.** 55°
9. 90° **11.** 65°

Just for Fun, page 473 $x = 12$

Written Exercises, page 475 1. 69°
3. 125° **5.** 49° **7.** yes **9.** yes **11.** no
13. $US = 15$ **15.** $\angle R = 65°$
17. $AB = 2\sqrt{34}$ **19.** $BC = 2\sqrt{5}$
21. $AB = x\sqrt{2}$

Problems, page 476 1. 90°, 18°, 72°
3. 18°, 54°, 108° **5.** 70°, 35°, 75° **7.** 22°,
46°, 112° **9.** 32°, 78°, 70°

Just for Fun, page 476

Written Exercises, page 478 1. $\angle D$ and
$\angle K$, $\angle E$ and $\angle L$, $\angle F$ and $\angle J$, $\overline{DE}$ and
$\overline{KL}$, $\overline{EF}$ and $\overline{LJ}$, $\overline{DF}$ and $\overline{KJ}$ **3.** false
5. false **7.** $EF = 6$, $DF = 8$ **9.** $DE = 2$,
$DF = 4$ **11.** $DE = 5\dfrac{1}{3}$, $EF = 6\dfrac{2}{3}$

Problems, page 479 1. 12 cm **3.** 10 m
5. 3 m

Just for Fun, page 479 The reasoning for
the parallelogram is logical, but the
reasoning for the canaries is not. There
could be canaries in other parts of the
Canary Islands.

Written Exercises, page 482 1. $\cos A = \dfrac{3}{5}$,

$\sin A = \dfrac{4}{5}$, $\tan A = \dfrac{4}{3}$, $\cos B = \dfrac{4}{5}$,

$\sin B = \dfrac{3}{5}$, $\tan B = \dfrac{3}{4}$ **3.** $\cos A = \dfrac{5\sqrt{41}}{41}$,

$\sin A = \dfrac{4\sqrt{41}}{41}$, $\tan A = \dfrac{4}{5}$, $\cos B = \dfrac{4\sqrt{41}}{41}$,

$\sin B = \dfrac{5\sqrt{41}}{41}$, $\tan B = \dfrac{5}{4}$

5. $\cos A = \dfrac{2\sqrt{14}}{9}$, $\sin A = \dfrac{5}{9}$, $\tan A = \dfrac{5\sqrt{14}}{28}$, $\cos B = \dfrac{5}{9}$, $\sin B = \dfrac{2\sqrt{14}}{9}$, $\tan B = \dfrac{2\sqrt{14}}{5}$ **7.** $\cos A = \dfrac{b}{c} = \sin B$

9. $(\sin A)^2 + (\cos A)^2 = \left(\dfrac{a}{c}\right)^2 + \left(\dfrac{b}{c}\right)^2 = \dfrac{a^2 + b^2}{c^2} = \dfrac{c^2}{c^2} = 1$ **11.** $\dfrac{8}{10}$ **13.** $\sin D = \dfrac{20}{29}$, $\cos D = \dfrac{21}{29}$

Written Exercises, page 484 For Exercises 1-11, answers are given in the order $\sin A$, $\cos A$, $\tan A$ **1.** 0.3420, 0.9397, 0.3640 **3.** 0.5736, 0.8192, 0.7002 **5.** 0.2924, 0.9563, 0.3057 **7.** 0.6820, 0.7134, 0.9325 **9.** 0.8829, 0.4695, 1.8807 **11.** 0.9563, 0.2924, 3.2709 **13.** 28° **15.** 68° **17.** 23° **19.** 44° **21.** 21° **23.** 86°

Written Exercises, page 487 **1.** 16 **3.** 10 **5.** 53 **7.** $BC \approx 40$, $AC \approx 50$ **9.** $BC \approx 17$, $AB \approx 62$ **11.** $\angle M \approx 61°$, $\angle R \approx 29°$ **13.** $\angle M \approx 18°$, $\angle R \approx 72°$ **15.** $YZ \approx 39$, $XZ \approx 31$ **17.** $YZ \approx 19$, $XZ \approx 43$

Problems, pages 487-489 **1.** 98 m **3.** 15 m **5.** 3° **7.** 87 km **9.** 167 m **11.** 284 m **13.** 74° **15.** 8 m and 14 m

Review, page 490 **1.** a **3.** d **5.** c **7.** c **9.** a

EXTRA PRACTICE

Chapter 1, page 491 **1.** 22 **3.** 220 **5.** 2 **7.** 14 **9.** 1 **11.** 3 **13.** 2 **15.** 14 **17.** 1 **19.** no solution **21.** {4} **23.** {4} **25.** {2, 4, 6, 8, 10} **27.** no solution **29.** $n + 3$, or $3 + n$ **31.** $\dfrac{3}{n}$, or $3 \div n$ **33.** $2(n - 5)$ **35.** $x + 2$ **37.** $2r$ **39.** $22 - d$ **41.** $m - p$ **43-53.** Answers may vary. **43.** $4x = 32$ **45.** $12t = 8$ **47.** $m + (m + 1) + (m + 2) = 4224$ **49.** $x + 3x = x(3x)$ **51.** $7x = 175$ **53.** $r + (2r + 3) = 11.4$

Chapter 2, page 492 **1.** -5 **3.** 2 **5.** -5 **7.** 0 **9.** 6 **11.** -15 **13.** -2 **15.** 4 **17.** -6 **19.** -19 **21.** 17 **23.** -3

25. -21 **27.** -33 **29.** -30 **31.** 2 **33.** -7 **35.** -18 **37.** 0 **39.** {4} **41.** {2, 4} **43.** {-4, 4} **45.** {-2, 2} **47.** -14 **49.** 10 **51.** -3 **53.** -96 **55. a.** 3, -2, 7, 2 **b.** 10 **c.** 10 spaces **57. a.** 20, -8, 2, -1.5 **b.** 12.5 **c.** 12.5°C **59.** 7 **61.** 4 **63.** 2100 **65.** $4x$ **67.** $-20a$ **69.** x **71.** $12 + 14y$ **73.** $-8h$ **75.** $100x + 200$ **77.** $2.4x + 5.6$ **79.** $11k + 1 + 5m$ **81.** 8 **83.** 6 **85.** 0 **87.** -24 **89.** 0 **91.** -300 **93.** -1.8 **95.** 18 **97.** 14 **99.** -21 **101.** $-2x + (-6)$ **103.** $-16x + 6y$ **105.** -55 **107.** $\dfrac{1}{63}$ **109.** -5 **111.** 370 **113.** $11x + 22y$ **115.** $2x + 4y$

Chapter 3, page 495 **1.** 14 **3.** 9 **5.** -12 **7.** -14 **9.** -612 **11.** 12 **13.** 6 **15.** 30 **17.** 0 ' **19.** -59 **21.** -7 **23.** -1 **25.** -1 **27.** 0 **29.** z **31.** $9x$ **33.** $2m + 14$ **35.** -11 **37.** 5 **39.** -4 **41.** 15 **43.** -3 **45.** -7 **47.** 14 **49.** -14 **51.** -17 **53.** -34 **55.** 50 **57.** 11 **59.** -6 **61.** 1 **63.** 22 **65.** -4 **67.** -40 **69.** 15 **71.** -42 **73.** 63 **75.** -7 **77.** -7 **79.** 3 **81.** 1 **83.** 126 **85.** -21 **87.** 9 **89.** -2 **91.** $\dfrac{5}{2}$ **93.** 0 **95.** $-\dfrac{12}{5}$ **97.** 4 **99.** 2 **101.** $\dfrac{3}{5}$ **103.** -1 **105.** 5 **107.** $\dfrac{3}{8}$ **109.** 2

Chapter 4, page 497 **1.** 25 **3.** 625 **5.** $\dfrac{1}{4}$ **7.** $\dfrac{1}{4}$ **9.** -25 **11.** -4000 **13.** 18 **15.** -78 **17.** -2 **19.** $3x^2 - 7x + 7$ **21.** $-4x - 2y - 10$ **23.** $5a + 5b + 5c + 5d$ **25.** 5 **27.** -9 **29.** a^{12} **31.** $60x^{18}$ **33.** $-8n^7m^3$ **35.** a^4b^2 **37.** $6xy^2$ **39.** 1 **41.** $8x^3$ **43.** x^{12} **45.** $4x^2y^4$ **47.** $-27x^4$ **49.** $10a^4b^4$ **51.** $8u^6v^{10}$ **53.** -64 **55.** 0 **57.** 4 **59.** $-3x^3 - 15x^2 - 18x$ **61.** $-3x^4 - 15x^3 - 18x^2$ **63.** $-6x^2$ **65.** $-t^3 + 60t$ **67.** x **69.** 4 **71.** -3 **73.** -20 **75.** $m^2 - m - 6$ **77.** $m^2 - 5m + 6$ **79.** $2x^2 + 5x - 12$ **81.** $2x^2 - 11x + 12$ **83.** $9x^2 + 12x + 4$ **85.** $8x^3 - 1$

Chapter 5, page 498 **1.** 1, 2, 3, 4, 6, 11, 12 **3.** 1, 2, 3, 6, 11 **5.** 1, 2, 3, 6 **7.** 1, 2, 3, 4, 5,

6, 8, 10, 12 **9.** $2^3 \cdot 5 \cdot 7$ **11.** $2^2 \cdot 3^2 \cdot 7$ **13.** $\dfrac{x^3}{6}$

15. $2x^3$ **17.** $2r^3 - r$ **19.** $2r^2 - 4r$

21. $\dfrac{2}{y} - \dfrac{3}{x} + \dfrac{1}{2xy}$ **23.** 198,000 **25.** 144

27. $8xy(x - 1)$ **29.** $2\pi r(r - 1)$

31. $\pi rh\left(\dfrac{1}{3}r + 1\right)$ **33.** $-3x(x - 2)$, or

$3x(-x + 2)$ **35.** $5xy(2x - y)$

37. $5mr(2m^2 - 4r + 3)$ **39.** $2m^2 - m - 3$

41. $2m^2 + m - 3$ **43.** $16x^2 + 40x + 25$

45. $10w^2 - 11w + 3$ **47.** $(2x + 1)(2x - 1)$

49. $(b^2 + 40c)(b^2 - 40c)$ **51.** $(4a + b)^2$

53. $(k + 7)(k + 5)$ **55.** $(m - 6)(m - 1)$

57. $(p + 6)(p + 2)$ **59.** $(k + 10)(k + 2)$

61. $(y - 20)(y - 1)$ **63.** $(x - 3)(x - 2)$

65. $(x + 8)(x - 1)$ **67.** $(x + 4)(x - 2)$

69. $(y + 10)(y - 2)$ **71.** $(a + 4)(a - 3)$

73. $(r + 11)(r - 3)$ **75.** $(m + 20)(m - 1)$

77. $(p + 1)(8p - 7)$ **79.** $(8x + 7)(x - 1)$

81. $(2r + 1)(4r - 7)$ **83.** $(4y + 7)(2y - 1)$

85. $(6x + 1)(x - 2)$ **87.** $(2x + 1)(x - 3)$

89. $(4d + 1)(3d - 2)$ **91.** $(3x - 4)(2x - 3)$

93. $(x + 6)(3x - 4)$ **95.** $(a + 3)^2$

97. $(x + y)(x + 2)$ **99.** $(x + 1)^2(x - 3)$

101. $(a^4 + 64)(1 + a)(1 - a)$ **103.** $\{-1\}$

105. $\{5\}$ **107.** $\left\{-\dfrac{1}{2}, -7\right\}$

109. $\{0, -1, -2\}$ **111.** $\{12, -2\}$

113. $\left\{3, -\dfrac{1}{2}\right\}$ **115.** $\left\{5, -\dfrac{2}{3}\right\}$

117. $\left\{-\dfrac{1}{2}, 1\right\}$ **119, 121.** Answers may

vary. **119.** $x^2 - x - 2 = 0$

121. $x^2 - 49 = 0$

Chapter 6, page 500 **1.** 4 **3.** $\dfrac{2}{3}$; $x \neq -y$

5. $\dfrac{1 + b}{2}$; $a \neq 0$ **7.** $\dfrac{y + a}{xy + y}$; $x \neq 0$, $x \neq -1$,

$y \neq 0$ **9.** $\dfrac{4r + 1}{4r - 1}$; $r \neq \dfrac{1}{4}$, $r \neq -\dfrac{1}{4}$

11. $\dfrac{k - 4}{k - 5}$; $k \neq 4$, $k \neq 5$ **13.** -1; $x \neq \dfrac{1}{2}$

15. $-\dfrac{3x - 1}{3 - x}$, or $\dfrac{3x - 1}{x - 3}$; $x \neq \dfrac{5}{2}$, $x \neq 3$

17. $\dfrac{-2}{1 - 2a}$; $a \neq 0$, $a \neq \dfrac{1}{2}$ **19.** 2 **21.** $3m$

23. $10r$ **25.** $\dfrac{c}{c + 1}$ **27.** $\dfrac{x - 3}{(x + 3)(x + 2)}$

29. $3b^3$ **31.** $\dfrac{7}{a + b}$ **33.** $\dfrac{1}{3x + y}$ **35.** $\dfrac{2x}{a + b}$

37. $\dfrac{3}{2(3x + 5)}$ **39.** $\dfrac{1}{a - 1}$ **41.** $\dfrac{m^2}{m + r}$

43. $\dfrac{12x + 5}{(2x + 1)(3x + 1)}$ **45.** $-\dfrac{2r}{(r + 2)^2}$

47. 0 **49.** $\dfrac{2}{(x - 3)(x - 2)(x - 1)}$

51. $\dfrac{5a^2 - 2a - 32}{(a + 2)^2(a - 2)}$ **53.** $\dfrac{1}{2x - 1}$

55. $5x + 4$ **57.** $6a + 5$ **59.** $x^2 + 2x + 4$

61. $x^2 - 2x + 2$ **63.** $k - 1$

65. $p^2 + 3 - \dfrac{3p}{p^2 + p + 1}$

67. $-3m^3 - m^2 + m + 2$

Chapter 7, page 502 **1.** $5:8$ **3.** $7:32$

5. $3:200$ **7.** $\dfrac{1}{3}$ **9.** $\dfrac{10}{17}$ **11.** 19 **13.** -3

15. 15 **17.** 45 **19.** -5 **21.** 5 **23.** 2

25. 2 **27.** 7 **29.** $-\dfrac{1}{2}$ **31.** 2.97 **33.** 0.314

35. 80 **37.** 222 **39.** $57\dfrac{1}{7}$ **41.** 33

Chapter 8, page 503 **1.** $y = 8 - 2x$

3. $y = 6 - \dfrac{3}{2}x$ **5.** $y = \dfrac{1}{2}x - 2$

7. $y = 2x - 5$ **9.** $y = \dfrac{10}{3} - \dfrac{2}{3}x$ **11.** 1

13. 1 **15.** $-\dfrac{52}{5}$ **17. a.** $(20, 0)$ **b.** $(0, -5)$

19. a. $(10, 0)$ **b.** $(0, -2)$ **21. a.** $(100, 0)$

b. $(0, 30)$

23. **25.**

27. **29.**

31.

33.

31.

35. $(9, -3)$ **37.** $s + a = 640$

39. $a = 2s + 160$ **41.** $\left(5, -\dfrac{25}{2}\right)$

43. $(5, -1)$ **45.** $(-3, -4)$ **47.** $n + 6$

49. $2(n + d)$ **51.** $20t + 2u$ **53.** $\dfrac{3n}{d - 7}$

55. $s - r$

Chapter 9, page 504 **1.** 2 **3.** -4 **5.** $\dfrac{1}{2}$

7. -2 **9.** -1 **11.** $\dfrac{5}{2}$ **13.** yes; $\dfrac{4}{3}$ **15.** yes;

$-\dfrac{3}{2}$

17.

19.

21–25. Answers may vary.
21. $5x - y = -10$ **23.** $6x + 2y = 1$
25. $2x - y = -4$

27.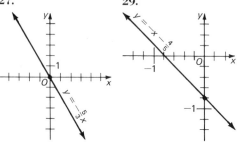

29.

33–37. Answers may vary.
33. $2x - y = 2$ **35.** $4x - y = 0$ **37.** $y = 4$

39. a. 7 **b.** $5\dfrac{1}{2}$ **41. a.** 8 **b.** $\dfrac{9}{16}$ **43.** 2

and 3 **45.** $(2, -4)$ **47.** $(-1, 3)$

49. $\left(4\dfrac{1}{2}, 1\dfrac{1}{2}\right)$ **51.** 25 **53.** 13 **55.** 12

57. 2 **59.** 1 **61. a.** 3 **b.** 12 **63. a.** $\dfrac{1}{2}$

b. 2 **65.** $C = kd$; $\dfrac{C_1}{d_1} = \dfrac{C_2}{d_2}$ (Answers may

vary.) **67.** inverse; 3 **69.** direct; 3 or $\dfrac{1}{3}$

71. direct; 7.5 **73.** direct; cannot be

determined **75.** inverse; $\dfrac{1}{8}$ **77.** 2

79–85. Answers may vary. **79.** $bh = k$;
$b_1 h_1 = b_2 h_2$ **81.** $p = kv^2$ **83.** $V = klwd$
85. $F = \dfrac{kv^2}{r}$

Chapter 10, page 507

1.

3.

5. $\left\{\text{the real numbers less than } \dfrac{23}{3}\right\}$

7. $\left\{\text{the real numbers greater than } \dfrac{2}{3}\right\}$

9. $\left\{\text{the real numbers less than } \dfrac{2}{3}\right\}$

11. false **13.** true **15.** $\left\{\dfrac{1}{2}, -\dfrac{1}{2}\right\}$

17. $\{9, 7\}$ **19.** $\left\{3, -\dfrac{5}{3}\right\}$ **21.** {the real

numbers greater than 2 or less than -2}
23. {the real numbers between -5 and -3}
25. $\left\{\text{the real numbers between } -\dfrac{1}{2} \text{ and } \dfrac{9}{2}\right\}$

27–35. Answers may vary.

27. $n(n + 1) > 152$ **29.** $d \geq 42$ **31.** $p \leq 3$
33. $c \leq 28$ **35.** $6c \geq b + 4$ **37.** {2 and the real numbers between 0 and 2} **39.** {4}
41. {the real numbers between -4 and 0}
43. {the real numbers} **45.** $\left\{\text{the real numbers greater than } \frac{1}{2} \text{ or less than } -1\right\}$
47. $\left\{1 \text{ and the real numbers between } \frac{2}{3} \text{ and } 1\right\}$ **49.** no **51.** yes
53.

55.

57.

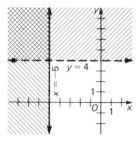

Chapter 11, page 508 1–5. Answers may vary **1.** $\frac{13}{10}$ **3.** $\frac{3}{25}$ **5.** $-\frac{21}{8}$ **7.** $>$
9. $<$ **11.** $<$ **13.** $>$ **15.** $>$ **17.** 10
19. $\frac{7}{15}$ **21.** $-\frac{31}{39}$ **23.** $\frac{11}{7}$ **25.** $0.\overline{6}$
27. 28.1 **29.** 1.75 **31.** $0.\overline{135802469}$
33. 1.8 **35.** $7.\overline{36}$ **37.** $\frac{7}{50}$ **39.** $\frac{14}{5}$ **41.** $\frac{62}{99}$
43. $\frac{111}{90}$ **45.** 0.75, or $\frac{3}{4}$; 0.875, or $\frac{7}{8}$
47. 0.11; 0.165 **49.** 0.38; -2.31 **51.** 31
53. 42 **55.** 252 **57.** $\frac{4}{25}$ **59.** $\frac{3}{5}$ **61.** 0.9
63. 6.32 **65.** 91.10 **67.** 0.14 **69.** 6.16
71. 5.08 **73.** $9m^2$ **75.** $|a + 1|$
77. $m^{50}n^{100}$ **79.** $|4a - 1|$ **81.** {38, −38}
83. $\left\{\frac{1}{6}, -\frac{1}{6}\right\}$ **85.** {29, −29}
87. {3.3, −3.3} **89.** {2.7, −2.7} **91.** 10
93. 3.16 **95.** 25 **97.** $4\frac{1}{6}$ **99.** $6\sqrt{21}$

101. $10\sqrt{2}$ **103.** $\frac{\sqrt{26}}{13}$ **105.** $\frac{\sqrt{2}}{3}$
107. $6\sqrt{5}$ **109.** $32x$ **111.** $9x$ **113.** $\frac{1}{3}$
115. 3 **117.** $2\sqrt{2}$ **119.** $13\sqrt{7}$ **121.** $\frac{9}{2}\sqrt{2}$
123. $-\frac{4}{3}\sqrt{15}$ **125.** 0 **127.** $25\sqrt{2}$
129. $-8\sqrt{15}$ **131.** 23 **133.** 37 **135.** 7
137. $32 - 10\sqrt{7}$ **139.** $9 + 2\sqrt{14}$
141. $2\sqrt{3} + 3$ **143.** $25 + \frac{25}{2}\sqrt{3}$
145. $95 - 5\sqrt{21}$ **147.** $9\sqrt{3} - 11\sqrt{2}$
149. $\frac{4\sqrt{7} + 10}{3}$ **151.** 2 **153.** $14 + 2\sqrt{35}$
155. {−4} **157.** {30} **159.** $\left\{\frac{17}{2}\right\}$
161. {5}

Chapter 12, page 512 1. $(x + 3)^2$
3. $(x - 11)^2$ **5.** $\left\{\frac{1}{5}, -\frac{1}{5}\right\}$ **7.** {1, −17}
9. $\left\{\frac{\sqrt{42}}{6}, -\frac{\sqrt{42}}{6}\right\}$
11. $\{3 + \sqrt{7}, 3 - \sqrt{7}\}$ **13.** $\left\{1, \frac{1}{3}\right\}$
15. 36; 6 **17.** $\frac{49}{4}$; $\frac{7}{2}$ **19.** {2, −8}
21. $\{6 + \sqrt{46}, 6 - \sqrt{46}\}$
23. $\{4 + 9\sqrt{17}, 4 - 9\sqrt{17}\}$ **25.** {50, −32}
27. $\left\{\frac{-1 + \sqrt{5}}{2}, \frac{-1 - \sqrt{5}}{2}\right\}$ **29.** $\left\{\frac{1}{2}, -3\right\}$
31. $\{-1 + \sqrt{3}, -1 - \sqrt{3}\}$
33. $\{4 + \sqrt{15}, 4 - \sqrt{15}\}$
35. $\{5 + \sqrt{15}, 5 - \sqrt{15}\}$ **37.** $\left\{2, \frac{3}{2}\right\}$
39. $\left\{\frac{2 + \sqrt{22}}{6}, \frac{2 - \sqrt{22}}{6}\right\}$ **41.** 13; two
43. −36; none **45.** 4; two **47.** −104; none **49.** $\left\{\frac{2 + \sqrt{19}}{3}, \frac{2 - \sqrt{19}}{3}\right\}$
51. {0, −2} **53.** $\{3 + \sqrt{19}, 3 - \sqrt{19}\}$
55. $\{2 + 2\sqrt{3}, 2 - 2\sqrt{3}\}$

Problems, Chapter 3, page 514 1. −134
3. −23 **5.** 345 cm **7.** $12 - (-6) = 18$; 18°C **9.** $1230 - (-22) = 1252$; 1252 points
11. $-38.87 - (-78) = 39.13$; 39.13°C
13. 18 **15.** 18 **17.** 94 **19.** 4 kg
21. $4.50 **23.** 4 km **25.** −32 **27.** $2.16
29. 11 **31.** soup, 85¢; salad, $1.70
33. $192 **35.** −4 **37.** 2

Problems, Chapter 4, page 516 1. 31, 32, 33
3. −20, −19, −18 **5.** 43, 45 **7.** 4, 5, 6
9. 6 years ago **11.** 14 student tickets
13. mathematics, 6 h; music, 4 h **15.** 11:12
A.M. **17.** 22 m by 15 m **19.** 20 m by 20 m

Problems, Chapter 5, page 517 1. 2 cm by
1 cm **3.** −11, −9 **5.** 11 m by 3 m **7.** 35 m
by 15 m

Problems, Chapter 7, page 517 1. 15 cm,
36 cm, 39 cm **3.** $11,250 **5.** 700 L **7.** 120
families **9.** 5 cm, 5 cm, 2 cm **11.** 3
13. 2, 5 **15.** 476 people **17.** $532
19. $7\frac{1}{2}$% **21.** $32.13 **23.** 30 kg
25. 10 kg of peppers; 5 kg of onions
27. about 3.4 h **29.** 4 d

Problems, Chapter 8, page 520 1. ninth-
grade, 45 bags; tenth-grade, 20 bags

3. engineer, $80; assistant, $60 **5.** first
number, 2; second number, 4 **7.** tape
player, $96; radio, $49 **9.** apples, $6;
apricots, $4 **11.** father, 36 years; son, 10
years **13.** 85 **15.** $\frac{16}{20}$ **17.** plane,
270 km/h; wind, 90 km/h

Problems, Chapter 9, page 521 1. 119 L of
oil **3.** 435 kg **5.** 63 r.p.m. **7.** $4900
9. 33.75 cm

Problems, Chapter 10, page 522 1. 4, 6
3. 38 km/h, 42 km/h

Problems, Chapter 11, page 522 1. 19.2 cm
by 6.4 cm **3.** 69.3 cm **5.** 3.32 m **7.** 100
9. 10

Problems, Chapter 12, page 523 1. 6 cm
3. 42, 44; −42, −44 **5.** 8 cm, 10 cm
7. 15 cm long, 10 cm wide, 11 cm high